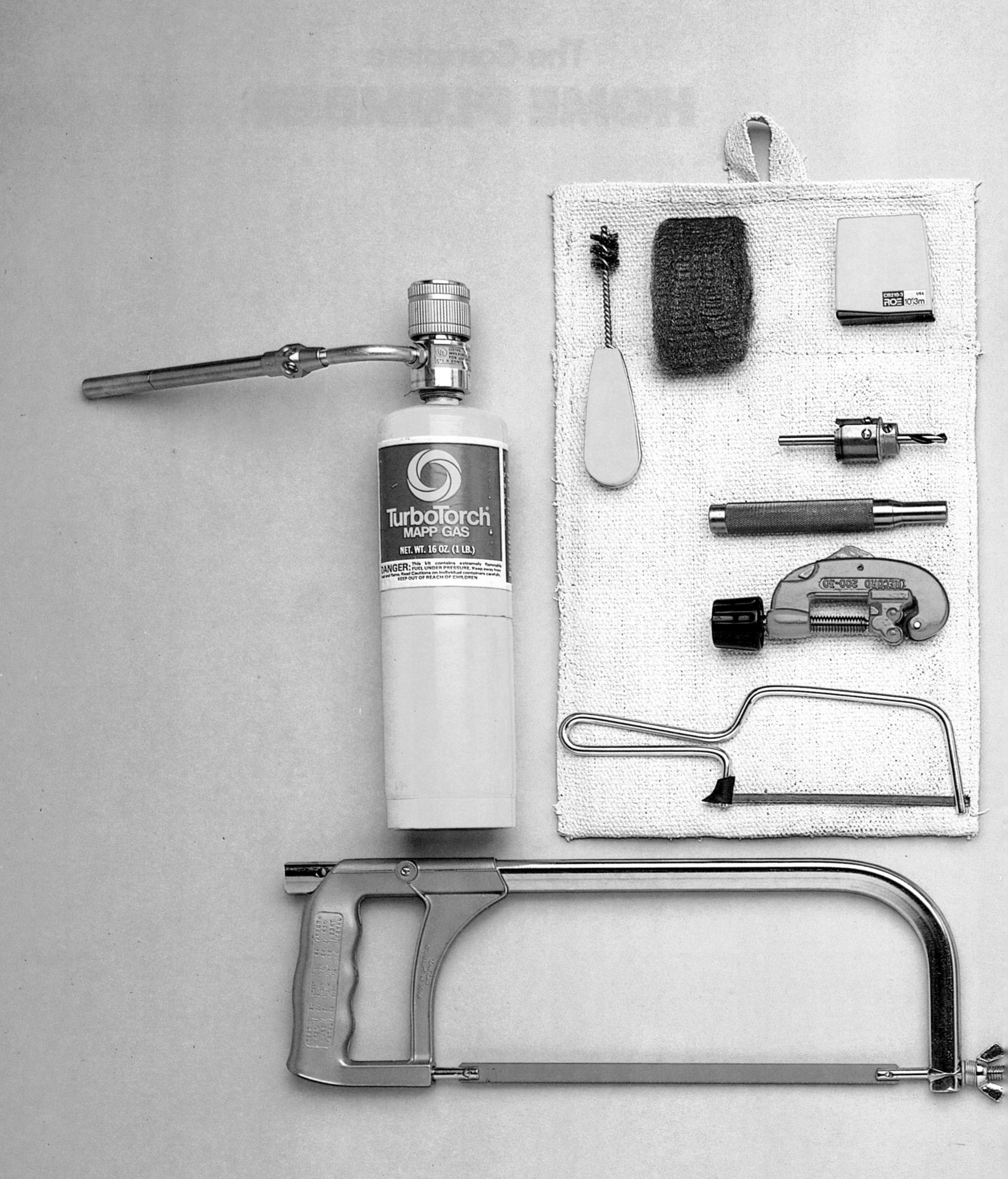
TurboTorch
MAPP GAS
NET. WT. 16 OZ. (1 LB.)
DANGER:

# The Complete HOME PLUMBER: Techniques, Projects and Materials

Edited by Mike Lawrence

Macdonald Orbis

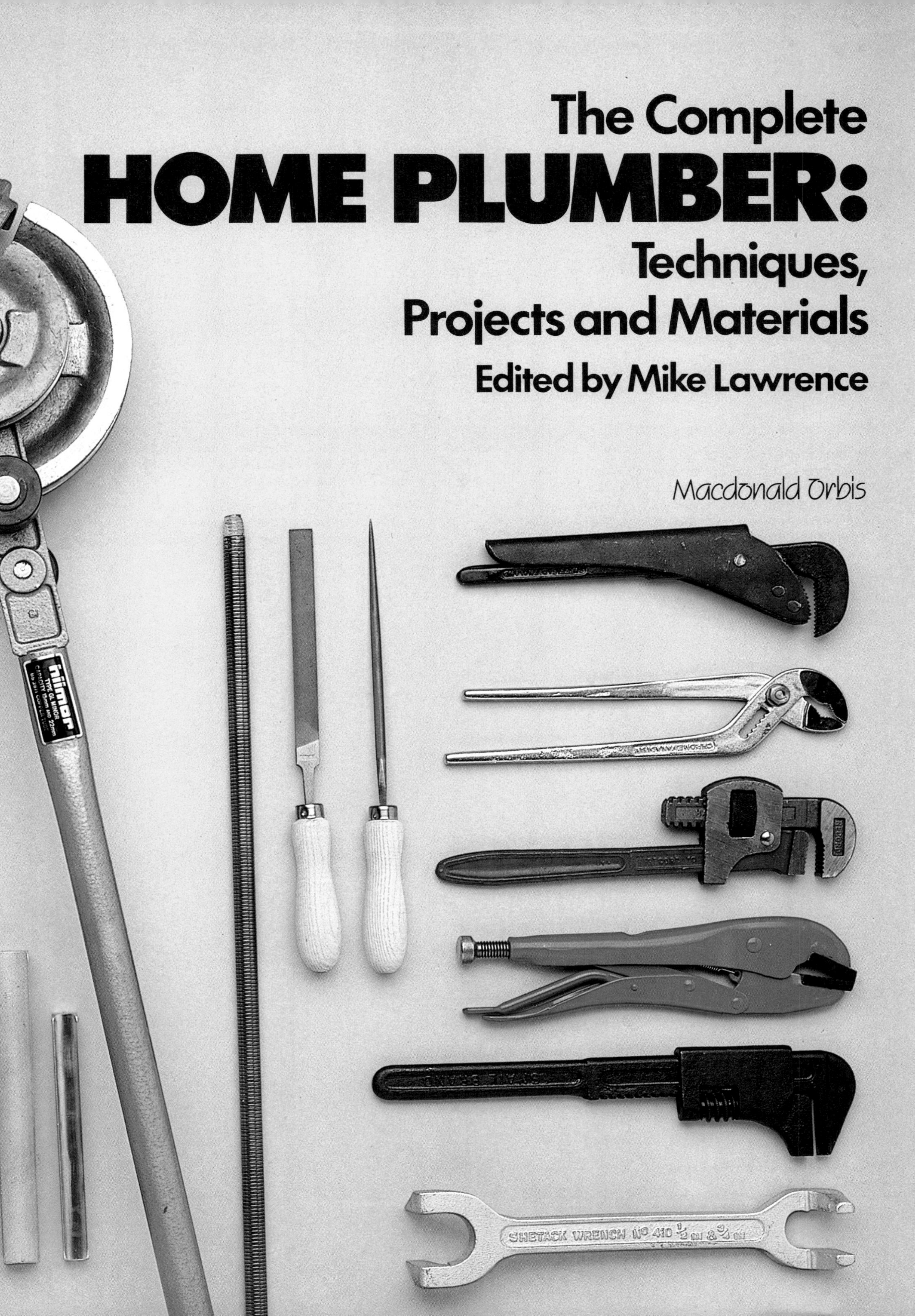

A Macdonald Orbis Book.

First published in Great Britain in 1986
by Orbis Publishing Ltd.

This edition published in Great Britain in 1988
by Macdonald & Co (Publishers) Ltd.
London & Sydney.

A member of Pergamon MCC Publishing Corporation plc.



Printed in Yugoslavia

ISBN: 0-356-15901-9

Acknowledgements
Photographers: Jon Bouchier, Simon Butcher, Paul Forrester,
Simon Gear, Jem Grischotti, Barry Jell, Keith Morris,
Karen Norquay, Roger Tuff.

Artists: Roger Courthold Associates, Bernard Fallon,
Nick Farmer, Trevor Lawrence, Linden Artists, David Pope,
Mike Saunders, Ed Stuart, Craig Warwick, Brian Watson.

Macdonald & Co (Publishers) Ltd.,
Greater London House,
Hampstead Road,
London NW1 7QX.

# CONTENTS

# INTRODUCTION

Many people take their plumbing systems for granted – so long as water flows from the taps when they are turned on and disappears again when the plug is pulled, they think no more about it. Most of the time their faith is justified; the average plumbing system often functions perfectly well for years with no trouble at all. When something does go wrong, or they want improvements or alterations carried out, they simply turn to a professional plumber. Only then do they realise how much his expertise costs, and wonder whether they could after all tackle some plumbing work themselves.

There is no reason why they shouldn't. The fear many do-it-yourselfers have about plumbing work is that any mistakes will cause an unholy mess, yet the skills needed to make watertight connections are not hard to learn. In fact, it takes a lot less skill to carry out most plumbing jobs than to make a success of a woodworking, decorating or bricklaying project, especially since the arrival of a whole new family of easy-to-use plumbing components. Furthermore, you need comparatively few specialist tools, so setting yourself up as a home plumber need not be an expensive business either.

One of the most important things you need to acquire is an understanding of how your home's plumbing and central heating systems work, and what rules and regulations you have to follow when you are carrying out extensions and alterations to them. *The Complete Home Plumber* aims to give you all this essential background information, and guide you through a wide range of plumbing repair and improvement projects.

The book begins by setting out water supply and waste systems in detail, so that you will be able to track down and identify all the pipework in your home. It then describes the traditional plumbing skills you'll need to know about before you begin to work on your system; many of the jobs you'll be carrying out will involve disconnecting existing fittings and pipe runs, so it's vital to understand how the plumber put everything together to begin with. Alongside these, you will find information on all the latest developments in DIY plumbing – plastic pipework for water supply as well as waste runs, push-fit and solvent-weld connectors that mean you can make up pipe runs without ever having to wield a spanner or blowlamp, corrugated pipes you can bend by hand, and many more. There is also a guide to the tools and accessories you will need to be a successful home plumber (and details of a handy basic tool kit every home should have ready for plumbing emergencies), plus an illustrated checklist for all the different types of plumbing fittings you are ever likely to need. Armed with this, you'll be able to ask confidently for a 'tee for copper, one end and branch reduced, 22 x 15 x 15mm' at your local plumber's merchant without causing hilarity among the queuing tradesmen!

The plumbing jobs covered in step-by-step detail include a number of common repair and replacement tasks that will help to keep your system running properly – everything from dealing with dripping taps and blocked waste pipes to fixing ball valves that don't open and close properly and radiators that leak. You will also find sections explaining a wide range of improvement projects – jobs like fitting new sinks and bathroom equipment, adding extra fittings such as bidets, showers and bedroom washbasins, and plumbing in appliances like washing machines and dishwashers. In each of these, the background to the job is explained fully so that you know exactly what is involved before you start work and are therefore able to plan every stage of the job in detail; what's more, tips from the professionals are given throughout to help you save time and get the best results.

The missing ingredient is for you to provide: it's the confidence to give home plumbing a try. Once you have familiarised yourself with the way your own home's plumbing and heating systems work, and practised some of the basic plumbing techniques on your workbench, there is no limit to the jobs you can tackle. The rewards at the end of the day will be two-fold: pride in your own achievements, and substantial savings on the fee you would have to pay a professional plumber.

We mentioned rules and regulations earlier. It's important to remember that any plumbing work you carry out in your home should comply where appropriate with your local water authority's Model Water Bye-laws and with the Building Regulations. You are obliged by law to notify your water authority of any changes you intend to make to the supply side of your system, and your local authority Building Control Officer or District Surveyor of alterations or additions to existing waste or drainage arrangements. They will check over your proposals and, if they're in order, give official approval. Don't start work without it.

CHAPTER 1

# WATER SUPPLY AND DRAINAGE NETWORKS

**Very few people are aware of what is involved in supplying clean, drinkable water to their homes, or indeed what happens to waste water when it disappears down a drain. Yet beyond the taps and the waste outlets is a vast network of underground pipes, drains and sewers, pumping stations, reservoirs, water towers and treatment works, all designed to ensure an efficient and constant supply of fresh water and the swift removal of waste.**

# UNDERSTANDING WATER SUPPLY

**Each one of us uses about 160 litres (35 gallons) of water a day, and takes it for granted. Only in a long spell of dry weather comes an awareness that we should use it carefully. Our use is controlled by the supply system – this is how it works.**

In the last 50 years the consumption of water has almost doubled. Rising standards of living have given rise to increased consumption, and a greater awareness of the need for hygiene has also played a large role in increasing the demand. Faced with this high demand, supply sources have been hard pressed to keep up.

### Where it comes from

Water is supplied by the local water authority (or the 'Undertaking' as it is known in the plumbing trade). After falling as rain it is collected in reservoirs which are fed by streams and rivers, or is pumped from underground wells. Water varies a lot in its chemical makeup since it picks up minerals and gases as it flows. If it picks up calcium, magnesium and sodium salts it will be 'hard' – the menace of pipe systems. Before being distributed it is usually filtered through sand and pebble beds to remove solids and organisms, and may have chlorine added to it to ensure that it is 'potable' – drinkable. Fluoride is also sometimes added for the protection of teeth.

Distribution is carried out by a network of pipes starting with 'trunk mains' which may be as much as 610mm (24in) in diameter. These split into mains and sub-mains which run underneath streets and side streets. It is these sub-mains which are tapped by individual houses for their supply.

The house system may be 'direct' in which all cold water supplies are piped direct from the rising main, with the cistern only being used to supply the hot water tank. Or it may be an 'indirect' system in which all cold-water supplies are taken from the cistern, with the exception of a direct supply to the kitchen sink for drinking purposes.

For water to flow through the trunk mains – and eventually into your house – it must be under a certain amount of pressure. This pressure is assisted by pumps but it is vital that somewhere in the mains system the water should reach a height in a reservoir or water tower, higher than any domestic system it has to supply. The vertical distance through which the water 'falls' is known as the 'pressure head' and without it our cisterns would never fill up without a lot of expensive additional pumping. The storage cistern also provides a pressure head inside the house, which is why it's preferable to have it in the roof space.

### The house system

The sub-main underneath the road is tapped by the 'communication pipe' which ends at the authority's stop-valve. This is usually situated under the pavement about 300mm (1ft) outside the boundary of your property. The stop-valve is located at the bottom of a vertical 'guard' pipe – about 1 metre (39in) deep – which is covered at the surface by a hinged metal cover. It should only be operated by the water authority and requires a special key to turn it. But in a real emergency you may be able to turn it yourself. In old houses it may be the only way of turning off the water supply. After this stop-valve the water enters the service pipe and from then on all pipes become your responsibility.

The service pipe continues under the wall of the property at a depth of at least 750mm (2ft 6in) to protect it from frost – though some water authorities insist that it should be 900mm (3ft) deep. As it travels under the house wall or foundation it usually goes through an earthenware pipe to protect it

## Ready Reference

### TURNING OFF THE WATER

It's essential you know where to turn off the mains water supply in case of an emergency. Check for stop-valves:

- under the kitchen sink
- in a utility room
- under the stairs
- just outside the boundary fence of your property. This one should only be turned off by the water authority, unless it's an emergency and you have no option
- in the front garden near the path and about a metre (39in) down. Look for a hinged metal cover. You might have to use a home-made wooden 'key' to reach the tap

## INDIRECT COLD SUPPLY

*The most common system of water supply in the UK is called 'indirect' because most taps take water from the storage cistern in the roof and not direct from the mains. The cistern is fed by the rising main which in turn is fed by the distribution pipe from the mains.*

*Water input to the cistern is controlled by a high pressure ball-valve. If this valve jams open the water level rises to flow out of the overflow or 'warning' pipe which should stick well out from the wall.*

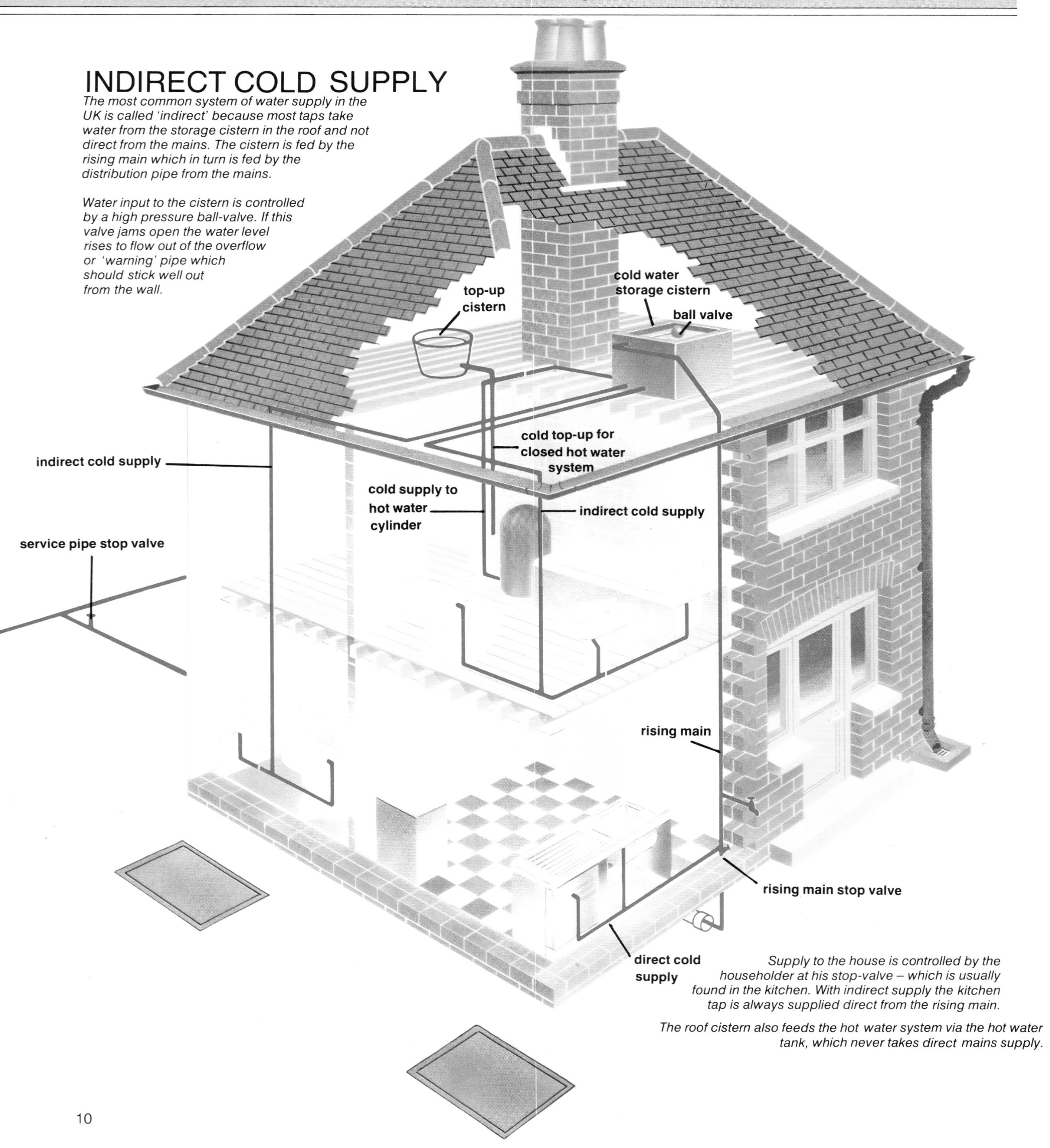


*Supply to the house is controlled by the householder at his stop-valve – which is usually found in the kitchen. With indirect supply the kitchen tap is always supplied direct from the rising main.*

*The roof cistern also feeds the hot water system via the hot water tank, which never takes direct mains supply.*

from possible settlement which might cause it to fracture. To prevent any risk of freezing in cold weather the service pipe should not emerge above ground level until it is at least 600mm (2ft) inside the inside wall surface.

Up to about 40 years ago, service pipes were usually made of lead (in fact the word plumbing originally stemmed from the Latin word for lead – *plumbum)*. Today copper and polythene are used instead. The latter is particularly good as it is a poor conductor of heat and is less prone to freezing and fracture.

### The service pipe

The service pipe continues under the wall near the kitchen sink, which means that it is often attached to the inner face of the outside wall. This is contrary to the recommendation that it should be attached to an inside wall, and so such a pipe should be lagged with insulation material. The pipe should also be insulated if it comes through any sub-ground floor cavity where it would be subjected to the icy blasts of winter from under-floor ventilation. Again these precautions are both intended to minimise the risk of frost damage.

When the service pipe rises above the ground floor it is called the 'rising main' and it eventually terminates in the supply cistern, which is usually in the roof cavity. The householder's main stop-valve is usually found on the rising main a little way above floor level. This is the most important 'tap' in the house. In any plumbing emergency – when bursts or leaks occur, for example, your first action should be to turn this tap off, thus isolating the house system from the mains water supply. The stop-valve should always be turned off when you go away if the house is going to be empty. In old houses the location of the stop-valve may vary considerably, it may be in the cellar, under the stairs, or even under a cover beneath the front path – or it may not exist at all, in which case the authority's stop-valve is the only control.

### Branch supply pipes

At least one 'branch' supply pipe leaves the rising main close above the stop-valve and drain tap – this is to the tap over the kitchen sink. This tap must be supplied direct from the main supply as it is supposed to provide all drinking and cooking water. Water which has been in a storage cistern is no longer considered drinkable, sometimes termed 'potable', as it may be slightly contaminated by debris in the storage cistern.

Other branches may be taken at this point to an outside tap, or to a washing machine or dishwasher.

The rising main continues upwards and while its ultimate destination is the cold water storage cistern the pipework in between will vary from house to house, depending on

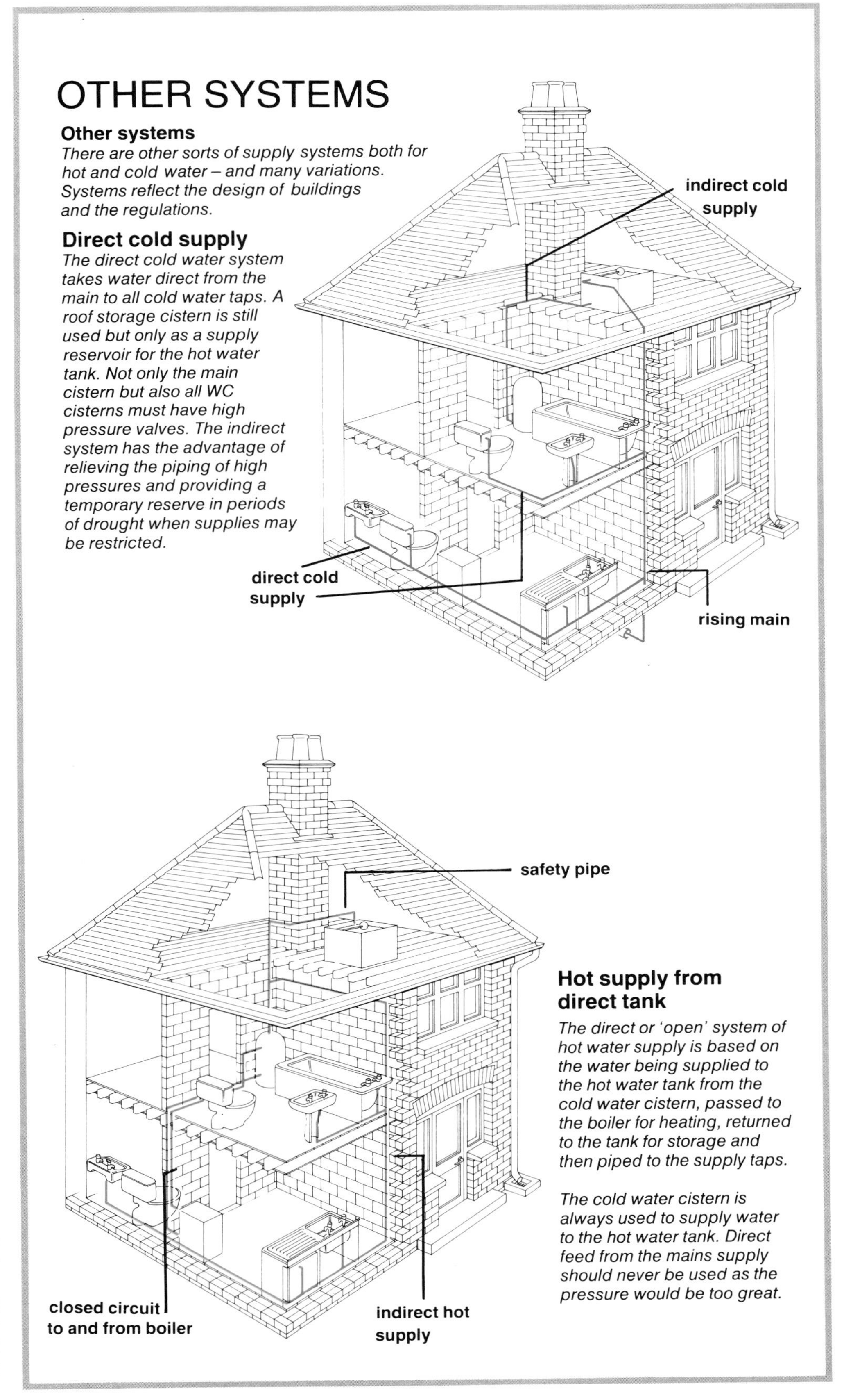


## OTHER SYSTEMS

### Other systems

*There are other sorts of supply systems both for hot and cold water – and many variations. Systems reflect the design of buildings and the regulations.*

### Direct cold supply

*The direct cold water system takes water direct from the main to all cold water taps. A roof storage cistern is still used but only as a supply reservoir for the hot water tank. Not only the main cistern but also all WC cisterns must have high pressure valves. The indirect system has the advantage of relieving the piping of high pressures and providing a temporary reserve in periods of drought when supplies may be restricted.*

### Hot supply from direct tank

*The direct or 'open' system of hot water supply is based on the water being supplied to the hot water tank from the cold water cistern, passed to the boiler for heating, returned to the tank for storage and then piped to the supply taps.*

*The cold water cistern is always used to supply water to the hot water tank. Direct feed from the mains supply should never be used as the pressure would be too great.*

# INDIRECT HOT WATER SUPPLY

*In an indirect or 'closed' hot water system a closed pipe runs from the boiler, through a heat exchanger in the hot water tank and back to the boiler again. This closed system contains water which never comes into contact with the hot water used by the household. The closed circuit between boiler and hot water cylinder loses water very slowly, and is topped up automatically by water from a small reservoir cistern in the loft. A safety pipe returns over-heated water to this or the main cistern.*

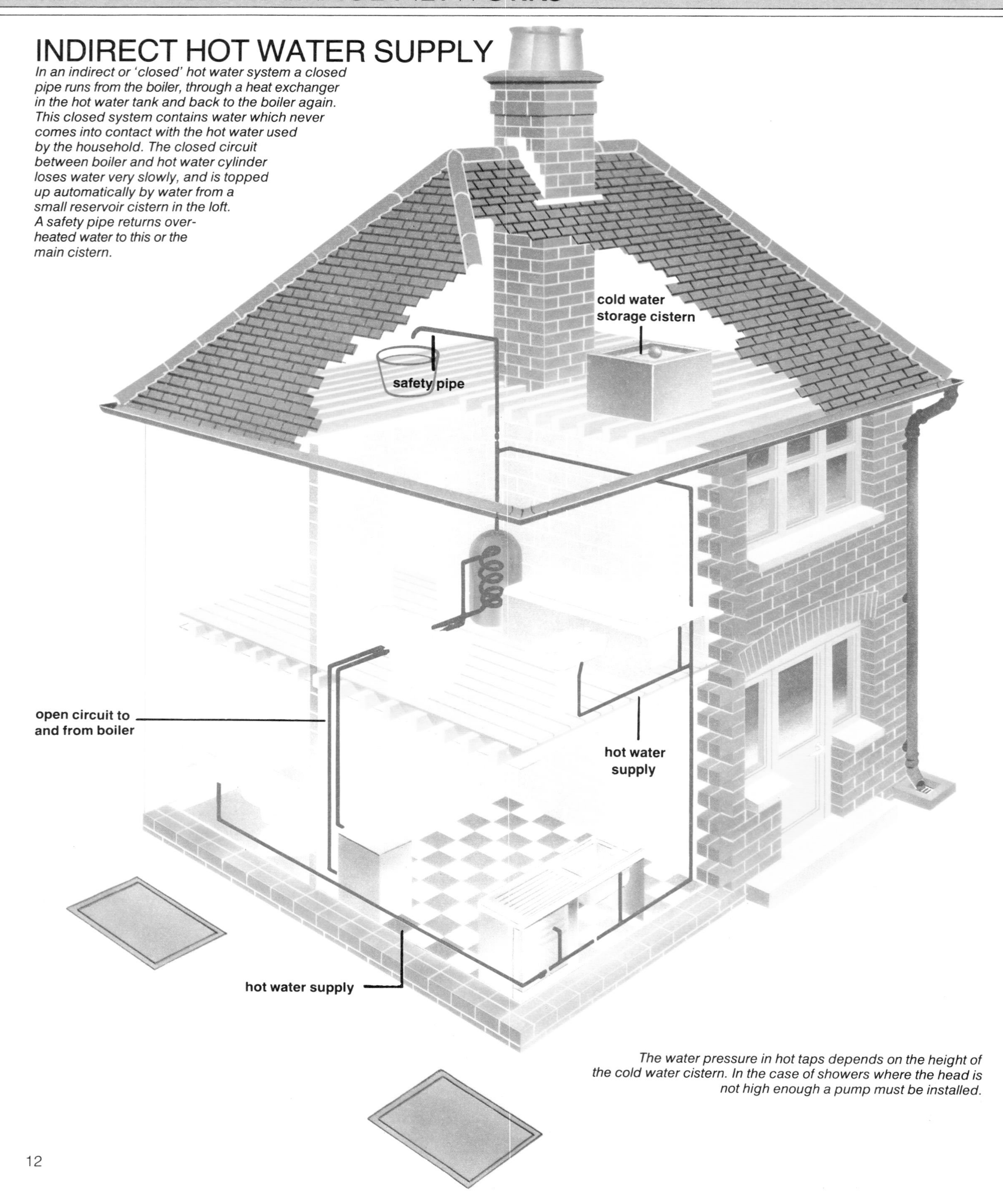


*The water pressure in hot taps depends on the height of the cold water cistern. In the case of showers where the head is not high enough a pump must be installed.*

whether a 'direct' or 'indirect' system has been installed.

In many areas indirect systems must be installed in new buildings, yet in Western Europe direct systems are the rule. Indirect systems have been encouraged because of the difficulty in maintaining constant mains pressure particularly at times of peak demand. Routing of most supplies through the storage cistern evens out fluctuations, and it also rules out the risk of 'back siphonage' whereby dirty water could be sucked back into the mains supply – though this rarely occurs. The 1976 drought in the UK provided good reason for indirect systems, since each house had an emergency supply in the storage cistern if the mains water had to be shut off.

### Cisterns

The 'tank' in your loft or attic is in fact a 'cistern'. Cisterns are not sealed – though they should be covered – and so are subject to atmospheric pressure. Tanks are completely sealed – as with a hot water storage tank – and are not subject to atmospheric pressure.

Cold water cisterns ,have traditionally been made of galvanised mild steel and it is quite likely that you will find one like this in your loft. They are still available, but are not usually installed in new houses. Other materials used have been asbestos, cement, copper and glass fibre, but today the most common material is plastic, of which glass fibre reinforced polyester (GRP), polythene and polypropylene are the most common varieties.

The advantages plastics have over all other cistern materials are their lightness in weight, resistance to corrosion and flexibility. Galvanised steel is heavy and liable to corrode, while asbestos and cement are not only heavy but can become porous and are prone to accidental damage. Don't forget the capacity of a typical cistern is 227 litres (50 gallons), and this water alone weighs nearly 0.25 tonne (1/4 ton), so all cisterns must be fully supported on the joists. With rigid materials such as steel the cistern can rest across the joists, but with plastic and glass fibre a platform should be installed to support the whole area of the bottom, otherwise the material may develop local weaknesses.

Cisterns should be covered to prevent any contamination of the water. Where the underside of the roof is exposed dust and dirt are liable to fall in. The top and sides should also be insulated to minimise the risk of freezing. The bottom is left uncovered to allow rising warm air from rooms below to keep the water above freezing point, and so you shouldn't insulate the roof space under the cistern.

Cisterns were often installed before the roof was put on and if you want to replace yours, perhaps because it's made of steel and is corroding, you may not be able to get it through the trap door. While it is sometimes suggested that a cistern should be cut up to get it out this is in fact a very heavy and arduous job in such a confined space and it would be better to manoeuvre it to one side and leave it in the loft, installing a new cistern alongside. Modern plastic cisterns can literally be folded up so they can be passed through small loft hatches.

### Pipes and taps

Water leaves the storage cistern in distribution pipes which are usually 22mm (3/4in) or 15mm (1/2in) in diameter. In a direct system, supply from the cistern will usually only be to the hot water tank, and in an indirect system this link must also be direct – but other distribution pipes are used with branches to supply the other appliances – basins, baths and WC cisterns. Distribution pipes usually end in taps but in the case of a WC a low pressure ball-valve controls the flow.

The WC in an indirect system has a low pressure ball-valve because when the water leaves the storage cistern it is no longer at mains pressure but at normal atmospheric pressure which is pressing down on the surface of the stored water. This means that the higher up the house a tap or other outlet is situated the lower will be the water pressure. In practice this means that you can't have a tap in an indirect system which is above the level of its distribution outlet from the cistern. Showers are particularly affected by this difference of pressure, and if there is not sufficient 'head' to 'drive' the shower a special pump may have to be installed.

Cold water supplied to the hot water tank is heated in two different ways again called indirect and direct systems – or, respectively, closed and open. In the latter the cold water is circulated through the boiler, where it is heated, and returned to the tank from where it flows to tapped outlets. In the indirect system the cold water supplied never actually goes to the boiler, instead it is heated in the tank by a coiled pipe or jacket containing hot water which is continuously circulating through the boiler. In either case a pump often helps the water flow through the boiler, and supplementary or alternative heat may come from an immersion heater. If there is no boiler but only an immersion heater in the tank the system is essentially direct with the heating of the water taking place in the tank rather than in the boiler.

### Draining the system

Just above the rising main stop-valve should be a drain cock. With the stop-valve turned off the drain cock can be used to drain part of the cold water system when repairs are necessary – the hot water system has its own drain cock.

## Ready Reference

### PIPE SIZES AND THEIR USES

**Distribution pipes**

- 22mm (3/4in) pipe – water supply to bath and hot water cylinder
- 15m (1/2in) pipe – WC, basin, bidet and shower supplies
- 28mm (1in) pipe – for use with multiple appliances, but usually unnecessary.

**Warning pipes (Overflows)**

- these must have a diameter greater than that of the inlet pipe to prevent cold water cisterns and WC cisterns from overflowing.

### CONNECTIONS AT COLD WATER CISTERN

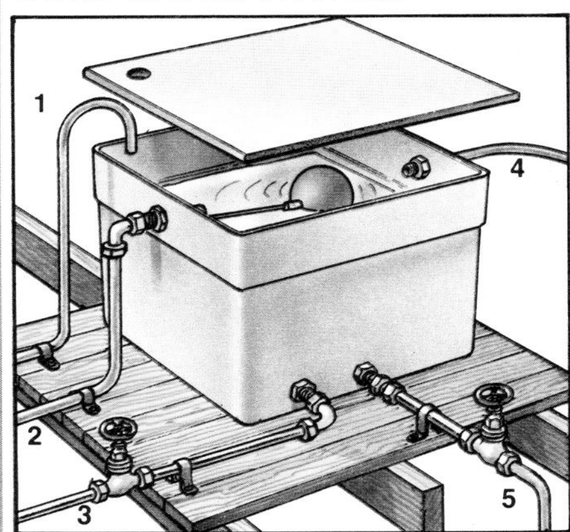


**1 safety pipe** **2 rising main** **3 cold supply to taps** **4 overflow** **5 cold supply to hot water tank**

### DRAINING THE SYSTEM

To drain the system from the mains stop-valve to cistern, turn off the stop-valve and attach one end of the hose to the drain cock, which should be just above the stop-valve, and run the other end to a drain. Then open the drain cock.

Drain remainder of system by turning off

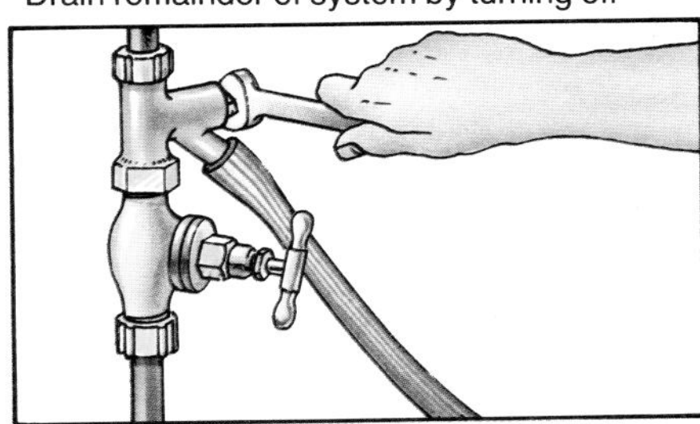

mains supply and opening cold water taps. The hot water system has its own drain cock, usually found close to the boiler.

# WASTE WATER SYSTEMS

**A waste water system must be able to dispose of used water from the kitchen and bathroom efficiently and hygienically, and some also have to cater for rainwater falling on the roof. Here's how it's done.**

The supply of hot and cold water to the taps in your house is really only half the domestic plumbing story. You also need a waste system to remove what you've used or don't want. And besides coping with the dirty water from the bath, basin and sink and the waste from the WC, the system also has to deal with the rainwater which falls on the roof.

The drainage system therefore has to be efficient and durable, and for obvious reasons of hygiene, self-cleansing. Waste matter mustn't be allowed to remain in the pipes and if blockages occur it should be possible to remove them easily.

## How the drainage system works

There are several domestic drainage systems but each of them can be broken down into five separate sections. When waste water leaves an appliance of any sort, it will go immediately through a 'waste trap' – a 180° bend containing a water seal which fills the trap whenever the waste pipe empties. This keeps drain smells out of the room and prevents insects and the like from entering the home. With WCs it also makes self-cleansing easier. WC traps are cast as an integral part of the WC pan, but on other appliances they are separate, and are attached to the outlet pipe by a large retaining nut.

From the trap, waste water enters a branch pipe which leads to the main vertical drainage 'stack'. This takes it below ground level to the first underground section of the drainage system where it flows through at least one inspection chamber (covered with a manhole cover) and into the public sewer, which is usually situated underneath the road. The sewer is provided by the public health authority and it is their responsibility to remove all waste running into it.

Often rainwater from the roof is fed into the drainage system to flow into the public sewer. But some authorities provide a separate street drain for it or insist on the provision of soakaways (pits filled with rubble and gravel which allow the water to soak into the surrounding earth) near the house. Tanks and cisterns rarely overflow, but when they do they discharge clean water, so it's not necessary for the overflow pipes to be located over a drain. The water can fall directly onto the ground.

The cost of laying public sewers in rural areas means that the waste from many houses in these parts flows into a cess pool or septic tank. These are specially constructed pits for storing effluent (and in the case of a septic tank, for breaking it down into harmless matter). Both of these require periodic pumping out, cess pools much more often as they store all the waste. If you're buying a house with one of these systems, check how often this has to be done, who does it and how much you may have to pay.

## How it all began

Proper plumbing systems have only been around for about 100 years. The large urban expansion which took place during the Industrial Revolution lead to squalid housing conditions, and disease was rife. Eventually, enclosed sewers were introduced along with piped water supplies and pottery WC pans. By the 1870s many homes were equipped with a basin, a WC and a sink; but an acute shortage of qualified plumbers lead to ridiculous installations which often produced as great a health threat as before. The London County Council took the lead in sorting things out by laying out a set of rules in 1900, establishing the 'two-pipe' system – one stack for waste water from basins and sinks, another for 'soil water' from WCs.

The amount of pipework needed with the two-pipe system, and the increased siphonage problems on tall buildings, led to the introduction of the 'one-pipe' system. This system was the forerunner of the modern 'single stack' system and abandoned the distinction between the soil and the waste pipe stacks. It was only used extensively on multi-storey buildings.

On the one-pipe system all discharges flowed into a single stack which had an open-ended outlet at roof level. All traps had deep seals and each branch pipe was also connected to a vent pipe which rose to eaves level.

The single stack system was developed in the UK in the late 1940s to overcome the drawbacks and complications of the two-pipe systems, and to simplify the installation – everyone must be familiar with the untidy cluster of pipes on the outside walls of houses with these systems.

The advent of light plastic piping helped in this development, as it made the production of accurate mouldings easier, and cut down the installation time because plastic was quicker to join than the old metal piping.

## The single stack system

This consists of a single waste stack into which all the branch pipes discharge. However, ground floor waste doesn't have to go

# TWO-PIPE WASTE SYSTEM

*The traditional two pipe system takes all soil to the underground drain by one pipe, and all the waste from baths, basins etc down another. It is found in most pre-war houses, and is still used, particularly in bungalows where the installation is spread out.*

*Roof drainage may flow into the same underground drainage system; it may go into a separate storm drain (out in the street) in areas of high rainfall; or it may drain into a soakaway in the garden.*

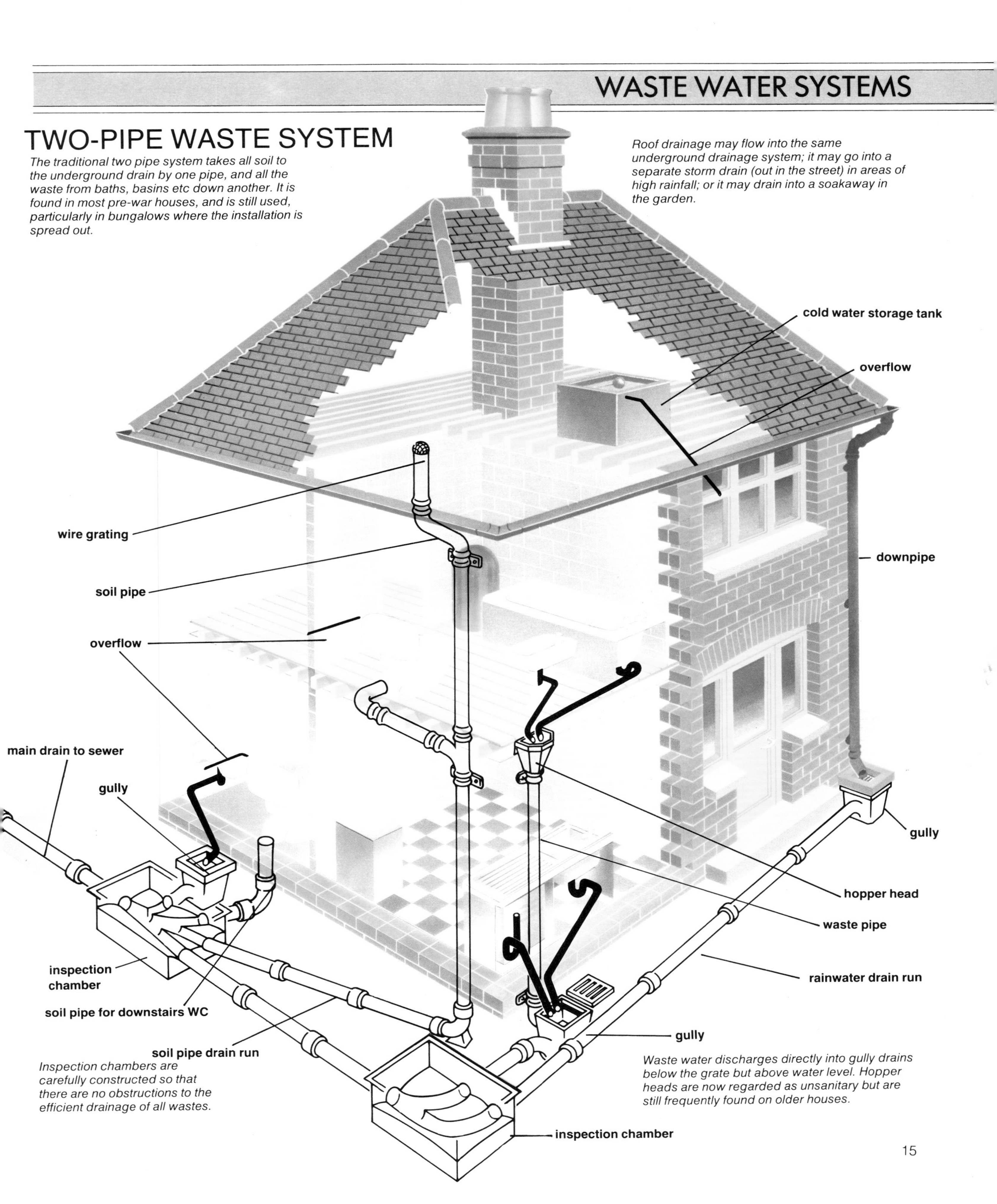


*Inspection chambers are carefully constructed so that there are no obstructions to the efficient drainage of all wastes.*

*Waste water discharges directly into gully drains below the grate but above water level. Hopper heads are now regarded as unsanitary but are still frequently found on older houses.*

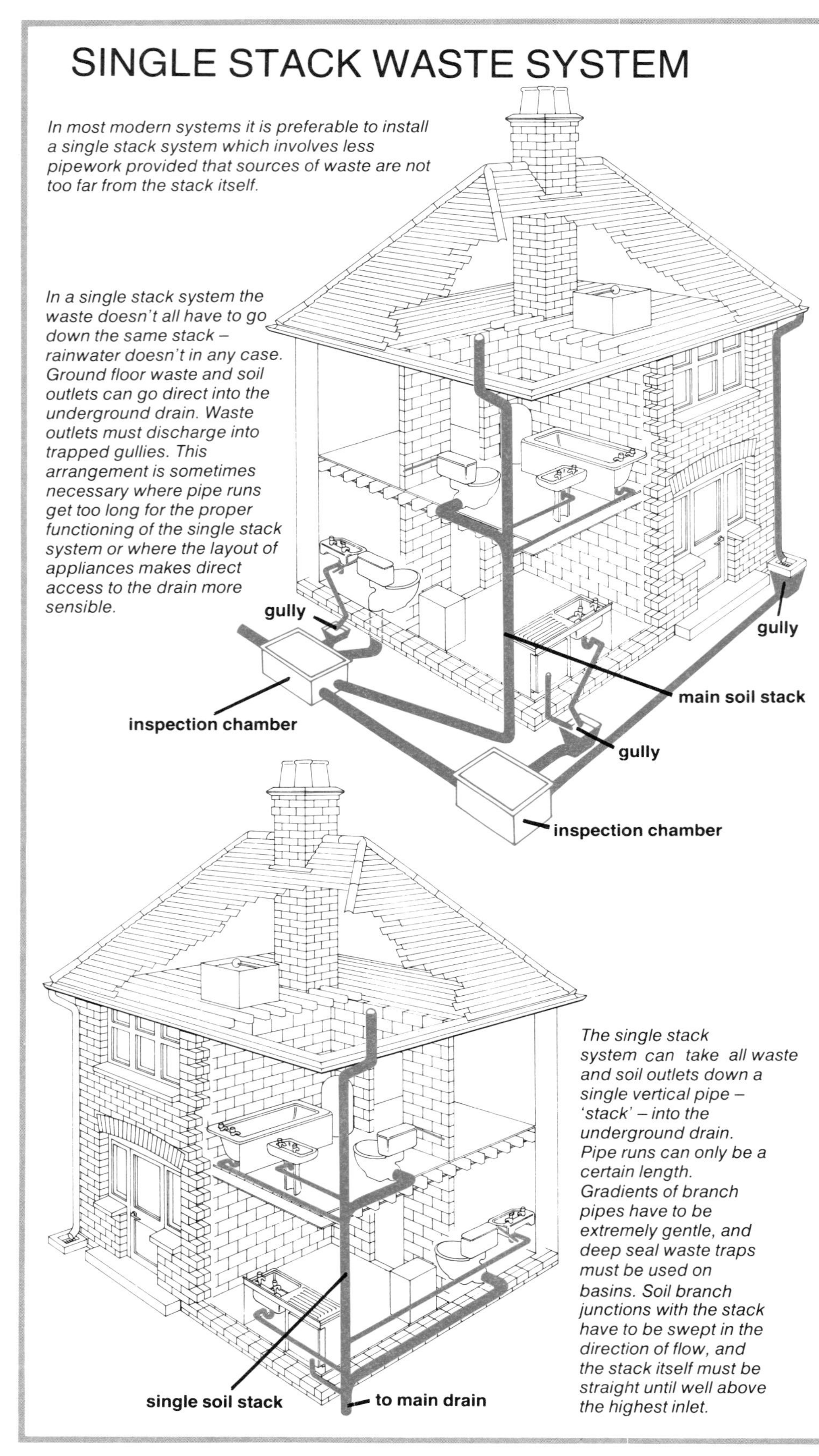


into the stack. Sink waste water may flow into a trapped gully and ground-floor WCs may be connected directly into the underground drain. This avoids any risk that a blockage at the base of the stack (where it bends to join the underground drain) could lead to waste water being forced back along the waste pipes to ground-floor appliances.

In appearance the single-stack system is the simplest waste system of all and the most economical to install. As a result it is incorporated in the majority of new houses. But because the branches have to be comparatively short, the system is less useful in bungalows where appliances are likely to be spread out. Usually all the pipework is sited indoors, which means a neater appearance for the house exterior; it also reduces the possibility of frost damage. All you'll see of the system is a tell-tale vent pipe poking up through the roof.

In order to make the system work properly a number of technical regulations have to be taken into account when it's being installed. These relate to the length, diameter, bend radii and angles of bend of the branch pipes, the use of P-traps and S-traps on waste pipes other than WCs (see *Traps for each appliance),* the positioning of the stack connectors, and the dimensions of the stack itself. While the system may look simple, considerable research has been done to ensure that problems of siphonage aren't likely to occur.

### The two-pipe system

The principles of the two-pipe system were based on a belief that all kinds of disease were caused by the 'bad air' in drains, and the system aimed to keep this out of homes. The basic principle was that the 'soil' discharge from WCs went directly down one stack into the underground drain. All other discharges, termed 'waste', went down another stack which led into a trapped gully (a cast drain incorporating a water trap) at ground level and from there joined the soil discharge under-ground. Sometimes waste had to fall into a channel at ground level before running into the drain.

All waste and soil pipework had to be fixed to the outside of the building. The soil pipe was continued upwards to eaves level where it terminated open-ended in a wire cover to keep nesting birds from causing a blockage. This allowed free passage of air from the underground drain.

When the two-pipe system came into existence, most homes only had an outside WC (quite often shared) and a kitchen sink, so discharge was entirely at ground level, but when upstairs bathrooms became popular waste was directed into hoppers attached to stand-pipes, which caused new problems. Hoppers were not self-cleansing and soapy water drying on the inside could start to smell; draughts could also blow up the pipe to the hopper, bringing smells from the drain at the bottom. This led to some authorities banning hoppers and insisting on discharge direct into another stack which meant installing an eaves-level vent as with the soil stack.

On buildings over two storeys high this created another problem known as 'induced siphonage'. When water flowing down the waste stack from one outlet passed another outlet where it joined the stack, it could cause a partial vacuum in the second pipe which could suck out the contents of the water trap. To cure this problem the upper part of each trap had to be connected to a branch vent pipe which either connected to a separate vertical stack to eaves level, or joined the vented waste stack at least 900mm (3ft) above the level of the highest waste connection. If you live in a tall house you may have this system, and any repairs to vent pipes should follow the existing system. The alternative is to take out the entire system and replace it with a single stack arrangement.

### Traps for each appliance

The traditional trap was a simple U-shaped bend attached to a horizontal branch outlet – today called a 'P' trap. If the branch outlet is vertical this trap bends round again into a double 'U' or 'S' outlet. In systems with lead pipes, the traps were often formed from lengths of pipe, while with modern plastic waste systems the traps are separate and easily detachable. The plastic bottle trap, which performs the same function, is also now widely used, and this is more compact and neater in appearance.

The depth of the water-filled part of the trap is known as the 'depth of seal'. Shallow traps have a seal depth of around 50mm (2in), 38mm (1½in) or 19mm (¾in), while 'deep-seal' traps have a 75mm (3in) seal.

Lead traps usually allow access for clearing blockages, and this is obtained by unscrewing an access cap or 'eye'. Modern plastic traps are connected by screwed collars at both ends and can be completely removed for cleaning if blocked. The lower part of bottle traps likewise completely unscrews. Adjustable plastic traps are available for fixing to existing pipework where access is difficult and special adaptors are used to link to copper and iron pipes.

Traps must remain filled with water and it is against the bye-laws if they don't. This is the most important and lasting principle handed down from the waste disposal thinking of the last century.

The water seal can be lost from traps for lots of reasons. Siphonage is the worst problem and where it occurs it's usually due to a badly designed system. Simply, if the air pressure beyond the trap is slightly less than the normal atmospheric pressure acting on the surface of the water in the trap, the water will drain away. This is more likely with 'S' traps than 'P' traps, and with shallow rather than deep traps. The problem of siphonage led to the introduction of venting systems and dictated the dimensions in the single stack system (and also excluded the use of 'S' traps).

### Overflow pipes

There are two sorts of overflow pipes – those which are connected to storage cisterns and WC cisterns, and those which are attached to or form a part of appliances such as basins and baths. They are known in the trade as warning pipes. Both sorts should be fitted to avoid the risk of overflows damaging your home. This may be caused when you forget to turn off the bath, or by mechanical failure when the ball-valve on the water storage tank jams open.

In sinks, basins and baths the overflow must discharge into the branch waste pipe between the trap and the appliance, or into the trap above the water level of the seal, and must be able to cope with the flow of water from one tap turned full on.

Sink and basin overflows are usually built into the design of the appliance, while those for baths are supplied as part of the plumbing and connect to a slot in the waste outlet casting.

Overflows from tanks and cisterns consist of a length of pipe of a minimum 22mm (⅞in) internal diameter, capable of discharging water as quickly as any incoming flow. They usually emerge through the outside wall and stick out far enough to avoid any water flow sluicing down the wall surface, which could be a potential source of damp.

### Pipe and trap materials

All waste and soil pipes are today mainly manufactured in plastic. Branch pipes were made of lead or copper, stack pipes of cast iron, traps of lead or brass and underground pipes of vitrified clay. Only the latter still predominantly utilize the traditional material.

### Your legal position

Drainage regulations fall under the Public Health Acts as well as the Building Regulations, so it's important to know where you stand. The householder is responsible for the entire drainage system until it enters the public sewer – even though this is usually beyond the boundary of the property. While blockages beyond the lowest inspection chamber are rare, any clearance work can be very expensive – particularly if you use a '24-hour' plumbing service. The public

## Ready Reference

### SINGLE STACK SYSTEMS

Single stack waste systems must be built and modified correctly in order to be acceptable to the authorities and to work properly. Here are some rules to remember:

- 'P' traps must be used on all appliances – 'S' (integral) traps are only allowed on WCs – and the depth of seal should always be 75mm (3in)
- wash basins and bidets need a 32mm (1¼in) diameter trap and branch pipe, if the branch is up to 1.7m (5ft 7in) long. If more – up to a maximum of 2.3m (7ft 6in) – use a 38mm (1½in) trap and pipe
- baths, sinks and showers use a 38mm (1½in) diameter trap and branch pipe
- washing machines use a vertical stand pipe (usually about 600mm/24in high) with a 32mm (1¼in) diameter trap at the bottom ('P' or running 'P'). There must be an air gap where the hose enters the standpipe
- WC branch pipes are usually 100mm (4in) in diameter to correspond with the outlet; branch lengths can be up to 6m (20ft) long
- branch pipe gradients should be at a minimal angle – preferably 1-2½° (18-45mm fall per metre or ¾-1¾in per 39in)
- ground floor WCs can connect directly into the underground drain as long as the top of the trap is less than 1.5m (5ft) from the point of entry into the main drain
- there should be no connection nearer than 200mm (8in) below the WC branch connection from the opposite side of the stack
- the lowest connection to the stack must be at least 450mm (18in) above the bottom of the bend at the base of the stack
- the bend at the base of the stack(below ground) must have a radius of at least 200mm (8in)
- stack pipes must be at least the same diameter as the WC outlet
- the top of the stack pipe, capped with a grille, must be above the eaves and at least 0.9m (35in) above any window which is within 3m (10ft) of the pipe.

sewer is provided by the public health authority and is their responsibility.

If your house was built as one of a group of houses, then it's quite possible that you'll have shared drainage facilities. This means there is one drainage pipe collecting the waste of several homes before it discharges into the public sewer. The system was adopted because it saved installation costs. If your house was built before 1937, it's still the responsibility of the local authorities to cleanse the shared drainage runs, although you're responsible for clearing blockages and for maintenance. But if you live in a post-1937 house then the responsibility for the shared drains rests collectively on all the owners concerned and if a blockage is caused by someone else you will have to pay a proportion of the bill. It is therefore important when moving house to check out the exact position. If this is difficult to ascertain, try the Environmental Health Officer for advice; he should also be consulted if you want to change the system.

## PLASTIC WASTE TRAPS

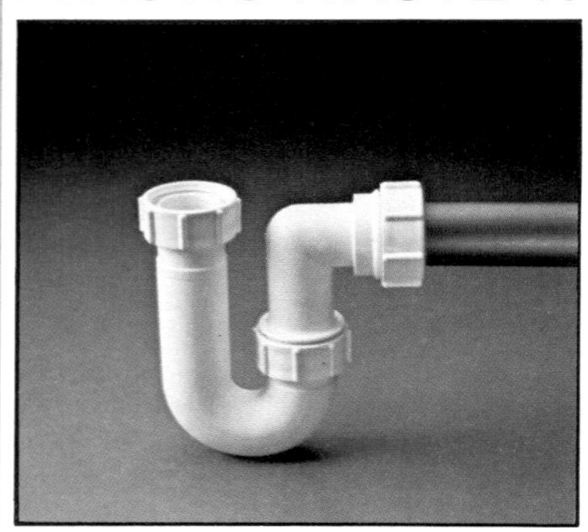

**The modern U-bend** *is made from one of several plastic materials.*

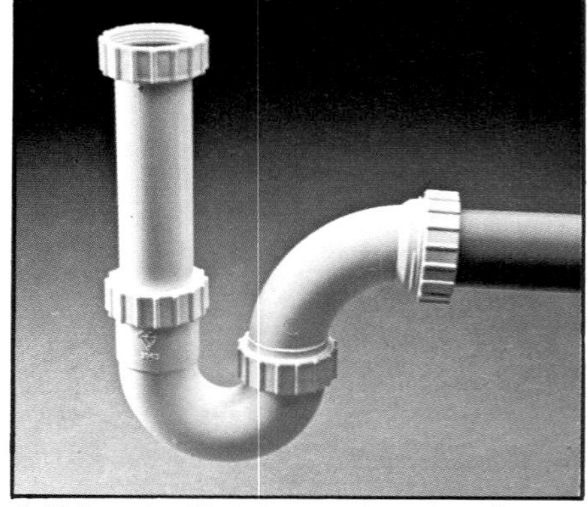

**A U-bend with telescopic extension** *can be adjusted to existing appliances.*

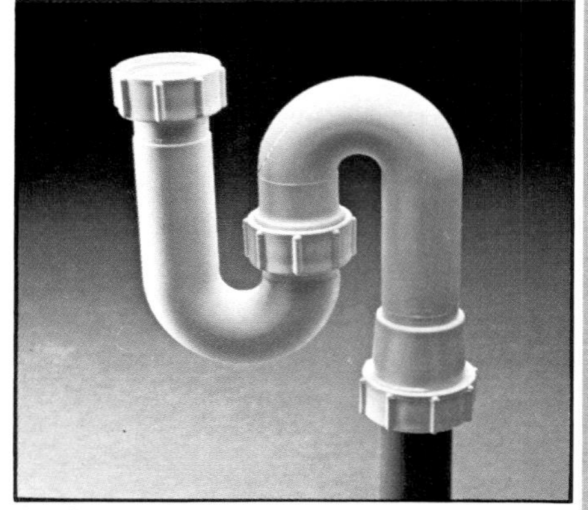

**An S-bend** *is designed for use where the outlet is vertical.*

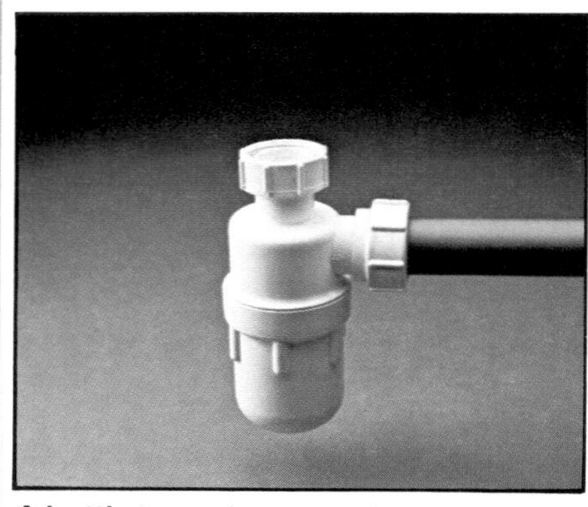

**A bottle trap** *gives a neater appearance, but is less efficient.*

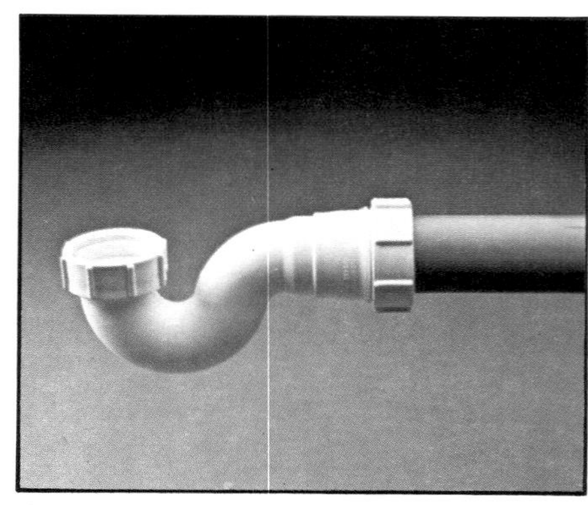

**A shallow trap** *is used beneath a bath or shower where space is crucial.*

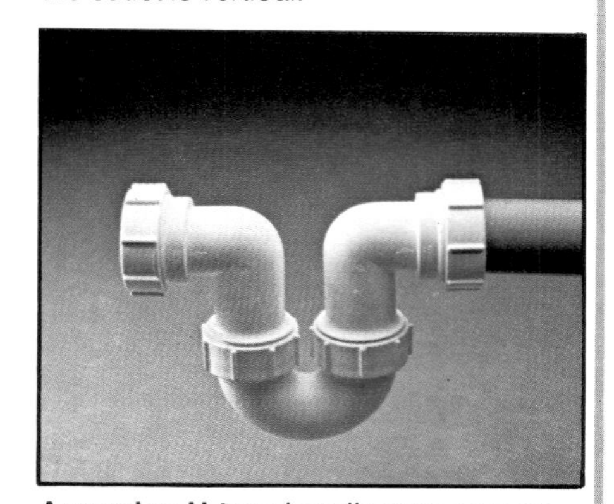

**A running U-trap** *handles two or more untrapped appliances piped together.*

**A dip partition bottle trap** *has a base which unscrews.*

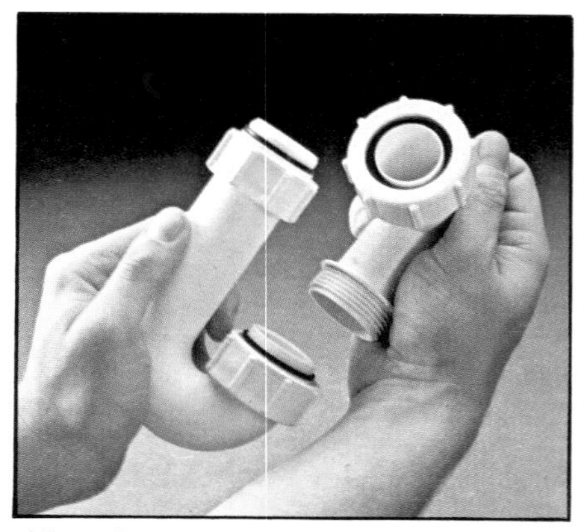

*All modern traps come apart for easy cleaning and installation.*

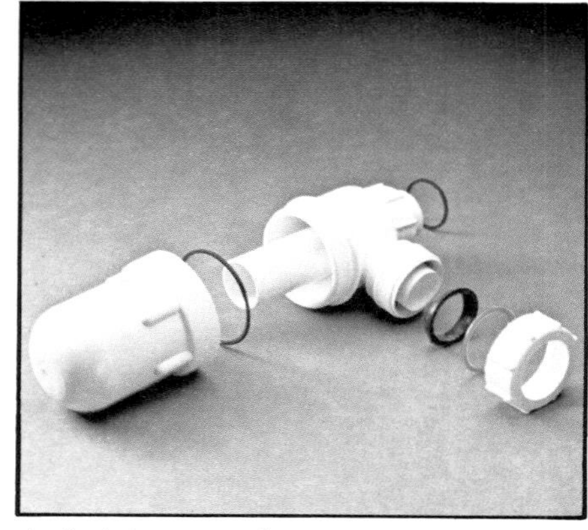

*A dip tube trap taken apart to show the O rings and washers.*

## CHAPTER 2

# BASIC SKILLS AND TOOLS

**There is no doubt that a professional plumber is a highly skilled person and matching his expertise would take you many years of study and training. However, you can acquire sufficient skills without too much trouble, allowing you to carry out most of the plumbing jobs you will come up against, provided you take care in what you are doing.**

# JOINTS FOR COPPER PIPE

**Joining copper pipe is one of the basic plumbing skills. Compression and capillary joints are easy to make and once you've mastered the techniques, you'll be prepared for a whole range of plumbing projects.**

Connecting pipes effectively is the basis of all good plumbing as most leaks result from poorly constructed joints. For virtually all domestic plumbing purposes you will only have to use compression or capillary joints. Compression joints are easy to use but expensive, while capillary joints are cheap but need some care in fitting.

If you are making a join into an existing pipe system remember to make sure the water supply has been turned off at the relevant stop-valve (see EMERGENCY PIPE REPAIRS, pages 76 and 77) and the pipe completely drained.

## Preparing the pipes

Before joining pipes together, check that the ends are circular and have not been distorted. If they have been dented, cut back to an undamaged section of the pipe using a hacksaw with a sharp blade or a wheel tube cutter (see pages 25 to 27).

The ends should also be square and a simple way of checking this is shown on page 23 (see *Ready Reference)*. Use a file to make any correction and remove ragged burrs of metal. If you're using a capillary joint clean up the sides of the pipe with abrasive paper or steel wool.

## Compression joints (friction joints)

A compression joint, as its name implies, is made by compressing two brass or copper rings (known as olives or thimbles) round the ends of the pipes to be joined, so forming a watertight seal. There are two main types of compression joint – the non-manipulative fitting and the manipulative fitting.

Although not the cheapest means of joining a pipe, a non-manipulative joint is the easiest to use and requires only the minimum of tools. It comprises a central body made of brass or gunmetal with a cap-nut at each end which, when rotated, squeezes the olive tightly between the pipe end and the casing. This is the most commonly used type of compression joint suitable for most internal domestic plumbing purposes.

A manipulative joint is now rarely used in indoor domestic water systems. Because it cannot be pulled apart it is sometimes used for underground pipework, but capillary joints will do equally well in these situations.

The joint usually comprises a male and a female union nut. These are slipped over the pipe ends which are then flared ('manipulated') using a special steel tool called a *drift*. Jointing compound is smeared on the inside of the flares and a copper cone is inserted between them. The nuts are then screwed together to complete the seal.

## How a compression joint works

The olive (thimble) is the key part of a non-manipulative compression joint. When the cap-nut is rotated clockwise the olive is forced between the casing and the pipe and is considerably deformed in the process.

A watertight seal is dependent upon the pipe ends having been well prepared so they butt up exactly to the pipe stop in the casing. This forms a primary seal and ensures that the pipe is parallel to the movement of the rotating cap-nut. An even pressure is then applied to the olive so that it does not buckle under the strain of tightening.

## What size of pipework and fittings?

Pipework is now sold in metric dimensions, but plumbing in your home may be in imperial sizes. The metric sizes are not exactly the same as their imperial equivalents – check the table *(Ready Reference,* right) which shows the different ways pipe can be bought.

These differences can cause problems. With capillary joints you have to use adaptors when converting pipe from one system to another. Adaptors are also needed for some compression joints although the 12mm, 15mm, 28mm and 54mm sizes are compatible with their imperial equivalents. This means if you already have imperial compression joints you can connect in new metric pipework, without replacing the joints.

Adaptors are made with different combinations of metric and imperial outlets to fit most requirements. A supplier will advise on what replacements to use.

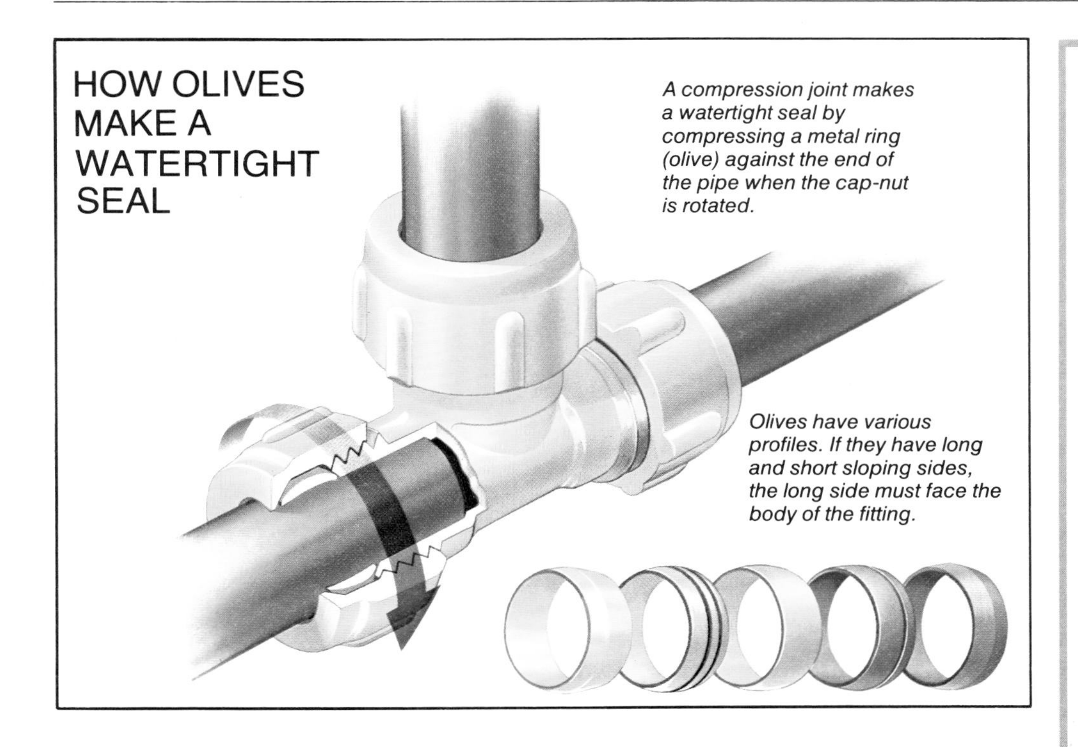


## Capillary joints

A capillary joint is simply a copper sleeve with socket outlets into which the pipe ends are soldered. It is neater and smaller than a compression joint and forms a robust connection that will not readily pull apart.

Because it is considerably cheaper than a compression joint it is frequently used when a number of joints have to be made and is particularly useful in awkward positions where it is impossible to use wrenches.

Some people are put off using capillary fittings because of the need to use a blow-torch. But modern gas-canister torches have put paid to the fears associated with paraffin lamps and are not dangerous.

## How a capillary joint works

If two pipes to be joined together were just soldered end to end the join would be very weak because the contact area between solder and copper would be small. A capillary fitting makes a secure join because the sleeve increases this contact area and also acts as a brace to strengthen the connection.

Molten solder is sucked into the space between the pipe and fitting by capillary action, and combines with a thin layer of copper at the contact surface thus bonding the pipe to the fitting. To help the solder to

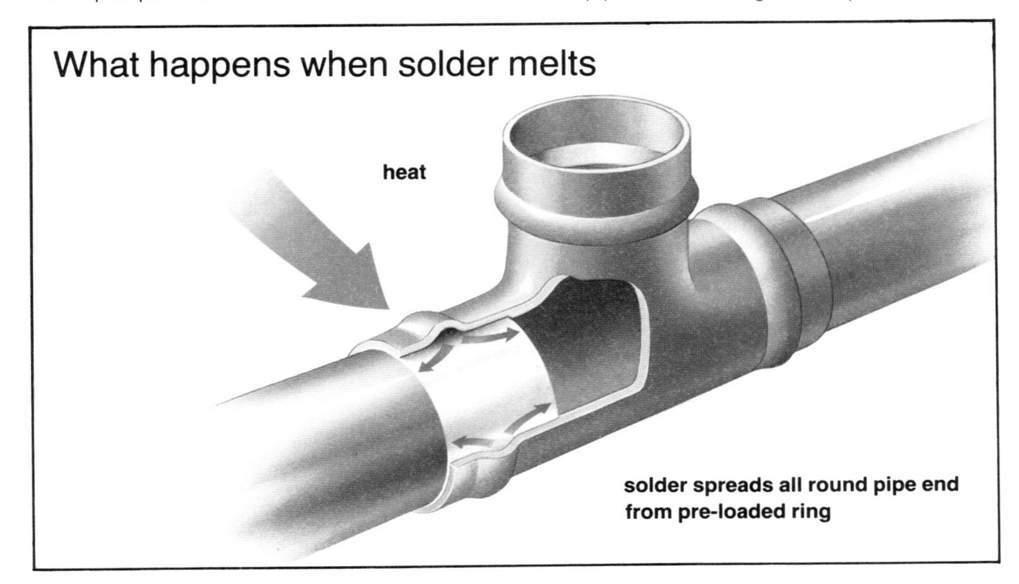


# Ready Reference

## WHICH TYPE OF FITTING?

**Capillary fittings** are
- cheap to buy
- unobtrusive when fitted
- useful in confined spaces
- very quick to install – and to unmake during alterations, BUT
- using them requires a blow-torch to melt the solder
- if the joint leaks you have to completely remake it.

**Compression fittings** are
- easy to assemble – you'll only need two wrenches or adjustable spanners – BUT
- they're much more expensive than capillary fittings
- they are much bulkier and obtrusive on exposed pipe runs
- in awkward places you may not be able to get wrenches in to tighten up the joint. Leaks can sometimes be cured by further tightening.

## MATCHING UP PIPEWORK

Matching new pipe to old isn't always as easy as it sounds because even if your existing pipework is copper it may have been manufactured to imperial sizes – and all new copper pipe comes in metric sizes.
- metric/imperial equivalents for the most widely used sizes are given below

| **UK metric** (external diameter) | **Imperial** (internal diameter) | **Australian metric** (internal diameter) |
|---|---|---|
| 12mm | 3/8in | – |
| 15mm | 1/2in | 10mm |
| 22mm | 3/4in | 20mm |
| 28mm | 1in | 25mm |
| 35mm | 1 1/4in | 32mm |

- if you're using integral-ring capillary fittings (where the solder is pre-loaded into the fitting) you'll always need special adaptors to join new copper pipe to old – these adaptors are just ordinary fittings with one end slightly larger than the other
- end-feed capillary fittings can be made to work simply by adding more solder – but it requires more skill
- if you're making compression joints, the 12mm, 15mm and 28mm fittings will work with old 3/8in, 1/2in and 1in pipe. For other imperial pipe sizes, again you'll need special adaptors.

## SAFETY TIPS

When using a blow-torch always
- wear thick heat-resistant gloves
- put down a lighted blow-torch on a firm flat surface with the flame pointing into space
- clear any flammable material from the area where you are working

## MAKING A COMPRESSION JOINT

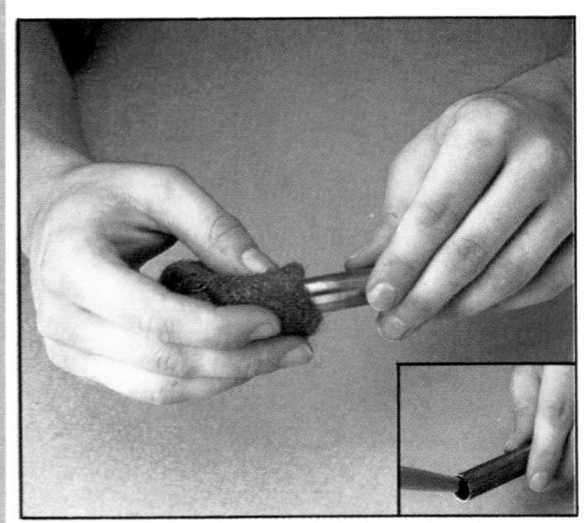

**1** *Check that the end of the pipe is square using a file to make any correction and to remove burrs. Clean pipe end and olive with steel wool.*

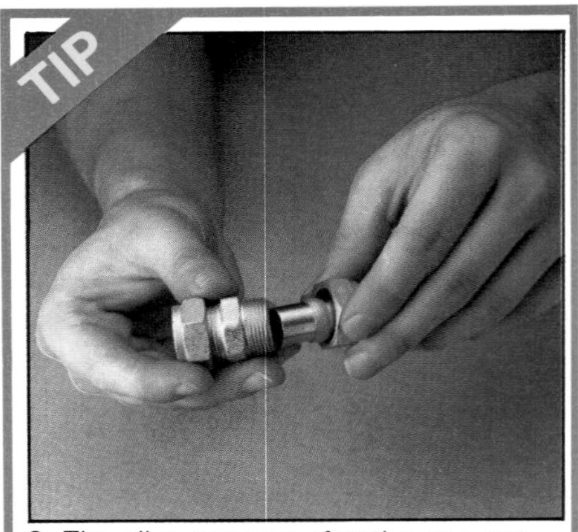


**2** *The olive goes on after the cap-nut. If it has both long and short sloping sides, make sure the long side faces the main body of the compression fitting.*

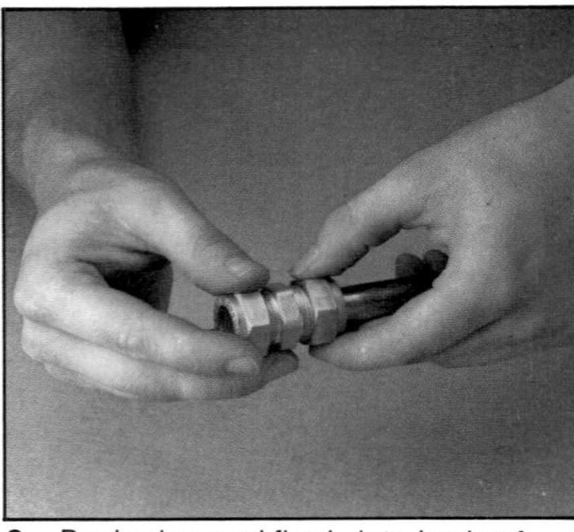

**3** *Push pipe end firmly into body of fitting so that it rests squarely against pipe stop. Screw up cap-nut tightly with your fingers.*

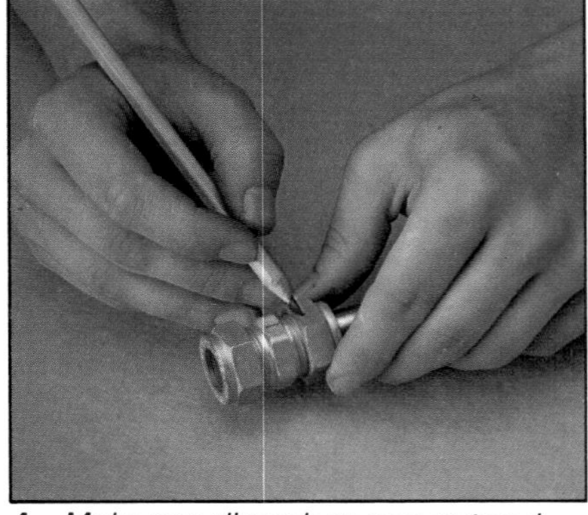

**4** *Make pencil mark on cap-nut and another aligning on body of fitting to act as guide when tightening cap-nut with wrench.*

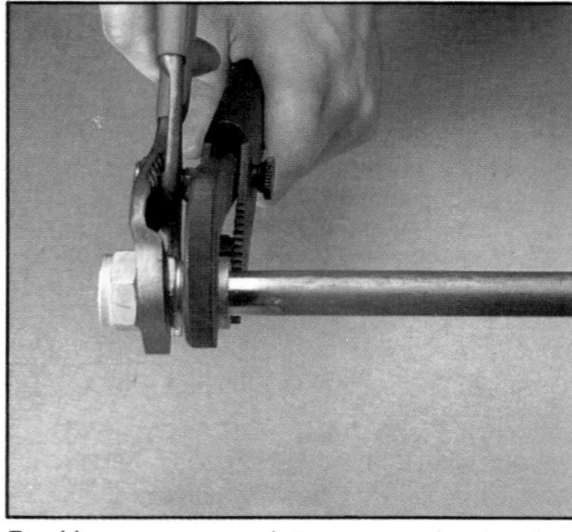

**5** *Use one wrench to secure body of fitting and the other to rotate the cap-nut clockwise. About 1 1/2 turns is sufficient to give a watertight seal.*

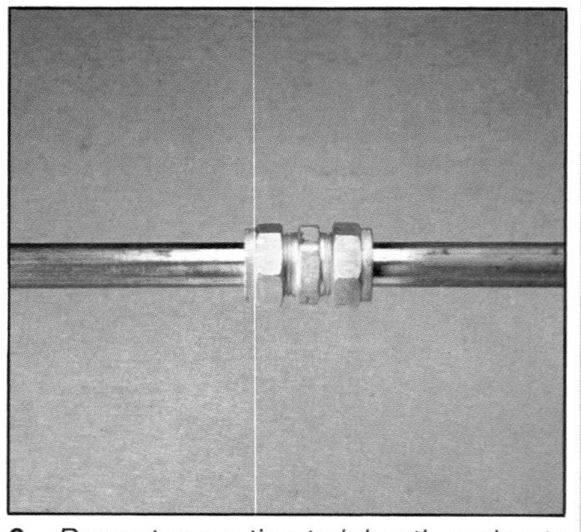

**6** *Repeat operation to join other pipe to fitting. If water seeps through when supply is turned on, tighten cap-nut further by half a turn.*

'take' the copper needs to be clean and shining. Therefore flux is applied to prevent oxides forming which would impair the solder-copper bond.

### Types of capillary joint

The most common type of capillary joint has a ring of solder pre-loaded into the sleeve. It is known as an integral ring or 'Yorkshire' fitting – the name of a leading brand.

The 'end feed' type of capillary joint is virtually the same as an integral ring fitting, but you have to add the solder in a separate operation. The sleeve is slightly larger than the pipe and liquid solder is drawn into the space between by capillary action.

### Flux and solder

Essential in the soldering operation, flux is a chemical paste or liquid which cleans the metal surfaces and then protects them from the oxides produced when the blow-torch heats the copper so a good metal-solder bond is formed. Mild non-corrosive flux is easy to use as it can be smeared onto the pipe and fitting with a clean brush or a sliver of wood. Although it is best to remove any residue this will not corrode the metal. There is an acid-corrosive flux which dissolves oxides quickly, but this is mostly used with stainless steel. The corrosive residue must be scrubbed off with soapy water.

Solder is an alloy (mixture) of tin and lead and is bought as a reel of wire. Its advantage in making capillary joints is that it melts at relatively low temperatures and quickly hardens when the heat source (blow-torch) is removed.

### Blow-torches

A blow-torch is an essential piece of equipment when making capillary joints. It is easy, clean and safe to use providing you handle it with care. Most modern torches operate off a gas canister which can be unscrewed and inexpensively replaced (larger cans are relatively cheaper than small). Sometimes a range of nozzles can be fitted to give different types of flame, but the standard nozzle is perfectly acceptable for capillary joint work.

### Using a blow-torch

When using a blow-torch it's most convenient to work at a bench, but you'll find most jointing work has to be carried out where the pipes are to run. Pipework is usually concealed so this may mean working in an awkward place, such as a roof space, or stretching under floorboards. However, always make sure you are in a comfortable position and there's no danger of you dropping a lighted blow-torch.

## MAKING A CAPILLARY FITTING

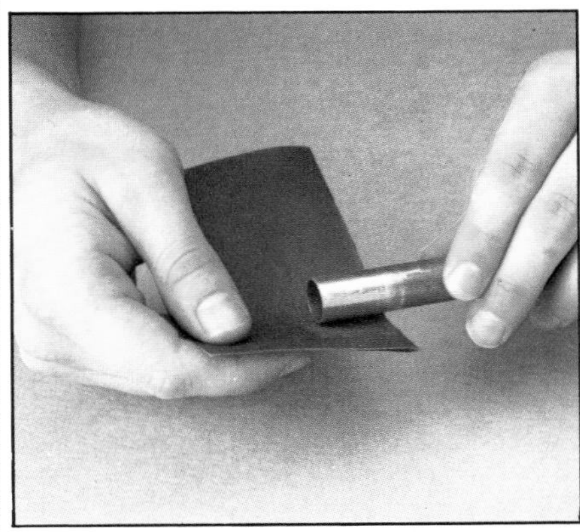

*1 Make sure the pipe end is square, then clean it and the inner rim of the fitting with steel wool or abrasive paper until shining.*

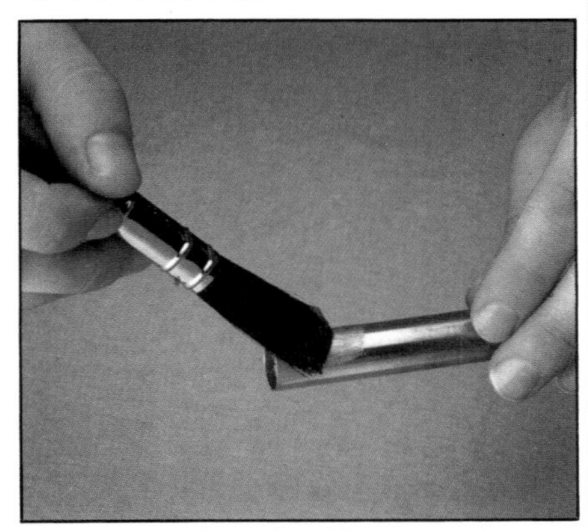

*2 Flux can be in liquid or paste form. Use a brush, rather than your finger, to smear it over the end of the pipe and the inner rim of the fitting.*

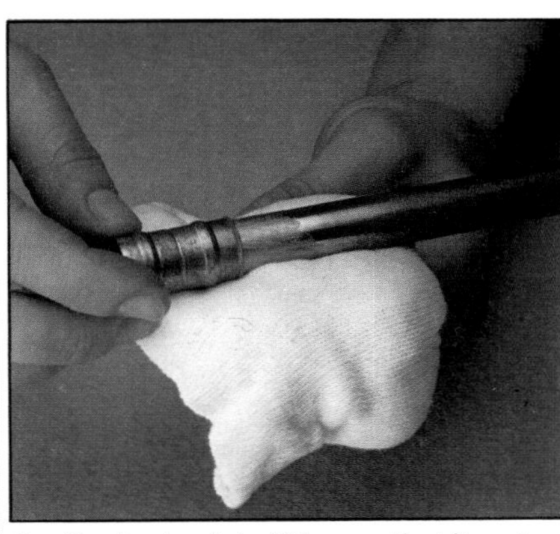

*3 Push pipe into fitting so that it rests against pipe stop, twisting a little to help spread the flux. Remove excess flux with a cloth.*

*4 When you're making up a whole pipe-run, it helps to make corresponding pencil marks on pipe ends and fittings as a guide for correct lining up.*

*5 Make other side of joint in same way, then apply blow-torch. Seal is complete when bright ring of solder is visible at ends of fitting.*

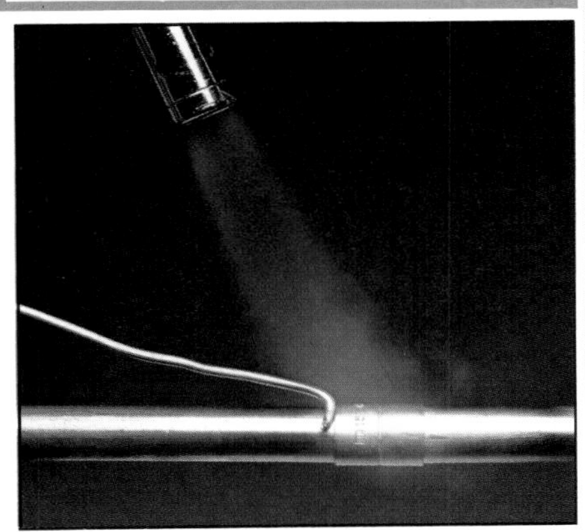

*6 For an end feed fitting, heat the pipe, then hold the solder to mouth of joint. A bright ring all the way round signifies a seal.*

## Ready Reference

### WHICH TOOLS?

**For cutting pipe:**
- hire a **wheel tube cutter** (which ensures perfectly square pipe ends)

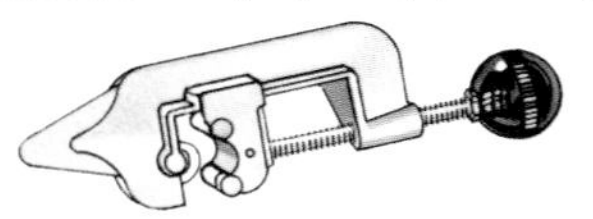

or use a **hacksaw**
- use a **metal file** for removing ragged burrs of metal and for squaring ends of pipe that have been cut with a hacksaw. A half-round 'second-cut' type is ideal.

**For compression joints:**
- use two adjustable **spanners** or **pipe wrenches** (one to hold the fitting, the other to tighten the cap-nut)

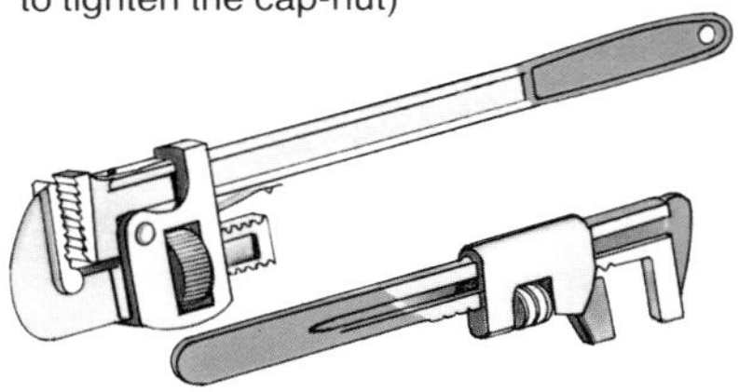

- **steel wool** to clean the surface of pipes before assembling a joint.

**For capillary joints:**
- a **blow-torch** to melt the solder
- **steel-wool** for cleaning pipe surfaces
- **flux** to ensure a good bond between the solder and copper
- **solder** because even if you're using integral ring fittings (which already have solder in them) you may need a bit extra
- **flame-proof glass fibre** (or a ceramic tile) to deflect the torch flame from nearby surfaces.

### TIP: CUTTING PIPE SQUARELY

For a perfect fit, pipe ends must be cut square. If you're using a hacksaw, hold a strip of paper round the pipe so its edges align and saw parallel to the paper edge. Use the same trick if you have to file an inaccurately-cut end.

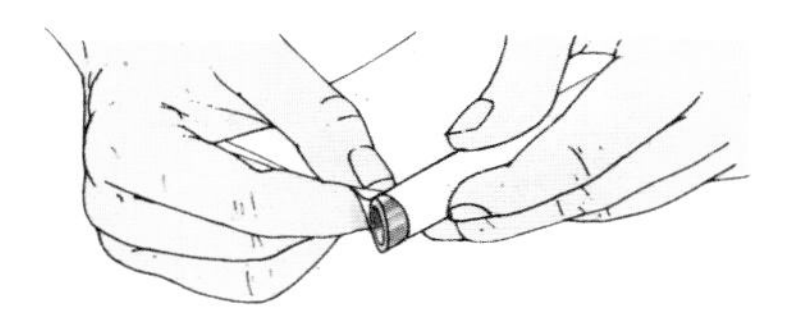

### TIP: PROTECT NEARBY JOINTS

With capillary fittings, the heat you apply could melt the solder in nearby fittings. To help prevent this, wrap them in wet cloths.

When working near to joists and floorboards, glass, paintwork and other pipework with capillary joints it is important to shield these areas with flame-proof glass fibre matting.

### Applying the heat

When making a capillary joint gradually build up the temperature of the copper by playing the flame up and down and round the pipe and then to the fitting. When the metal is hot enough the solder will melt and you can then take away the flame. The joint is complete when a bright ring of solder appears all round the mouth of the fitting. Stand the torch on a firm level surface and turn it off as soon as you have finished. Where two or more capillary joints are to be made with one fitting, for example the three ends of a tee, they should all be made at the same time. If this is not possible wrap a damp rag round any joints already made.

### Repairing a compression joint

If a compression joint is leaking and tightening of the cap-nut doesn't produce a watertight seal you'll have to disconnect the fitting and look inside – after turning off the water supply. If a cap-nut is impossible to move, run a few drops of penetrating oil onto the thread. If that doesn't do the trick, you'll have to cut it out and replace the fitting and some piping.

Once you have unscrewed one of the cap-nuts there will be enough flexibility in the pipe run to pull the pipe from the casing. Usually the olive will be compressed against the pipe. First check that it is the right way round (see page 21) and if it isn't replace it with a new one making sure that it is correctly set.

Sometimes the olive is impossible to remove and needs to be cut off with a hacksaw – make the cut diagonally. Reassemble the joint following the procedure on page 22 and repeat the operation for the other end of the pipe. Turn on the water supply to check that the repair is watertight.

### Repairing a capillary joint

Poor initial soldering is usually the reason why a capillary fitting leaks. You can try and rectify this by 'sweating' in some more solder but if this doesn't work you'll have to remake the joint.

Play the flame of the blow-torch over the fitting and pipe until the solder begins to run from the joint. At this stage you can pull the pipe ends out of the sockets with gloved hands. You can now reuse the fitting as an end feed joint or replace it with a new integral ring capillary connection.

If you reuse the fitting clean the interior surface and the pipe ends with abrasive paper or steel wool and smear them with flux. Then follow the procedure for making an end feed capillary joint.

## REPAIRING A COMPRESSION JOINT

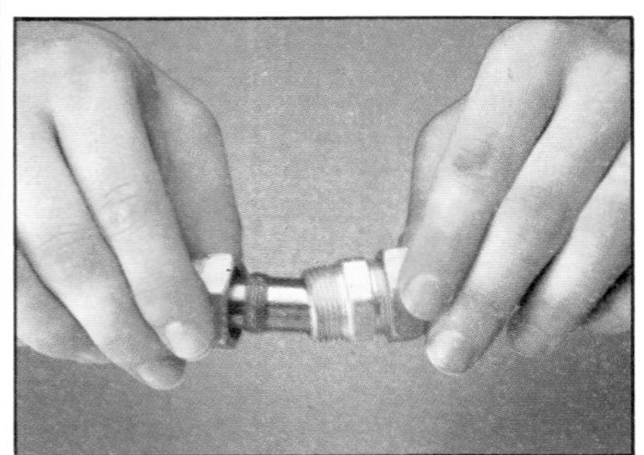

**1** *Unscrew cap-nut using wrenches. There's enough flexibility in pipe run to pull pipe from casing. Check that olive fits, and isn't damaged.*

TIP

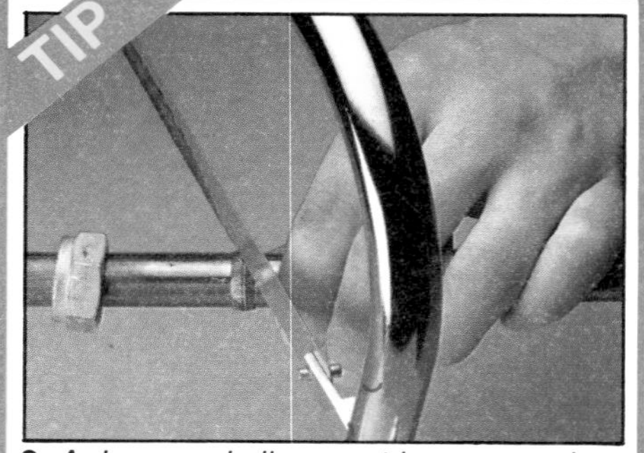

**2** *A damaged olive must be removed. Use a hacksaw and to make it easier make the cut on the diagonal – but take care not to cut into the pipe itself.*

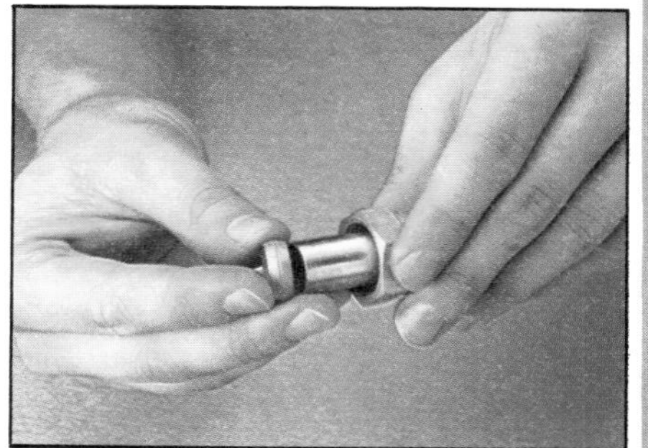

**3** *Prepare end of pipe with steel wool or abrasive paper. Slip on new olive and finger tighten cap-nut. Rotate cap-nut 1½ turns using wrenches.*

## REPAIRING A CAPILLARY JOINT

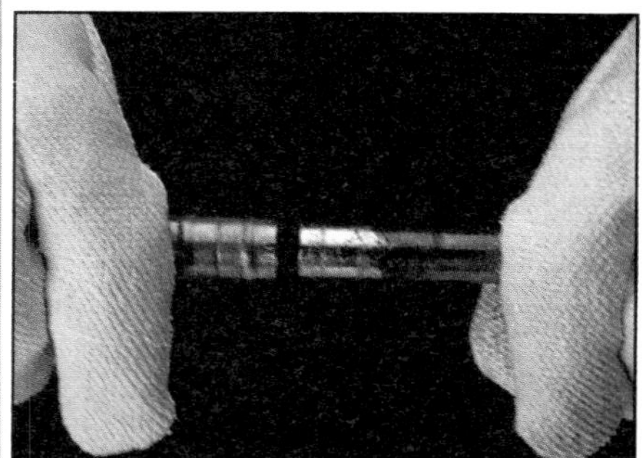

**1** *Drain pipe and wrap a damp cloth round nearby joints. Play flame on fitting and pull pipe from rim using gloved hands.*

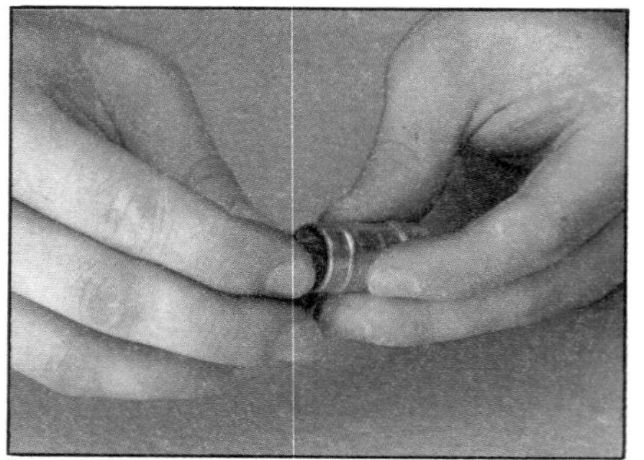

**2** *If you remake both sides of joint use a new fitting. A spent integral ring fitting, thoroughly cleaned, can be used as an end feed joint.*

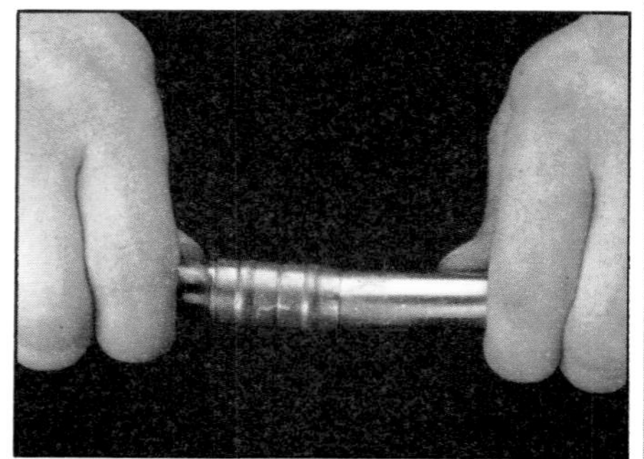

**3** *Use steel wool to clean end of pipe and inside of fitting. Brush with flux and push pipe into socket. Apply blow-torch to melt solder.*

# CUTTING & BENDING COPPER PIPE

**One of the advantages of domestic copper pipe is that it's easy to cut and bend. Few tools are required and even if you've only a few bends to make in a pipe run, it makes sense to know how it's done. Making accurate bends may need some practice, but it's cheaper than buying specially-shaped fittings.**

In all plumbing water has to be carried from a source to a fixture and often then to some type of exit where it can disperse as waste. Basic to all of this is that water must run smoothly with nothing causing resistance to the flow — an important factor when the pressure is low.

Generally the best plumbing practice is to make pipe runs as straight and direct as possible. But sometimes bends are unavoidable (like, for example, when pipe has to go around a room or to turn down into an area below) and if available fittings are neither right for the angle nor attractive to look at, then you'll have to bend the pipe to suit.

Copper piping, because it is both light and resistant to corrosion, is a popular choice for home plumbing work. It can be joined with either capillary or compression fittings (as described on pages 20 to 24) and when bends are needed you can create the angles in several ways.

The first essential is to accurately work out the pipe lengths you require. Once you've made the measurement double check it — it's quite easy to forget to allow for the pipe that will fit into the socket ends of the joints. You can make the actual marks on the pipe with pencil as this is clearly visible on copper and is a good guide when you come to cutting.

## Cutting pipe accurately

For smaller pipe sizes, a sharp-bladed hacksaw is the best tool to use to make the cut. You'll need to hold the pipe firmly, but if you use a vice be careful not to over-tighten the jaws and crush the bore of the pipe (see *Ready Reference*, on page 27).

It's important to cut the pipe square so that it butts up exactly to the pipe stop in the joint. This will ensure the pipe is seated squarely in the fitting which is essential for making a watertight seal. It will also help to make that seal. It's surprising how near to square you can get the end just cutting by eye. But the best way to make a really accurate cut is to use a saw guide. This can be made very easily by placing a small rectangle of paper round the pipe with one long edge against the cut mark. By bringing the two short edges of the paper together and aligning them you effectively make a template that's square to the pipe. All you then have to do is hold the paper in place and keep the saw blade against it as you cut. Any burr that's left on the cut edges can be removed with a file.

If you intend to carry out a lot of plumbing, or are working mainly in the larger pipe sizes, it may be worthwhile buying (or hiring) a wheel tube cutter. Of course using one of these is never absolutely essential, but it does save time if you've more than, say, half a dozen cuts to make. And once you have one you'll use it for even the smallest jobs. It's quick to use and will ensure a square cut without trouble every time. You simply place the pipe in the cutter and tighten the control knob to hold it in place. The cutter is then rotated round the pipe and as it revolves it cuts cleanly into the copper. This circular action automatically removes burr from the outside of the pipe, but burr on the inside can be taken away with the reamer (a scraping edge) which is usually incorporated in the tool.

## Bending copper pipe

If a lot of changes of direction are necessary in a pipe run it's cheaper and quicker to bend the pipe rather than use fittings. This also makes the neatest finish particularly if the pipework is going to be exposed. Under a pedestal wash-basin, for example, the hot and cold supply pipes rise parallel to each other in the pedestal before bending outwards and upwards to connect to the two tap tails.

### Ready Reference

#### GETTING BENDS RIGHT

The trickiest part of bending copper pipe is getting the bends in the right place.
To avoid mistakes

- don't try to make too many bends in one pipe length
- mark the position for one bend at a time.

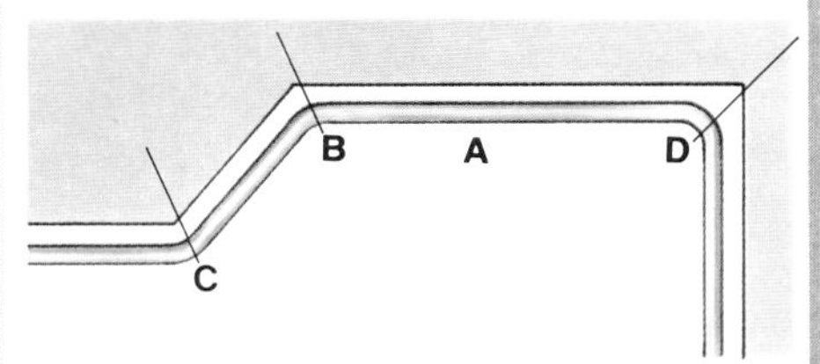


**Example:** To make up the pipe run in our sketch, plan to divide up the run at A; here two pipe lengths will be joined by a straight coupling after the bends have been formed.

- form bend B at approximately the right distance from point A
- offer up bend B to the wall, mark the start of bend C where the pipe touches the corner point
- form bend C and check for fit.

To get bend D in the right place on the second length of pipe

- measure the distance from A into the corner of the wall
- form bend D at this distance from the pipe end
- lay the two lengths in place, cut off any overlap and connect them with a straight coupling.

Using fittings in this situation would be more costly as well as possibly being unsightly, while the cheaper alternative, making bends, means the pipework is less conspicuous. The pipe can also be bent to the exact angle required so this method of changing direction is not limited by the angles of the fittings. And with fewer fittings in a pipe system there are fewer places where leaks can occur.

The smaller sizes of copper pipe, those most commonly used in domestic plumbing (15mm, 22mm and 28mm), can be bent quite easily by hand. The technique of annealing — heating the pipe to red heat in the vicinity of the bend to reduce its temper (strength) and so make bending easier — is unnecessary when working in these pipe sizes. But you will need to support the pipe wall, either internally or externally, as the bend is made. If you don't you'll flatten the profile of the pipe. Using it in this condition would reduce the flow of water at the outlet point.

For small jobs a bending spring is the ideal tool, supporting the pipe internally. It is a long hardened steel coil which you push into the pipe to the point where the bend will be made. It's best used for bends near the end of the pipe, since the spring can be easily pulled out after the bend is made. However, it can be used further down the pipe if it is attached to a length of stout wire (which helps to push it into place, and is vital for retrieving it afterwards).

### Bending techniques

You actually bend the pipe over your knee, overbending slightly and bringing back to the required angle. The spring will now be fixed tightly in the pipe and you won't be able simply to pull it out. However, its removal is quite easy. All you have to do is to insert a bar — a screwdriver will do — through the ring at the end of the spring and twist it. This reduces the spring's diameter and will enable you to withdraw it. It's a good idea to grease the spring before you insert it as this will make pulling it out that much easier (also see *Ready Reference* page opposite).

Slight wrinkles may be found on the inside of the bend, but these can be tapped out by gentle hammering. It's wise not to attempt this before taking out the spring. If you do you'll never be able to remove it.

Bending springs are suitable for 15mm and 22mm diameter pipe. But although it is possible to bend 28mm pipe as well, it's advisable to use a bending machine instead. This is also preferable if you have a lot of bends to make. And if you don't want to go to the expense of buying one, you can probably hire a machine from a tool hire shop.

A bending machine consists of a semi-circular former that supports the pipe externally during the bending operation and a roller that forces the pipe round the curve when the levers of the machine are brought together. The degree of bend depends on how far you move the handles.

### Flexible pipe

This is a kind of corrugated copper pipe which can be bent easily by hand without any tools. You can buy it with two plain ends for connection to compression joints or with one end plain and one with a swivel tap connector for connection to a tap or ball-valve.

As it's the most expensive way of making a bend, it's not cost effective to use it when you have to make a number of changes of direction in a pipe run. It's not particularly attractive to look at so it is best used in places where it won't be seen. As such it's most commonly used for connecting the water supply pipes to the bath taps in the very confined space at the head of the bath. And it can make the job of fitting kitchen sink taps easier, particularly when the base unit has a back which restricts access to the supply pipes.

## CUTTING COPPER PIPE

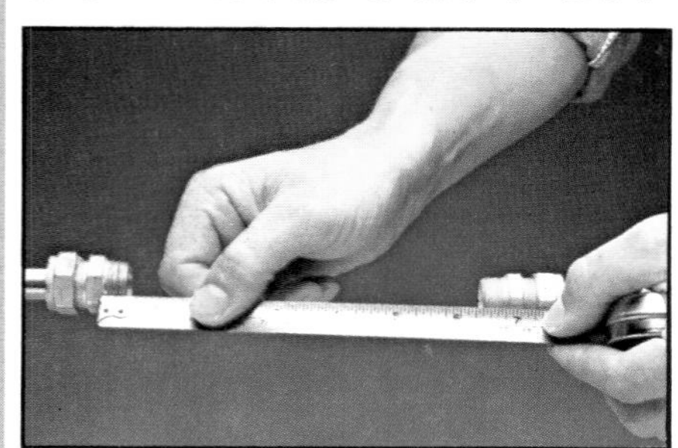

**1** *Make an accurate measurement of the proposed pipe run. Don't forget to allow extra for the pipe that will fit inside the joints.*

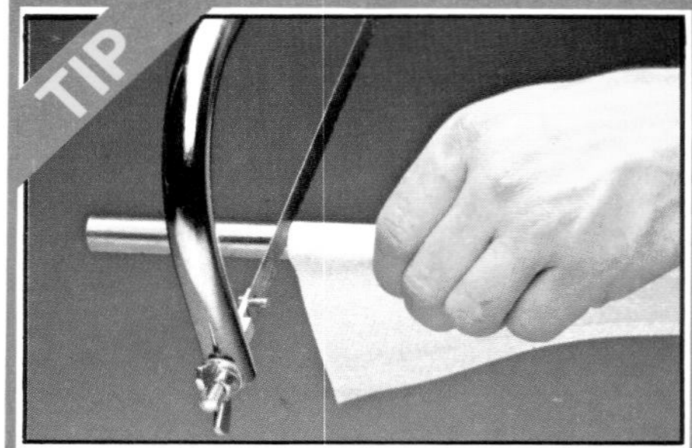


**2** *Use a simple paper template to help you cut pipe squarely. Wrap the paper round the pipe and align the edges.*

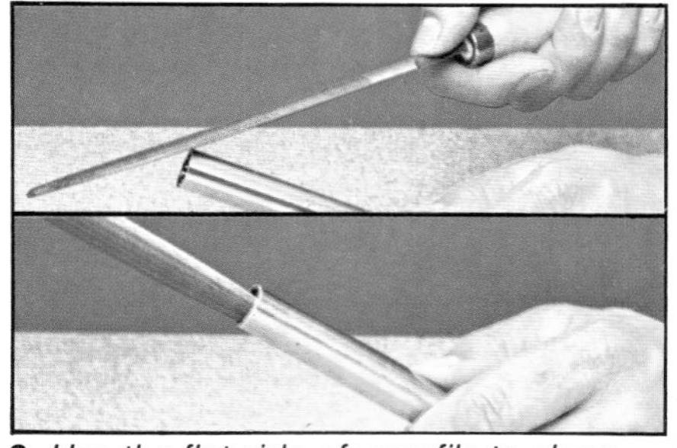

**3** *Use the flat side of your file to clean any burr from the outside of the pipe. The curved side of the file can be used to clean the inside.*

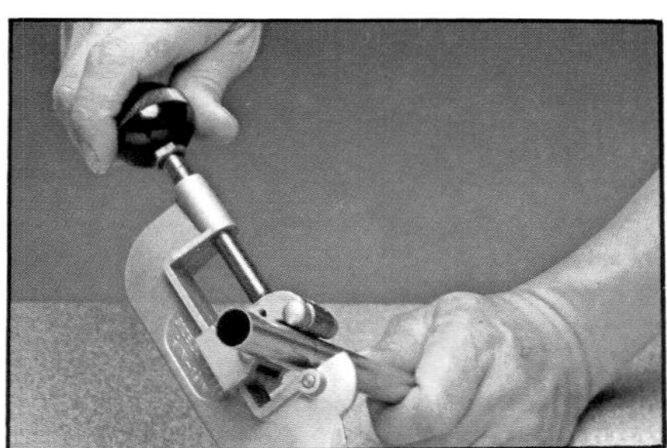

**4** *When using a wheel tube cutter, position the cutting mark on the pipe against the edge of the cutting wheel, then tighten the control knob.*

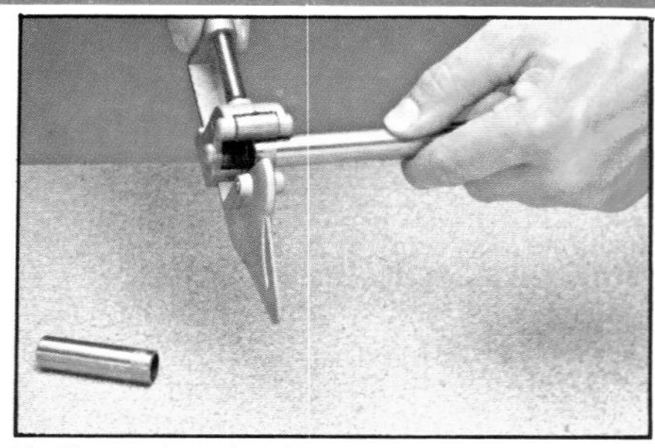

**5** *Once the pipe is clamped in place, rotate the cutter so it makes an even cut. The rollers on the tool will keep the blade square to the pipe.*

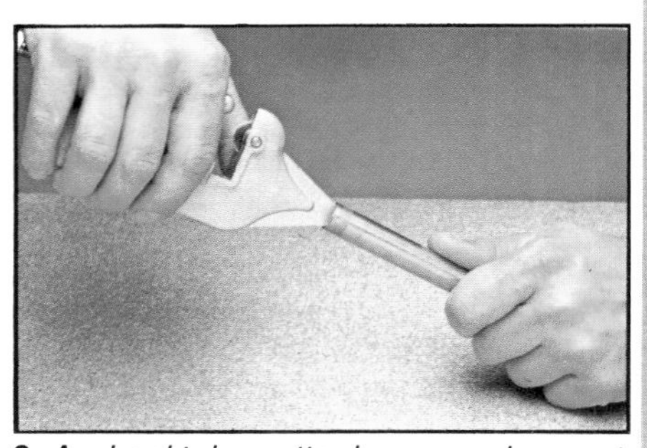

**6** *A wheel tube cutter leaves a clean cut on the outside of the pipe, but any burr on the inside can be removed with the reamer (an attachment to the tool).*

# BENDING COPPER PIPE

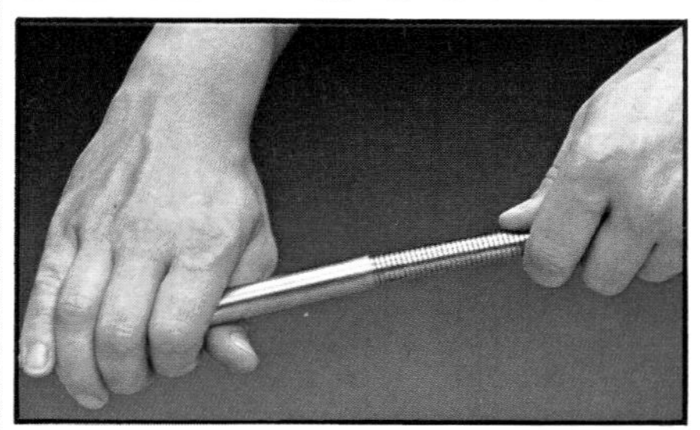

**1** *Always use a bending spring which is compatible in size with the pipe. Smear it with petroleum jelly.*

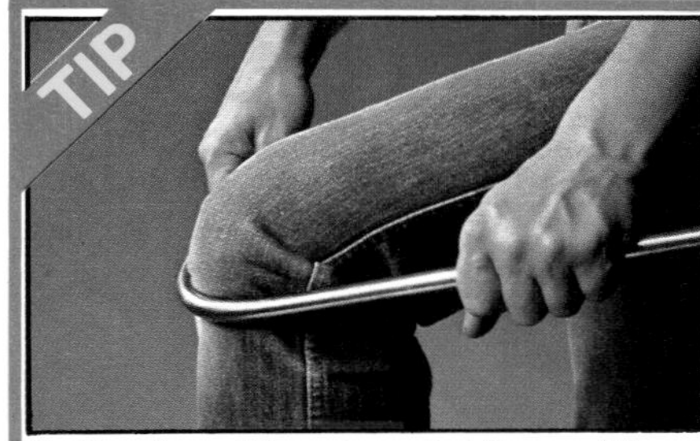


**2** *Overbend the pipe slightly, and then bend it back to the required angle.*

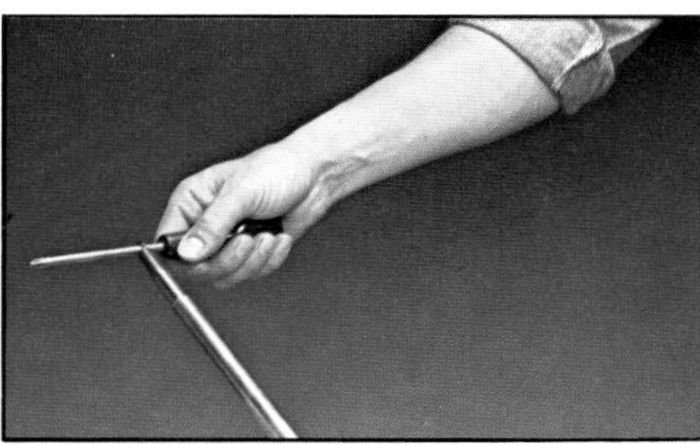

**3** *Put a screwdriver through the ring at the end of the spring. Twist it, then pull the spring out.*

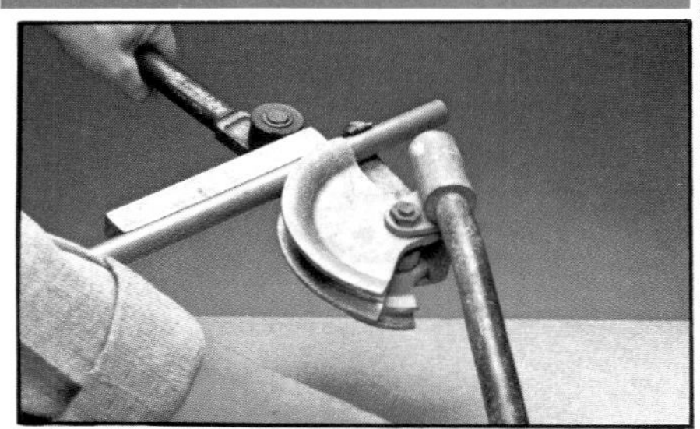

**4** *To use a bending machine, open the levers and position the pipe as shown, then slide the straight former on top.*

**5** *Raise the levers so the wheel runs along the straight edge and the pipe is forced round the circular former.*

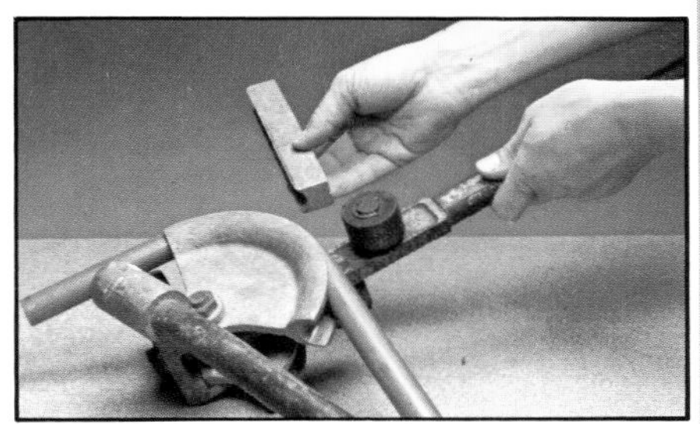

**6** *Bend the pipe to the required angle, then remove by opening the levers, and taking out the straight former.*

# FLEXIBLE COPPER PIPE

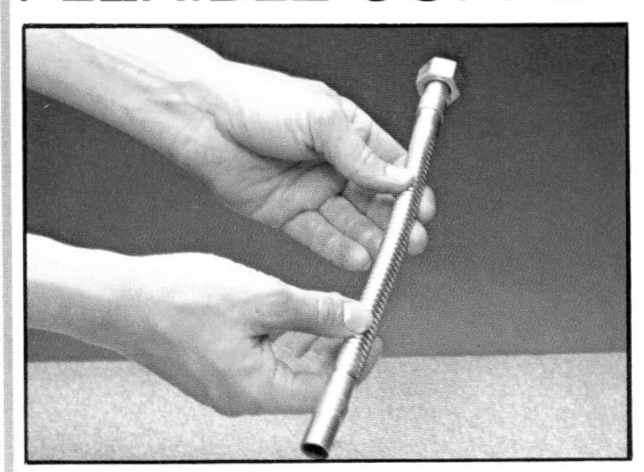

**1** *Although relatively expensive, flexible pipe is ideal for making awkward bends in the pipe run to connect to taps.*

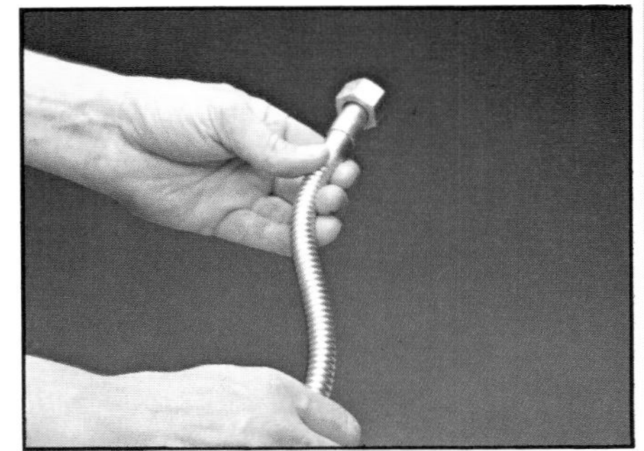

**2** *It's easy to hand bend the pipe to the required shape, but don't continually flex it or the thin wall will split.*

## Ready Reference

### PIPE LENGTHS

Draw a rough sketch plan of the complete pipe run, then work out:

- how many 2 metre lengths you'll need
- where to join them in on the straight (not at a bend)
- how many fittings you'll need to connect the pipes to each other.

### TIP: CUTTING PIPE

Copper pipe can be crushed in the jaws of a vice so use a bench hook when cutting with a hacksaw. Pin a scrap of wood beside it to hold the pipe snugly.

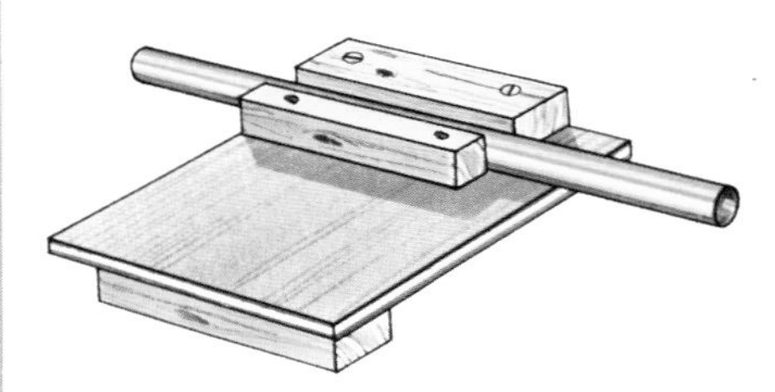

### BENDING AIDS

For 15mm and 22mm pipe use a *bending spring* to match the pipe size. It's a flexible coil of hardened steel about 600mm (2ft) long.

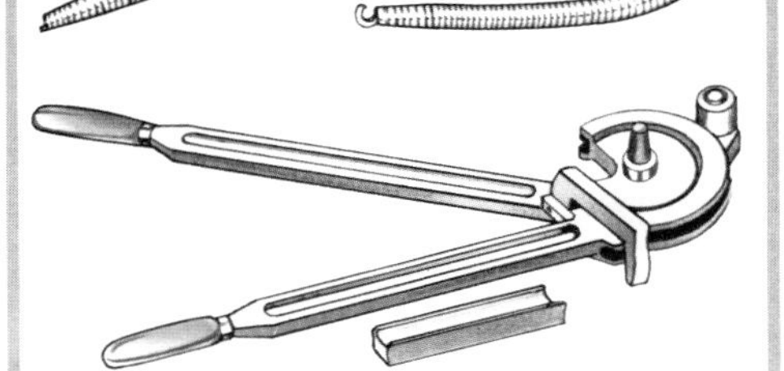

For 28mm pipe hire a *pipe bending machine* which supports the outside of the pipe wall as it bends.

### TIP: REMOVING BENDING SPRINGS

For bends over 600mm (2ft) from the pipe end use a wire coathanger with a hooked end to turn and withdraw the spring.

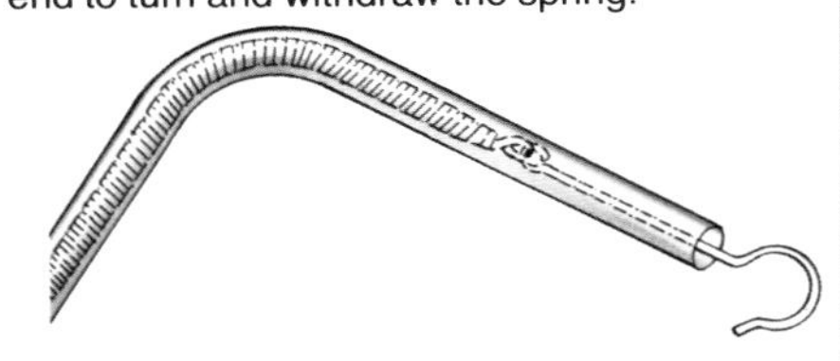

# CONNECTING NEW PIPES TO OLD

**Improvements or additions to a domestic plumbing system inevitably involve joining new pipework into old. How you do this depends largely upon whether the existing pipework is made of lead, iron or more modern materials – copper, polythene or even unplasticised PVC.**

The principle of joining into existing pipework is quite straightforward. You decide where you will need your new water supply – at a bedroom basin or an outside tap, for example – and then pick a convenient point on the plumbing system to connect up your 'branch line'. At this point you have to cut out a small section of the old pipe and insert a tee junction into which the branch pipe will be fitted. That's all there is to it: laying the branch pipe will simply involve routine cutting, bending and joining of new pipe, and final connection to the new tap or appliance at the other end.

Before you can begin the job, however, you have to do some reconnaissance work to identify what sort of existing pipework you have. You might be tempted to relate the plumbing to the age of the house, thinking that an old house will have an old system with lead or iron pipework. But this isn't a reliable guide. Many old properties have been modernised and so may actually have a more up-to-date system than a house built relatively recently.

Until the 1950s the only types of pipe used in domestic plumbing were lead and iron, but then these were superseded by thin-walled copper piping. Today there are other alternatives too: stainless steel is sometimes used as an alternative to copper, and polythene and UPVC (unplasticised polyvinyl chloride) pipes can be installed for cold water supplies only.

Check the table (see *Ready Reference*, right) for the type of pipe you can use. While copper is the most common one for new work, it must *never* be joined to galvanised iron because of the severe risk of electrolytic corrosion of the iron if the galvanising is not in perfect condition.

## First things first

Before cutting into a pipe run you'll first have to turn off the water supply to the pipe and then drain it by opening any taps or drain cocks connected to it (as described on pages 49 to 51). But this need not be too inconvenient if you make up the complete branch line before you turn the water off so you are without water only while you make the final branch connection.

## Connecting into copper pipe

When taking a branch from a copper pipe it's probably easier to use a compression tee fitting rather than a capillary fitting. A compression fitting can be made even if there is some water in the pipe run – capillary joints need the pipe to be dry – and you won't have to worry about using a blow-torch and possibly damaging other capillary joints nearby (if they are heated up, their solder will soften and the joint will leak).

It's quite easy to work out how much pipe to cut out of the main run in order to insert a tee junction (of either compression or capillary fittings). Push a pencil or stick into the tee until it butts up against the pipe stop. Mark this length with your thumbs, then place the stick on top of the fitting so you can mark the outside to give a guide line. Next you have to cut the pipe at the place where the branch has to be made and prepare one of the cut ends (see the pictures on page 30). Now connect to the pipe the end of the tee that doesn't have the guide line marked on the casing and rest the tee back against the pipe. You will now be able to see where the pipe stop comes to and you can then mark the pipe to give you the second cutting point. Remove the section of pipe with a hacksaw and prepare the pipe end.

With a compression fitting put on the other cap-nut and olive. If you gently push the pipe and tee sideways to the pipe run this will give you more room to position the body before you allow the pipe end to spring into place. When this is done the cap-nut can be pushed up to the fitting and can be tightened with your fingers. Both sides of the tee can then be tightened using your wrenches to give the cap-nuts about one-and-a-half turns.

Remember that you must use a second wrench to grip the body of the fitting so it stays still as the cap-nut is tightened. If it should turn, other parts of the joint which have already been assembled will be loosened or forced out of position, and leaks will result. The connection into the main pipe run is now complete and you can connect up the branch pipe.

If you are using a capillary tee fitting there are a number of points to bear in mind. It's easiest to use one with integral rings of solder (this saves the bother of using solder wire) and after the pipe ends and the inside rims have been prepared and smeared with flux the fitting can be 'sprung' into place. The branch pipe should also be inserted at this stage so all the joints can be made at the same time.

When using the blow-torch, it is important to protect the surrounding area from the effects of the flame with a piece of flame-proof glass fibre matting or the back of a ceramic tile. It's also worthwhile wrapping damp cloths round any nearby capillary joints to protect them from accidental over-heating and thus 'sweating'.

# IDENTIFYING YOUR PIPEWORK

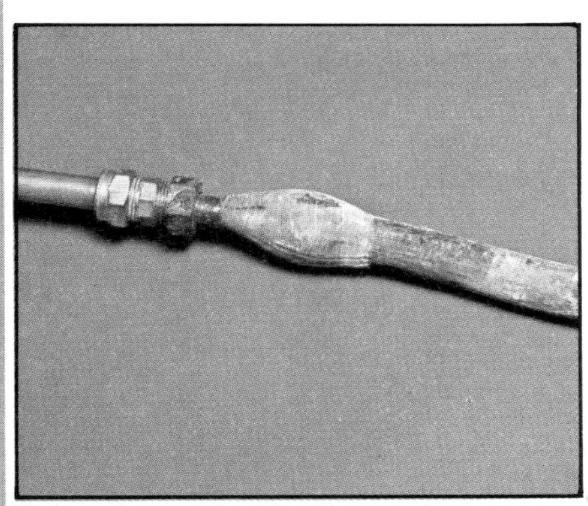

*1 Lead pipes are grey and give a dull thud when knocked. You can nick the surface with a knife. Look for smooth bends and neat even swellings – these are 'wiped' soldered joints. Repairs are often made using copper pipe.*

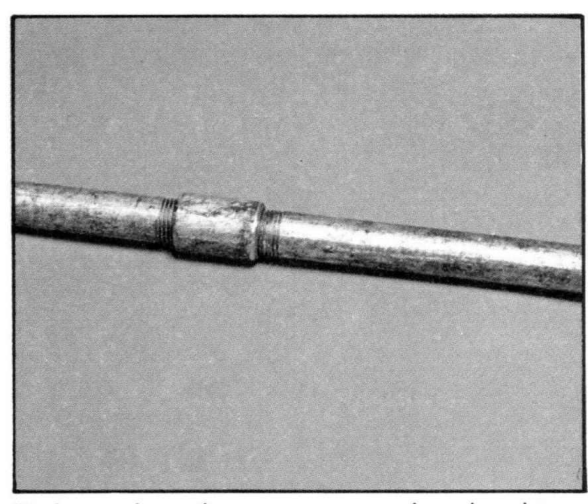

*2 Iron pipes have a grey galvanised or black finish and give a clanging sound when knocked. A knife will only scrape along the surface. Look for the large threaded joints which appear as a collar on the pipe or at a bend.*

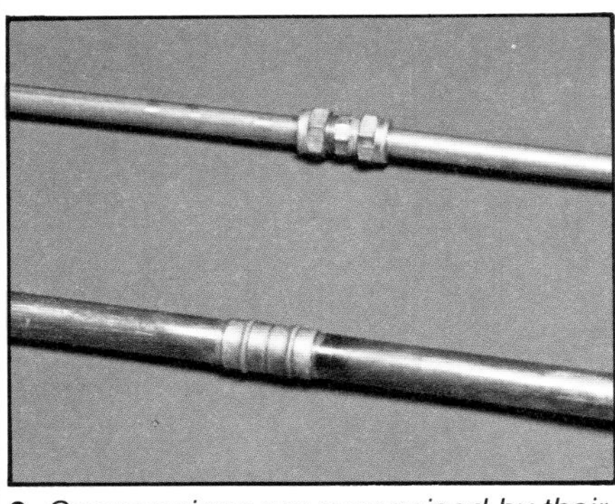

*3 Copper pipes are recognised by their familiar copper colour. Changes of direction are often made by bends in the pipe itself or by using angled fittings. The joints will be either the compression or capillary type.*

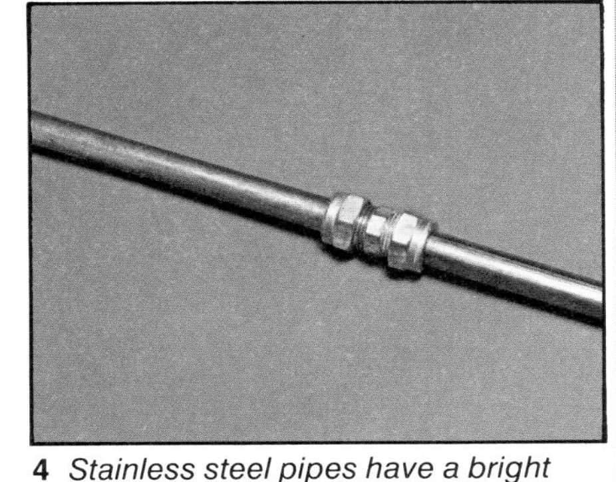

*4 Stainless steel pipes have a bright silvery surface. They come in the same sizes as copper and can be joined in the same way. Bends are only found in sizes up to 15mm. These pipes are not commonly used in the home.*

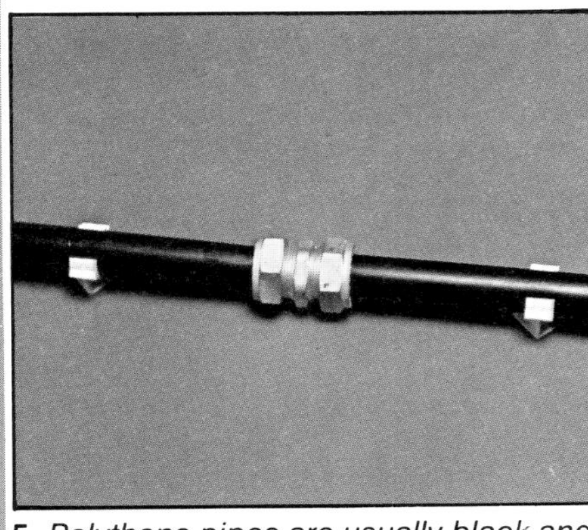

*5 Polythene pipes are usually black and are soft enough to be slightly compressed between the fingers. Joints are made with metal compression fittings which require special gunmetal olives and liners.*

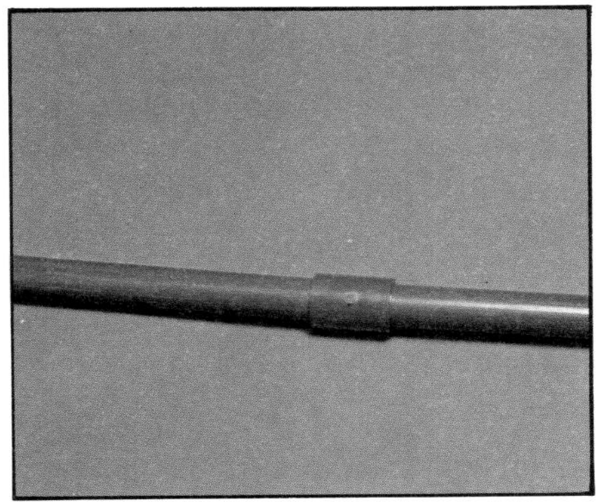

*6 UPVC pipes are grey and rigid. Connections and changes in direction are made by angled joints which fit like slim collars over the ends of the pipes. These are fixed in place using solvent weld cement.*

## Ready Reference

### WHAT JOINS TO WHAT?

Use this table as a guide to choosing new pipework – the first material mentioned is the best or most usual choice.

| Existing pipe | New pipework |
|---|---|
| copper | copper, stainless steel, polythene |
| lead | copper, stainless steel, polythene |
| iron | iron, stainless steel, polythene |
| stainless steel | stainless steel, copper, polythene |
| polythene | polythene, copper, stainless steel |
| UPVC | copper, stainless steel, polythene |

### CONNECTING OLD TO NEW

Fitting metric to imperial pipework can be complicated by the slight differences in pipe diameters. The problem connections are:

**copper to copper (compression fittings)**
- some metric fittings can be used directly with imperial-sized pipes (eg, 15mm fittings with ½in pipe and 28mm fittings with 1in pipe)
- with other sizes you need to buy special adaptors or larger olives to replace those inside the fittings, so to connect a 15mm branch into existing ¾in pipe you'll need a tee 22 x 22 x 15mm with special olives for the 22mm ends of the tee.

**copper to copper (capillary fittings)**
- metric capillary fittings with integral solder rings are not compatible with imperial pipes, but straight adaptors are available to connect the two sizes of pipe
- use these to join in short lengths of metric pipe, the other ends of which are connected to opposite ends of the metric tee
- with end-feed type fittings, extra solder can be added to make a good joint with imperial-sized pipe.

**copper to stainless steel** – as for copper to copper connections, but usually compression fittings only.

**stainless steel to copper** – as above for copper to stainless steel.

**stainless steel to stainless steel** – as for copper to copper.

### Connecting into lead pipe

Inserting a tee junction into lead pipe involves joining the run of the tee into two 'wiped' soldered joints. Join short lengths of new copper pipe into opposite ends of a compression tee. Measure the length of this assembly, and cut out 25mm (1in) less of lead pipe. Join the assembly in with wiped soldered joints – a job that takes a lot of practice, and one you may prefer to leave to a professional plumber until you have acquired the skill. You then connect the branch pipe to the third leg of the tee.

### Connecting into iron

Existing iron pipework will be at least 25 years old, and likely to be showing signs of corrosion. Extending such a system is not advisable – you would have difficulty connecting into it, and any extension would have to be in stainless steel. The best course is to replace the piping completely with new copper piping.

### Connecting into polythene pipe

If you have to fit a branch into a polythene pipe it's not a difficult job, especially if you use the same material. Polythene pipes are joined by compression fittings similar to those used for copper. Polythene hasn't yet been metricated in the UK and each nominal pipe size has a larger outside diameter than its copper equivalent. So you'll have to use either special gunmetal fittings for polythene pipe (still made to imperial sizes) or else an ordinary metric brass fitting a size larger than the pipe – 22mm for ½in polythene.

You also need to slip a special metal liner inside the end of the pipe before assembling each joint to prevent the pipe from collapsing as the cap-nuts are tightened. In addition, polythene rings are used instead of metal olives in brass fittings. Apart from these points, however, inserting a tee in a length of polythene pipework follows the same sequence as inserting one into copper.

### Connecting into UPVC pipe

As with polythene it's an easy job to cut in a solvent weld tee – a simple collar fitting over the ends of the pipe and the branch. After you've cut the pipe run with a hacksaw you have to roughen the outsides of the cut ends and the insides of the tee sockets with abrasive paper and then clean the surfaces with a spirit cleaner and degreaser. Solvent weld cement is smeared on the pipe ends and the insides of the sockets, and the pipe ends are then 'sprung' into the sockets.

You have to work quickly as the solvent begins the welding action as soon as the pipes meet. Wipe surplus cement off immediately, and hold the joint securely for 15 seconds. After this you can fit your branch pipe to the outlet of the tee.

## CUTTING INTO METRIC COPPER PIPE

TIP

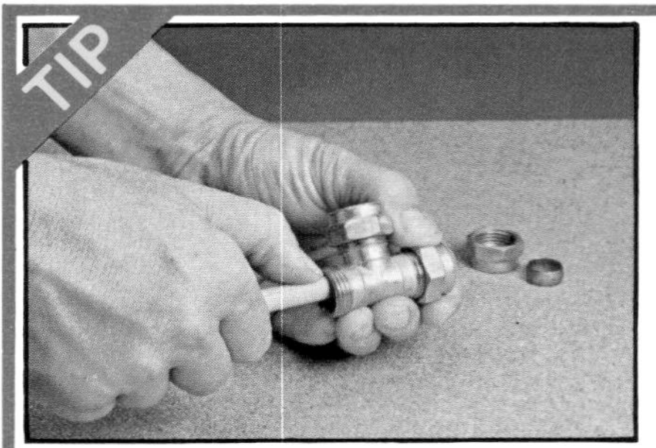

*1 On one side of the tee, push a pencil or piece of dowelling along the inside until it butts against the pipe stop. Mark this length with your thumb.*

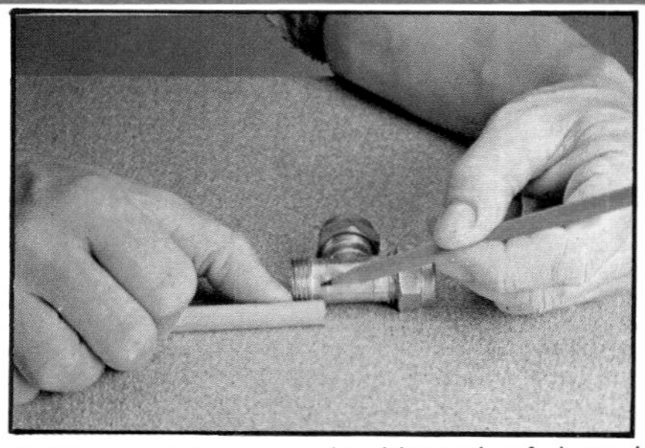

*2 Now hold the marked length of dowel against the outside of the fitting so you can see exactly where the pipe stops. Mark this position on the fitting.*

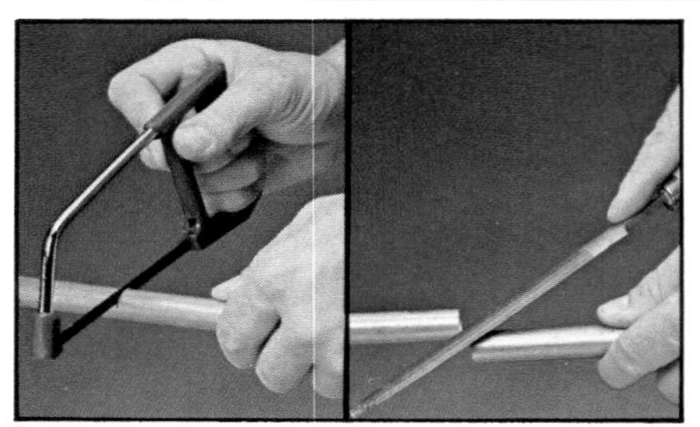

*3 Having turned off the water and drained the supply pipe, cut it at the place where you want the branch to join in. Clean one of the ends with steel wool.*

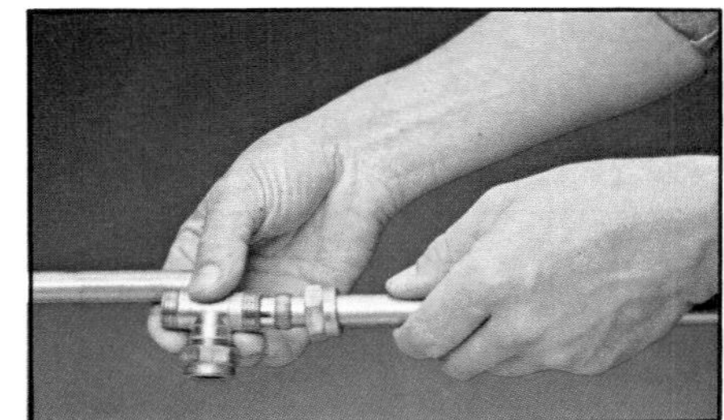

*4 Now slip a cap-nut and then an olive over the cleaned pipe end and connect up the unmarked end of the tee fitting to the pipe.*

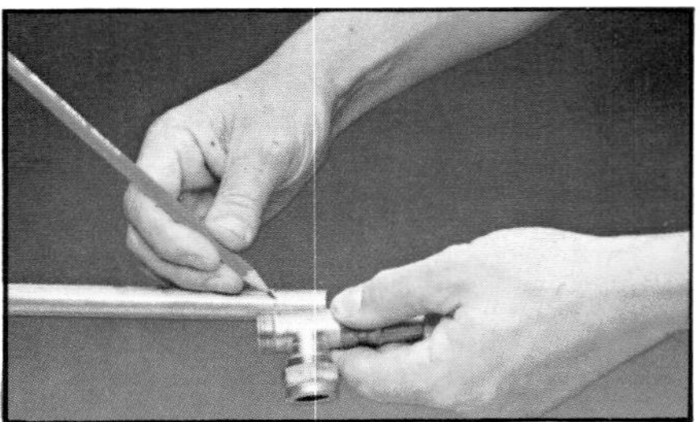

*5 Allow the tee to rest alongside the pipe run. The mark on the front of the fitting is your guide to where the pipe has to be cut again.*

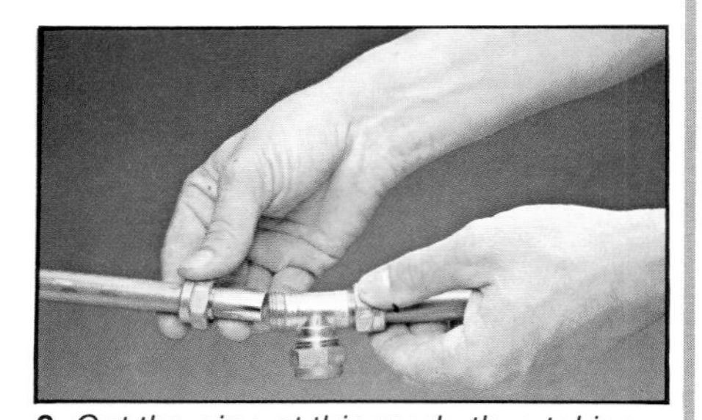

*6 Cut the pipe at this mark, thus taking out a small section. Clean the end and slip a cap-nut and olive into place. Spring the pipe end into the tee.*

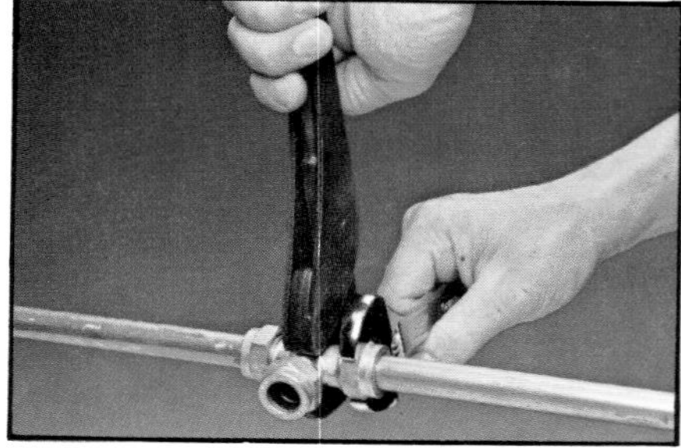

*7 Support the fitting with a wrench while tightening the cap-nuts on both ends of the tee with an adjustable spanner or wrench.*

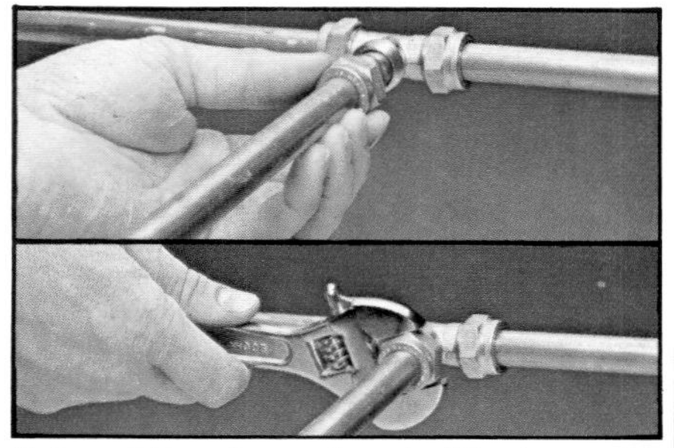

*8 Insert the cleaned end of the branch pipe into the tee and tighten the cap-nut 1½ turns with a wrench, holding the fitting to stop it from twisting.*

# JOINING METRIC TO IMPERIAL PIPE

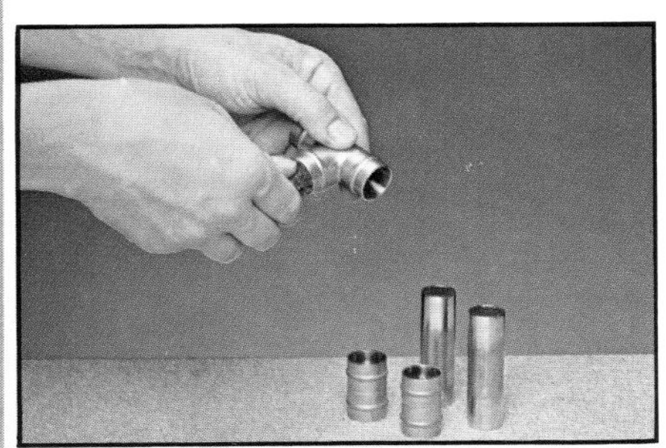

**1** *Cut two short lengths of metric pipe and prepare the pipe ends, the metric/ imperial adaptors and also the tee junction.*

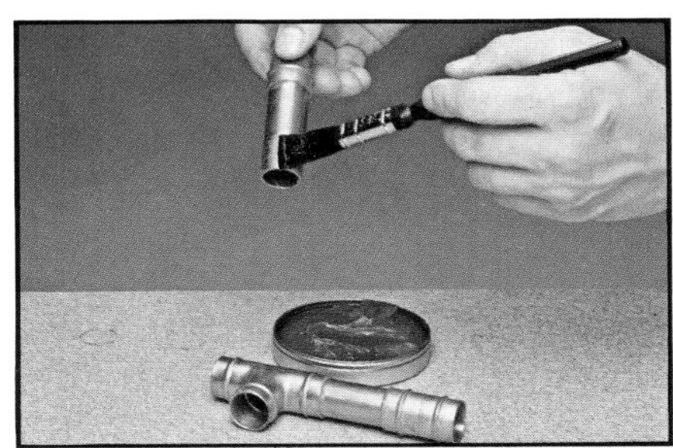

**2** *Smear flux over the ends of the pipe, inside the rims of the adaptors and each opening on the tee. Then assemble the fitting.*

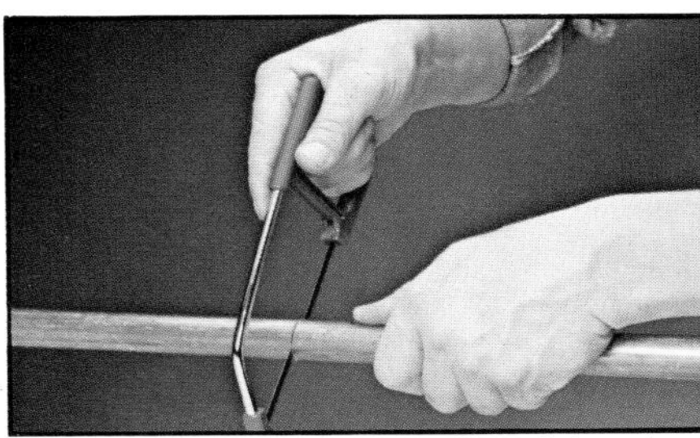

**3** *With the water turned off and the pipe drained, cut it where you want to make the connection. Prepare one of the ends with steel wool.*

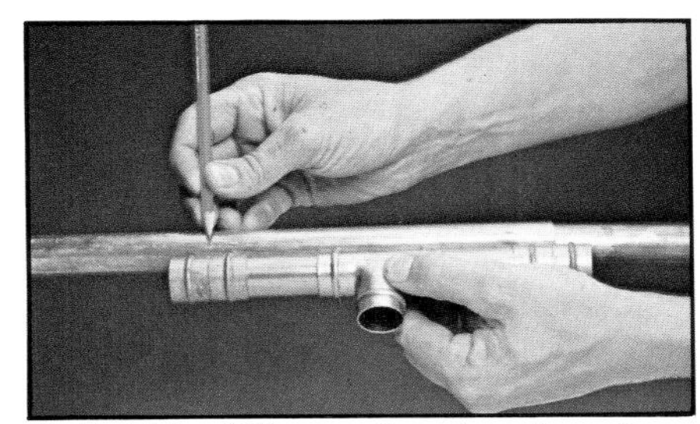

**4** *Hold the fitting so the pipe stop of one adaptor rests against the cut. Now you can mark the other pipe stop position on the pipe run.*

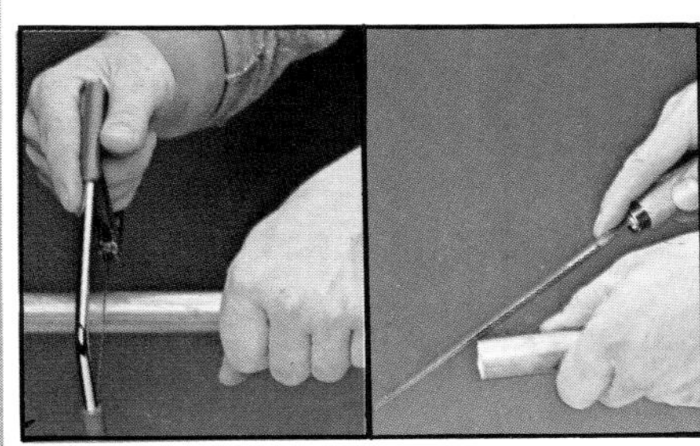

**5** *Cut out the section of pipe and prepare the newly-cut end. Don't forget to apply the flux, smearing it on the outside of both pipe ends.*

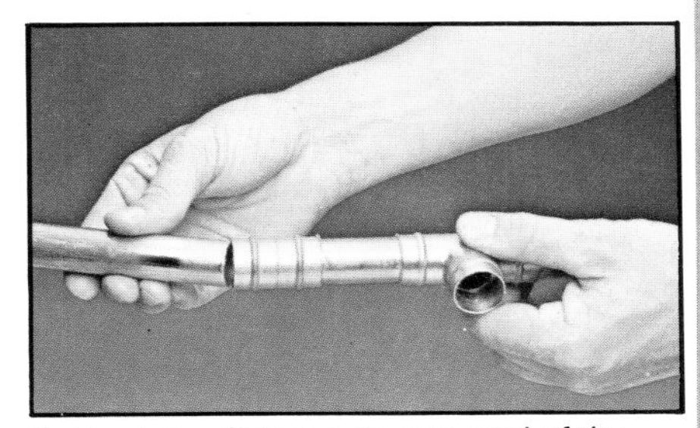

**6** *Push the fitting onto one end of the supply run, then gently spring the other end into place so that the tee junction is correctly positioned.*

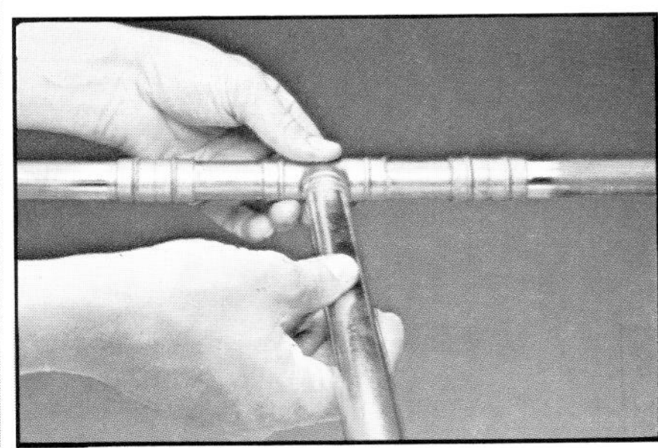

**7** *Prepare the end of the branch pipe and push it into the tee. Make sure that all the pipe ends are butting up fully against the pipe stops.*

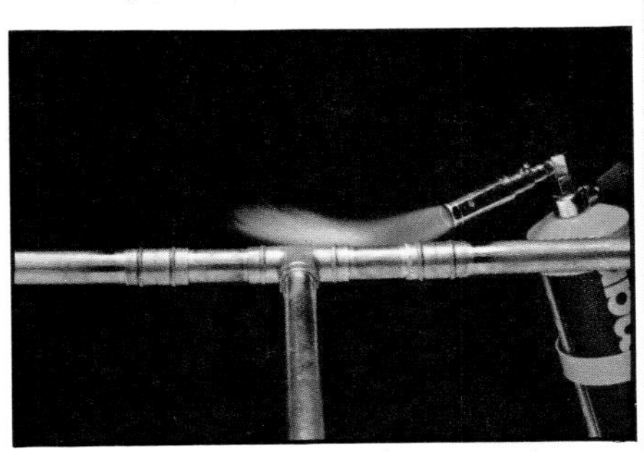

**8** *Make all the joints at the same time. Rings of solder round the mouths of the fittings indicate that sound, watertight connections have been made.*

## Ready Reference

### CONVENIENT CUTTING

Try to join into existing pipework at a point where you have room to manoeuvre.
If space is very tight
- use a junior hacksaw instead of a full-sized one, or
- use a sawing wire for cutting pipes in corners

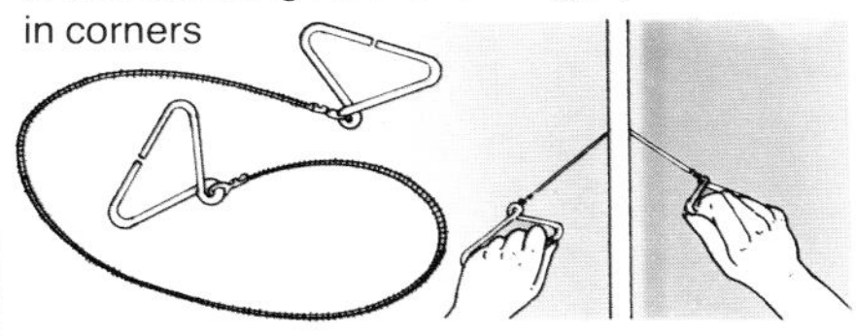

### THE RIGHT TEE

Your branch line may be the same diameter as the main pipe, or smaller (it should never be larger). Tees are described as having all ends equal (eg, 15 x 15 x 15mm), or as having the branch reduced (eg, 22 x 22 x 15mm).

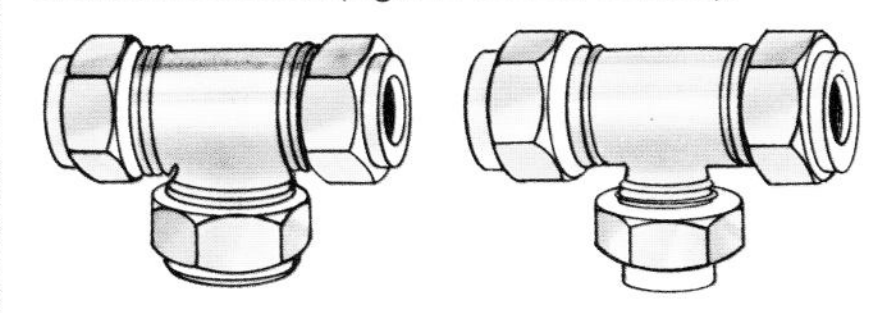

### SUPPORTING THE PIPEWORK

All pipework needs supporting at intervals along its length with pipe clips (usually plastic or metal). Fit them at
- 1.2m (4ft) intervals on horizontal pipe runs
- 1.5m (5ft) intervals on vertical pipe runs.

### TO SAVE TIME AND TROUBLE

- hold the body of a compression fitting securely with one wrench or spanner while doing up the cap-nut with another
- wrap nearby capillary fittings in damp cloths when soldering in new ones
- make up the entire branch line before cutting in the branch tee
- have cloths handy for mopping up when cutting into existing pipework
- if you're using compression fittings on a vertical pipe run, stop the lower cap-nut and olive from slipping down the pipe by clipping a clothes peg or bulldog clip to it
- keep a replacement cartridge for your blow-torch in your tool kit so you don't run out of gas in the middle of a job.

## JOINING INTO PLASTIC PIPES

**1** *Polythene pipe is joined by a compression fitting with a larger olive than usual (right hand) and pipe liners to support the pipe walls.*

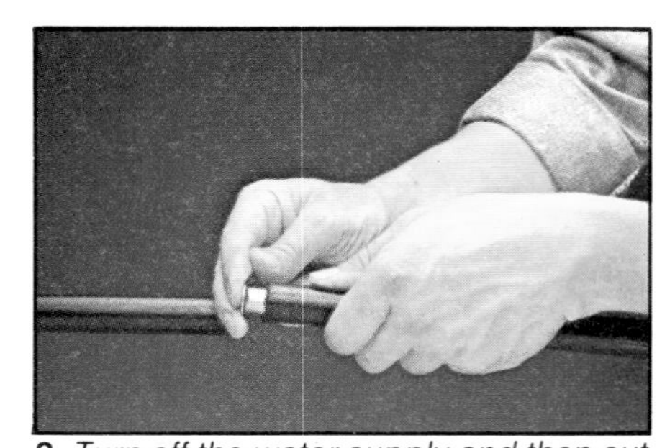

**2** *Turn off the water supply and then cut the pipe. Use a file to remove any rough edges and then insert a liner into one end of the pipe.*

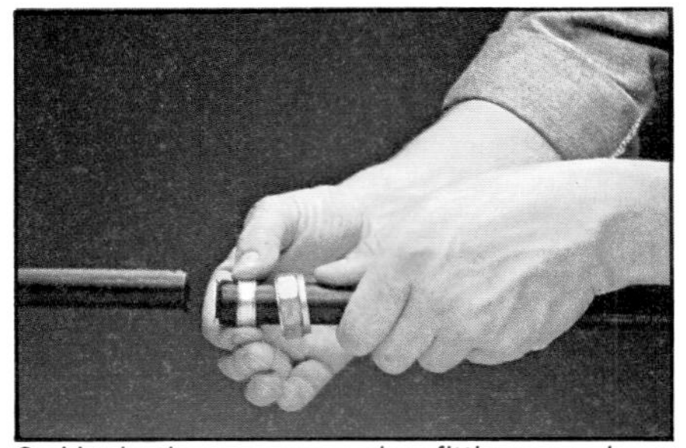

**3** *Undo the compression fittings and slip a cap-nut over the pipe end containing the liner; then slip on the olive.*

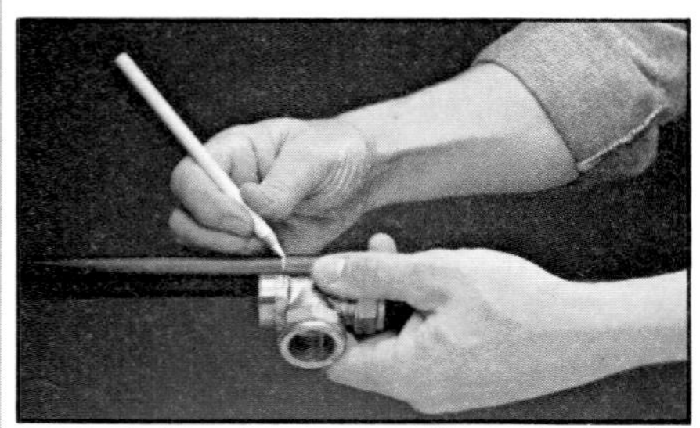

**4** *Mark the pipe stop on the outside of the tee, join the tee to the prepared end, then mark across the pipe stop to show where the pipe is to be cut.*

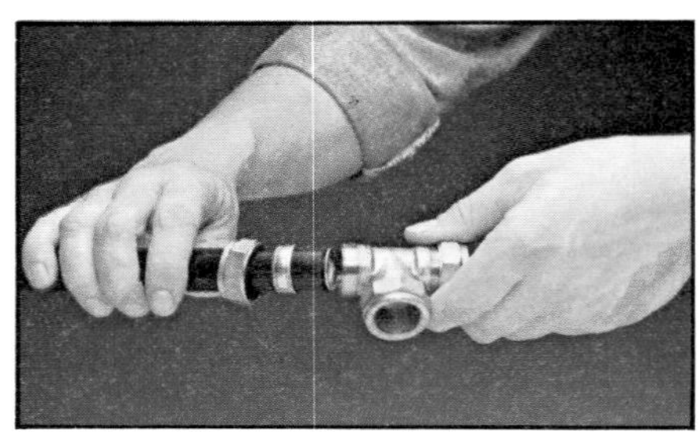

**5** *Cut out the section of pipe and connect the other end of the tee. Hold the fitting securely while you tighten the cap-nuts 1 1/2 turns.*

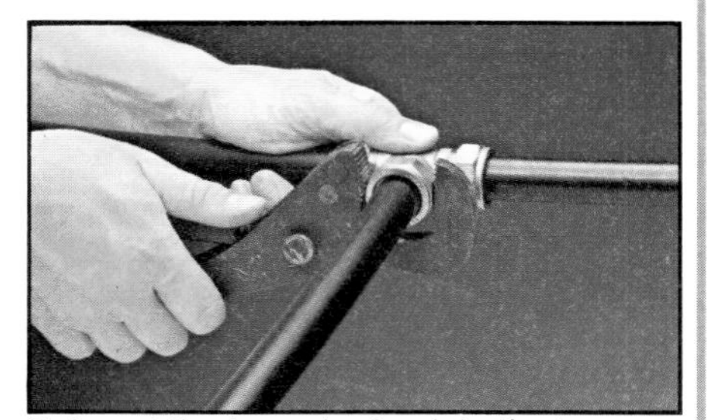

**6** *Insert the branch pipe into the tee fitting and again use a wrench or adjustable spanner to give the cap-nuts 1 1/2 turns.*

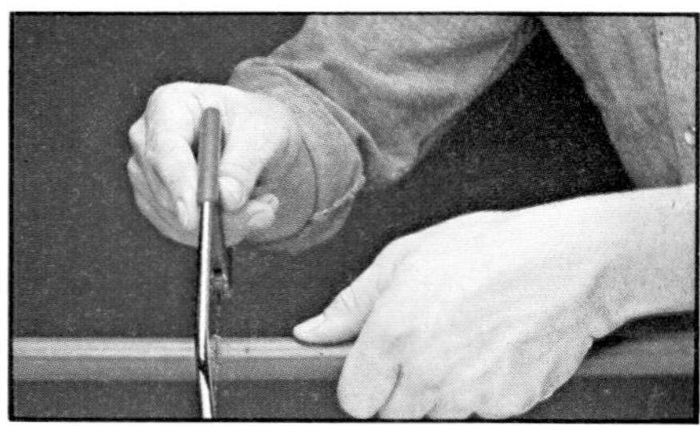

**7** *With UPVC pipe, mark the pipe stops on the outside of the tee. Use these as a gauge to cut out a small section of pipe with a hacksaw.*

TIP

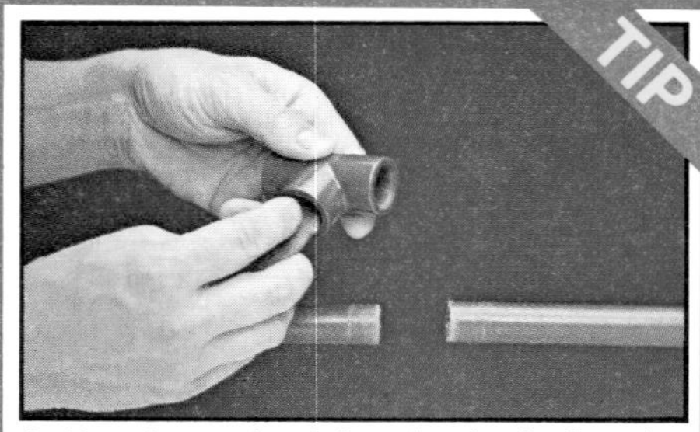

**8** *Key the ends of the pipe including the branch and the inside of the tee with abrasive paper. This is essential when using solvent-weld cement.*

**9** *Thoroughly clean the ends of the pipes with a degreaser, which you apply with a brush, and leave until completely dry.*

**10** *Once you've done this, spread solvent weld cement on the contact surfaces. Take care not to inhale the fumes as you work.*

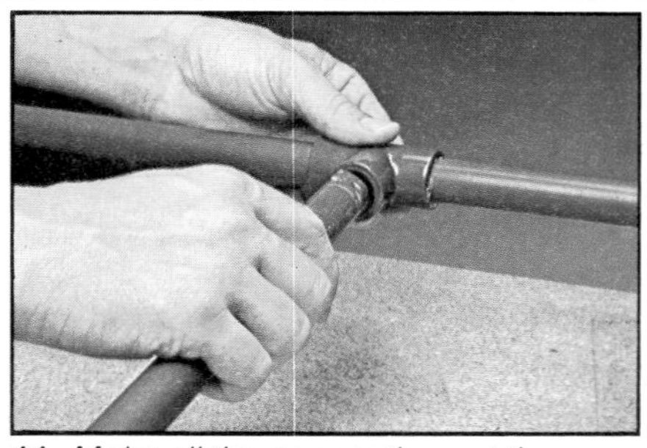

**11** *Make all the connections at the same time, and check to ensure that all the pipes are pushed right into the tee. Hold for 30 seconds.*

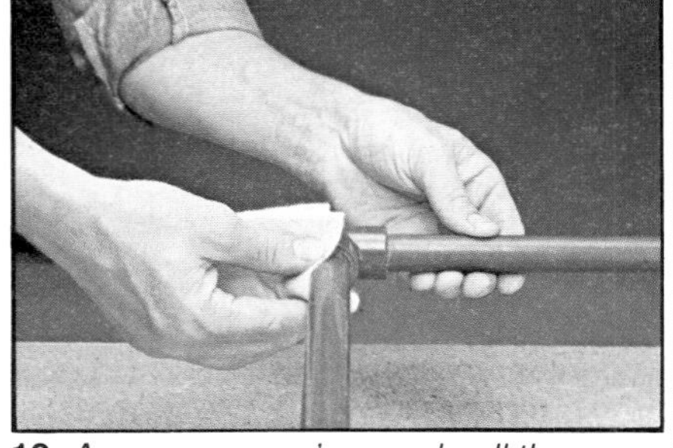

**12** *As soon as you've made all the connections, use a cloth to remove any surplus cement from the pipes. Water shouldn't be turned on for 24 hours.*

# USING PLASTIC PIPE AND FITTINGS

**Plastic pipe and fittings can now be used for hot water supplies and central heating. They are easy to work with and allow the DIY plumber to tackle a wide range of jobs.**

Over the last twenty years plastic has become the most popular plumbing material for above and below ground drainage, for rainwater collection and disposal, and for subsoil drainage. In the form of black polythene tubing it has also become a material widely used for water transportation on camping sites and farms. In the home, however, it has not proved popular. Although this lack of interest can partly be attributed to the conservatism of plumbers and householders, the main reason has been that up until now the plastic pipes that have been available have been suitable for cold water supplies only. This has meant that plumbers, who have had no choice but to use copper or some other metal for the hot water or central heating system, have almost always tended to use the same material when dealing with the cold water system. Householders have doubted the ability of plastic pipework to do a good, life-long job, and have also tended to resist its use on grounds of taste: quite simply, in places where pipework is exposed to view the combination of plastic and copper (or stainless steel or iron) is not one that is very pleasing to the eye.

Now, however, all this has changed. Recently the National Water Council (NWC) gave its approval to two proprietary systems of plastic plumbing, one made out of polybutylene and the other of chlorinated polyvinyl chloride (CPVC), both of which can now be used for cold *and* hot water supply as well as for wet central heating systems. These two rival plumbing systems should hold a special appeal for the DIY enthusiast and – now that they have gained the NWC's approval – there is nothing to prevent them gaining widespread acceptance.

## The advantages of plastic pipework

The most obvious advantage is the lightness of the pipework, which makes for ease of handling, but the most important benefit is the ease with which plastic can be cut and joined. This means that the level of skill you require to undertake a particular plumbing task is greatly reduced, as is the amount of time you require to carry it out. Both systems are also strong and durable, more resistant to frost than a traditional plumbing system and, unlike the latter, not subject to corrosion. Last but not least, they are competitively priced.

Plastic pipes are less vulnerable to frost because plastic is a poor conductor of heat compared to metal (which means that, unlike metal, it provides a certain amount of insulation), and because it has greater elasticity. This means that plastic pipes are not only less likely to freeze than metal ones, but also that in the event of their doing so they are much less likely to burst. The greater degree of insulation that plastic provides also brings other benefits: it results in less heat being lost from pipe runs between radiators (or between the hot water cylinder and the hot taps), as well as meaning that less insulation is necessary for pipework that needs to be protected against the cold.

Plastic pipes aren't subject to corrosion for the simple reason that plastic isn't attacked by the water supply. Electrolytic corrosion, which results in the build up of hydrogen gas and black iron oxide sludge (magnetite) and can ultimately lead to leaky radiators and early pump failure, is therefore far less of a problem when a central heating system is fitted with plastic pipes.

This also means that plastic is a safer material to use for your drinking water supply pipes than metal, the use of which can, under some circumstances, present a health risk.

One final point to be borne in mind before you replace metal pipes with plastic ones is that plastic is a non-conductor of electricity. This means that all-plastic plumbing systems cannot be used to earth a domestic electricity supply (see *Ready Reference*).

You can obtain both polybutylene and CPVC tubing in the 15mm (½in), 22mm (¾in) and 28mm (1in) diameters commonly used in domestic hot and cold water supply and in small-bore central heating. However, in other respects – particularly as regards the flexibility of the two different types of tubing and methods of cutting and jointing – the two systems differ. So, before you undertake a plumbing task using plastic pipes and fittings, you'd do well to consider which system best suits your particular application.

## Polybutylene tubing

Polybutylene tubing is brown in colour and naturally flexible; in this respect it differs from CPVC tubing, which is rigid. As well as being available in 3m (10ft) lengths in all three diameters, it is also obtainable as a 100m (325ft) coil in the 15mm (½in) size, and as a 50m (162ft) coil in the 22mm (¾in) size. This flexibility, and the long lengths in which the tubing is available, is particularly useful as it cuts down the time you need to spend on installation, and reduces the number of fittings necessary (which means less cost). You can thread polybutylene pipes under floors and between joists with minimal disturbance, their flexibility also allowing you to take them through apertures and round obstacles that would otherwise present serious difficulties. You can bend the tubing cold to easy bends with a minimum radius of eight times the pipe diameter; 15mm (½in) tube can therefore be bent to a minimum radius of 120mm (4¾in) and 22mm (¾in) to a minimum radius of 176mm (7in). You must, however, provide a clip on either side of the bend to secure it. The flexibility of polybutylene tubing means that

## POLYBUTYLENE PIPE AND FITTINGS

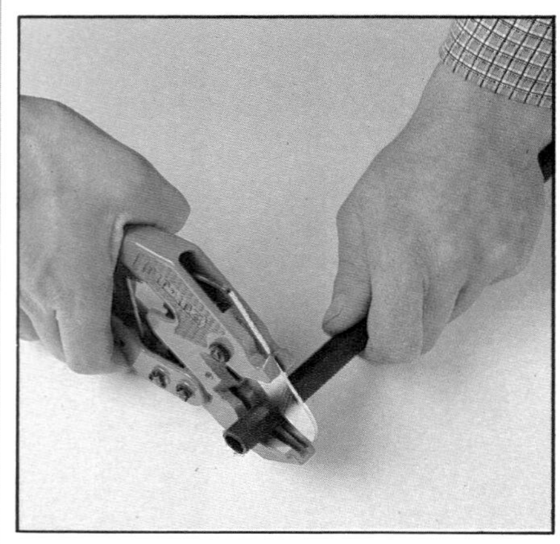

**1** *The best way to cut polybutylene pipe is with the manufacturer's shears. These are easy to use and ensure that you get a square-cut pipe end every time.*

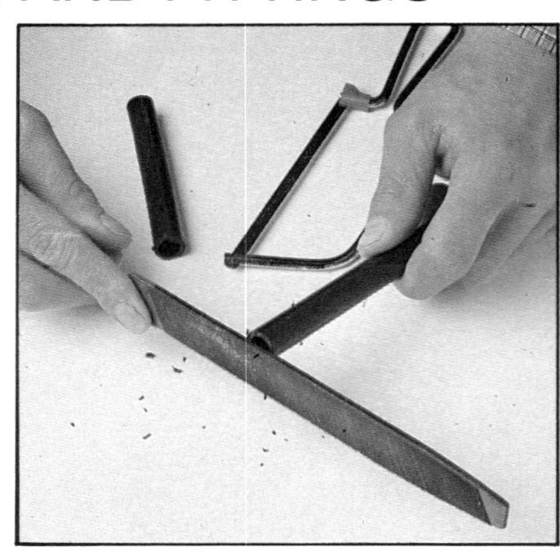

**2** *Alternatively, you can cut polybutylene pipe with a hacksaw or a sharp knife. If you use this method don't forget to clean off any burr or swarf with a file.*

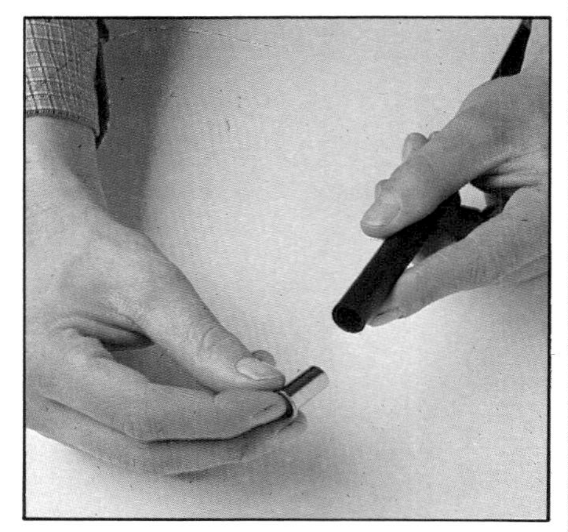

**3** *Before jointing the pipe, insert a stainless steel support sleeve into the pipe end. This prevents the tube end getting crushed within the fitting.*

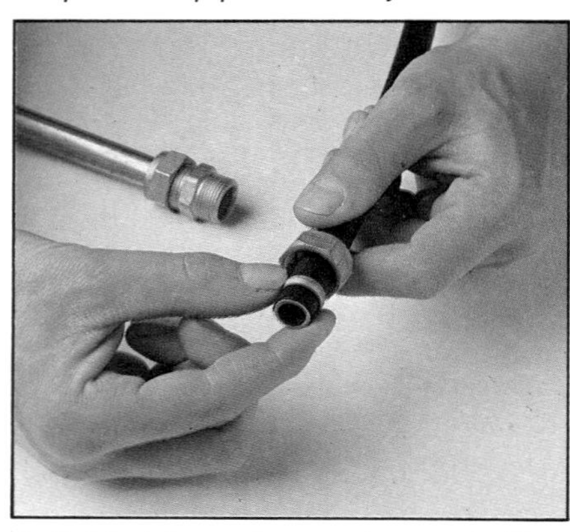

**4** *Polybutylene pipe can be used with ordinary compression fittings. The joint is made in exactly the same way as one made using ordinary copper pipe.*

**5** *Within a polybutylene fitting a grab ring holds the pipe in place, while an 'O' ring ensures a watertight seal. The two are separated by a spacer washer.*

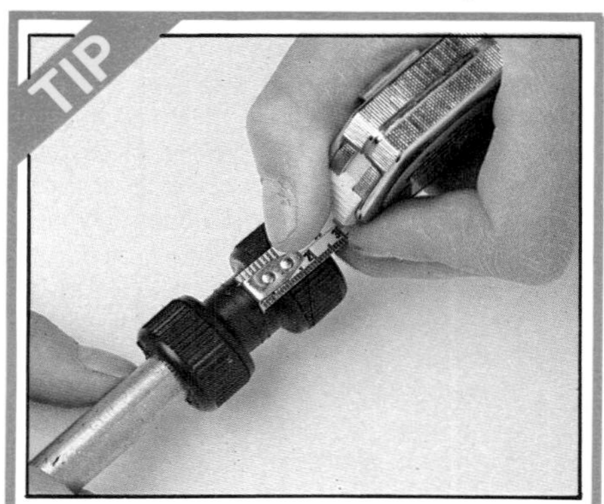


**6** *The witness lines on the body of the fitting indicate the length of pipe hidden within it when the joint is assembled. Remember to allow for this.*

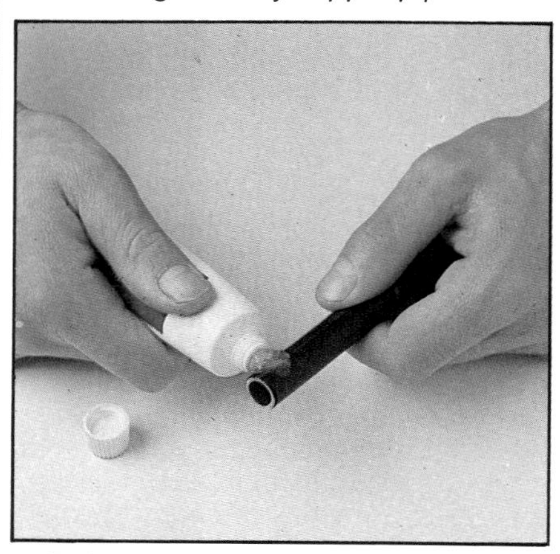

**7** *Before inserting polybutylene pipe into a polybutylene fitting, apply a special lubricant to both the pipe end and the interior of the socket.*

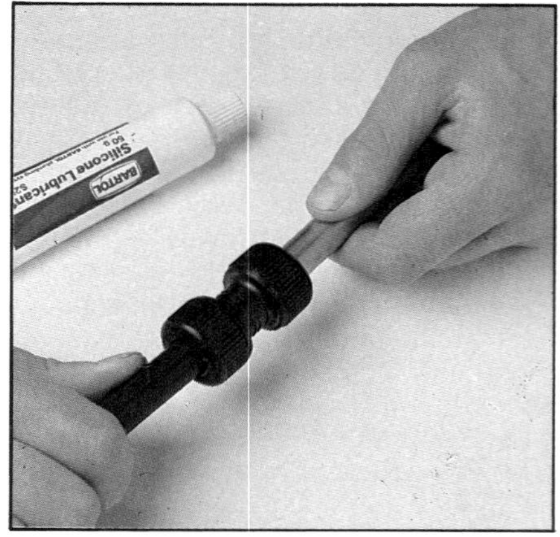

**8** *Make the joint without unscrewing or even loosening the cap-nuts. Simply thrust the pipe end into the socket until it meets the pipe stop inside.*

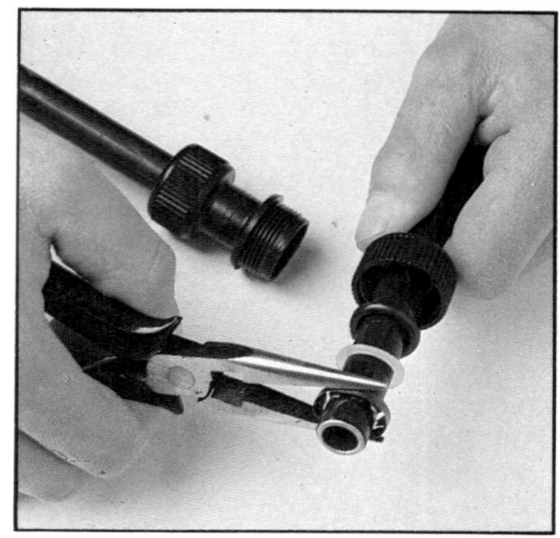

**9** *The pipe can be withdrawn only if you unscrew the cap-nut. To re-use the joint, crush and discard the grab ring, and then replace it with a new one.*

# CPVC PIPE AND FITTINGS

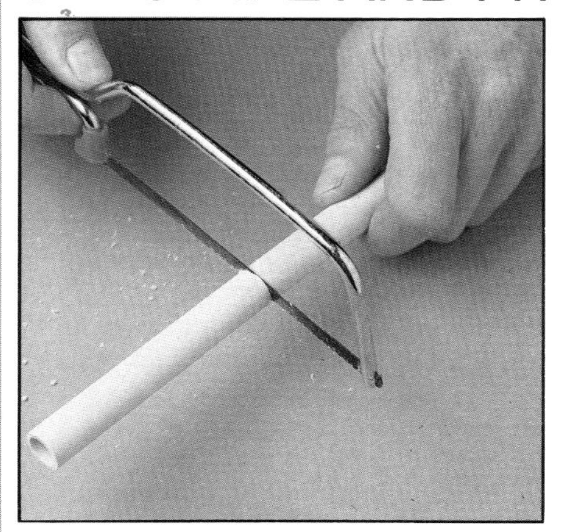

**1** *You can cut CPVC pipe with either a fine-toothed saw or an ordinary pipe cutter. If using a saw, make sure that you hold it at right-angles to the pipe.*

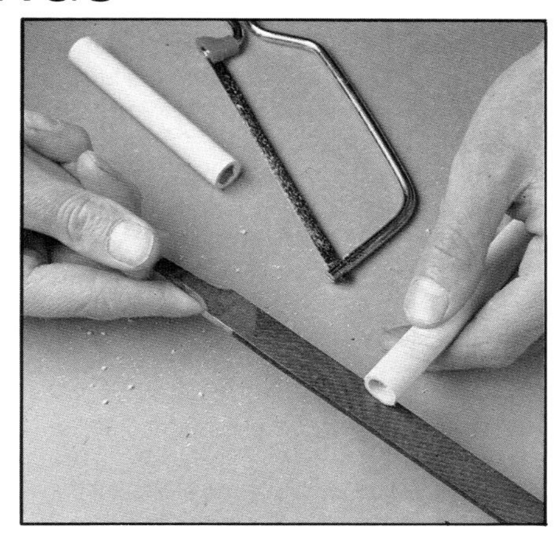

**2** *Use a file or a knife to remove the swarf from the pipe end. Check that the pipe fits snugly in the socket, and that the fitting is free from imperfections.*

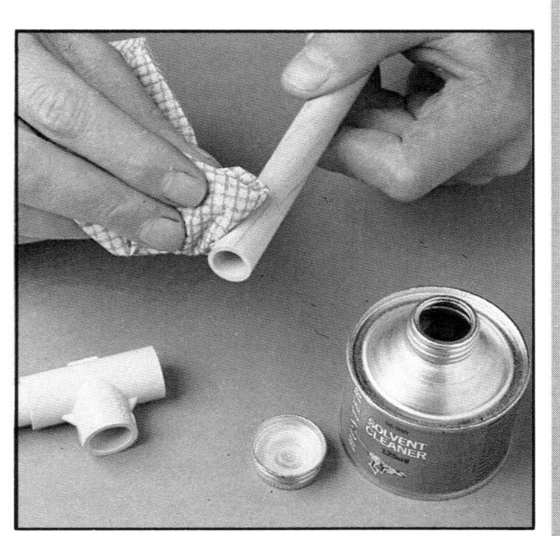


**3** *Before making a joint with CPVC the surfaces to be solvent-welded must first be cleaned. Use the manufacturer's special solvent cleaner for this purpose.*

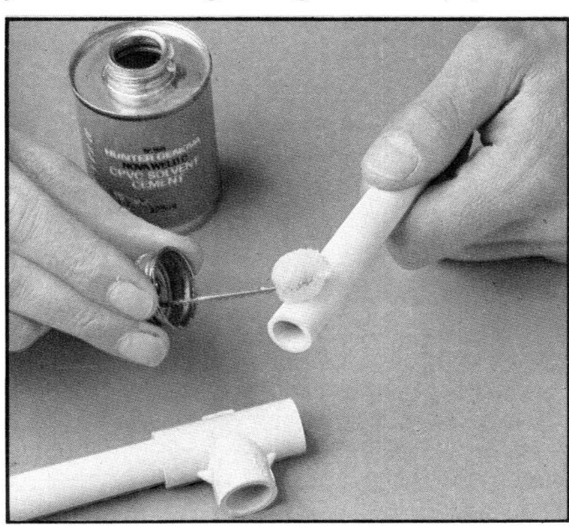

**4** *Immediately afterwards, apply the solvent weld cement, brushing this liberally on the tube end and only sparingly in the interior of the fitting socket.*

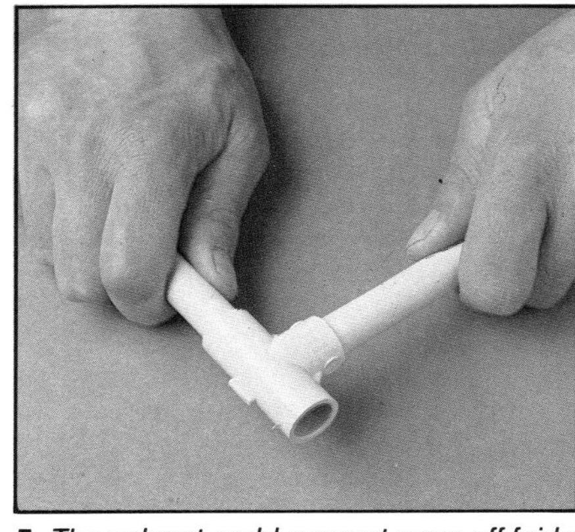

**5** *The solvent-weld cement goes off fairly rapidly, so you must make the joint as soon as you've applied it. Push the pipe home with a slight twisting motion.*

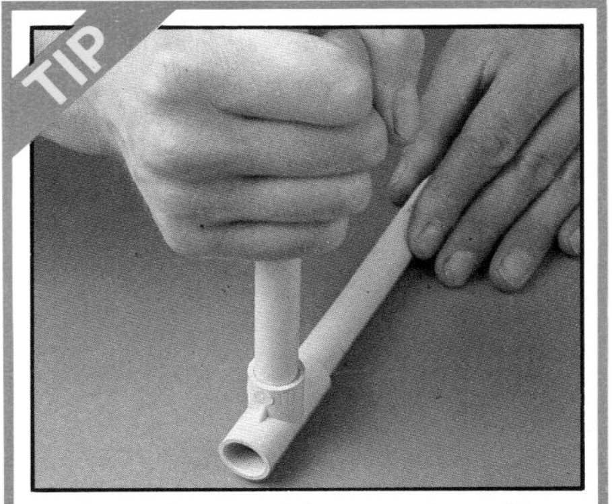


**6** *The solvent-weld cement's rapid setting time also means you must make adjustment for alignment immediately. Do not remove surplus cement.*

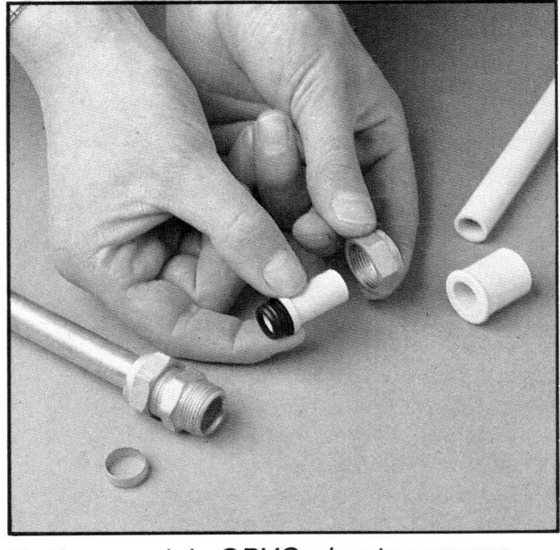

**7** *You can join CPVC pipe to copper using a compression fitting and a two-part adaptor. Discard the olive as the first part of the adaptor is self-sealing.*

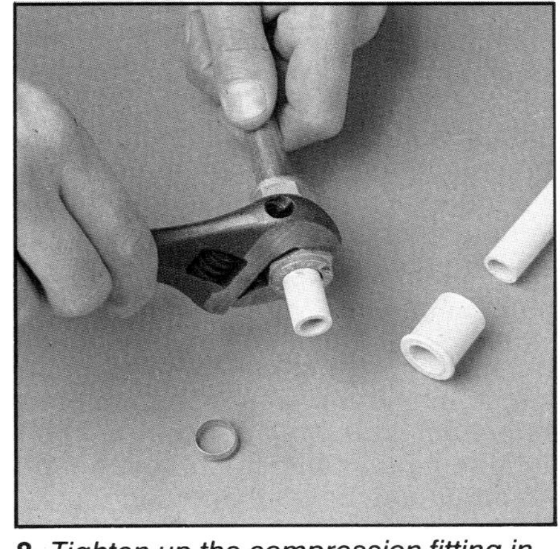

**8** *Tighten up the compression fitting in the usual way. Use a second spanner to hold the body of the fitting before giving the coupling nut a final turn.*

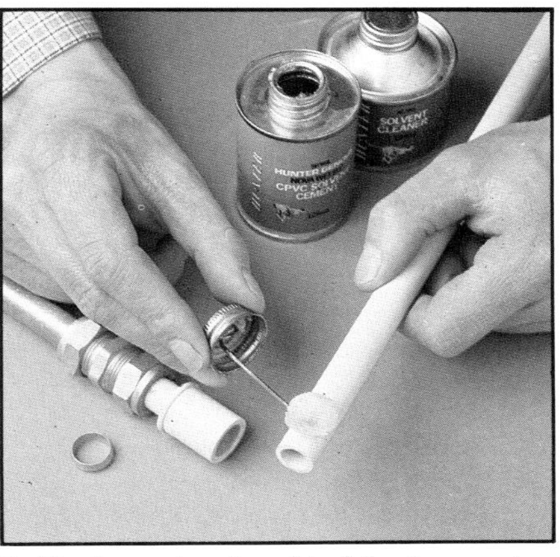


**9** *Having solvent-welded the two parts of the adaptor together, complete the fitting by solvent-welding the CPVC pipe to the second part of the adaptor.*

you will have to give continuous support to any visible horizontal pipe runs in order to eliminate the possibility of unsightly sagging (see *Ready Reference*).

You can cut polybutylene tube with a sharp knife or a hacksaw. However, for speed of operation and to ensure an absolutely square cut pipe end every time, the manufacturers recommend that you use their specially designed pipe shears. It would certainly be worthwhile investing in a pair of these shears before embarking on a major project that involved the making of a large number of joints.

You can join polybutylene tubing by using either non-manipulative (Type 'A') compression joints (as used with copper), or else the manufacturer's own patent push-fit connectors. One of the advantages of being able to use Type 'A' compression joints with tubing is that it enables you to replace a length of copper pipe with polybutylene tubing using the existing compression tee or coupling.

When using polybutylene tubing with this type of joint the procedure you follow is identical to that which you adopt with copper pipe (as described on pages 20 to 24). But in order to prevent the collapse of the tube end when the cap-nut is tightened, you must insert a purpose-made stainless steel support sleeve into it. And if you use jointing compound to complete a threaded fitting connected to polybutylene pipe, make sure none comes into contact with the polybutylene.

The patent polybutylene joints and fittings are available in the usual range of straight couplings, tees, elbows, reducing fittings and tap and tank connectors, and in appearance they resemble their brass compression counterparts. But there is one important difference – you don't have to loosen or unscrew the cap-nuts to make a joint. To make a connection you simply have to push the prepared pipe end into the fitting (see step-by-step photographs). Polybutylene fittings have one further advantage in that they allow you to rotate a pipe that has been inserted into one of them, even when it is filled with water. This means, for example, that a polybutylene stop-valve can rest neatly against a wall until you need to use it. You then pull the handle away from the wall so you can open and close it easily.

### CPVC tubing

CPVC tubing differs from the polybutylene type in two basic ways. First, it is rigid rather than flexible, which means that it is only available in relatively short lengths of 2m (6ft 6in) or 3m (9ft 9in). Secondly, it is joined by a process known as solvent welding, a slightly more involved procedure than making a push-fit or compression connection (see step-by-step photographs). Superficially, CPVC tubing can be distinguished from polybutylene by its off-white colour. An hour after the last joint has been made you can flush through the system and fill it with cold water; before filling with hot water you need to wait at least four hours.

CPVC pipe does expand when hot water passes through it, but this won't cause a problem in most domestic systems unless one of the pipe runs exceeds 10m (33ft), which is unlikely. In this case you will have to create an expansion loop using four 90° elbows and three 150mm (6in) lengths of pipe.

The manufacturers of CPVC tubing provide an exceptionally wide range of fittings to meet every eventuality. There are 90° and 45° elbows, equal and unequal tees, reducing pieces, tap and ball-valve connectors, stop-valves and gate-valves, and provision for connection to existing copper or screwed iron fittings. The connectors for copper tubing have a solvent-weld socket at one end and a conventional Type 'A' compression joint at the other. Those for iron fittings have a solvent-weld fitting at one end and either a male or female threaded joint at the other. If you are connecting a fitting to an existing iron socket, make sure that you render the screwed connection watertight by binding plastic PTFE tape round the male thread before screwing home.

### What system to use

Neither system is 'better' than the other, and each has its merits and its drawbacks. The polybutylene tubing is flexible and available in extremely long lengths which reduce the number of joints you will have to use, as well as enabling you to get through or round obstacles that might prove difficult were you using the CPVC system. On the other hand the push-fit polybutylene joints are bulkier and more obtrusive than those used with the CPVC system.

Bearing in mind this, and the fact that the rigid CPVC pipes will be less prone to sagging than the flexible polybutylene tubing, the CPVC system is probably the more acceptable one in situations where plumbing is exposed to view. The more complex construction of the polybutylene joints – the cause of their bulkiness – also makes them relatively expensive: which means that the smaller number necessary for carrying out a given plumbing task won't always cost you less than the greater number necessary with CPVC. However, polybutylene joints, unlike CPVC ones, can be used more than once.

Lastly, in case your decision to opt for one system or the other is influenced by the colour of the material out of which it is made (dark brown for polybutylene and off-white for CPVC), you can paint both systems with ordinary household paints.

## Ready Reference

### TIP: CHECK EARTHING

Metal plumbing systems were often used to earth the domestic electricity supply. Since plastic pipework doesn't conduct electricity, it's vital that the house's earthing arrangements are checked by an electrician if you replace any part of the plumbing system with plastic.

### BENDING POLYBUTYLENE PIPE

You can form bends in polybutylene pipe to a minimum radius of eight times the pipe diameter.

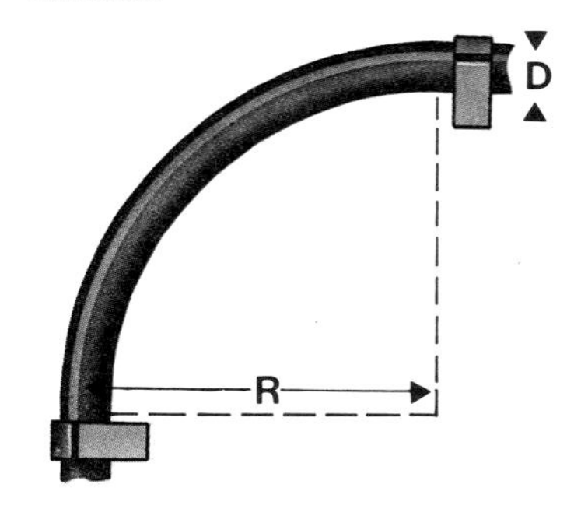


### CONNECTING POLYBUTYLENE TO IMPERIAL COPPER PIPES

You can use 15mm (½in) polybutylene fittings with ½in imperial-sized copper pipe without adaptation. If you wish to use 22mm (¾in) fittings with ¾in imperial-sized copper pipe, you have to replace the sealing ring with a purpose-made one of larger size.

### SUPPORTING PIPE RUNS

With CPVC pipe, space pipe brackets at 500mm (20in) intervals on horizontal pipe runs, at 1m (39in) intervals on vertical ones. With polybutylene pipe, use the following spacings:

| Pipe size | Horizontal run | Vertical run |
|---|---|---|
| 15mm (½in) | 400mm (16in) | 800mm (31in) |
| 22mm (¾in) | 600mm (24in) | 1m (39in) |

Reduce these by 25 per cent for pipes carrying water over 60°C (140°F), increase them by 25 per cent for cold pipe runs.

### CONNECTIONS TO BOILERS

Although polybutylene and CPVC pipes are suitable for all other applications, you can't connect them directly to a boiler. Instead you should

- connect short lengths of copper pipe to the boiler flow and return tappings
- link the plastic pipe to the copper using the appropriate type of fitting. The copper pipe tails should be
- 380mm (15in) long with CPVC pipe
- 1m (39in) long with polybutylene pipe.

## COMPARING THE SYSTEMS

*To show how the two plastic systems look in use, here is the pipe run involved in teeing off a spur to a washing machine, assembled using the appropriate fittings in each case. For comparison the same run has been assembled using copper pipe with capillary and compression fittings too.*

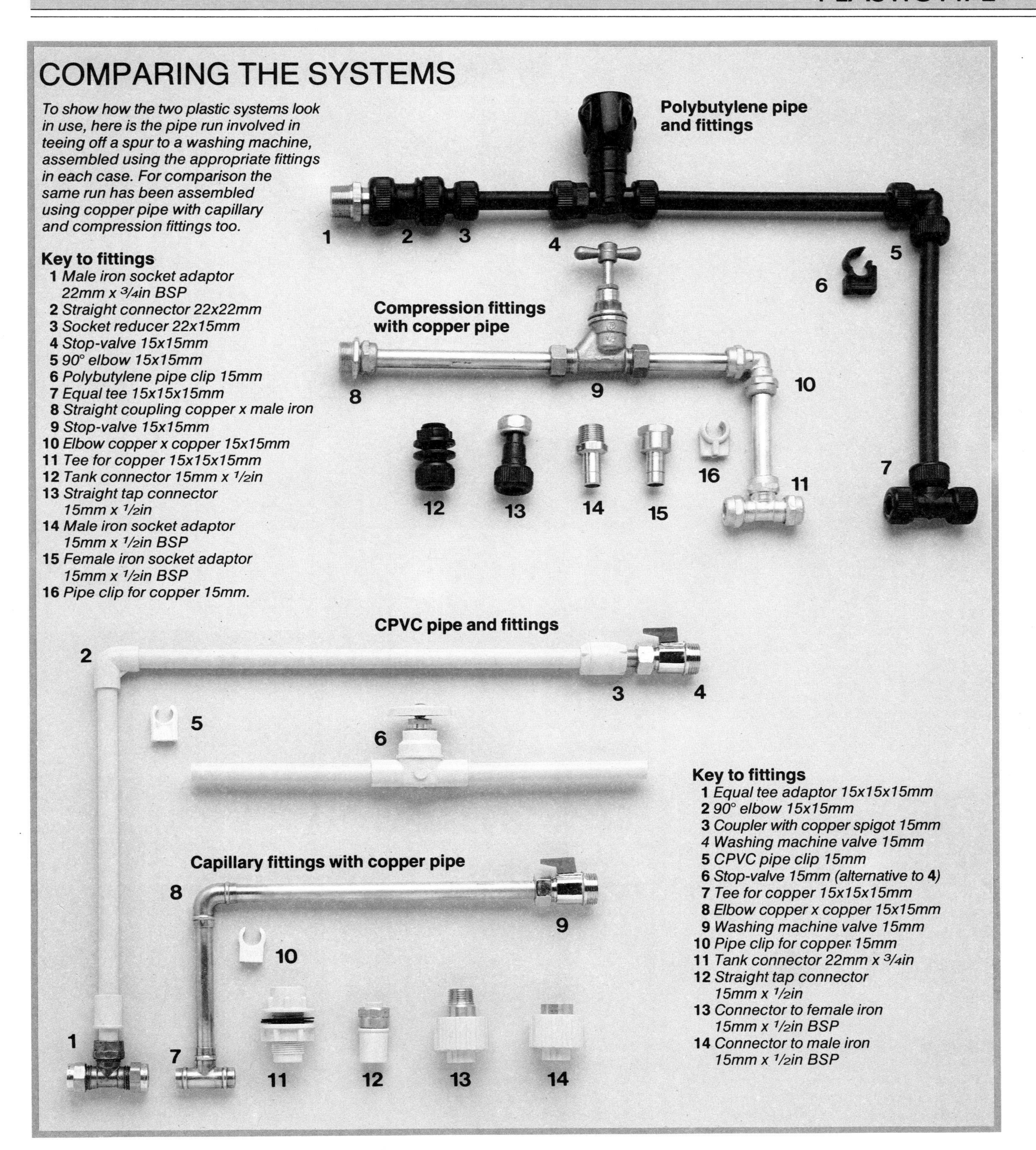


**Key to fittings**

**1** *Male iron socket adaptor 22mm x 3/4in BSP*
**2** *Straight connector 22x22mm*
**3** *Socket reducer 22x15mm*
**4** *Stop-valve 15x15mm*
**5** *90° elbow 15x15mm*
**6** *Polybutylene pipe clip 15mm*
**7** *Equal tee 15x15x15mm*
**8** *Straight coupling copper x male iron*
**9** *Stop-valve 15x15mm*
**10** *Elbow copper x copper 15x15mm*
**11** *Tee for copper 15x15x15mm*
**12** *Tank connector 15mm x 1/2in*
**13** *Straight tap connector 15mm x 1/2in*
**14** *Male iron socket adaptor 15mm x 1/2in BSP*
**15** *Female iron socket adaptor 15mm x 1/2in BSP*
**16** *Pipe clip for copper 15mm.*

**Key to fittings**

**1** *Equal tee adaptor 15x15x15mm*
**2** *90° elbow 15x15mm*
**3** *Coupler with copper spigot 15mm*
**4** *Washing machine valve 15mm*
**5** *CPVC pipe clip 15mm*
**6** *Stop-valve 15mm (alternative to* **4***)*
**7** *Tee for copper 15x15x15mm*
**8** *Elbow copper x copper 15x15mm*
**9** *Washing machine valve 15mm*
**10** *Pipe clip for copper 15mm*
**11** *Tank connector 22mm x 3/4in*
**12** *Straight tap connector 15mm x 1/2in*
**13** *Connector to female iron 15mm x 1/2in BSP*
**14** *Connector to male iron 15mm x 1/2in BSP*

# JOINING PLASTIC WASTE PIPES

**Most waste pipes installed today are made of plastic, which is cheap, lightweight and easy to work with. A little practice and careful measuring will enable you to replace all parts of your system. Here's how to join them together.**

Waste systems draining baths, basins and sinks used to be made of lead, heavy galvanised steel with screwed joints, or copper. Soil pipes from WCs were traditionally cast iron, as was all the outside pipework for both waste and soil disposal. Nowadays waste and soil pipes are made of one or other of a variety of plastic materials, which may be used for repairs, extension work or complete replacement of an existing system.

These plastic pipes are lightweight and easily cut, handled and joined. They are made of materials usually known by the initials of their chemical names – UPVC (unplasticised polyvinyl chloride), MPVC (modified polyvinyl chloride), ABS (acrylonitrile butadiene styrene) and PP (polypropylene). CPVC (chlorinated polyvinyl chloride) is usually used for hot and cold water supply pipes. Pipes and fittings are available in white, grey or a copper colour, depending on type and manufacture.

All these materials are satisfactory for domestic waste systems and – with one exception – can all be joined in the same way: either by push-fit (ring-seal) jointing or by solvent welding.

The exception is PP pipe. This was first developed because of its good resistance to very hot water and chemical wastes, and was therefore extensively used in industry. Nowadays, however, it is frequently used in the home for waste or rainwater drainage. The big difference between PP and other plastic pipes used in waste drainage is that it cannot be solvent-welded. All joints must be push-fit. In most situations this is no great disadvantage but it does make it important to be able to distinguish PP from other plastics. It has a slightly greasy feel and, when cut with a fine toothed saw, leaves fine strands of fibrous material round the cut edges.

### Sizes

When buying plastic pipe and components it is wise to stick to one brand only. Pipes and fittings from different makers, though of the same size, are not necessarily interchangeable. Most suppliers stock the systems of only one manufacturer, although the same

## PREPARING THE PIPE ENDS

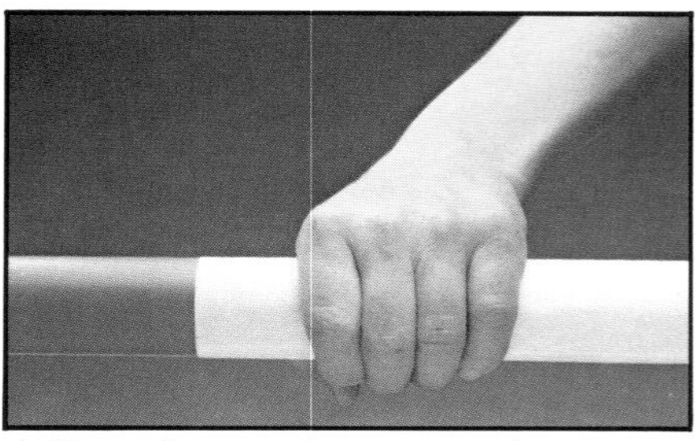

*1 To make sure that you cut the pipe squarely, hold a sheet of paper around it so that the edges meet and overlap each other. This is your cutting line.*

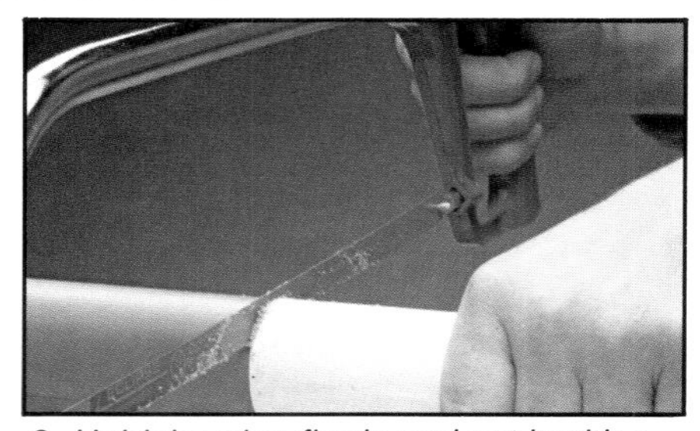

*2 Hold the pipe firmly and cut it with a hacksaw, using gentle strokes. You may find it easier to use a junior hacksaw, which gives a finer cut.*

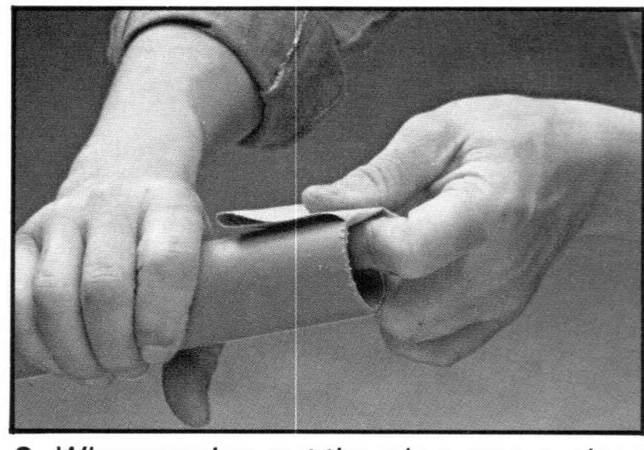

*3 When you've cut the pipe, use a piece of fine glass paper to clean off the burr left by sawing.*

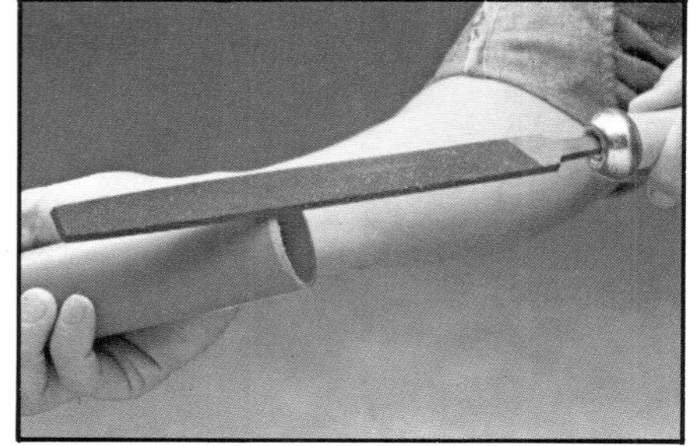

*4 Now take a file and chamfer the end of the pipe all round the edge to a 45° angle. Try to keep the chamfer even.*

## SOLVENT-WELD JOINTING

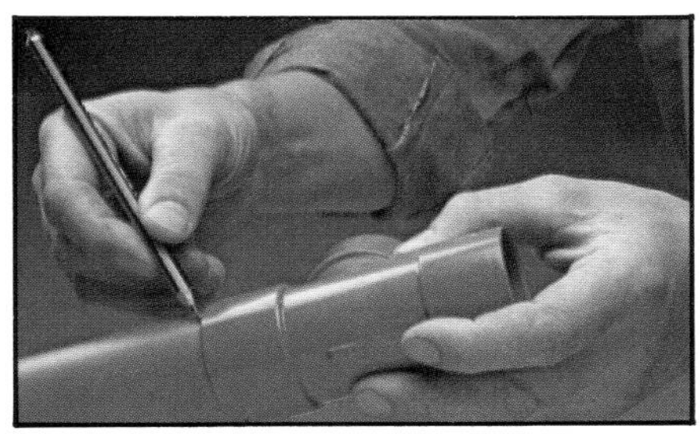

*1 Push the end of the pipe into the socket of the fitting as far as it will go. Mark the pipe at this point with a pencil as a guide to the length within the joint.*

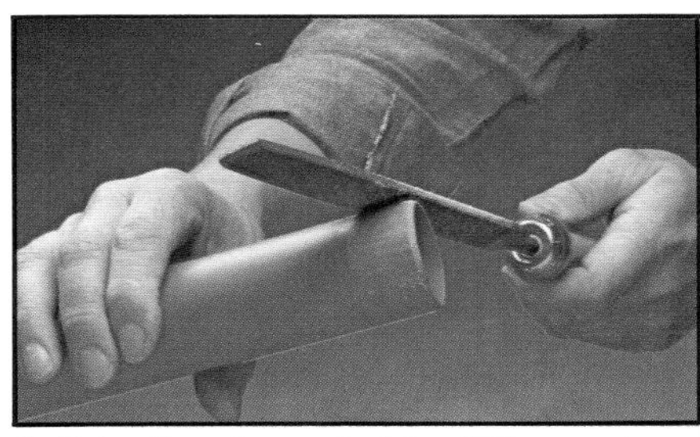

*2 Take the pipe out of the fitting and, with a file, roughen the whole of the end surface that will be inside the fitting up to the pencil mark.*

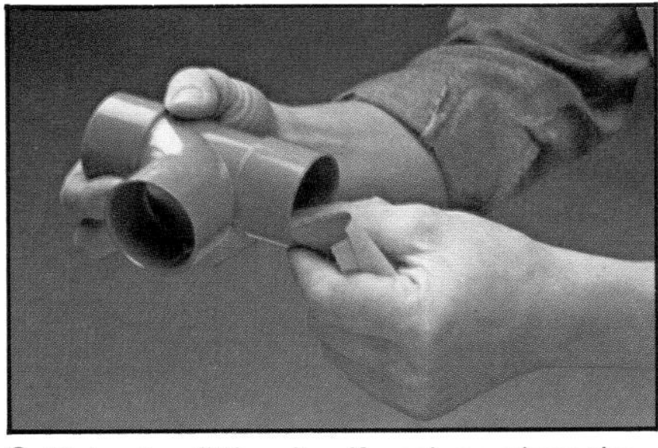

*3 Take the fitting itself and roughen the inside of the socket with fine glass paper. This will provide a key for the solvent cement.*

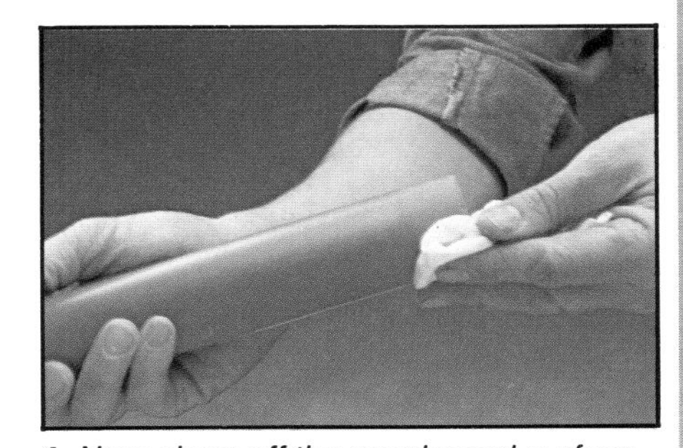

*4 Now clean off the roughened surface of the pipe and socket with spirit as recommended by the manufacturer to remove all dust and debris.*

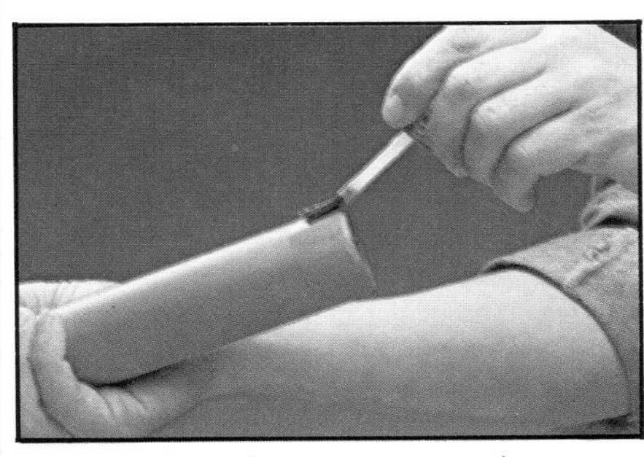

*5 Apply the solvent cement to the roughened end of the pipe, making sure that the whole roughened area is covered. Try and keep it off your fingers.*

*6 Also apply solvent cement to the socket of the fitting. Try to use brush strokes along the line of the pipe.*

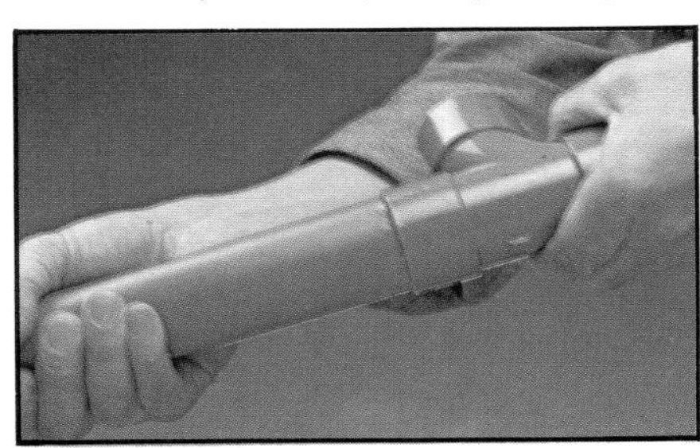

*7 Gently push the pipe fully home into the socket. Some manufacturers suggest a slight twisting action in doing this but check their instructions first.*

TIP

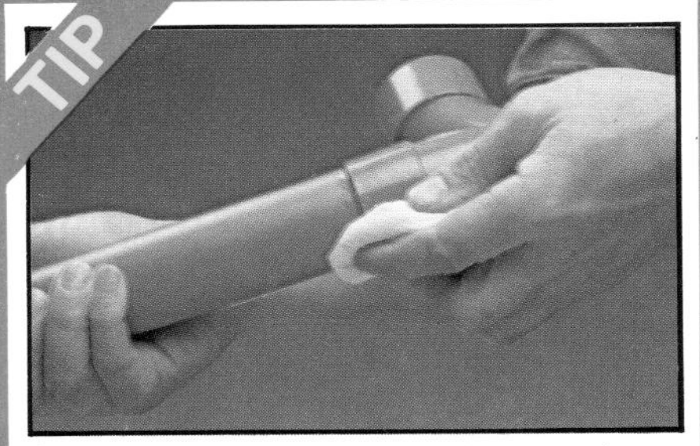

*8 Remove any excess solvent at the edge of the socket with a clean cloth, hold the joint in position for 30 seconds.*

## Ready Reference

### THE TOOLS YOU'LL NEED

- hacksaw – a junior or larger – for cutting the lengths of pipe as you need them
- piece of paper – to help cut the pipe truly square
- tape measure
- file – for chamfering the pipe ends
- fine glasspaper – to abrade pipes and sockets for solvent-welding, and for cleaning up the ends of pipes where you have cut them
- pencil – for marking the cutting points and socket depths to find the working area of the pipe.

### VITAL ACCESSORIES

- solvent cement – for solvent-welding
- cleaning fluid – for cleaning the pipe ends and socket fittings when making solvent-weld joints
- petroleum jelly – for lubrication when inserting the pipe into the socket in push-fit joint assemblies
- tissues or rag for cleaning off excess solvent or petroleum jelly.

### TYPES OF PIPE

**Unplasticised PVC** (UPVC) is used for all waste pipe applications.
**Modified PVC** (MPVC) has rubber or some other plasticiser added to make it more resistant to shock.
**Chlorinated PVC** (CPVC or MUPVC) is used where very hot water discharge occurs, such as washing machine out-flows.
**Polypropylene** (PP) is an alternative to PVC and can withstand hot water – but it expands a lot and is only suitable on short runs.
**Acrylonitrile butadiene styrene** (ABS) is stronger than UPVC and is used for waste connection mouldings.

### SAFETY TIPS

- don't smoke when you are solvent-weld jointing – solvent cement and solvent cement cleaner become poisonous when combined with cigarette smoke
- don't inhale the fumes of solvent-weld cement or cleaning fluid – so avoid working in confined spaces
- don't get solvent-weld cement on any part of the pipe you're not joining as this can later lead to cracking and weaknesses, especially inside sockets where the solvent cement can easily trickle down
- hold all solvent-weld joints for 15 seconds after joining and then leave them undisturbed for at least 5 minutes – if hot water is going to flow through the pipe don't use it for 24 hours.

## PUSH-FIT JOINTING

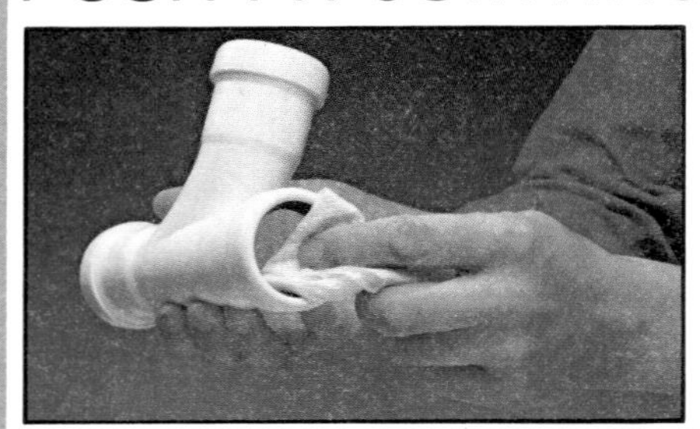

*1 Cut the pipe squarely as in solvent-weld jointing and remove the burr, then take the fitting and clean the socket out with the recommended cleaner.*

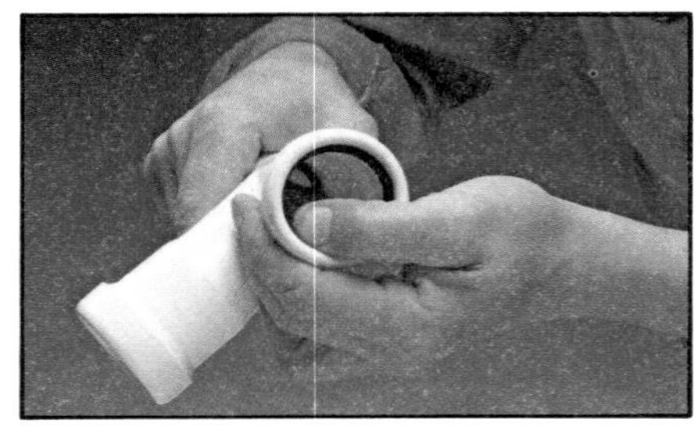

*2 Check that the rubber seal is properly seated in the socket. You may find seals are supplied separately and you will have to insert them.*

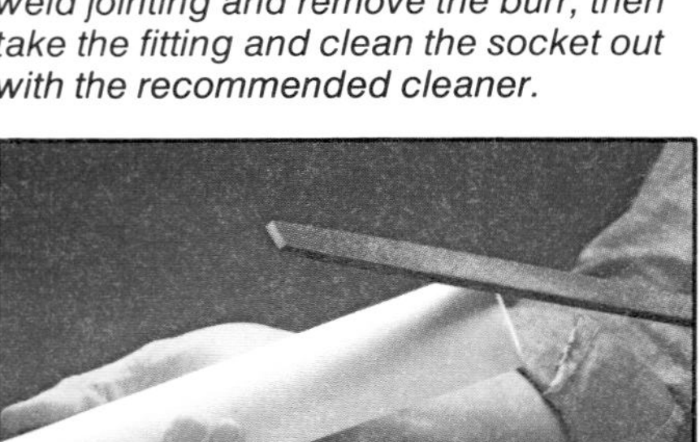

*3 Now chamfer the end of the pipe to an angle of 45°, and smooth off the chamfer carefully with fine glass paper so that no rough edges remain.*

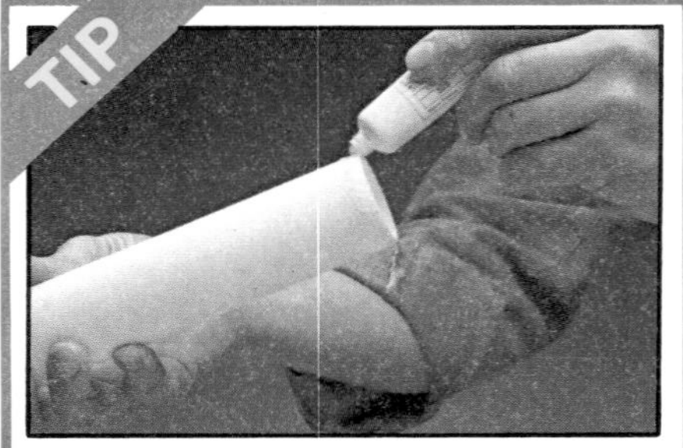


*4 Lubricate the end of the pipe with petroleum jelly over a length of about 5mm (3/16in).*

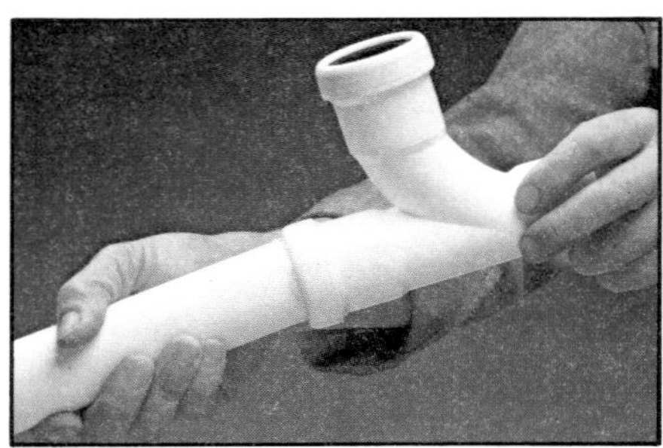

*5 Push the pipe into the socket gently but firmly. Then push it fully home and check that all is square, otherwise you may damage the sealing ring.*

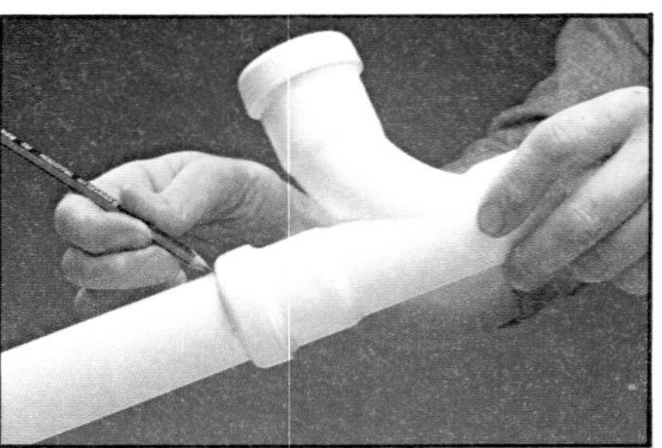

*6 Now make a pencil mark on the pipe at the edge of the socket – you can easily rub it off later if you want to – to act as a guide in setting the expansion gap.*

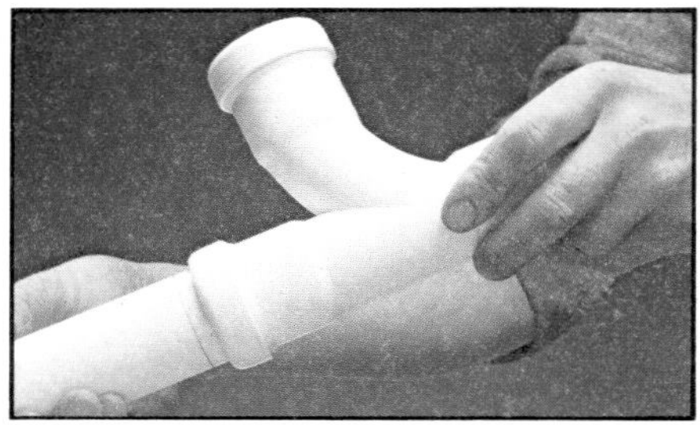

*7 Gently pull the pipe out from the fitting so that your pencil mark is about 10mm (⅜in) away from the fitting to allow for expansion when hot water is flowing.*

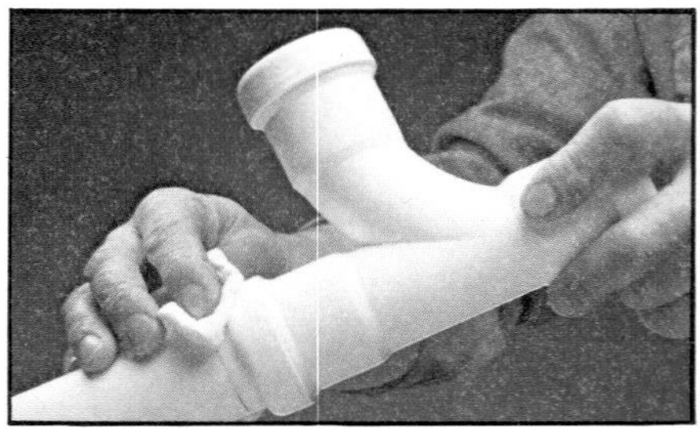

*8 The joint is now complete. Wipe off any excess petroleum jelly. Don't lose the expansion allowance when joining the other side of the fitting.*

manufacturer may make both PP and either PVC or ABS systems.

It is worth asking the supplier if there is an instruction leaflet supplied by the maker. There are slight variations in the methods of using each particular make of pipe and fitting. The manufacturer's instructions, if available, should be followed to the letter.

### Buying new pipe

Existing waste pipe is likely to be imperial in size – 1½in internal diameter for a sink or bath and 1¼in internal diameter for a wash basin.

Metric sized plastic pipes are normally described – like thin-walled copper tubes – by their external diameter, though at least one well-known manufacturer adds to the confusion by using the internal diameter. Both internal and external diameters may vary slightly – usually by less than one millimetre between makes. This is yet another reason for sticking to one make of pipe for any single project.

The outside diameter of a plastic tube that is the equivalent of a 1¼in imperial sized metal tube is likely to be 36mm and the inside diameter 32mm. The outside diameter of the equivalent of a 1½in pipe is likely to be 43mm and the inside diameter 39mm. If in doubt, it is usually sufficient to ask the supplier for waste pipe fittings for a basin waste or – as the case may be – a bath or sink waste. Plain-ended plastic pipe is usually supplied in 3m (10ft) lengths, though a supplier will probably cut you off a shorter piece.

### Joining solvent-weld types

Solvent-weld fittings are neater and less obtrusive than push-fit ones and they offer the facility of pre-fabrication before installation. However, making them does demand a little more skill and care and – unlike push-fit joints – they cannot accommodate the expansion (thermal movement) that takes place as hot wastes run through the pipe. A 4m (13ft) length of PVC pipe will expand by about 13mm (½in) when its temperature is raised above 20°C (70°F). For this reason, where a straight length of waste pipe exceeds 1.8m (6ft) in length, expansion couplings must be introduced at 1.8m intervals if other joints are to be solvent-welded. This rarely occurs in domestic design, however, and use of push-fit or solvent-weld is a matter of personal preference.

Although the instructions given by the different manufacturers vary slightly, the steps to making solvent-weld joints follow very similar lines. Of course, the first rule is to measure up all your pipe lengths carefully. Remember to allow for the end of the pipe overlapping the joint. When you've worked out pipe lengths cutting can start.

# JOINING SOIL PIPES

*These are joined in the same way as plastic waste pipes but are much bigger – about 100mm (4in) in diameter – so they take longer to fit. They also have some different fittings, such as a soil branch for use where the outlet pipe joins the stack, and access fittings with bolted removable plates for inspection. There are also special connectors to link to the WC pan, via a special gasket, and to link to the underground drainage system which is traditionally made of vitrified clay.*

*The accurate moulding of the fittings and the ease of assembly means that you can confidently tackle complete replacement of a soil system.that you can confidently tackle complete replacement of a soil system.*

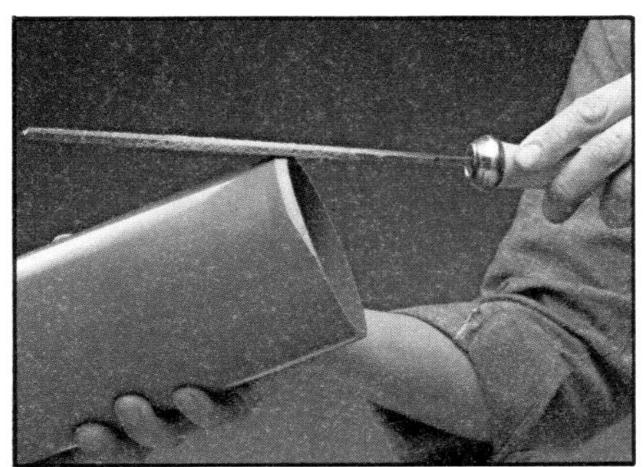

**1** *Soil pipes are joined in the same way as their narrower waste counterparts, but as they're bigger take special care with cutting and chamfering.*

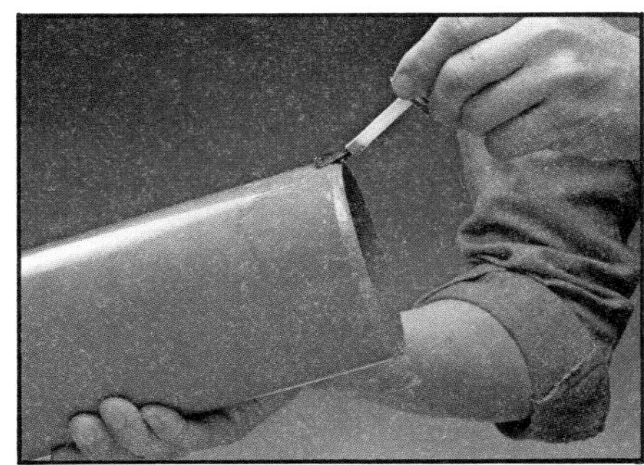

**2** *You have got a lot more area to cover with the solvent cement so you must work speedily – but don't neglect accurate application.*

**3** *The soil branch pipe has a swept entry into the main stack fitting. This is one of the most important joints in the system, so make sure you get it right.*

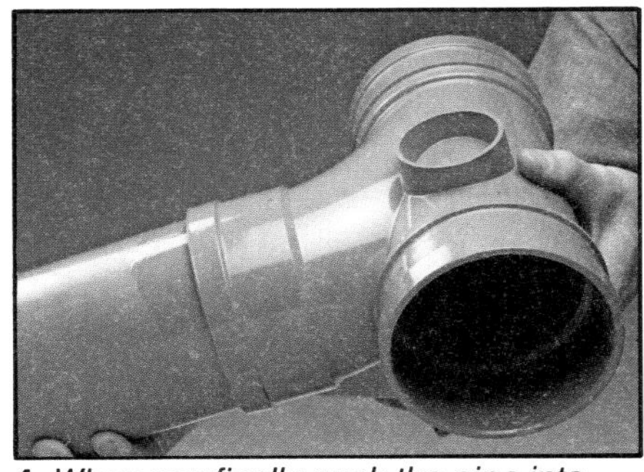

**4** *When you finally push the pipe into the fitting socket make quite sure that it goes right home against the pipe stop inside the fitting.*

Cut the pipe clean and square with a hacksaw or other fine-toothed saw. A useful tip to ensure a square cut is to fold a piece of newspaper over the pipe and join the edges beneath it. The paper will then act as a template.

Remove all internal and external burrs or roughness at the end of the pipe, then use a file to chamfer the outside of the pipe end to about 45°. Not all manufacturers recommend this, but it does provide an extra key for the solvent.

Insert the pipe end into the fitting and mark the depth of insertion with a pencil. Using medium grade abrasive paper, or a light file, lightly roughen the end of the pipe, as far as the pencil mark, and also roughen the interior of the socket. Thoroughly clean the roughened surfaces of the socket and the pipe end using a clean rag moistened with a spirit cleaner recommended by the manufacturer of the fittings.

Select the correct solvent cement (PVC pipes need a different solvent cement from ABS ones; once again, buy all the materials needed at the same time from the same supplier). Read the label on the tin and stir only if instructed.

Using a clean paintbrush, apply the solvent cement to the pipe end and to the

## Ready Reference

### TYPES OF FITTINGS

A number of fittings are available in both solvent-weld and push-fit systems – here are just a few of them. Check the complete range before you plan a new system – special bends and branches may exist that will make the job much easier.

**Solvent-weld 92½° bend**

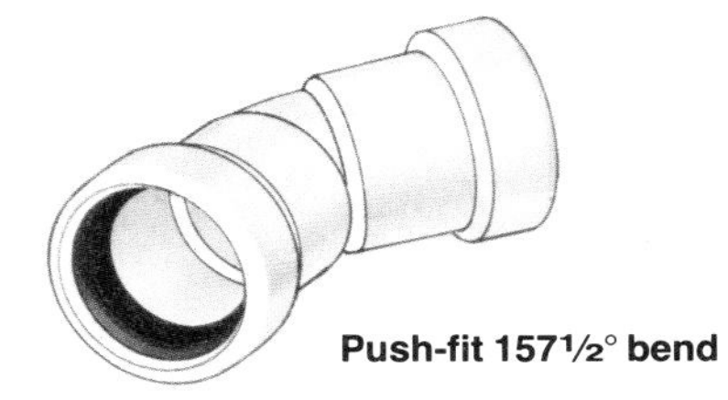

**Push-fit 157½° bend**

**Expansion coupling solvent-weld/push-fit**

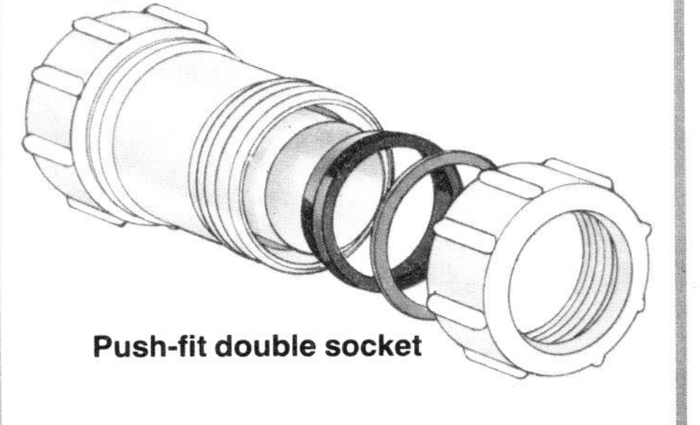

**Push-fit double socket**

**Solvent-weld adaptor**

inside of the fittings, brushing in the direction of the pipe. It is usually necessary to apply two coats to ABS pipes and fittings. The second coat should be brushed on quickly before the first has dried.

Push the pipe fully home into the fitting (some, but not all, manufacturers suggest that this should be done with a slight twisting action). Remove excess solvent cement and hold the assembled joint securely in position for about 30 seconds. If hot water will be flowing through the pipe, don't use it for 24 hours to give time for the joint to set completely.

### Joining ring-seal types

Preparation for ring-seal or push-fit jointing is similar to that for solvent welding. The pipe end must be cut absolutely squarely and all the burr removed. You should draw a line round the cut end of the pipe 10mm from its end and chamfer back to this line with a rasp or shaping tool, then clean the recess within the push-fit connector's socket and check that the sealing ring is evenly seated. One manufacturer supplies sealing rings separately, and they should be inserted at this point. The pipe end should now be lubricated with a small amount of petroleum jelly and pushed firmly into the socket past the joint ring. Push it fully home and mark the insertion depth on the pipe with a pencil. Then withdraw it by 10mm (3/8in), which is the allowance made for expansion. The expansion joint that is inserted into long straight lengths of solvent-welded waste pipe consists of a coupling with a solvent-weld joint at one end and a push-fit joint at the other.

As with solvent-weld jointing, individual manufacturers may give varying instructions. Some, for instance, advise the use of their own silicone lubricating jelly. Where the manufacturer supplies instructions it is best to follow these exactly.

### Fittings

PVC pipe can be bent by the application of gentle heat from a blow-torch, but this technique needs practice and it is best to rely on purpose-made fittings. Sockets are used for joining straight lengths of pipe, tees for right-angled branches, and both 90° and 45° elbows are usually available. If you need to reduce the diameters from one pipe to another you can use reducing sockets. These are really sockets within sockets which can be welded together, one taking the smaller diameter pipe and the other the larger. Soil outlet pipes from WCs are joined in the same way; they are merely bigger – usually 100mm (4in) – in diameter. Sockets work in the same way, but the branch-junction with the main soil stack must be of a specially 'swept' design.

## HOW PLASTIC FITTINGS WORK

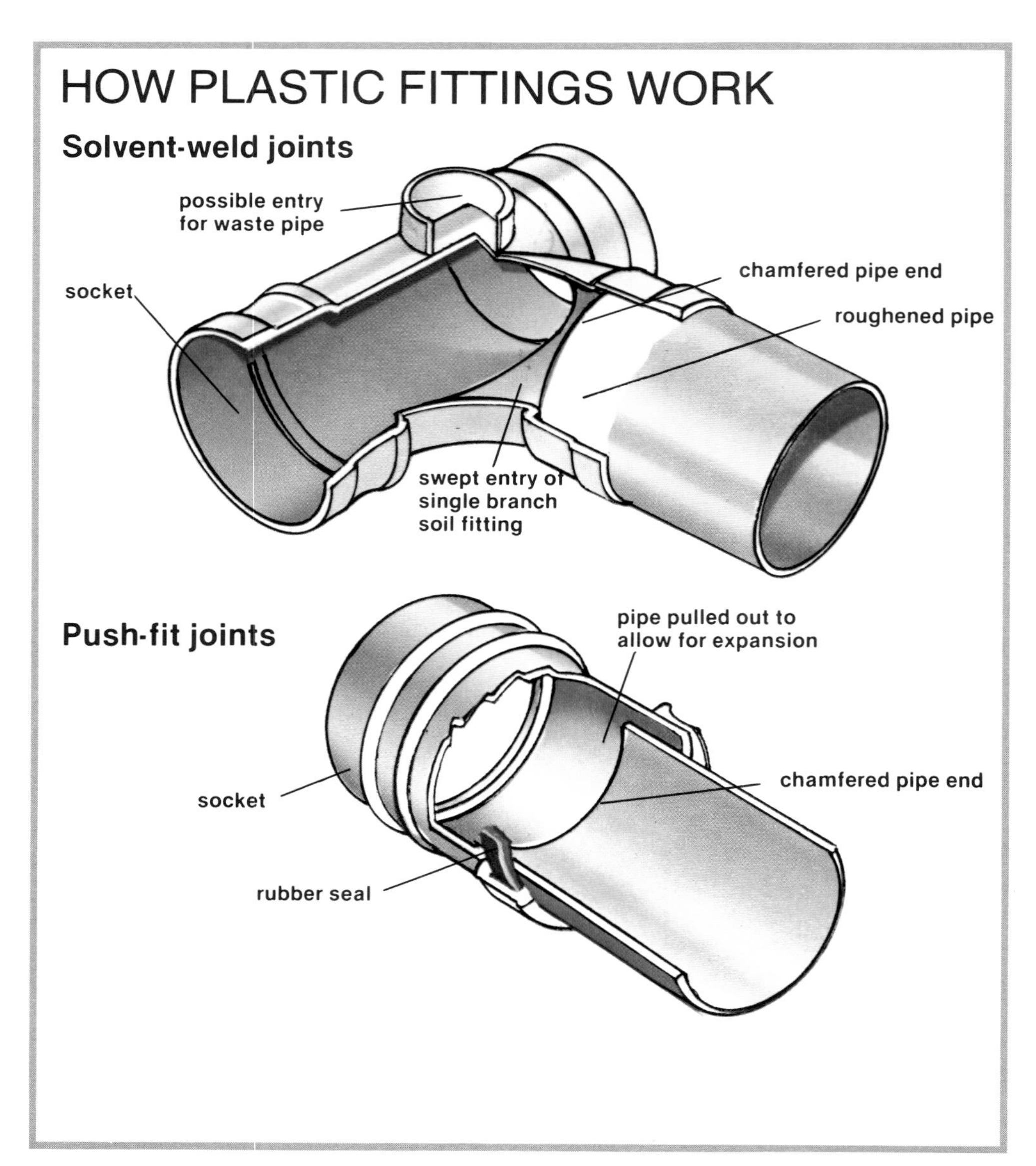


## SPECIAL FITTINGS

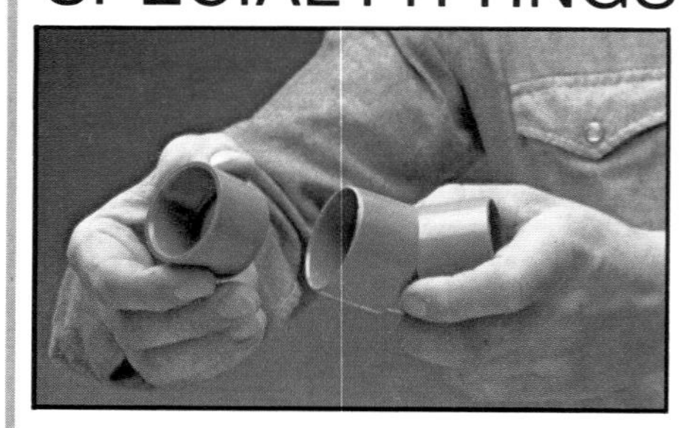

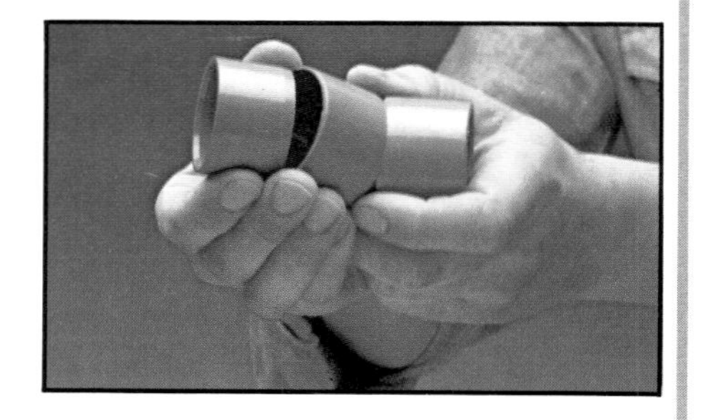

*Special fittings are available when pipe fitting is not straightforward. This is a reducing adaptor for push-fit fittings where you need to join a 32mm pipe to a 40mm pipe. You join the relevant pipe to the mating part of the adaptor and then join the two adaptor parts together.*

# TYPES OF PIPEWORK

**Lead and iron are no longer used as plumbing materials, having been replaced by copper or stainless steel. Now plastic pipework is revolutionising domestic plumbing.**

Virtually all **soil pipes** are now made from UPVC (1), which can be joined together using solvent welds or ring seals. Likewise, **overflow pipes** (2) are also made from UPVC, and lengths of these are connected with push-fit joins.

**Waste pipes**, made of UPVC and ABS plastic, are used for taking water away from baths, basins and sinks (3). Depending on the system they can be joined either by solvent welding or push-fit connections.

Plastic can also be used for water supply pipes. **Polybutylene pipes** (4) can take hot and cold water, the pipes being joined by compression fittings or special push-fit connectors. Similarly, **CPVC pipe** (5) can be used for hot and cold runs, but this is joined with solvent welds.

Black **polythene pipe** (6), the first plastic pipe to be used generally in domestic plumbing, is only suitable for cold water supplies, and consequently is mainly employed for garden and other outside water services.

**Rainwater downpipes** (7) are made from UPVC and have either circular or square profiles.

Half-hard temper **copper pipe** (8) is used for hot and cold distribution and central heating pipes, being easy to bend and join. **Stainless steel** (9) has also been used, mainly because it can be joined to copper and galvanised steel without causing electrolytic action.

**Flexible copper pipe** (10), which can be bent simply in the hands, is ideal for making the awkward connections between tap tails and the supply pipes without having to alter the existing runs.

# PLUMBING FITTINGS

**Putting in hot and cold pipes means you'll need a lot of different fittings at the pipe junctions, elbows, tees, valves and so on. Here is a basic selection to show you what's available.**

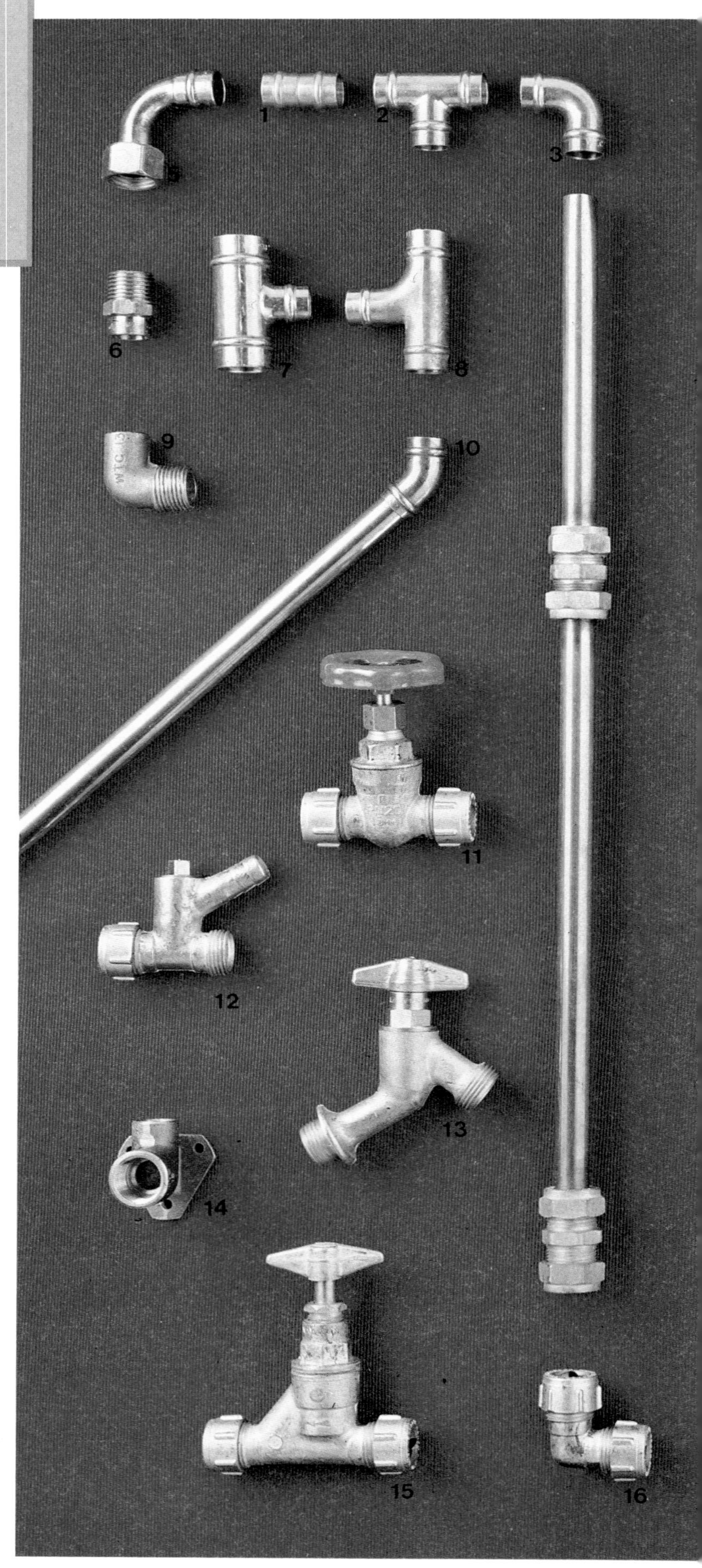


The most important skill required in any plumbing project involving hot or cold water pipe installation is that of making sound, water-tight joints between lengths of copper tubing and other pieces of plumbing equipment such as taps, ball-valves, and cold water cylinders. You will be required, for example, to take branches from existing water pipes and to make changes of direction in a pipe run.

To do all this, you need plumbing fittings, which make compression or soldered capillary joints (see pages 20 to 24). They are easily assembled using only a small tool kit. Type 'A' or non-manipulative compression joints are by far the more common. The other sort, type 'B' or manipulative joints are usually only used where the water authorities insist on them for underground pipe work.

It is possible to make Type 'A' compression fittings with only a couple of adjustable wrenches, a hacksaw and a metal file, but for a major project involving a number of joints, the purchase or hire of a wheel tube cutter is advisable; and to make soldered capillary joints some kind of blow-torch is also necessary, together with a pad of flame-proof glass fibre.

### Compression joints and fittings

Compression joints and fittings are made either of brass or gunmetal, although brass is the more common. As brass is an alloy of copper and zinc, impurities in the water supply in some areas may produce a phenomenon called dezincification. This is an electro-chemical reaction which results in the extraction of the zinc from the alloy, leaving the fitting unchanged in appearance but virtually without structural strength. Where dezincification is likely to occur, gunmetal fittings are traditionally used. Gunmetal is an alloy of copper and tin. However, a more economical alternative these days is to use one of the recently developed corrosion-resistant ranges of brass fittings.

### Sizes of compression fittings

Compression fittings are available for use with a number of sizes of copper or stainless steel pipe, but the only sizes likely to be required in domestic plumbing are 15mm, 22mm and 28mm. An existing plumbing system may well have imperial-sized pipe, and the imperial equivalents of 15mm, 22mm and 28mm are ½in, ¾in and 1in. The apparent difference between metric sizes and their imperial equivalents is accounted for by the fact that imperial-sized pipe is described by its internal diameter, and metric-sized pipe by its external diameter. You can use metric 15mm and 28mm compression joints and fittings to make connections with ½in and 1in imperial-sized pipe. When 22mm fittings are used with ¾in pipe, an adaptor is needed.

### Compression fitting range

The copper-to-copper coupling is the basic compression joint. There are reducing couplings to enable 28mm or 22mm tubing to be joined to tubes of smaller diameter. There are equal-ended and reducing T junctions (usually simply called 'tees') to enable branch supply pipes to be taken from existing pipes. There are elbow bends and 135° bends.

There are also fittings with one end a compression joint and the other a threaded outlet for direct connection to cisterns, cylinders or pipes of other materials. Male outlets are threaded on the outside, female ones on the inside. Threaded joints of this kind are made watertight by binding the thread with plumbers' PTFE tape.

### Soldered capillary joints

Capillary joints, which are neater and cheaper than compression joints, consist of a copper sleeve that fits fairly tightly over the tube ends so that solder may be run between the outside of the tube ends and the interior of the sleeve. 'Integral ring' or 'solder ring' capillary joints contain within the fitting sufficient solder to make the joint. With the cheaper 'end feed' fittings, solder has to be fed in separately from a reel of solder wire.

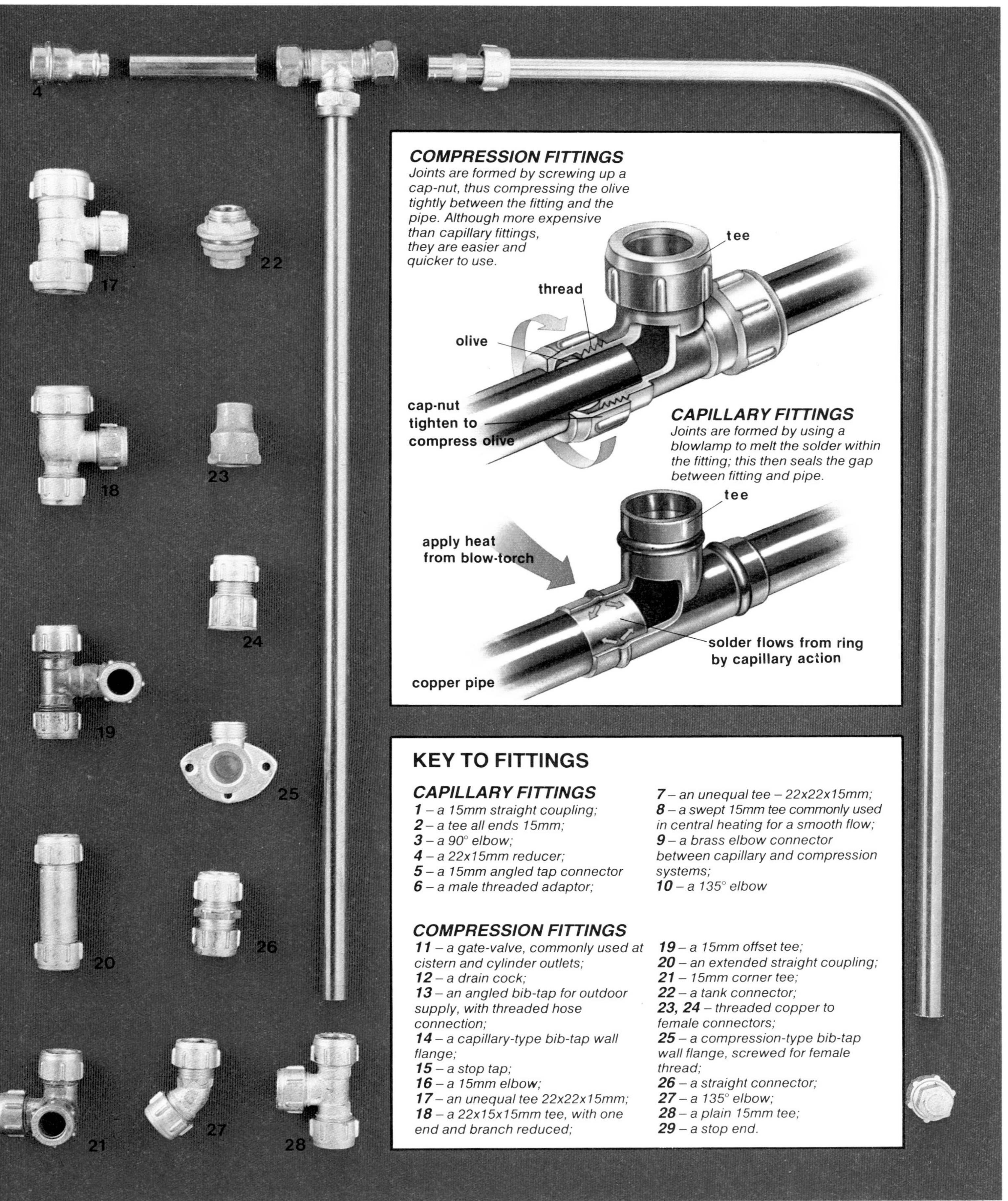


### *COMPRESSION FITTINGS*

*Joints are formed by screwing up a cap-nut, thus compressing the olive tightly between the fitting and the pipe. Although more expensive than capillary fittings, they are easier and quicker to use.*

### *CAPILLARY FITTINGS*

*Joints are formed by using a blowlamp to melt the solder within the fitting; this then seals the gap between fitting and pipe.*

## KEY TO FITTINGS

### *CAPILLARY FITTINGS*

***1*** *– a 15mm straight coupling;*
***2*** *– a tee all ends 15mm;*
***3*** *– a 90° elbow;*
***4*** *– a 22x15mm reducer;*
***5*** *– a 15mm angled tap connector*
***6*** *– a male threaded adaptor;*
***7*** *– an unequal tee – 22x22x15mm;*
***8*** *– a swept 15mm tee commonly used in central heating for a smooth flow;*
***9*** *– a brass elbow connector between capillary and compression systems;*
***10*** *– a 135° elbow*

### *COMPRESSION FITTINGS*

***11*** *– a gate-valve, commonly used at cistern and cylinder outlets;*
***12*** *– a drain cock;*
***13*** *– an angled bib-tap for outdoor supply, with threaded hose connection;*
***14*** *– a capillary-type bib-tap wall flange;*
***15*** *– a stop tap;*
***16*** *– a 15mm elbow;*
***17*** *– an unequal tee 22x22x15mm;*
***18*** *– a 22x15x15mm tee, with one end and branch reduced;*
***19*** *– a 15mm offset tee;*
***20*** *– an extended straight coupling;*
***21*** *– 15mm corner tee;*
***22*** *– a tank connector;*
***23, 24*** *– threaded copper to female connectors;*
***25*** *– a compression-type bib-tap wall flange, screwed for female thread;*
***26*** *– a straight connector;*
***27*** *– a 135° elbow;*
***28*** *– a plain 15mm tee;*
***29*** *– a stop end.*

# TOOLS FOR PLUMBING JOBS

**You should always check you've got the right tools to hand before starting any work, and plumbing is no exception. Here's a list of the ones you're most likely to need, plus some essential items to help you cope with emergencies.**

Anyone living in a fairly modern – or modernised – house with copper or stainless steel water supply pipes and a plastic waste water system can carry out all routine plumbing maintenance and repair work with only a minimal tool kit. In fact, many of the tools required for plumbing work will already be part of the general household or car tool kit. But, if you plan to do a lot of plumbing work you'll need a few specialised tools.

Before buying any expensive new tool ask yourself how often you will need to use it. If the honest answer is 'not more than once a year' then you should seriously consider hiring it instead.

### Spanners

You'll need a couple of adjustable spanners for tightening up compression fittings – one to hold the fitting steady while you use the other to tighten it up. You'll need them for many other types of fittings too.

A useful tool which can make life easier is the 'crows-foot' spanner. It's used to undo the virtually inaccessible back-nuts that secure bath and basin taps in position. Unless you have a lot of room beneath the taps you'll find it almost impossible to undo these nuts with an ordinary spanner.

### Wrenches

Only wrenches are capable of gripping and turning round objects such as pipes. There are two types used in plumbing. The pipe wrench looks like an adjustable spanner but its lower jaw is able to pivot slightly, and both jaws are serrated. As you use it, the lower jaw is able to open just enough to grip the pipe, then, as you turn it, the serrations dig in, pull in the jaws and grip even tighter. The harder you turn, the tighter they grip, so they're suitable for really stubborn jobs. Wrenches will only work in one direction; if you turn them the wrong way the jaws won't grip and the pipe will slip round.

The lockable wrench is slightly different. You adjust the jaw separation with a screw, then close them round the pipe, squeezing the handles to lock them on tightly.

### Pipe cutters

You can cut pipes with a hacksaw quite successfully, but if you plan to do a lot of plumbing work you should consider buying a pipe cutter. The pipe is placed between two hardened rollers and a thin cutting wheel; the tool is then rotated round the pipe while the cutting wheel is screwed down into the metal. A pipe cutter always produces a perfectly square and smooth cut – there is none of the rough metal burr that you'd get with a hacksaw. Yet it does round the end of the pipe inwards a little and the metal flange must be removed with a reamer which is usually incorporated in one end of the tool. Since pipe cutters need to be rotated round the rube they can't be used to cut existing pipes fitted close to a wall. So you will need a hacksaw as well.

### Pipe benders

Sharp bends in pipes are easiest to make with capillary or compression fittings. But you can bend pipe by hand it you want, and you'll have to if you want shallow curves. Copper pipe with a diameter of 22mm (3⁄4in) or less can be bent using bending springs or in a bending machine. The purpose of both springs and bending machine is to support the walls of the tube so that they don't flatten or wrinkle inside the curve as the bend is made. A bending spring supports the tube internally, while the bending machine supports it externally. As you're unlikely to want to bend copper pipe that often, these are tools it's best to hire when they're required.

### Thread sealers

Jointing compound and PTFE tape are both used to make a watertight – and gas-tight – seal on screwed fittings. Jointing compound is a sticky paste which you smear round the thread, and PTFE thread sealing tape is wound anticlockwise round the male fitting before the joint is assembled.

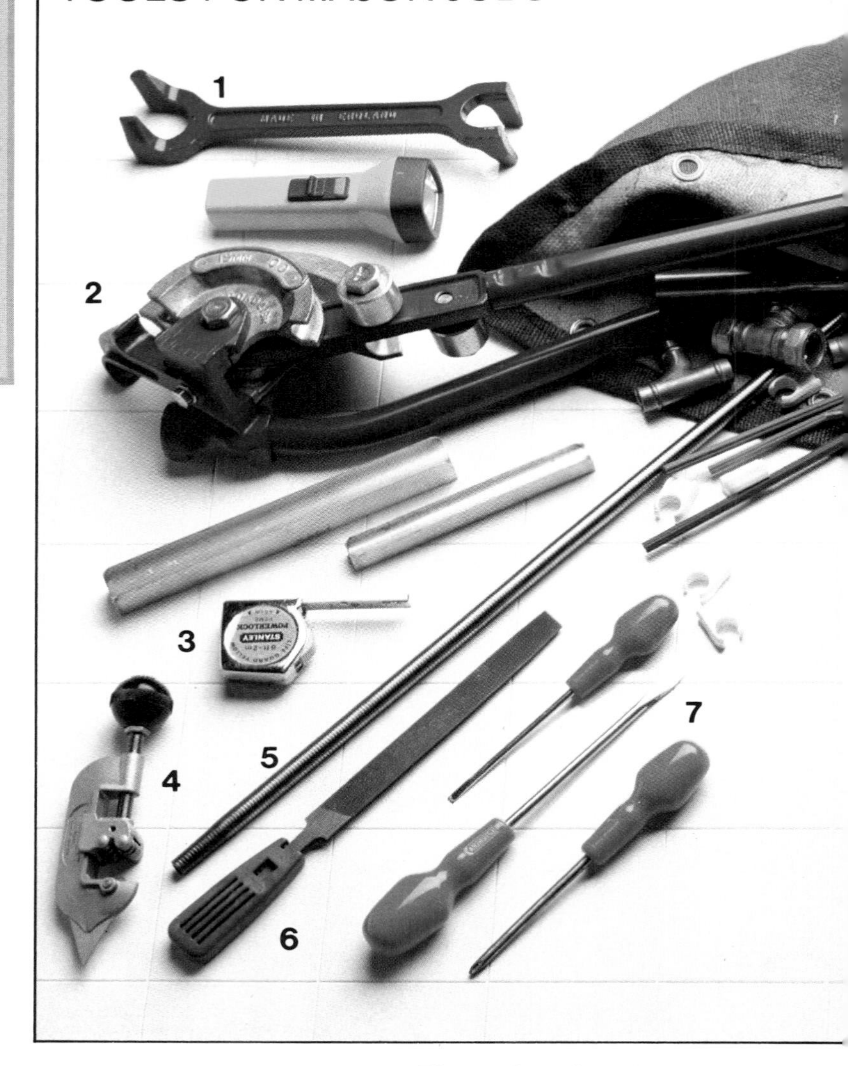


TOOLS FOR MAJOR JOBS

### Flame-proof gloves

If you're using a blowlamp and doing a lot of soldering then you'd be wise to invest in a pair of flame-proof gloves. Copper pipe conducts heat very efficiently so the gloves could prevent many burnt fingers.

### Torch

Very often you'll need to work at the back of sinks and baths or in dark, awkward corners in the loft, so a torch is essential. Change the batteries as soon as the bulb dims.

### Tape measure

You'll need a tape measure for accurate cutting of lengths of pipe and for positioning taps and fittings in the right place.

### Files and steel wool

A file is essential for removing burrs left by a hacksaw. Emery paper and steel wool are both used to clean the ends of copper pipe ready for making soldered joints. They're also used to roughen plastic pipe to provide a key for adhesives.

### Blowlamp

Unless you plan to use compression fittings for all your plumbing work you'll certainly need a blowlamp for making soldered joints. In most cases, a small blowlamp operating off a disposable canister of gas is easiest to use. Don't forget to keep a spare canister in your tool kit; they have a habit of running out at the most awkward moments.

### Other tools

Apart from the tools described above, you'll also need a power drill for drilling holes for fixing screws and pipes, a set of screwdrivers and a pair of pliers.

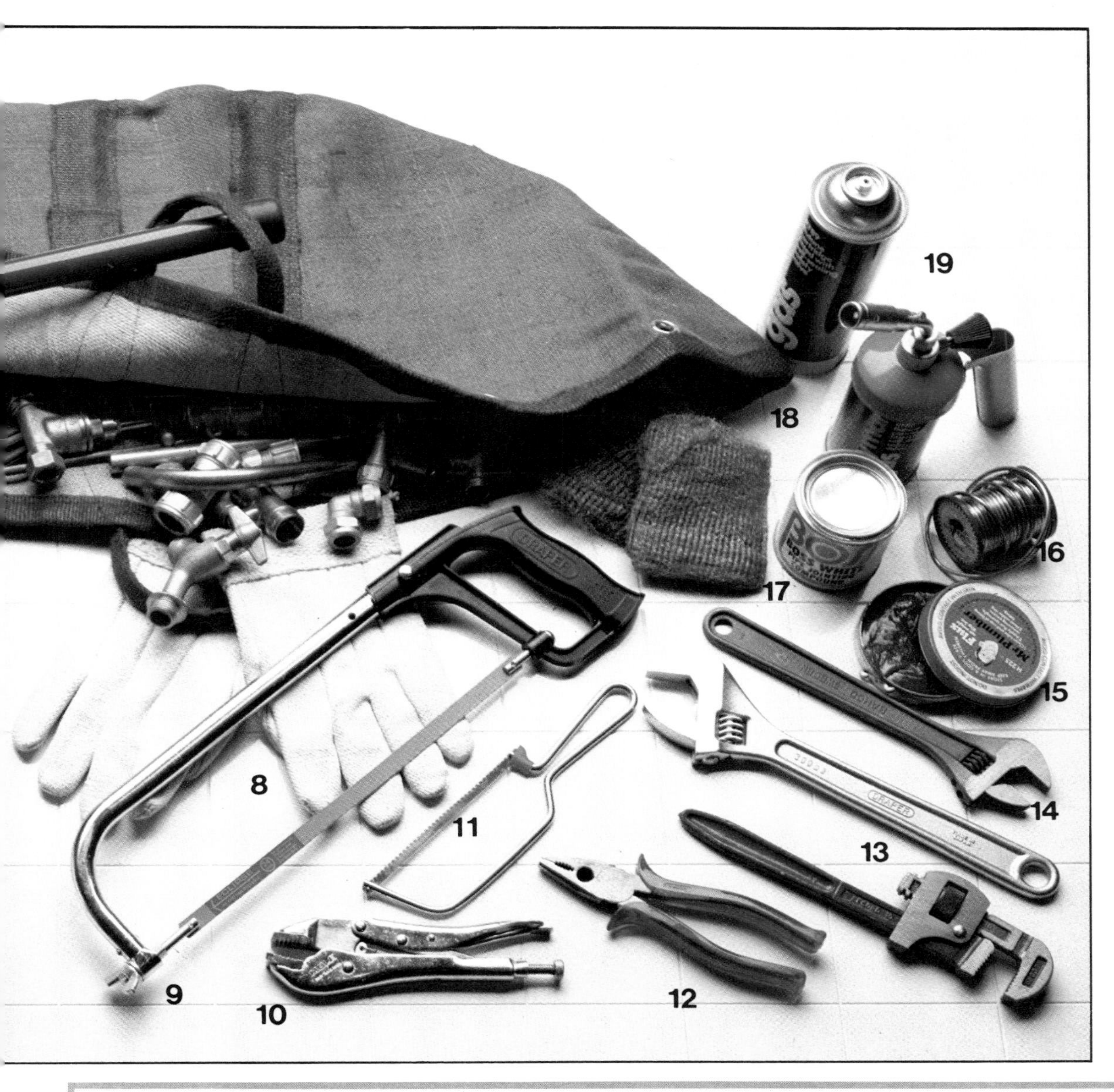


## KEY

### Tools for major plumbing work

**1** *crowsfoot spanner (one end for bath taps, the other for basins)*
**2** *pipe bender and formers for 15 and 22mm pipe*
**3** *retractable tape measure*
**4** *wheeled pipe cutter*
**5** *bending spring (available in 15 and 22mm sizes)*
**6** *half-round file*
**7** *screwdrivers for slotted and cross-head screws*
**8** *flame-proof gloves*
**9** *hacksaw with spare blades*
**10** *lockable wrench*
**11** *junior hacksaw*
**12** *pliers*
**13** *pipe wrench*
**14** *adjustable spanners*
**15** *flux paste for soldered capillary fittings*
**16** *solder in coil form for end-feed capillary fittings*
**17** *jointing compound (and/or PTFE tape) for threaded connections*
**18** *wire wool pads*
**19** *butane or propane blowlamp with replacement gas canisters.*

*In addition to the tools and items of equipment mentioned above, you are also likely to need:*

- *power drill with a selection of different sized masonry, twist drills and wood-boring bits*
- *pipe clips in 15 and 22mm sizes*
- *wallplugs (the stick type that you cut to length are the most economical)*
- *screws for mounting pipe clips, radiator brackets and so on*
- *a torch*
- *a bag to carry everything round the house in.*

## AN EMERGENCY PLUMBING KIT

There's really no point in assembling a full plumbing tool kit if you never intend to do any plumbing work. But emergencies can always happen so it's wise to keep a small tool kit to hand to stop an accident turning into a disaster. This should include an adjustable spanner, a locking wrench, a screwdriver and a pair of pliers, plus equipment to cope with bursts and leaks.

If you hammer a nail into a pipe you can easily make a quick repair with a two-part pack of epoxy resin sold especially for plumbing repairs. The adhesive and hardener are worked together in the hands and the material is moulded round the hole. This makes a permanent repair for small holes or leaking joints, but a larger hole is repaired more securely by cutting out the damaged section of pipe and inserting a straight compression coupling. So keep at least two of these in your tool kit – one each for 15mm and 22mm pipe.

Keep some penetrating oil for freeing jammed stop-valves or corroded nuts and, of course, an adjustable spanner to undo the latter. You'll also need a selection of tap washers – one for each type of tap, and some O-rings for the ball-valve. A few spare olives are always handy – compression fittings can be reused but you need a new olive each time. For clearing blocked waste pipes you'll need a 'force cup' or sink waste plunger, and a piece of flexible wire for clearing out blocked pipes and drains. Finally, mini-hacksaws are so cheap it's worth keeping one specially for your emergency tool kit. For more information see the following chapter.

## CHAPTER 3

# ROUTINE MAINTENANCE AND REPAIRS

**Looking after your home's plumbing system is essential if you are to get the best from it, and every member of the family should know what to do in an emergency when the system springs a leak, so that it can be dealt with quickly and effectively.**

# DRAINING PLUMBING SYSTEMS

**When you are carrying out repairs or alterations to your plumbing or wet central heating system, you will usually have to drain water from the parts you are working on. Here's what you'll have to do.**

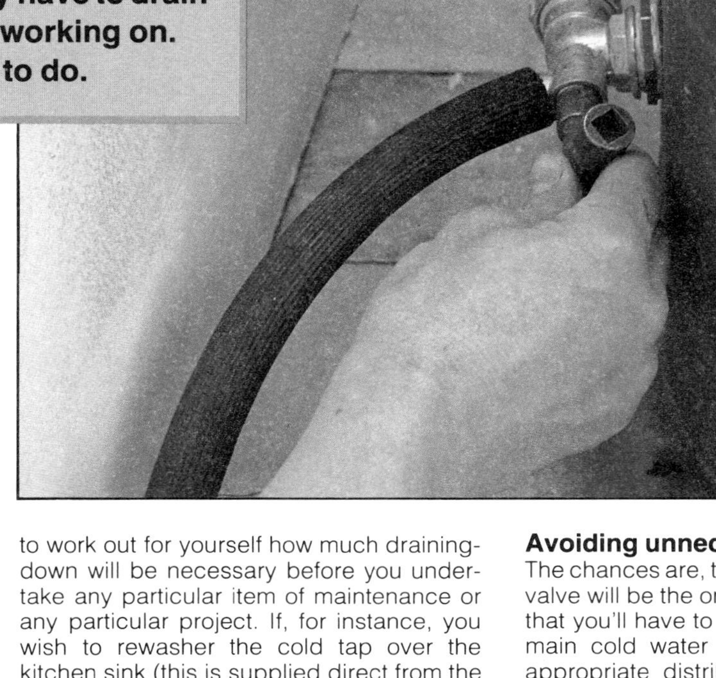

Virtually all major and many minor plumbing operations demand the partial or total drainage of either the domestic hot or cold water supply. If you have a 'wet' central heating system you'll also have to drain that before carrying out repairs or alterations. Before attempting this – long before the need for drainage arises, in fact – you should make yourself thoroughly familiar with the design and layout of these systems in your home. Here are some questions to which you should know the answers:

- Are all cold water draw-off points supplied direct from the rising main, or are the bathroom cold taps and the WC cistern supplied with water from a main cold water storage cistern (probably situated in the roof space)?
- Is the hot water system 'direct' or 'indirect' (see pages 9 to 13)?
- If the system is direct, is the domestic hot water heated solely by means of an electric immersion heater, solely by means of a domestic boiler (gas, oil or solid fuel), or are both means of heating available?
- If hot water is provided solely by means of an immersion heater, is there a drain-valve at the base of the cold supply pipe from the storage cistern to the hot water cylinder?
- If hot water is provided by means of a boiler, is there a drain-valve on the pipework beside the boiler, or possibly incorporated into the boiler itself?
- If the system is indirect, is it a conventional indirect system (indicated by the presence of a small feed-and-expansion tank in the roof space, feeding the primary circuit) or is it a self-priming indirect system such as the Primatic?
- Is there a 'wet' central heating system provided in conjunction with hot water supply?
- Where is the main stop-valve, and are there any other stop-valves or gate-valves fitted into distribution or circulating pipes in the system?
- Are there drain-valves at low points in the central heating circuit?

## Draining down for simple repairs

Once you are thoroughly familiar with the contents and layout of your own plumbing and central heating systems, you will be able to work out for yourself how much draining-down will be necessary before you undertake any particular item of maintenance or any particular project. If, for instance, you wish to rewasher the cold tap over the kitchen sink (this is supplied direct from the rising main) or to tee into the rising main to provide a garden water supply, all that you need to do is to turn off the main stop-valve and to turn on the kitchen cold tap until water ceases to flow from it. You will then have drained the rising main to the level of the cold tap. In many modern homes a drain-valve is provided immediately above the main stop-valve to permit the rising main to be completely drained.

Rather more drainage is necessary when you wish to renew the washer on a hot tap, or on a cold tap supplied from a storage cistern, or to renew a ball-valve in a WC cistern that is supplied with water from a storage cistern. First of all, see if there are any stop-valves or gate-valves on the distribution pipes leading to the particular tap or ball-valve. There could be gate-valves on the main hot and cold distribution pipes just below the level of the main cold water storage cistern. There could even be a mini-stop-valve on the distribution pipe immediately before its connection to the tail of the tap or ball-valve.

In either of these circumstances you're in luck!. All you have to do is to turn off the appropriate gate-valve or mini-stop-valve and then to turn on the tap or flush the lävatory cistern. You can then carry out the necessary repairs.

## Avoiding unnecessary drainage

The chances are, though, that the main stop-valve will be the only one in the system, and that you'll have to contemplate draining the main cold water storage cistern and the appropriate distribution pipes before you can get on with your task, by turning off the main stop-valve and draining the cistern and pipes from the taps supplied by the cistern. This, however, will mean that the whole of the plumbing system is out of action for as long as it takes you to complete the job. It is generally better to go up into the roof space and lay a slat of wood across the top of the cold water storage cistern. You can then tie the float arm of the ball-valve up to it, so that water cannot flow into the cistern. Then drain the cistern by opening the bathroom taps. In this way the cold tap over the sink will not be put out of action.

Here's another useful money-saving tip: even if you are draining down to rewasher a hot tap, there is no need to run to waste all that hot water stored in the hot water cylinder, *provided that your bathroom cold taps are supplied from the cold water storage cistern*. Having tied up the ball-valve, run the bathroom *cold* taps until they cease to flow and only then turn on the hot tap you want to work on. Because the hot water distribution pipe is taken from above the hot water storage cylinder, only a little hot water – from the pipe itself – will flow away to waste and the cylinder will remain full of hot water.

For the same reason, unless you expect to have the hot water system out of action for a

# WHERE TO DRAIN THE SYSTEM

*On a well-designed plumbing system you should find that drain-valves have been installed at several points, so that partial draining-down is possible.*

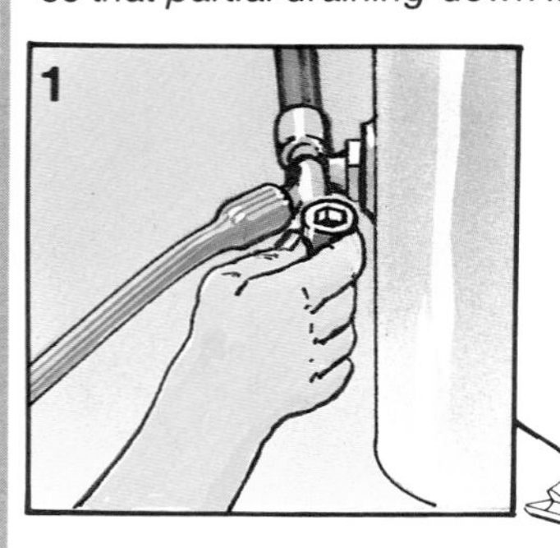


**1** *A drain-valve at the point where the cold feed from the storage cistern in the loft enters the hot water cylinder means that you can empty the main body of the cylinder (at least, down to the level of the inlet pipe) in the event of it springing a leak. Here a T-shaped drain-valve spanner is being used to open the valve.*

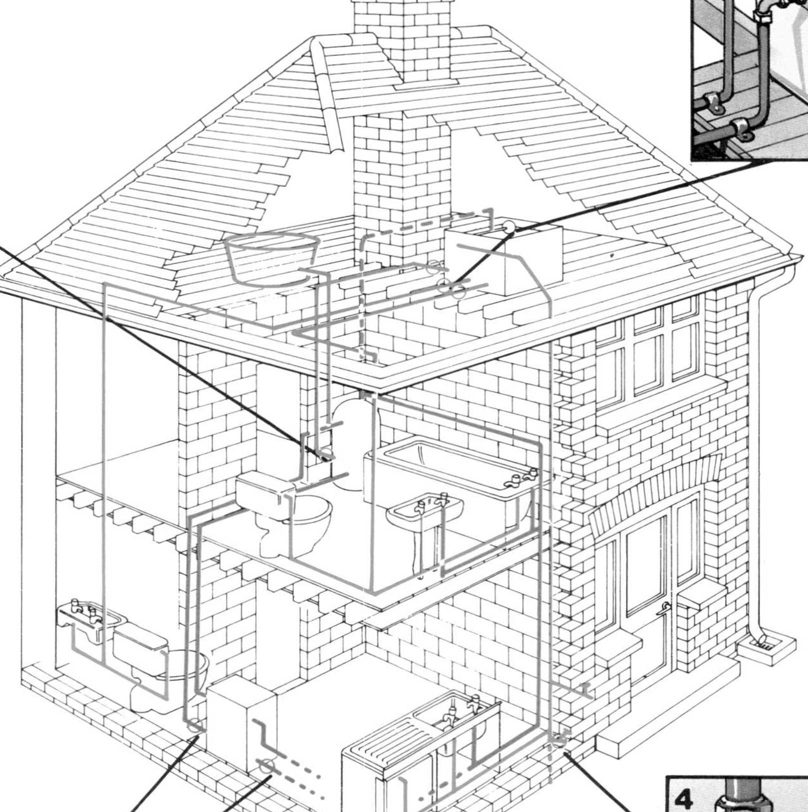

**2** *If gate-valves are fitted on the outlets from the cold water storage cistern, all you have to do to drain a pipe run is shut the appropriate valve and open the taps. If they are not fitted, you will have to drain the cistern too. To stop it filling, tie the float arm up to a piece of wood resting across the cistern.*

**4** *A drain-valve fitted above the rising main stop-valve allows you to drain the main and connect tees to it. The stop-valve saves you from having to tie up the storage cistern ball-valve when draining the cold supply pipes.*

**3** *Drain-valves fitted beside the boiler allow you to drain the primary circuit and the central heating system.*

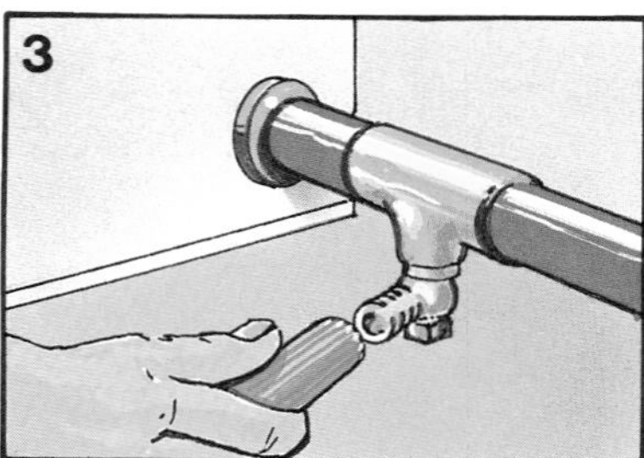


### Action checklist

*Which part of the system you drain, and how you go about it, depends on the job you're doing. Here's a brief checklist of the sequence of operations in each case.*

**Job:** *to rewasher/replace kitchen cold tap, tee off rising main for new supply pipe;*
- *turn off rising main stop-valve and drain rising main via drain-valve*
- *if no drain-valve fitted, open kitchen cold tap to drain main down to level of tee to kitchen sink.*

**Job:** *to rewasher/replace other cold tap, renew WC ball-valve, extend cold supply;*
- *if gate-valve fitted to outlet at cold cistern, close valve and open lowest appropriate cold tap; otherwise*
- *tie up arm of cold cistern ball-valve and drain cistern by opening cold taps.*

**Job:** *to rewasher/replace hot tap, extend existing hot supply;*
- *close gate-valve on outlet at cistern or tie up cistern ball-valve*
- *open cold tap until flow stops*
- *only then open hot tap.*

**Job:** *to replace hot cylinder;*
- *close gate-valve or tie up ball-valve arm*
- *turn off boiler or immersion heater*
- *empty cylinder via cylinder drain-valve*
- *close gate-valve on outlet from feed/expansion tank, or tie up ball-valve*
- *drain primary circuit via drain-valve at boiler.*

**Job:** *to replace cold cistern;*
- *close rising main stop-valve*
- *drain cistern by opening cold taps (hot water will still run from cylinder).*

**Job:** *to replace boiler;*
- *on* ***direct systems,*** *turn off boiler or immersion heater and also heating system*
- *close rising main stop-valve*
- *open all taps, and drain boiler from drain-valve nearby*
- *on* ***indirect systems,*** *turn off boiler*
- *close feed/expansion tank gate-valve*
- *drain primary and central heating systems from drain-valves at boiler.*

prolonged period there is no need to switch off the immersion heater or to let out the boiler when carrying out a maintenance operation on the bathroom hot tap.

### Problems with air locks

If your hot and cold water distribution systems are properly designed – with 'horizontal' runs of pipe actually having a slight fall away from the storage cistern or the vent pipe to permit air to escape – then the system should fill up with little or no trouble when you untie the ball-valve and permit water to flow into the cistern again. Should an air-lock prevent complete filling, try connecting one end of a length of hose to the cold tap over the kitchen sink and the other end to one of the taps giving trouble. Turn on first the tap giving trouble and then the one over the kitchen sink. Mains pressure from this cold tap should blow the air bubble out of the system.

### Draining the whole system

Very occasionally – perhaps because of a major reconstruction of the system or because of that most traumatic of all plumbing emergencies, a leaking boiler – it may be necessary to drain the whole system. Let's assume, first of all, that you have either a direct hot water system or a self-priming indirect one.

Switch off the immersion heater and let out or switch off the boiler. Turn off the central heating system if this is operated from the self-priming cylinder. Close the main stop-valve and open up every tap in the house – hot as well as cold. Connect one end of a length of hose to the drain-valve beside the boiler or, if the cylinder is heated by an immersion heater only, at the base of the cold supply pipe entering the cylinder, and take the other end of the hose to an outside gully. Open up the drain-valve and allow the system to drain.

If you have an indirect system you should again turn off the boiler and central heating system. Then close the gate-valve leading from the feed-and-expansion tank, or tie up it's ball-valve, and drain the system from the boiler drain-valves.

How you proceed depends upon the reason for which you have carried out the draining-down. Your aim should be to get as much of the plumbing system as possible back into operation quickly.

### Restoring partial supplies

The first step is to go up into the roof space and tie up the ball-valve on the main storage cistern as already described. Open up the main stop-valve and water supply will be restored to the cold tap over the kitchen sink.

It should also be possible to restore the bathroom cold water supplies. Trace the distribution pipe that takes water from the cold water storage cistern to the hot water cylinder.

## COPING WITH AIRLOCKS

*Clear supply-pipe airlocks by linking the affected tap to the kitchen cold tap with hose secured by worm-drive clips. Open the affected tap first, then the kitchen tap.*

*Avoid airlocks in primary or heating circuits by filling them upwards via a hose linking the kitchen cold tap and the boiler drain-valve. Close vents as radiators fill.*

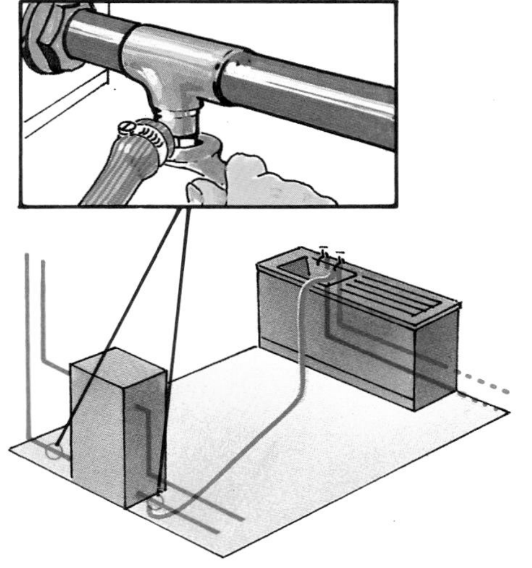

Find a cork of the correct size, lean into the cistern and push it into the pipe's inlet. Before doing so, it is a good idea to screw a substantial woodscrew part of the way into the cork to facilitate removal. You can then untie the ball-valve and allow the cistern to refill; no water will flow to the hot cylinder.

### Draining heating systems

If you have a conventional indirect hot water system – perhaps installed in conjunction with a central heating system – you can drain the primary circuit, together with the radiator circuit if there is one, without draining the water from the outer part of the storage cylinder. Because of the increased risk of corrosion that arises from water and air coming into contact with steel surfaces, a radiator circuit should be drained only when absolutely essential. When this has to be done – to add additional radiators, perhaps – you should tie up the ball-valve serving the feed-and-expansion tank and drain from both the drain-valve beside the boiler and from any drain-valves provided at low points of the system. You must, of course, let out or switch off the boiler before attempting this.

When refilling the primary circuit (or when refilling a direct system with boiler) it may help to prevent the formation of air-locks if you connect one end of your garden hose to the boiler drain-valve and the other end to the cold tap over the kitchen sink. Open them both up and the system will fill upwards, with air being driven out in front of the rising water. As the central heating circuit refills, open up all the radiator vents – and any other air vents that there may be in the system – and leave them open until water begins to flow through them. It is a good idea, when refilling a central heating system, to introduce a reliable corrosion-proofer into the feed-and-expansion tank to prevent future internal corrosion, but you can do this only if you fill the system from the top, not from the bottom.

### Winter precautions

One final point: if you are leaving your home empty during the winter months, you should drain the main cold water storage cistern and, if you have a direct hot water system and will be away for more than two or three days, you should drain the hot cylinder, the boiler and its circulation pipes as well. Human memory is fallible. Having done so, leave a conspicuous notice on the boiler and by the immersion heater switch saying 'SYSTEM DRAINED – DO NOT LIGHT BOILER OR SWITCH ON HEATER UNTIL IT HAS BEEN REFILLED'.

Because of the risk of corrosion already referred to, the primary circuit and any central heating system connected to it should not be drained in these circumstances. If you have a central heating system that is capable of automatic control, leave it switched on under the control of a frost-stat. This is a thermostatic control, usually positioned in a garage or in the roof space, that will bring the heating into operation when a predetermined, near-freezing-point temperature, is reached.

# STOPPING TAPS LEAKING

**Although taps are in frequent use, they rarely need maintenance. But if one starts to leak don't ignore it. Leaking taps are not only annoying and wasteful, but also, if they are hot taps, expensive — you've paid to heat the water going down the drain.**

A tap is a device for controlling the flow of water at an outlet point, and is opened and closed by turning a handle. This may be a 'tee' or 'capstan' type (so called because of the shape) fitted onto a spindle rising from the body of the tap. Or it may be a 'shrouded head', covering all of the upper part of the tap.

Turning the handle clockwise forces a jumper unit down onto a valve seating in the waterway of the tap and stops the flow of water. Because metal against metal doesn't make a very tight seal, a synthetic rubber disc — a washer — is attached to the base of the jumper so that it beds firmly onto the seating.

Turning the handle anti-clockwise raises the jumper from the seating and allows water to flow. An exception to this is the Supatap where the nozzle is rotated to control the flow. When you open a tap water pressure will also force water round the jumper unit and, unless there is some way of preventing it, this would escape from round the spindle. To get round this problem some taps have 'O' ring seals fitted to the spindle while older taps have greased wool packed tightly in a gland around the spindle. More modern taps have rubber tube for packing.

Mixers work in exactly the same way as ordinary taps except that they have only one spout that combines the flow of water from the hot and cold supplies. On kitchen mixers particularly this spout can be swivelled so that it can be pushed to one side to give better access to the sink or can supply a double sink.

When a tap starts to leak, there's a strong temptation either to ignore it or to try to stop it by closing it as tightly as you can. Such action is invariably ineffective and could lead to the valve seating being permanently damaged.

### Where leaks occur

Basically there are three places a tap can leak: at the spout, in which case the washer and perhaps the seating will need looking at; at the spindle when the tap is turned on, which means either the packing in the gland or the 'O' ring has failed; or at the swivel point at the spout of a mixer tap, which means that the 'O' ring is at fault. All these repairs are easy to deal with. But first you must know the type of tap and the terminology related to it.

### How washers are replaced

*Conventional pillar tap* This is the basic type of tap design and provides a good example of the procedure to follow when replacing a washer. These taps are commonly used for the hot and cold water supply over the kitchen sink and in this position they are probably the most frequently used taps in the house. It's quite likely that sooner or later the washers will need replacing.

To do this you'll first have to turn off the water supply either at the mains or, if you're lucky, at isolating stop-valves under the sink which when shut cut off the supply either to the hot or cold tap without affecting the rest of the system (see previous section and pages 76 to 77). Turn on the tap fully so it is drained before you start work.

Usually with a pillar tap the spindle rises out of a dome-like easy-clean cover, which you should be able to unscrew by hand. If this proves too difficult, you can use a wrench, but pad the jaws thoroughly with rag to avoid damaging the finish on plated taps.

With the tap turned on fully you can then raise the cover sufficiently to slip the jaws of a wrench under it to grip the 'flats' of the headgear — the main body of the tap which has a nut-shaped section to it. If you can't do this you'll need to take off the tap handle and easy-clean cover. First you'll have to remove the tiny grub-screw in the side of the handle which can then be lifted off. If this proves difficult a good tip is to open the tap fully, unscrew, then raise the easy-clean cover and place pieces of wood (a spring-loaded clothes peg will do) between the bottom of the easy-clean cover and the body of the tap. By turning the tap handle as if you were trying to close it the upward pressure on the easy-clean cover will force it off the spindle. However, you then have to replace it over the spindle just sufficiently to enable you to turn the tap on. When this is done take it off again and remove the easy-clean cover. While you are doing all this make sure

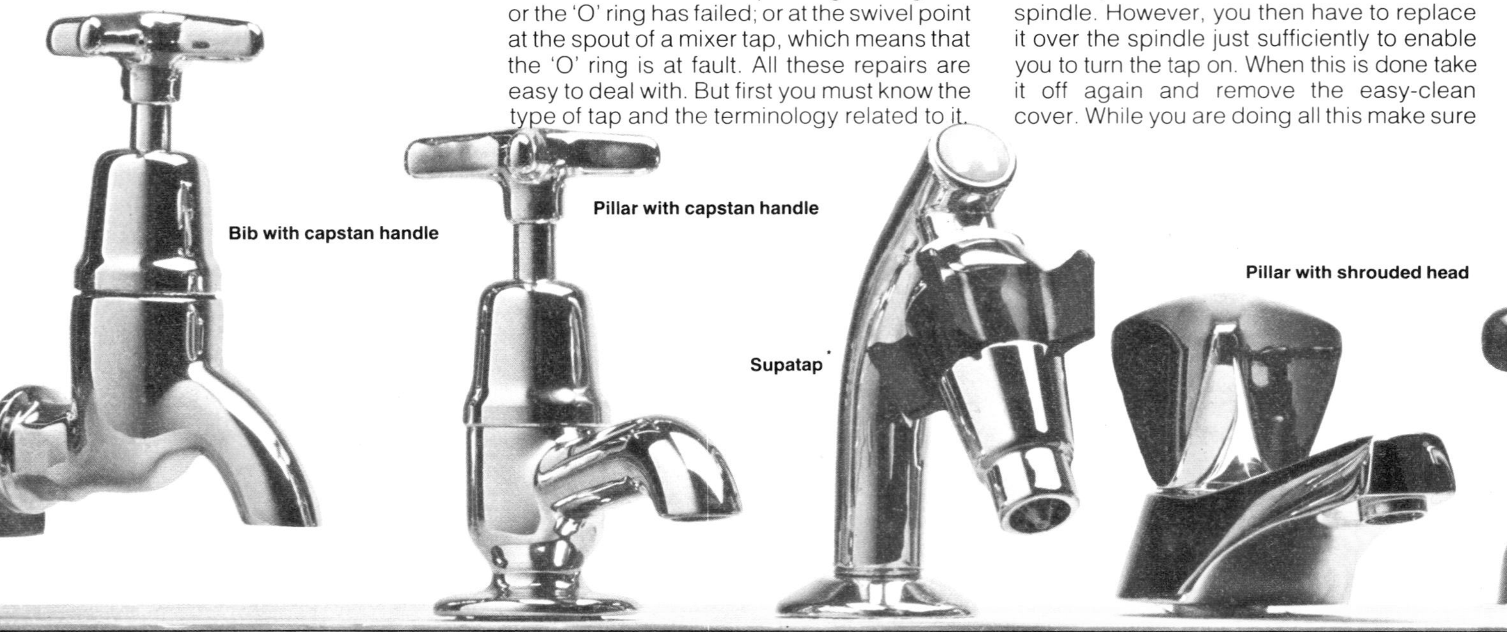

you hold the tap steady. If the headgear is stiff and the entire tap turns you could damage the part of the sink into which the tap fits.

You can now put the headgear to one side. You should be able to see the jumper, with the washer attached, resting on the valve seating within the body of the tap (though sometimes it gets stuck and lifts out with the headgear). Often the washer is held in position on the jumper by a tiny nut which has to be undone with pliers before the washer can be replaced. This may be easier said than done, and rather than waste time attempting the all-but-impossible, it's probably better to fit a new washer and jumper complete rather than just renewing the washer. Once this has been done the tap can be reassembled, and as you do this smear the screw threads with petroleum jelly.

*Tap with shrouded head* This is basically a pillar tap where the spindle is totally enclosed by an easy-clean cover that also acts as a handle to turn the tap on and off. Some shrouded heads are made of plastic and care is therefore needed when using wrenches. But the mystery of this tap is how to get to the inside — and methods vary with the make of tap.

Some shrouded heads can simply be pulled off, perhaps after opening the tap fully and then giving another half turn. Some are secured by a tiny grub-screw in the side. But the commonest method of attaching the head is by a screw beneath the plastic 'hot' or 'cold' indicator. Prise the plastic bit off with a small screwdriver to reveal the retaining screw (normally a cross-headed screw). When the shrouded head has been removed you'll find that you can unscrew the headgear to reach the interior of the tap in the same way as with an ordinary pillar tap. Rewashering can then be done in the same way.

If the jumper is not resting on the valve seating in the body of the tap, but is 'pegged' into the headgear so that it can be turned round and round but can't be withdrawn, it's slightly more of a problem to remove the washer-retaining nut. The easiest way is to fasten the jumper plate in a vice (although pliers will do) and turn the nut with a spanner. Some penetrating oil will help to free the thread. If after this you still can't loosen the nut, a good tip is to slip the blade of a screwdriver between the plate of the jumper and the tap headgear and lever it to break the pegging. A new jumper and washer can then be fitted complete, although the stem should be 'burred' or roughened with a file to give an 'interference fit' when it is slipped into the headgear.

*Bib taps* These taps are treated in exactly the same way as a conventional pillar tap. You might find with a garden tap that there's no easy-clean cover, so the headgear is already exposed.

**TOOLS FOR TAP REPAIRS**

- **thin screwdriver** is useful for prising off clipped on coverings, separating washer from jumper, removing 'O' rings, grub-screws
- **cross-headed screwdriver** might be needed for retaining-screw on some shrouded or mixer taps
- **adjustable wrench or spanner** is needed to remove the headgear.

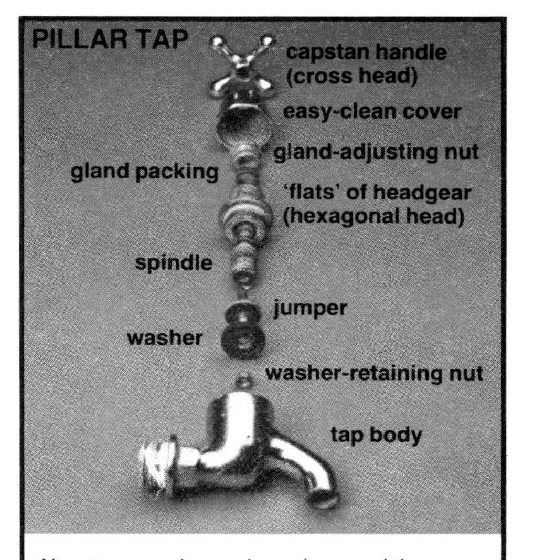


*New taps rarely need repairs – and the actuality is more likely to be taps like these which won't be bright and clean inside. In hard-water areas lime scale will have accumulated which can cause the tap to jam so remove it with wire wool when the tap's dismantled. This will also help you identify the parts.*

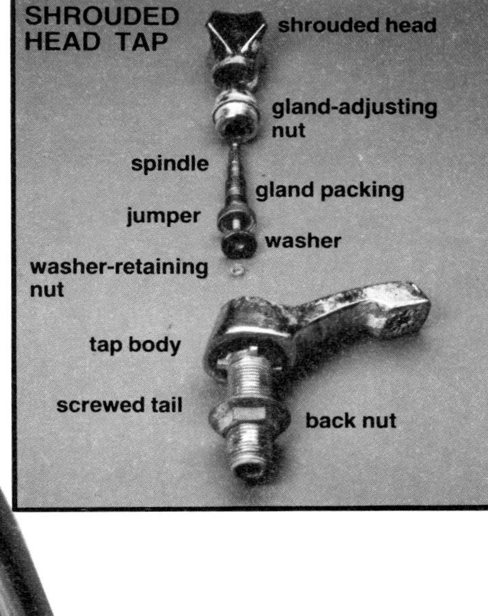

## REPLACING A PILLAR TAP WASHER

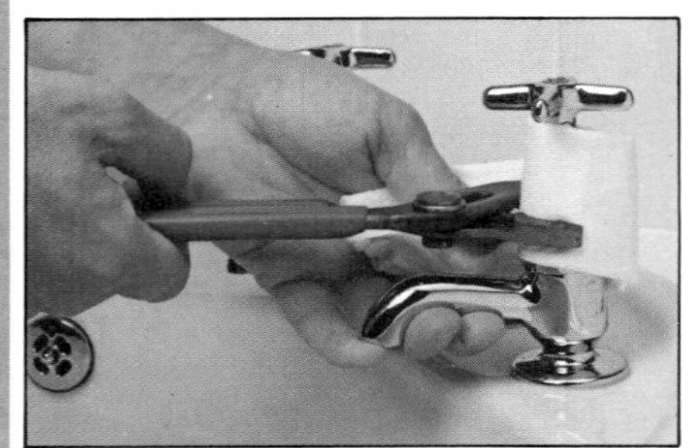

**1** *Pillar taps should be opened fully after turning off the water supply. Now unscrew the easy-clean cover.*

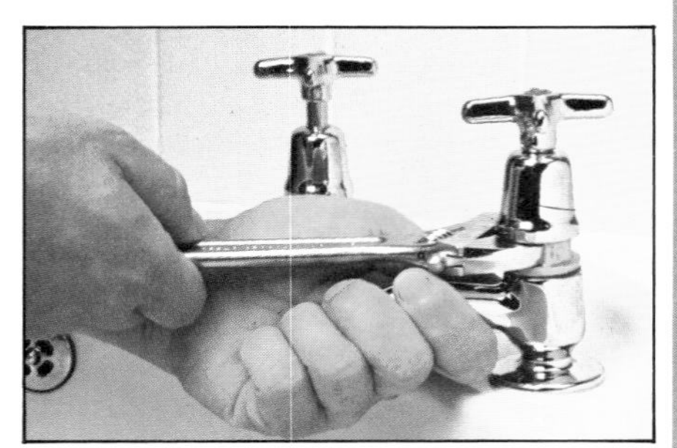

**2** *Lift up the easy-clean cover so you can slip an adjustable spanner or wrench in to undo the headgear.*

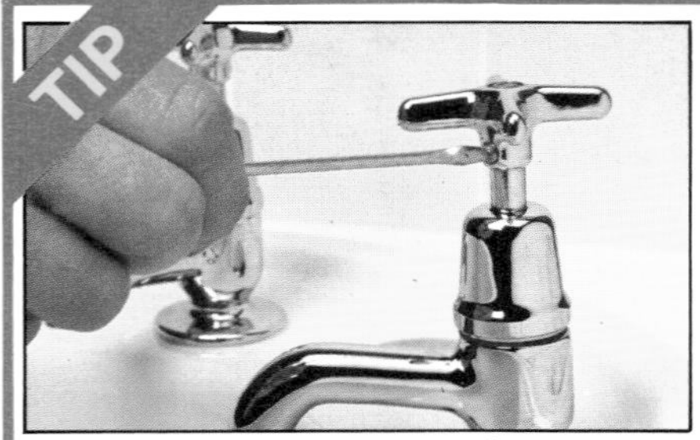


*If there isn't enough space for the spanner or wrench, undo the grub-screw and then remove the handle.*

*If the handle won't come out, put a wedge under the cover and try to close the tap and force the cover up.*

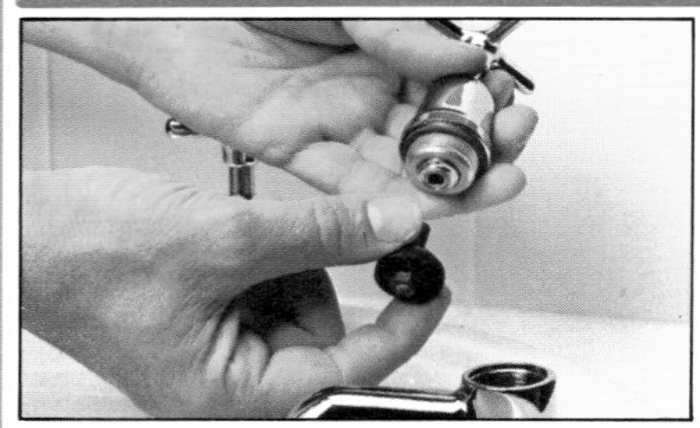

**3** *With the handle fully opened, the headgear can be removed and the jumper unit pulled away.*

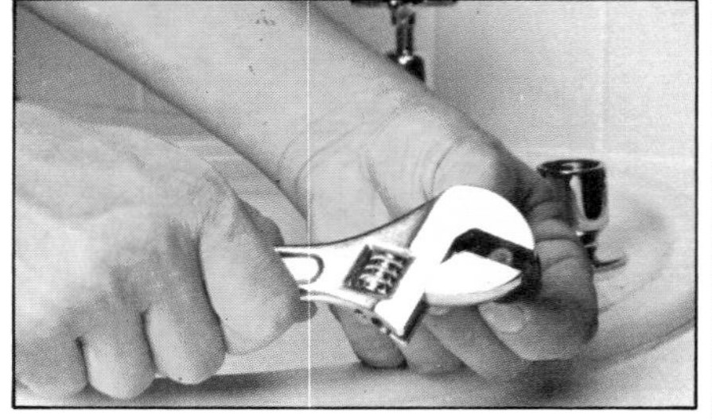

**4** *Some taps have the washer fixed to the jumper unit by a nut; in others it has to be prised off.*

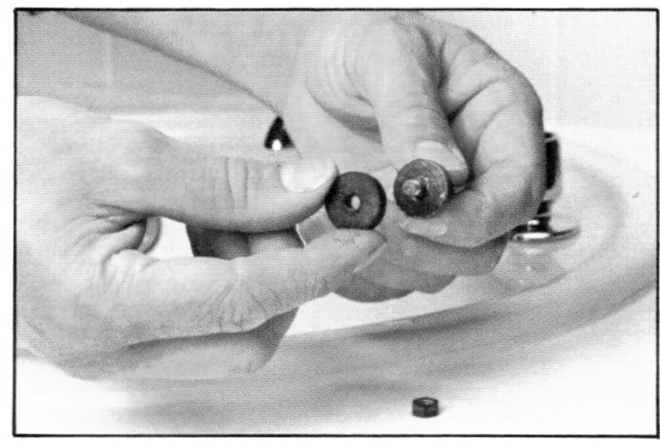

**5** *Push a washer of the correct size over the end of the jumper unit. If held by a nut clean it with steel wool before replacing it.*

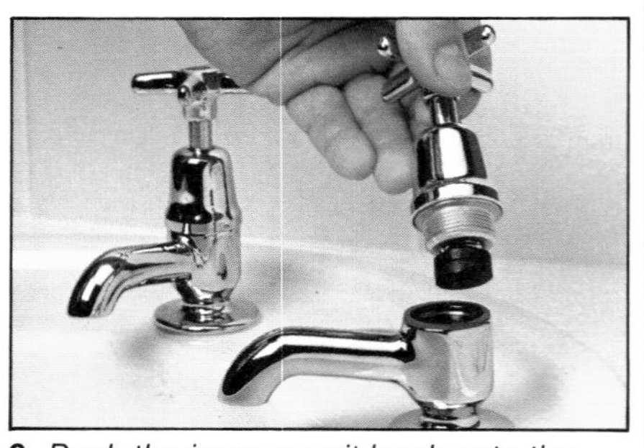

**6** *Push the jumper unit back onto the headgear and replace in the tap. Turn the handle to half close the tap, then restore the mains supply.*

Jem Grischotti

## SHROUDED TAP

**1** *With a shrouded head tap, you can either pull it off or prise off the indicator cap with a screwdriver after turning the water supply off and the tap on.*

**2** *Undo the retaining screw (probably a cross-headed type so you'll need the right screwdriver) and then you will be able to pull off the head.*

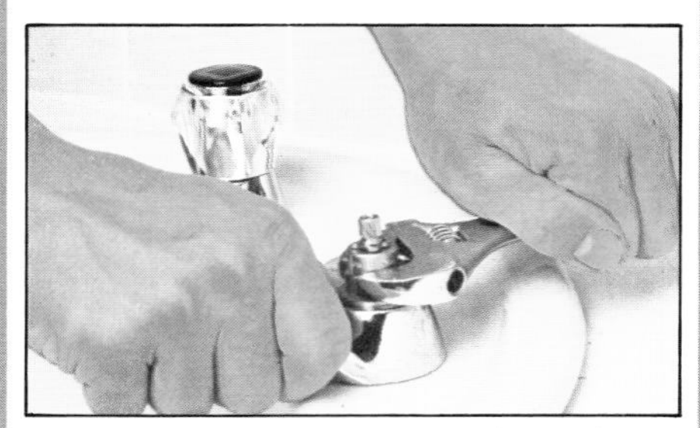

**3** *Hold the spout to prevent damaging the basin while you unscrew the headgear either using a spanner or an adjustable wrench.*

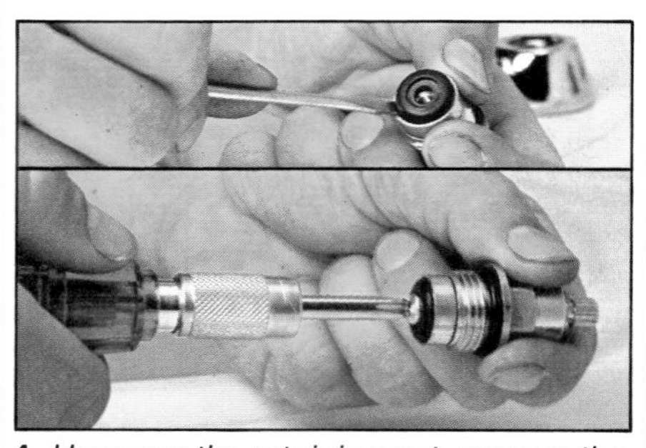

**4** *Unscrew the retaining nut, remove the old washer and replace with one of the correct size. Reassemble the tap, then restore the water supply.*

# RE-WASHERING A SUPATAP

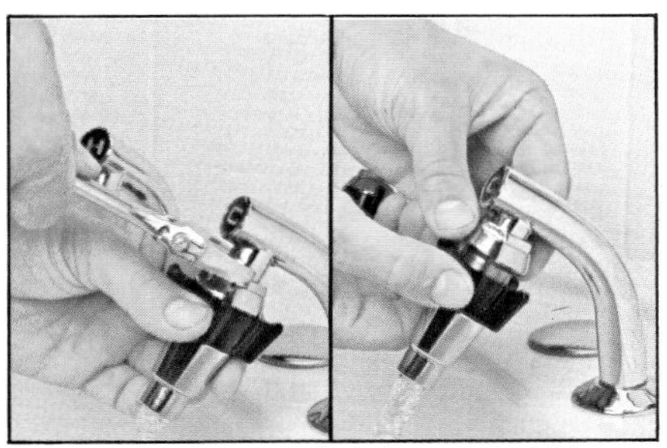

*1 Turn on the tap slightly and hold it while you undo the top nut. Open the tap fully, then turn the nozzle to unscrew it from the headgear.*

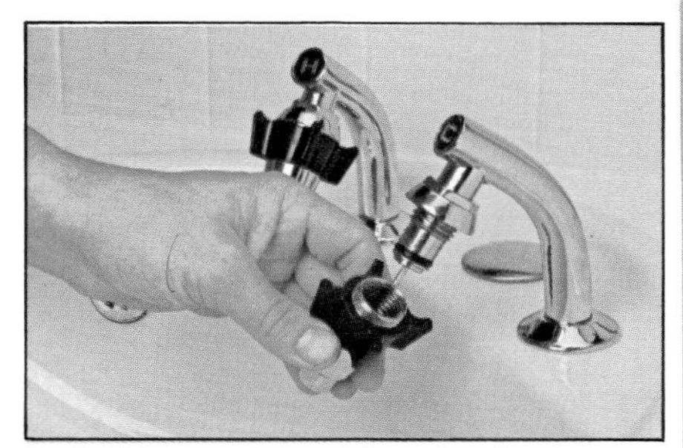

*2 As the nozzle comes away in your hand, a valve in the tap will automatically cut off the water so that you can make the repair.*

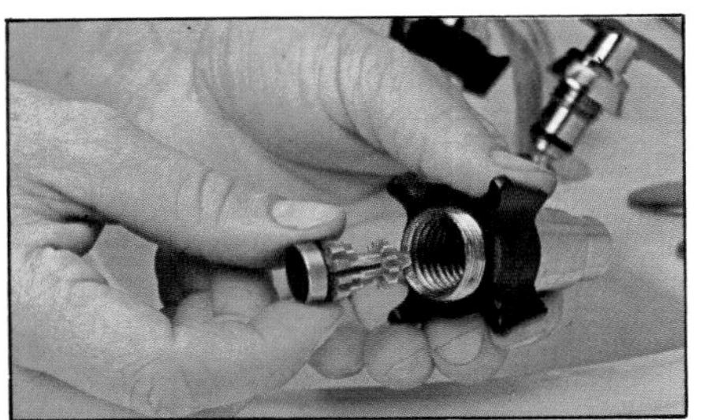

*3 Tap the nozzle on a hard surface so you can shake out the anti-splash device to which will be attached the jumper unit and the washer.*

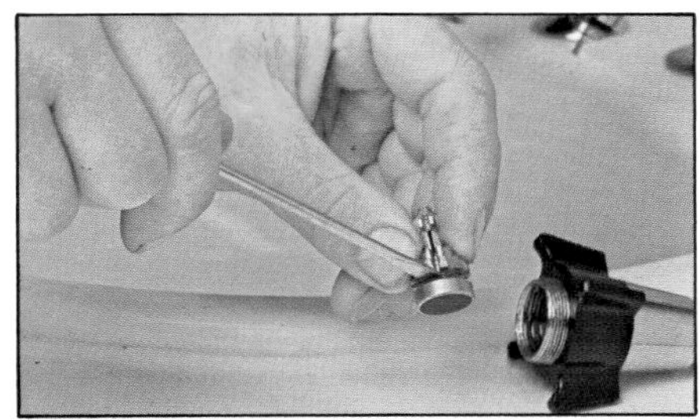

*4 Prise the old washer and jumper unit from the anti-splash device and press in a new complete unit. Now you can reassemble the tap.*

*Supataps* Changing the washer on this type of tap can be carried out in minutes, without the need to cut off the water supply first. Before you begin, check that you have a replacement Supatap washer and jumper unit. Once you've undone the retaining nut at the top of the nozzle you have to open up the tap fully — and then keep on turning. At first the flow will increase, but then, just before the nozzle comes off in your hand, a check-valve inside the tap will fall into position and stop the flow. You can separate the anti-splash device, (containing the washer and jumper unit) from the nozzle by turning it upside down and tapping the nozzle on a hard surface — not a ceramic sink or basin. The washer and jumper unit then need to be prised from the anti-splash device — you can use a knife blade or the edge of a coin to do this. A new washer and jumper unit can then be snapped in. When reassembling the tap it's necessary to remember that the nozzle has a left-hand thread and so has to be turned anti-clockwise to tighten it.

## Repairing a poor seating

Sometimes a tap will continue to drip although you've changed the washer. This is usually because the valve seating has become scored and damaged by grit from the mains, so the washer can't make a watertight connection.

You can use a reseating tool to put the problem right. This entails removing the headgear after the water has been turned off, inserting the tool into the body of the tap and turning it to cut a new seating. It won't be worthwhile buying one of these tools for what is a once-in-a-lifetime job, but you may be able to hire one from a tool hire company.

An alternative method, and certainly one that's a lot easier, is to use a nylon 'washer and seating set'. Again with the water supply off, the headgear and the washer and jumper are removed from the tap end and the nylon liner is placed in position over the seating. The jumper and washer are then inserted into the headgear, which is screwed back onto the tap. The tap handle is then turned to the off position. This action will force the liner into and over the old seating to give a watertight joint.

You can't, of course, use one of these sets to reseat a Supatap. However, the makers (Deltaflow Ltd) will supply a reseating tool on request, but these taps very rarely need reseating.

You can also use a domed washer to cure a poor seating. It increases the surface area in contact with the waterway and so

# Ready Reference

### WHAT'S GONE WRONG?

Check out the problem first.
**Washers** may be worn or disintegrating. Replace with 12mm (½in) or 18mm (¾in) synthetic rubber washers, available from hardware stores. A good tip for a temporary repair is to reverse the old washer.

**'O' rings** that look worn may also cause leaks. Choose the same size so they fit snugly.

**Valve seating** is damaged if rough and uneven. You can:

- use a domed, not a flat, washer

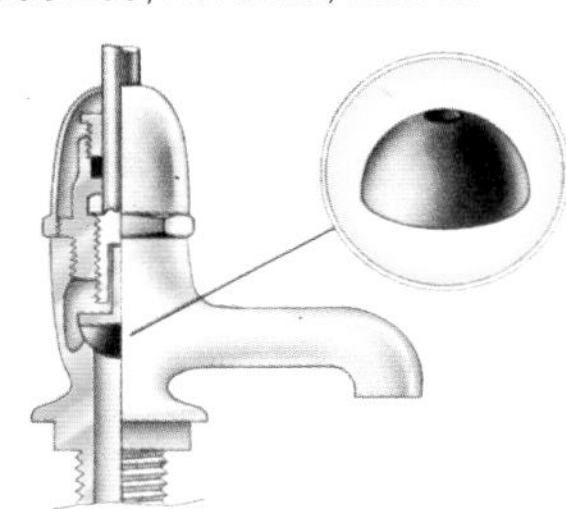

- fit a washer and seating set which covers up the damage
- buy or hire a reseating tool to grind the damaged seat smooth

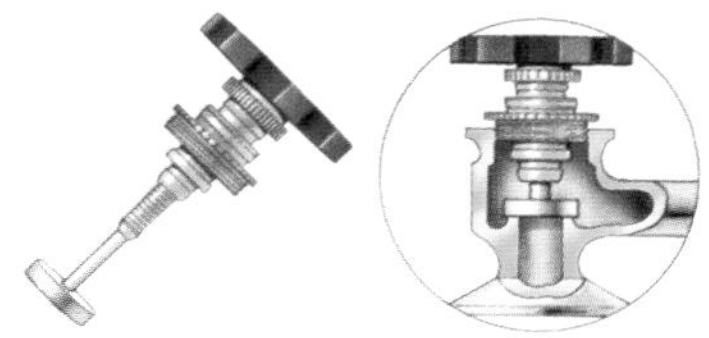

### TIPS TO SAVE TIME AND TROUBLE

- If you can't undo the nut holding the washer to the jumper, buy an all-in-one jumper and washer set.

- If a metal easy-clean cover is stuck pour very hot water over it. It should then unscrew.
- After repairing a tap, leave the water to run gently for 15 minutes to remove any air trapped in the pipes.

## LEAKAGE UP THE SPINDLE

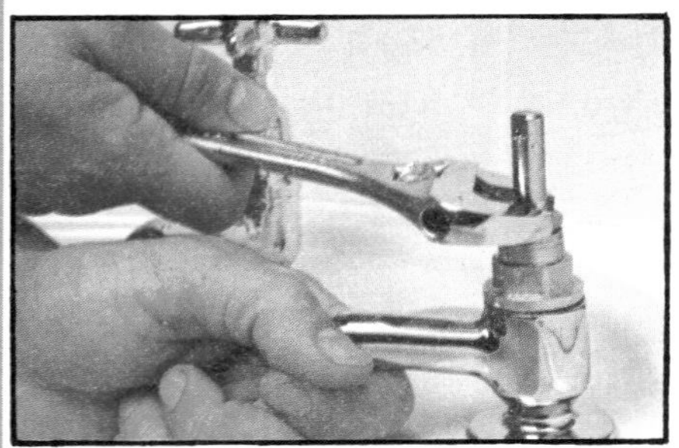

*1 If the tap has a stuffing box round the spindle, first try to tighten the gland-adjusting nut.*

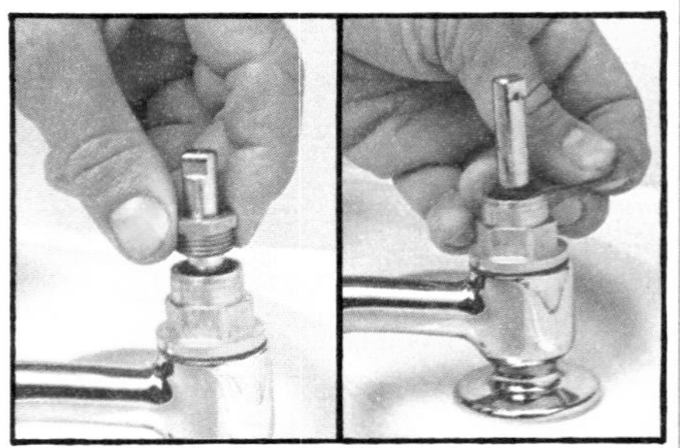

*2 If this fails to stop the leak, remove the nut and then pick out the old greased wool stuffing.*

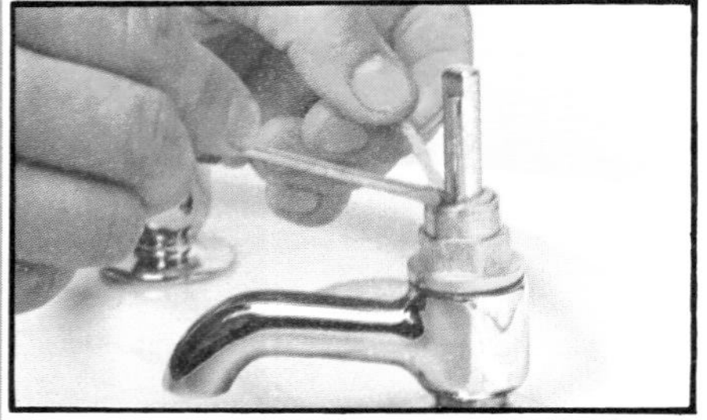

*3 Smear petroleum jelly on a length of knitting wool, then wind it around the spindle, packing it down tightly.*

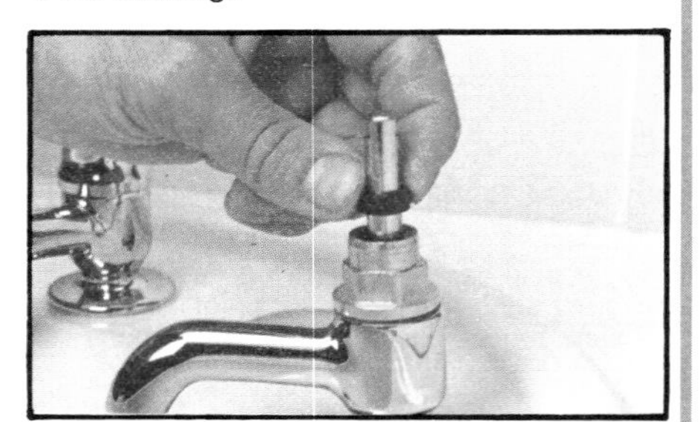

*4 Alternatively you may be able to use a rubber packing washer which just has to be slipped on.*

Keith Morris

## REPLACING 'O' RING SEALS

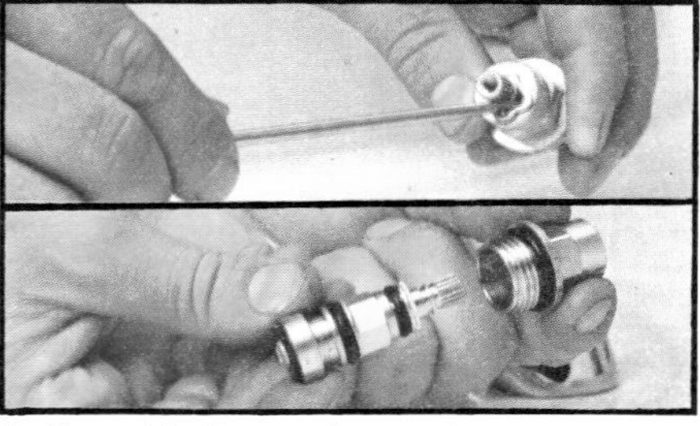

*1 To get to the seals on a tap, remove the headgear and prise off the circlip which holds the spindle in place.*

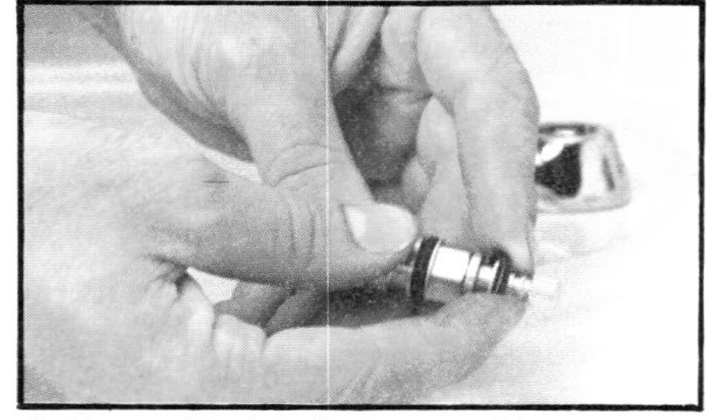

*2 Use a thin-bladed screwdriver to work off the worn 'O' rings and then replace them with new ones.*

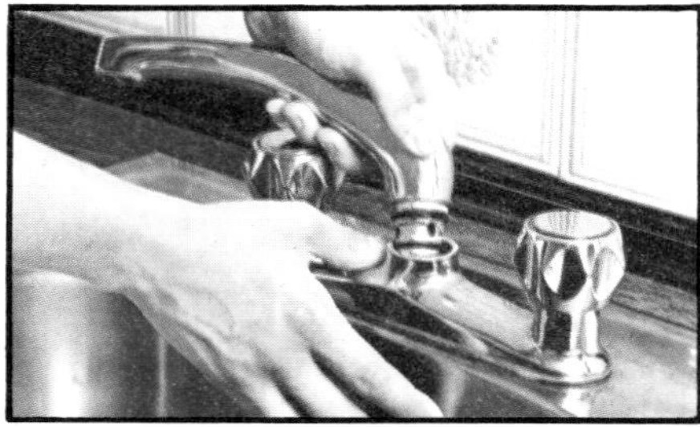

*3 At the swivel point of a spout, first undo any grub-screw. Now twist the spout to one side and gently ease it from the mounting.*

*4 Prise off the worn seals with a screwdriver and then slip new ones into position. Replace the spout back in the mounting, restore water.*

effectively cuts off the flow when the tap is turned off even though the top of the valve seating may not be smooth.

### Repacking a gland

This is necessary when you turn the tap on and water bubbles up the spindle towards the handle. At the same time the tap can be turned on and off far too easily — you might even be able to spin the handle with a flick of the fingers. This fault is a common cause of water hammer — heavy thudding following the closure of a tap or float-valve — that can result in damage to the plumbing system.

Leakage up the spindle is most likely to occur in rather old fashioned — but still very common — taps in which the spindle passes through a gland or 'stuffing box' filled with greased wool. It's inevitable that water containing detergent will be splashed onto the tap and this may result in the grease being washed out of the gland. The leakage can also be created if you run a garden or washing machine hose from the tap.

Fortunately, to make a repair you don't have to cut off the water supply to the tap, but you must be able to get at the gland-adjusting nut. This is the first nut through which the spindle passes.

Giving the gland-adjusting nut about half a turn may be enough to stop the leakage up the spindle, but eventually all the adjustment available will be taken up and you'll then have to repack the gland. When the gland-adjusting nut has been unscrewed and removed, the old gland packing material can be taken out and replaced with knitting wool saturated with petroleum jelly. The wool is wound round the spindle and packed down tightly before the gland-adjusting nut is put back and tightened until the tap handle can be turned fairly easily but without any leaks occurring.

### Replacing an 'O' ring

Many modern taps have 'O' ring seals instead of a packed gland or stuffing box. If an 'O' ring fails the remedy is simply to undo the gland-adjusting nut, pick out the old 'O' ring and replace it with a new one. Leaks from taps with this fitting are rare. 'O' rings are also found at the swivel point of many mixer taps and if a leak occurs here you have to remove the spout to make the change – but this is usually only held with a grub-screw.

Older Supataps aren't fitted with an 'O' ring seal but if water leaks from the top of the nozzle you can fit a ring round the valve casing. Modern Supataps have an 'O' ring already fitted and if it needs replacing, it's a simple matter of slipping it off and pushing on another — but choose one that fits snugly and doesn't move about. If this doesn't cure the leak you'll have to replace the anti-splash device which could have become worn.

# REPLACING TAPS

**Changing the old taps on your basin is a bright and practical way of making your bathroom more attractive. It may also be a good idea if they are old and inefficient. Here's what is involved.**

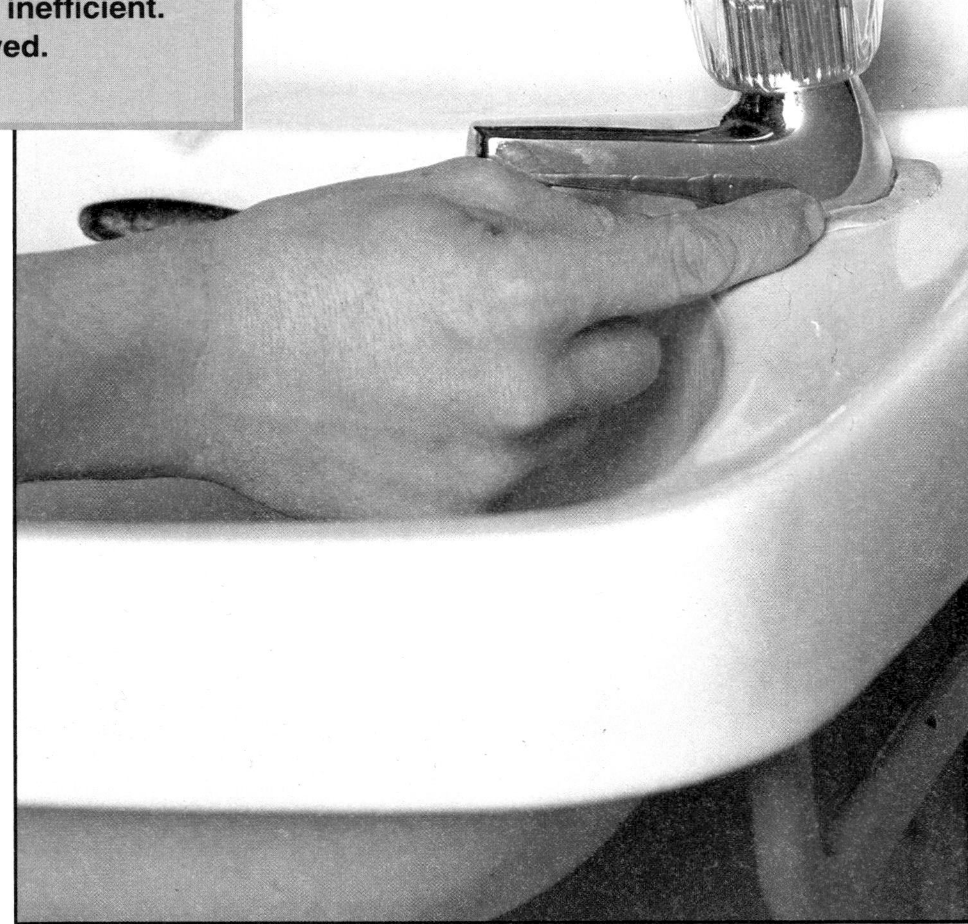

There may be a number of reasons why you wish to replace the taps supplying your sink, basin or bath. They may continually drip or leak, where new taps would give efficient, trouble-free service. Perhaps you want the advantages that mixers have over individual taps or perhaps it is simply that the chromium plating has worn off leaving the taps looking incurably shabby.

It is more likely, however, that appearance, rather than malfunction, will be your reason for changing. There are fashions in plumbing fittings as in clothing and furniture. Taps of the 1950s or 60s are instantly recognisable as out-of-date in a bathroom or kitchen of the 1980s. Fortunately, fashions in sinks, basins and baths have changed rather less dramatically over the past three decades. There is probably no more cost-effective way of improving bathroom and kitchen appearance than by the provision of sparkling new taps or mixers.

## Choosing taps

When you come to select your new taps you may feel that you are faced with a bewildering choice. Tap size, appearance, the material of which the tap is made, whether to choose individual taps or mixers and – for the bath – whether to provide for an over-bath shower by fitting a bath/shower mixer: all these things need to be considered.

Size is easily enough dealt with. Taps and mixers are still in imperial sizes. Bath tap tails are ¾in in diameter, and basin and sink taps ½in in diameter. There are, however, a few suppliers who are beginning to designate taps by the metric size, not of the taps themselves, but of the copper supply pipes to which they will probably be connected. Such a supplier might refer to bath taps as 22mm and sink and basin taps as 15mm.

Most taps are made of chromium-plated brass, though there are also ranges of enamelled and even gold-plated taps and mixers. Although taps and mixers are still manufactured with conventional crutch or capstan handles, most people nowadays prefer to choose taps with 'shrouded' heads made of acrylic or other plastic. In effect, these combine the functions of handle and easy-clean cover, completely concealing the tap's headgear. A still popular alternative is the functional 'Supatap', nowadays provided with plastic rather than metal 'ears' for quick and comfortable turning on and off.

There is also a very competitively priced range of all-plastic taps. These usually give satisfactory enough service in the home, but they cannot be regarded as being as sturdy as conventional metal taps, and they can be damaged by very hot water.

So far as design is concerned the big difference is between 'bib taps' and 'pillar taps'. Bib taps have a horizontal inlet and are usually wall-mounted while pillar taps have a vertical inlet and are mounted on the bath, basin or sink they serve.

## Taking out old basin taps

When replacing old taps with new ones the most difficult part of the job is likely to be – as with so many plumbing operations – removing the old fittings. Let's first consider wash basin taps.

You must, of course, cut off the hot and cold water supplies to the basin. The best way of doing this will usually be to tie up the float arm of the ball valve supplying the cold water storage cistern so as to prevent water flowing in. Then run the bathroom cold taps until water ceases to flow. Only then open up the hot taps. This will conserve most of the expensively heated water in the hot water storage cylinder.

If you look under the basin you will find that the tails of the taps are connected to the water supply pipes with small, fairly accessible nuts, and that a larger – often

## REMOVING OLD TAPS

**1** *It's best to change taps by removing the basin completely. Loosen the two tap connectors carefully with an adjustable spanner.*

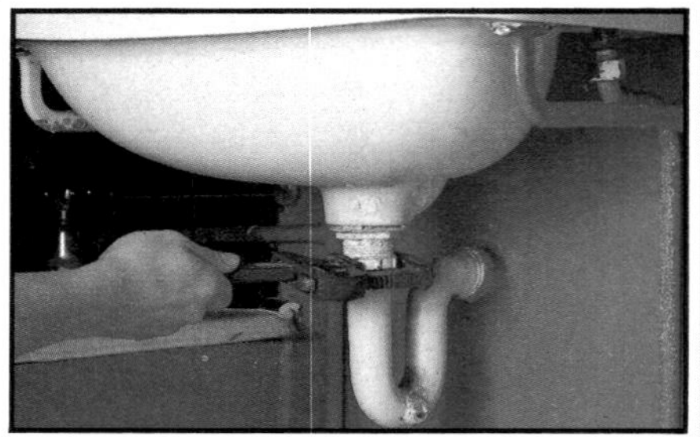

**2** *Disconnect the waste trap connector using an adjustable wrench. Take care not to damage the trap, particularly if it is lead or copper.*

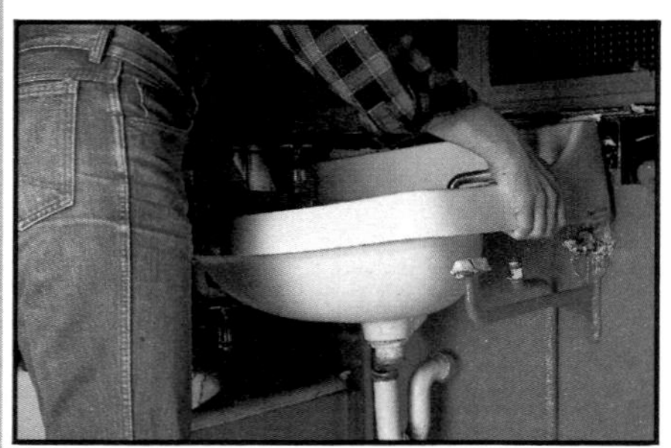

**3** *Undo any screws holding the basin to its brackets on the wall, and lift it clear of the brackets before lowering it carefully to the floor.*

**4** *Check the condition of the back-nuts, which may be badly corroded. It's a good idea to apply penetrating oil and leave this to work for a while.*

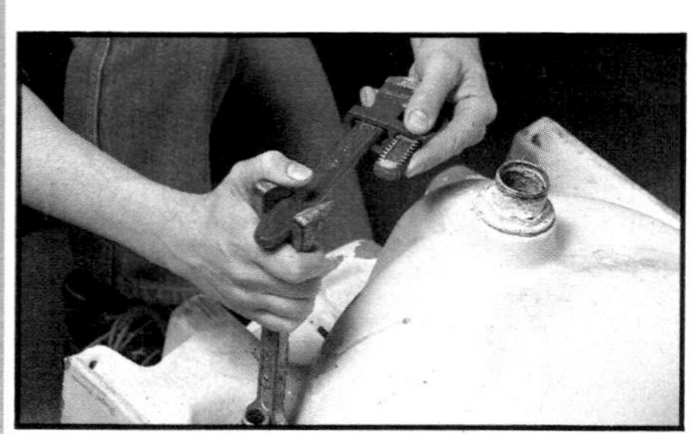

**5** *Use the crowsfoot (with extra leverage if necessary) to undo the back-nut. If more force is needed, grip the tap itself with a wrench to stop it turning.*

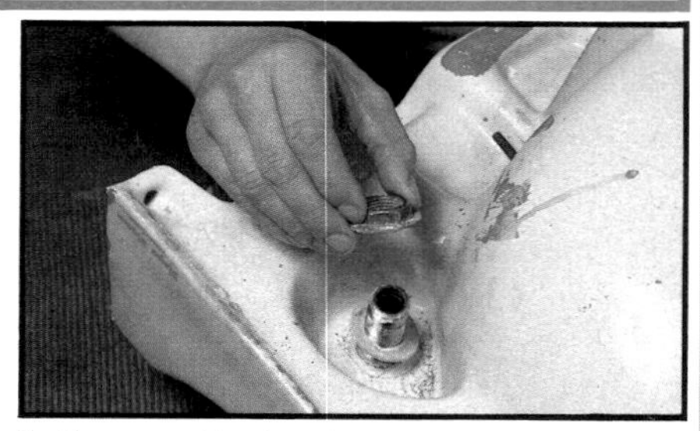

**6** *Remove the back-nut and any washers between it and the basin. Old washers like these should always be replaced with new washers.*

inaccessible – back-nut secures the tap to the basin. The nuts of the swivel tap connectors joining the pipes to the taps are usually easily undone with a wrench or spanner of the appropriate size. The back-nuts .can be extremely difficult – even for professional plumbers!

There are special wrenches and basin or crowsfoot spanners that may help, but they won't perform miracles and ceramic basins can be very easily damaged by heavy handedness. The best course of action is to disconnect the swivel tap connectors and to disconnect the trap from the waste outlet. These are secured by nuts and are easily undone. Then lift the basin off its brackets or hanger and place it upside down on the floor. Apply some penetrating oil to the tap tails and, after allowing a few minutes for it to soak in, tackle the nuts with your wrench or crowsfoot spanner. You'll find they are much more accessible. Hold the tap while you do this to stop it swivelling and damaging the basin.

### Fitting the new taps

When fitting the new taps or mixer, unscrew the back-nuts, press some plumber's putty round the tail directly below the tap body or fit a plastic washer at the top of the tail.

## Ready Reference

### EQUIPMENT CHECKLIST

For replacing existing taps, you will need the following tools and equipment:

- new taps of the right type and size
- an adjustable spanner
- a basin wrench ('crowsfoot')
- an adjustable wrench
- penetrating oil
- plastic washers (see below)
- plumber's putty
- PTFE tape

You may also need tap tail adaptors (if the new taps have shorter tails than the old ones) and new tap connectors (if your new taps have metric tails instead of imperial ones).

### WHAT ABOUT WASHERS?

With ceramic basins, use a plastic washer above and below the basin surface (A) so you don't crack the basin as you tighten the back-nut. You can use plumber's putty instead of the upper washer.

On thin basins, use a special top-hat washer between basin and back-nut (B).

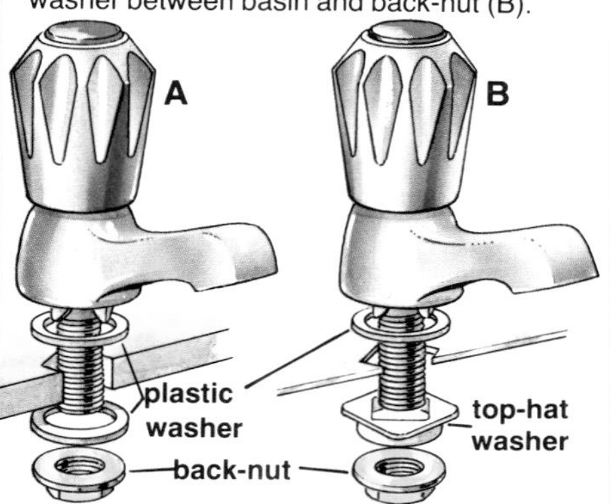


The lugs at the top of the tap tail are meant to stop it turning in square tap holes. Use special anti-rotation washers to stop new taps with smaller lugs from turning in old tap holes.

### TIPS TO SAVE TROUBLE

- to undo stubborn back-nuts, add extra leverage to the crowsfoot by hooking a wrench handle into its other end
- if this fails, squirt penetrating oil around the back-nuts. Leave for a while and try again
- in really stubborn cases, remove the basin completely, and turn it upside down on the floor so you have more room to work
- grip the tap body with an adjustable spanner to stop it turning as you use the crowsfoot; otherwise the tap lugs could crack the basin

## FITTING NEW TAPS

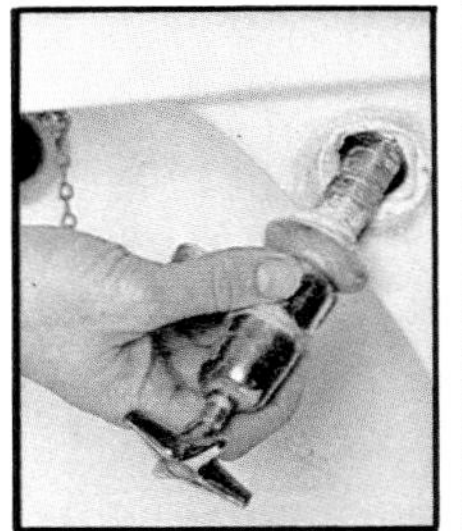
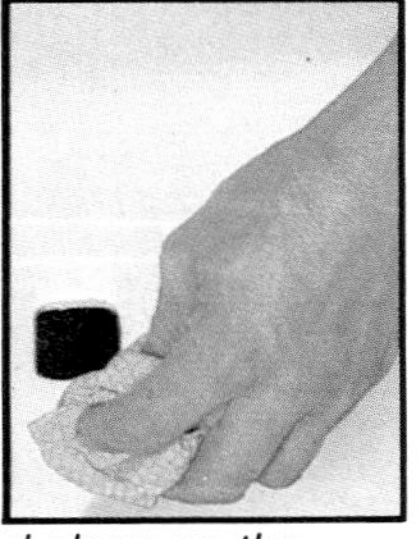

*1 Remove the tap and clean up the basin surround, chipping away scale and any old putty remaining from when the tap was originally installed.*

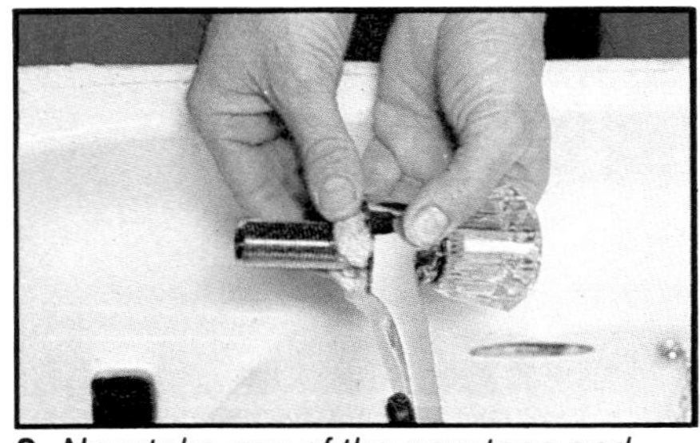

*2 Now take one of the new taps and fit a washer or plumber's putty around the top of the tail before pushing it into the hole in the basin.*

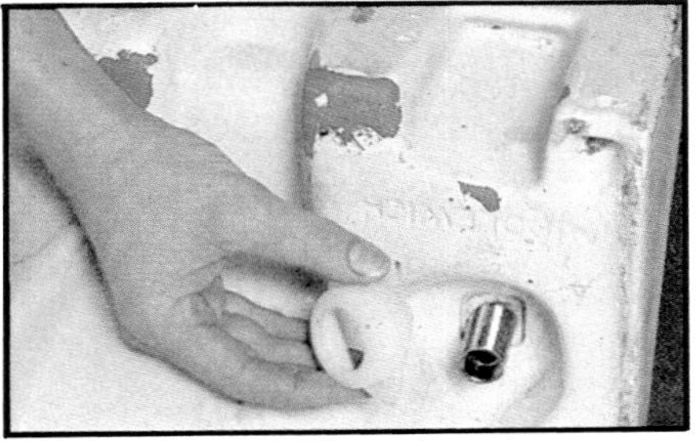

*3 Twist the tap so that it's at the correct angle to the basin and is firmly bedded on the putty. Then push a top-hat washer onto the tail.*

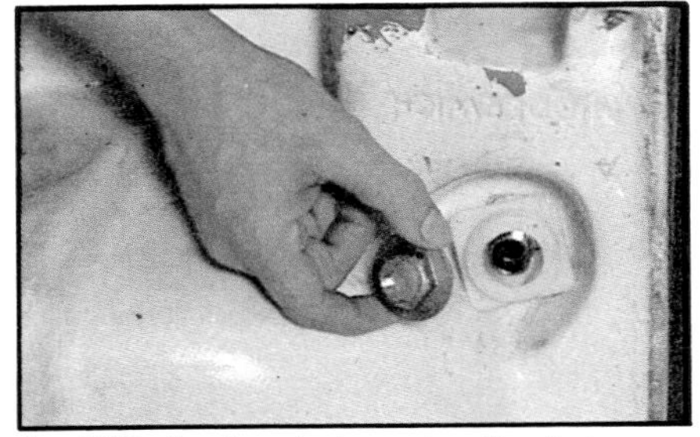

*4 With the top-hat washer firmly in place, take the new back-nut and screw it up the tail of the tap by hand.*

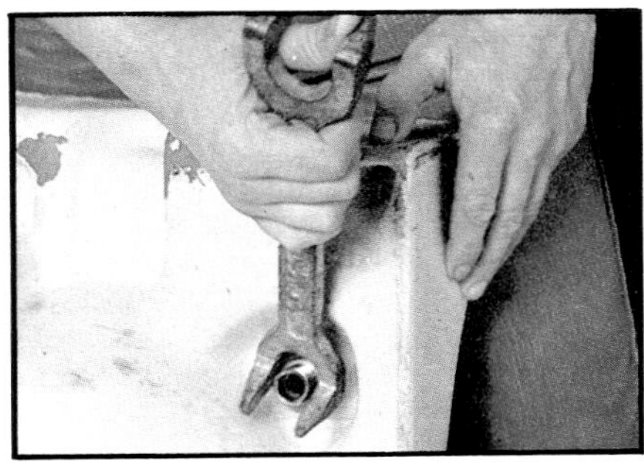

*5 Tighten up the back-nut until the tap assembly is completely firm, using the crowsfoot or an adjustable spanner. Repeat the process for the other tap.*

TIP

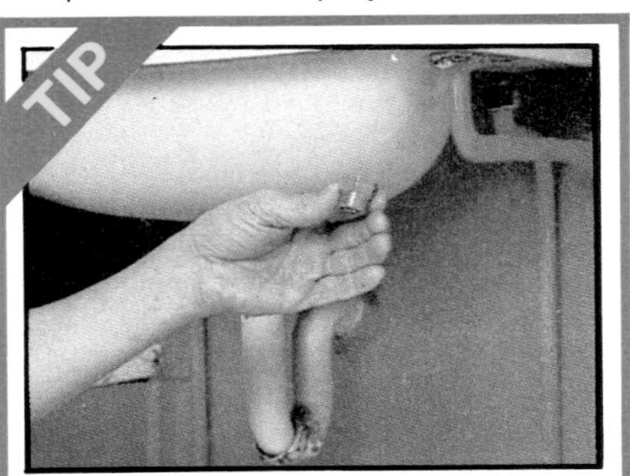

*6 Reconnect all the pipework. Use tap-tail adaptors if the new taps have shorter tails than the old ones.*

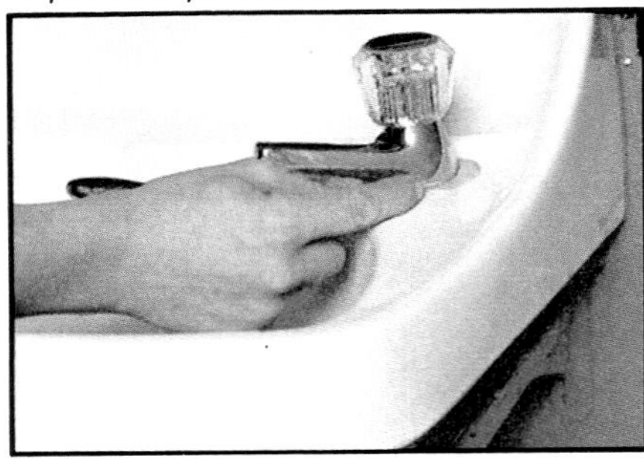

*7 When all is secure, remove any surplus putty from around the base of the taps, wiping it over with a finger to leave a smooth, neat finish.*

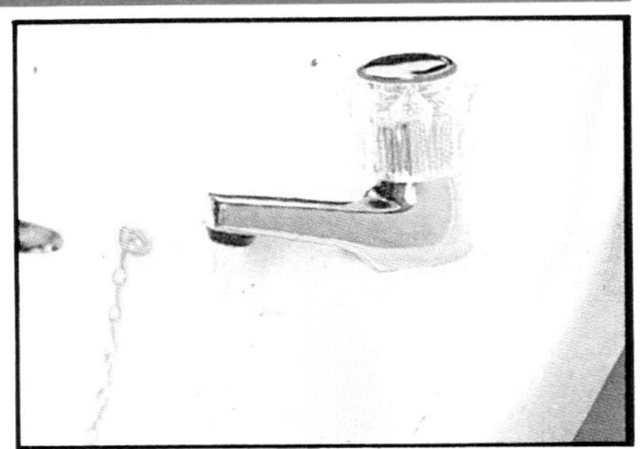

*8 Turn the water back on. Check that the flow from the taps is regular and that the waste trap is not leaking. If it is, tighten up its connectors slightly.*

Push the tails through the holes in the basin. Slip flat plastic washers over the tails where they protrude from beneath the basin, screw on the back-nuts and tighten them up. Make sure that the taps or mixer are secure, but don't overtighten them. To make tightening easier, (and undoing, if ever necessary) use top-hat washers.

All that remains to be done is to connect the swivel tap connectors to the tails of the new taps or mixer. You will see that a tap connector consists of a lining – with a flange – that is inserted into the tap tail and is then secured by the coupling nut. This nut is provided with a washer to ensure a watertight connection. When renewing taps you may well need to renew this small washer.

It is possible that when you come to connect the water supply pipes to the taps you will get an unpleasant surprise. The tails of modern taps are slightly shorter than those of older ones and the tap connectors may not reach. If the water supply pipes are of lead or of copper it is quite likely that they will have enough 'give' to enable you to make the connection but, if not, there are extension pieces specially made to bridge the gap.

### Bib taps

If you're replacing existing bib taps with those of a more modern design, it's a relatively simple matter of disconnecting and unscrewing the old ones and fitting the new taps in their place. However, it's quite possible that you'll want to remove the bib taps altogether and fit a new sink with some pillar taps. This will involve a little more plumbing work. To start with, turn off the water supply and remove the taps and old sink. If the pipework comes up from the floor, you'll need to uncover the run in the wall to below where the new sink will go. You should then be able to ease the pipes away from the wall and cut off the exposed sections. This will allow you to join short lengths of new pipe, bent slightly if necessary, to link the pipe ends and the tap tails. Alternatively, if the pipes come down the wall you'll have to extend the run to below the level of the new sink and use elbow fittings to link the pipe to the tap tails. In either case it's a good idea to fit the taps to the new sink first and to make up the pipe-work runs slightly overlong, so that when the new sink is offered up to the wall you can measure up accurately and avoid the risk of cutting off too much pipe. Rather than having to make difficult bends you can use lengths of corrugated copper pipe. One end of the pipe is plain so that it can be fitted to the 15mm supply pipes with either a soldered capillary or compression fitting; the other end has a swivel tap connector.

# STOP-VALVES AND BALL-VALVES

**The valves that control your household water system aren't difficult to understand – or to fit or repair. So the next time one of yours goes wrong, be prepared to put it right yourself.**

Stop-valves, gate-valves and ball-valves are all plumbing fittings that in different ways do precisely the same thing, which is to regulate the flow of water through pipes. Each of the three types of valve performs an important function in your water system, and it is therefore in your interest to know not only what they do and how they do it, but also how to put right any of the faults to which they are prone.

### Stop-valves

Your main stop-valve is perhaps the single most important plumbing fitting in your house. In the event of almost any plumbing emergency the very first thing that you should do is turn it off. This will stop the flow of water into your house and reduce the extent of any damage. Looking like a very basic brass tap, your main stop-valve will be found set into the rising main not far from the point where this pipe enters your house. Often it will be located under the kitchen sink.

If your house is fairly old then it could be that it won't be provided with a main stop-valve. If this is the case, then you will have to use the local water authority's stop-valve instead. You will find it under a hinged metal flap set into your garden path or the pavement outside your property. This sort of stop-valve usually has a specially-shaped handle that can only be turned with one of the water authority's turnkeys. So that you can deal promptly with any emergency you should make sure that you either have one of these turnkeys, or at least that you have ready access to one. However, both for the sake of convenience and because specialist gadgets like turnkeys have a habit of disappearing when they're most needed, you may decide to install a main stop-valve yourself – not a difficult task if the rising main is made of copper pipe (see step-by-step photographs).

The internal construction of a stop-valve is identical to that of an ordinary tap, and so it is prone to the same types of faults (see *Ready Reference*). But one further trouble that may afflict your stop-valve – which doesn't crop up with ordinary taps – is that of jamming in the open position as a result of disuse. It's a problem cured simply by applying penetrating oil to the spindle. However, you can prevent this happening by closing and opening the stop-valve regularly, and by leaving it fractionally less than fully open – a quarter turn towards closure will do.

### Gate-valves

Whereas stop-valves are always fitted to pipes that are under mains pressure, gate-valves are used on pipes that are only subject to low pressure. They are therefore found on hot and cold water distribution pipes and on those of the central heating system. Gate-valves differ from stop-valves in as much as they control the flow of water through them, not with a washered valve, but by means of a metal plate or 'gate'. You can distinguish them from stop-valves by the fact that their valve bodies are bigger, and by their wheel – as opposed to crutch – handles. Due to the simplicity of their internal construction gate-valves require little attention (see *Ready Reference*). Unlike stop-valves, which have to be fitted so that the water flowing through them follows the direction of an arrow stamped on the valve body, you can install a gate-valve either way round.

### Mini stop-valves

Mini stop-valves are useful little fittings that you can insert into any pipe run. Their presence enables you to re-washer or renew a tap or ball-valve (see below) or repair a water-using appliance such as a washing machine without disrupting the rest of your water system. They can also be used to quieten an excessively noisy lavatory flushing cistern that is fed directly from the rising main, since by slowing down the flow of water to the ball-valve you can reduce the noise without materially affecting the cistern's rate of filling after flushing. You usually fit a mini stop-valve immediately before the appliance that it is to control; and they can be turned off and on either with a screwdriver, or by turning a small handle through 180°.

### Ball-valves

Ball-valves are really just self-regulating taps designed to maintain a given volume of water in a cistern. While there are a number of different patterns they all have a float – not necessarily a ball these days – at one end of a rigid arm which opens or closes a valve as the water level in the cistern falls or rises. There are basically two types of ball-valve: the traditional type, generally made of brass, in which the water flow is controlled by a washered plug or piston; and the type that has been developed more recently in which the flow is controlled by a large rubber diaphragm housed within a plastic body.

### Croydon and Portsmouth ball-valves

The oldest of the traditional types of ball-valve is the Croydon pattern. You can easily recognise one of these by the position of its piston, which operates vertically, and by the fact that it delivers water to the cistern in two insufferably noisy streams. Due to their noisi-

# FITTING A STOP-VALVE

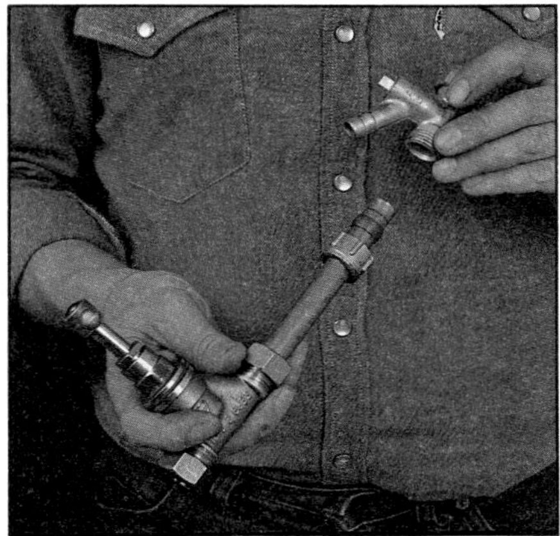

*1 When installing a main stop-valve use the type that has compression fittings. If it isn't combined with a drain-cock then fit one separately.*

*2 Make sure that you fit the stop-valve the right way round. The direction of the water flow is clearly indicated by an arrow stamped on the valve body.*

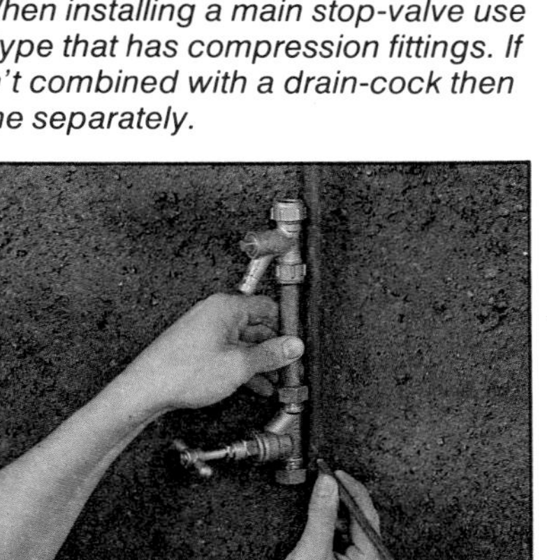

*3 Take care when marking off the rising main. The extent to which the pipe will penetrate the fitting is indicated by a shoulder; use this as your guide.*

*4 Turn off the water authority's stop-valve and cut it at the mark with a hacksaw. Some water will flow out as you do this; be prepared for it.*

*5 Spring the stop-valve into the cut pipe so that the two ends meet the pipe stops within the fitting. The valve handle should be angled away from the wall.*

*6 Tighten up the nuts, restore the water supply at the water authority's stop-valve, then turn on the stop-valve and check the fitting for leaks.*

## Ready Reference

### HOW A STOP-VALVE WORKS

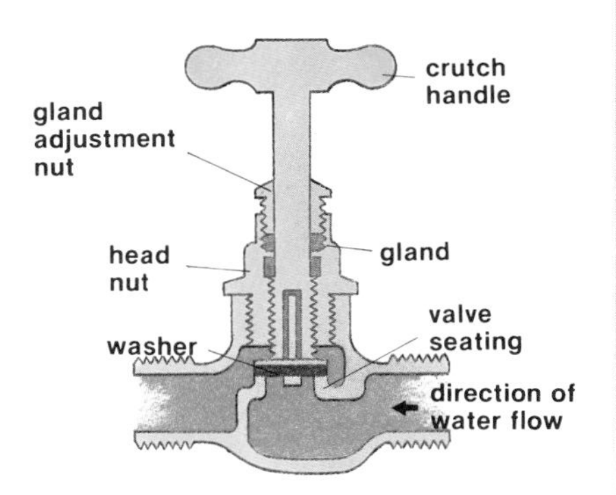


Because a stop-valve works in the same way as an ordinary tap its washer and gland are also subject to wear. You can:
- remove headgear to replace a worn washer (see pages 52 to 56), and
- deal with a worn gland by tightening the adjustment nut, or by re-packing the gland.

### HOW A GATE-VALVE WORKS

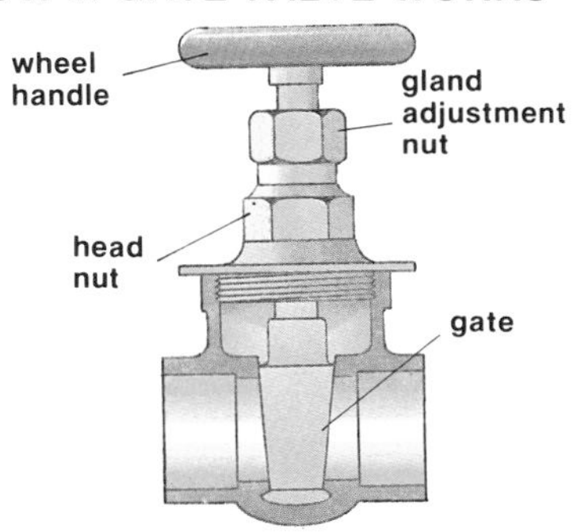


A gate-valve requires little attention. The only thing that may give trouble is the gland, which sometimes needs adjusting or renewing.

### DEZINCIFICATION

In areas where the water supply is unusually acidic the zinc content of pipe fittings made of brass (an alloy of copper and zinc) can be dissolved by the water. This phenomenom is known as dezincification, and it results in the fittings losing their structural strength. When it presents a problem, fittings made of gunmetal (an alloy of copper and tin) are usually used though cheaper corrosion-resistant brass fittings are also available. These usually have CR stamped on the valve body.

For more information on household water supply see pages 9 to 13.

## VALVE TYPES

*Apart from the float arm the only moving part on a diaphragm-type valve is a small plunger. When prompted by the float arm this plunger presses a large rubber diaphragm against the valve nozzle to close it.*

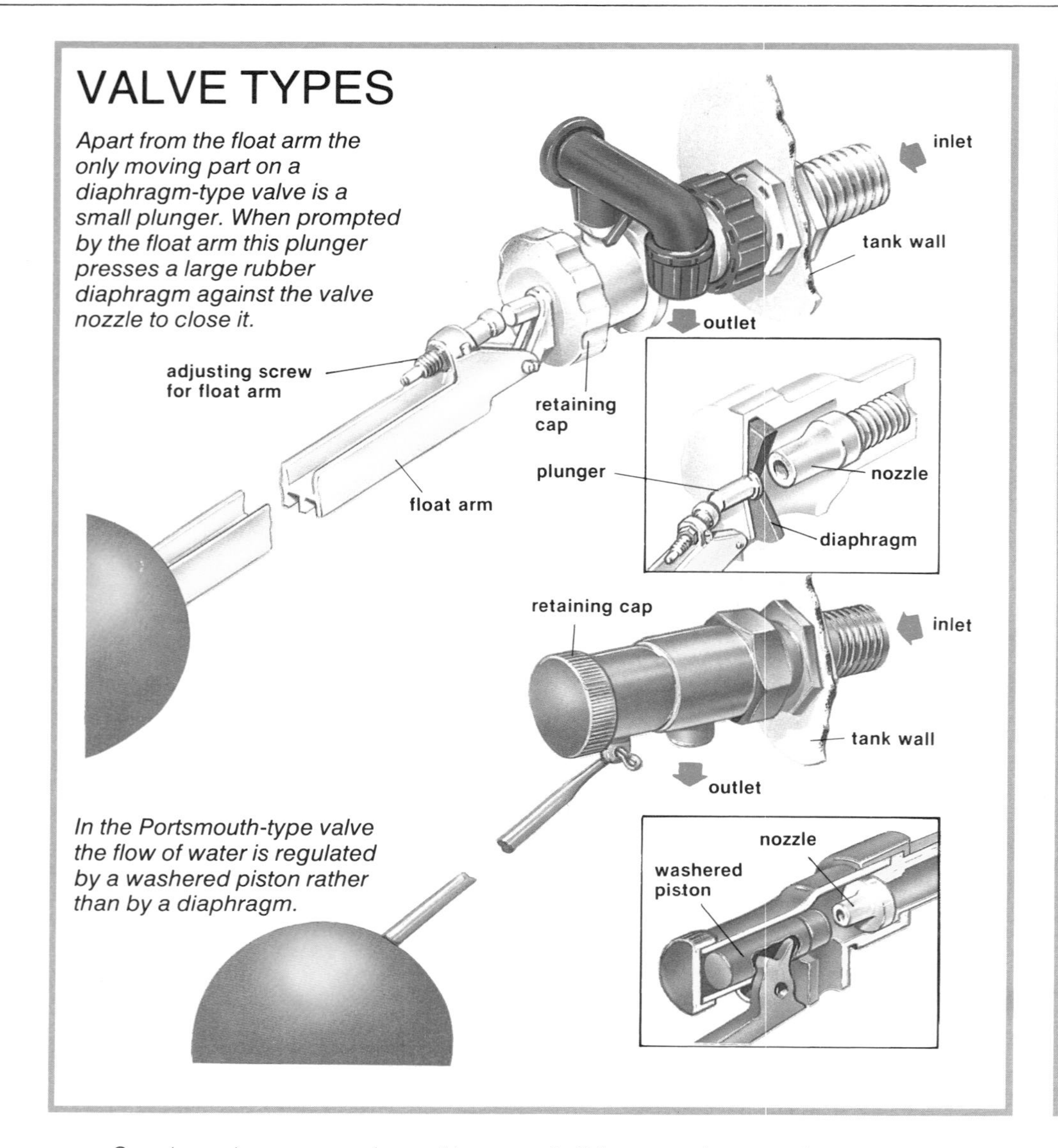


*In the Portsmouth-type valve the flow of water is regulated by a washered piston rather than by a diaphragm.*

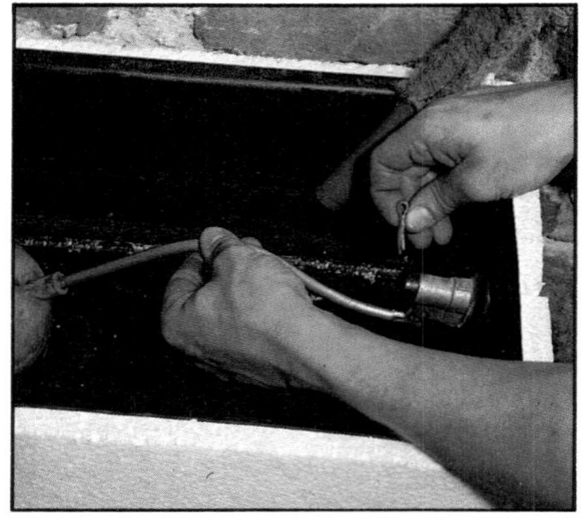

**1** *The first thing you do when faced with a faulty Portsmouth valve is examine the piston. In order to get at it you will first have to remove the float arm.*

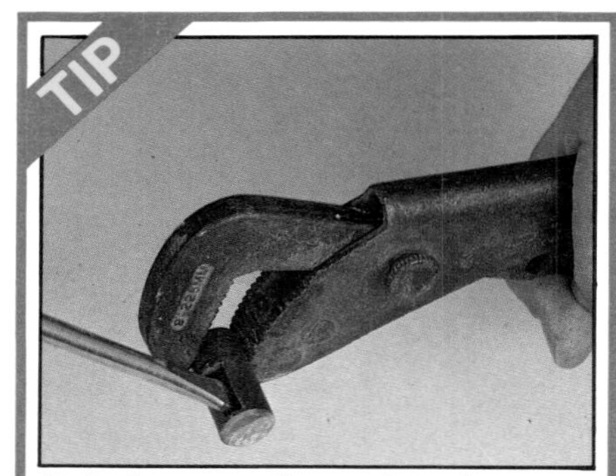


**5** *A piston usually consists of two parts. If it's hard to unscrew, slip a screwdriver into the slot and turn the washer-retaining cap with a wrench.*

ness, Croydon valves are now by and large obsolete, and if you do come across one you will almost certainly want to replace it. The traditional type of valve that superseded the Croydon pattern was the Portsmouth valve (see illustration). You can distinguish it from the former type by the fact that its piston operates horizontally; and as it is still popular with plumbers despite the development of more sophisticated diaphragm type valves, it is a pattern that you may well find in your home.

When one of your ball-valves goes wrong the first thing you will notice is water dripping from an outside overflow pipe. If the valve is a Portsmouth pattern then it is likely to have developed one of three faults. First, it could have jammed partially open as a result of the build-up of scale or the presence of grit; or, secondly, it could need re-washering. In either of these cases this will necessitate you turning off the water supply so that you can either clean the ball-valve or fit a new washer to it (see step-by-step photographs). Lastly, the valve could have been incorrectly adjusted to maintain the proper water level in the cistern – which should be about 25mm (1in) below the overflow pipe. Even modern Portsmouth valves are rarely provided with any specific means of adjusting the water level, so if you need to do so you will have to resort to bending the float arm.

Noise can be a problem with Portsmouth valves. It is caused either by the inrush of water through the valve nozzle, or by vibration created by the float bouncing on ripples on the surface of the water ('water hammer'). As silencer tubes are now banned by water authorities, you will have to try other methods to deal with this problem. Reducing the mains pressure by closing the rising main stop-valve slightly may help, and as vibration can be magnified by a loose rising main it is worth making sure that this pipe is properly secured with pipe clips. Another measure you could take would be to improvise a stabiliser for the float using a submerged plastic flowerpot tied to the float arm with nylon cord. However, if all the above measures fail you will have to consider replacing the Portsmouth valve with one of the modern diaphragm types.

### Diaphragm ball-valves

Diaphragm ball-valves, which are also referred to as BRS or Garston ball-valves, were specially developed to overcome the noisiness and inherent faults of the Croydon and Portsmouth valves. Since the moving parts of a diaphragm valve are protected from incoming water by the diaphragm (see illustration) there is no risk of them seizing as a result of scale deposits; and the problem of noisy water delivery is often overcome nowadays by an overhead sprinkler outlet which sprays rather than squirts the water into the cistern. Should you need to adjust the water

## REPAIRING A BALL- VALVE

**2** *Then unscrew the retaining cap and push out the piston. Do this by inserting a screwdriver into the slot in the underside of the valve body.*

**3** *If you can't get the piston out or if you suspect that your ball-valve needs a clean rather than a new washer, then you will have to remove the whole valve body.*

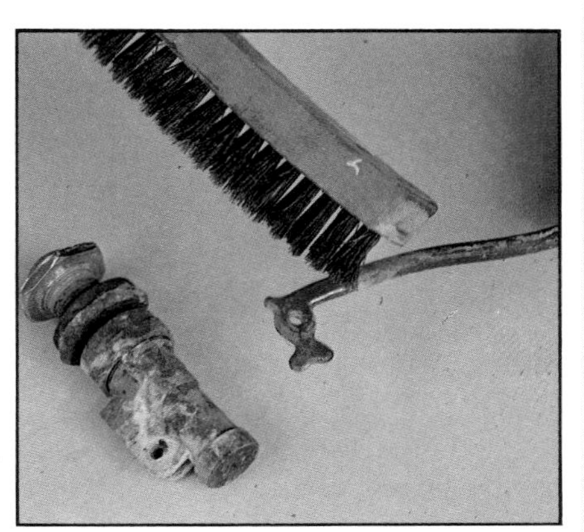

**4** *If a build-up of scale does turn out to be the cause of your problem, clean the valve and the end of the float arm with a wire brush.*

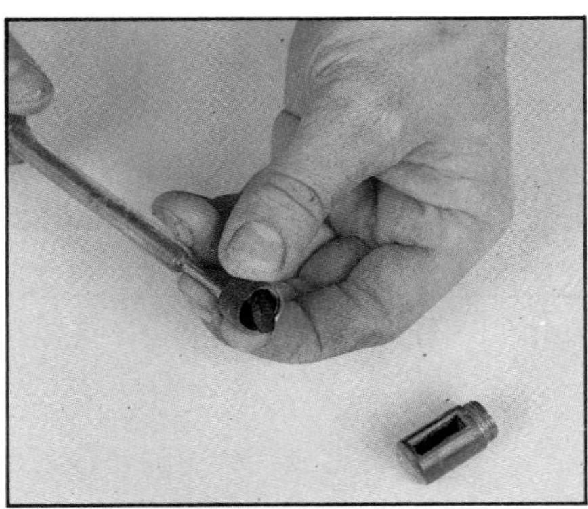

**6** *You'll find the old washer seated in the cap. Poke it out and substitute a new one. Smear the piston with petroleum jelly before replacing it in the valve.*

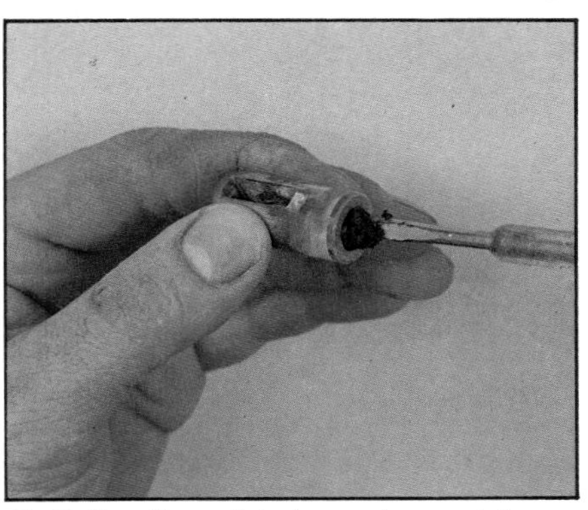

**7** *Rather than risk damaging a piston that refuses to unscrew, pick out the old washer with a point and force a new one back in its place.*

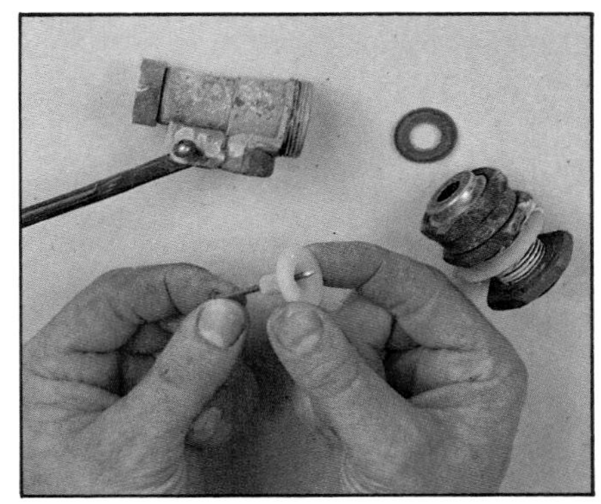

**8** *Debris caught in the valve nozzle can interrupt the water flow. Cure this problem by dismantling the valve and removing the debris with a nail.*

level in a cistern fitted with a diaphragm valve, then invariably you can by means other than bending the float arm. The only problems you are likely to encounter with diaphragm valves are jamming of the diaphragm against the valve nozzle, and obstruction of the space between the nozzle and diaphragm with debris from the main. You remedy these problems by unscrewing the knurled retaining cap and either freeing the diaphragm with a pointed tool or removing the debris.

### High and low pressure water supply

The water pressure under which a ball-valve operates is an important factor, as the size of the hole in the nozzle of the valve will be either smaller or larger according to whether it is under high pressure (ie, mains pressure) or low pressure (ie, supplied by water from a storage tank). Older Portsmouth valves have either HP (high pressure) or LP (low pressure) stamped on their bodies, and will only operate satisfactorily under the pressure for which they are designed. Modern valves, on the other hand, have interchangeable nozzles which allow you to convert them from low to high pressure or vice versa. If you fit a high-pressure valve (or nozzle) in a situation where a low-pressure one is required this will result in an agonisingly slow refill. A constantly dripping overflow may be the sign of a low-pressure valve that has been fitted to a cistern that is fed by the mains.

In some areas, mains pressure varies considerably throughout a 24-hour period. During the day, when demand is high, pressure will be low, whereas in the evening as demand falls off the pressure increases. These fluctuations in pressure don't affect low pressure valves but they do affect high pressure ones, which can perform erratically as a result. You can overcome this problem if it affects you by replacing your high pressure ball-valves with equilibrium valves.

### Equilibrium ball-valves

You can buy Portsmouth and diaphragm equilibrium valves. These are both designed to allow a small quantity of water to pass through or round the washered piston (or diaphragm) into a watertight chamber beyond. Acting as it does on the rear of the piston, and being at the same pressure as the mains, the water in the chamber ensures that the piston is held in equilibrium. What this means in practice is that the valve is operated solely by the movement of the float arm, rather than by a combination of the movement of the float arm *and* the pressure of the incoming water as is the case in an ordinary high-pressure valve. In addition to refilling your cistern promptly regardless of any fluctuations in mains pressure, equilibrium valves also eliminate the 'bounce' as the valve closes – a common cause of water hammer. A diaphragm equilibrium valve will give you a particularly rapid and silent refill.

# REPLACING A RADIATOR

**If one of your existing radiators is malfunctioning in some way, or else just out of character with the decor of your home why not replace it with a brand new one? You'll find this job straightforward if you follow our instructions.**

There are a number of reasons why you may want to replace an existing radiator in your home's central heating system. These can range from the aesthetic to the purely practical. At one time radiators were ugly and cumbersome, and if you have any still in use like this it's quite likely that they'll clash with the decor of your home. On the practical side, you may well find that a radiator in your system has developed leaks. This will mean both water and heat loss, as well as the inconvenience of cleaning up the mess. And, of course, you may simply feel that a modern radiator would produce more heat, and so improve the comfort in your home. Whatever your reasons for replacing a radiator, you'll have to choose a new one to go in its place, before actually removing the existing one.

### Choosing a new radiator

Modern radiators are usually made of 1.25mm (about 1/16in) thick pressed steel, and are designed to be space-saving, neat and attractive. For a simple replacement job, size will be among the most important considerations. If the new radiator can be successfully connected to the existing fittings, you won't need to alter or modify the circulating pipes. Consequently, the job will be that much easier. Radiators are available in a wide variety of sizes, ranging in height from 300mm (12in) to 800mm (32in) and in length from 480mm (19in) to 3200mm (10ft 6in) – so you shouldn't have too much difficulty in finding one that will fit into the space left by the old one. Special low, finned radiators are also available. These are usually fitted along the skirting and are both neat and unobtrusive – yet can be turned into decorative features in their own right.

But size isn't the only important consideration. After all, a radiator's job is to provide heat, so you'll have to shop around and find the one which, for its size, will produce most heat. A radiator's heat output is measured in kW – kilowatts – so you should look for the one with the highest kW rating for its size. Remember, it's always possible to turn off a radiator that makes a room too warm; it's far less easy to increase heat output in a room which, with the radiator

## THE FITTINGS

*A typical panel radiator is fitted with a flow control valve (below), a lock-shield valve (bottom right), an air-bleed valve (right) and a blanking off plug (far right).*

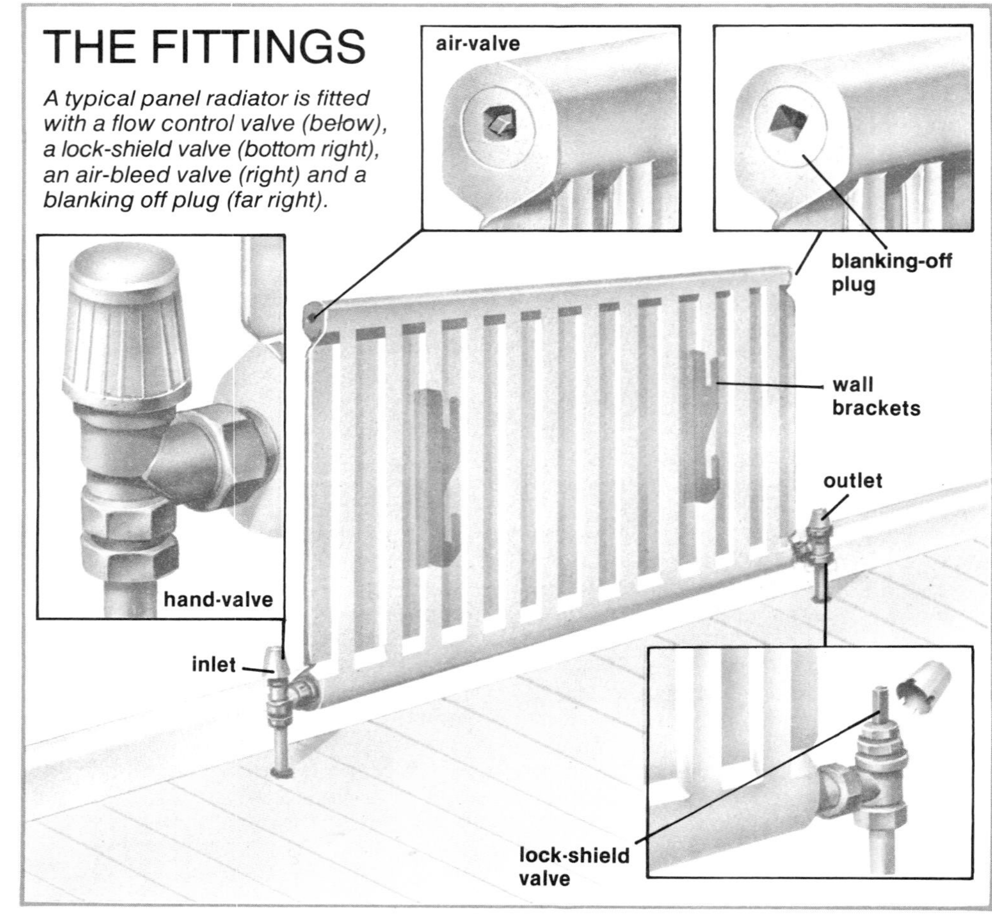

## REMOVING THE OLD RADIATOR

**1** *Turn off the flow control valve by hand, and the lock-shield valve by turning its spindle with pliers. Note how many turns are needed to close it completely.*

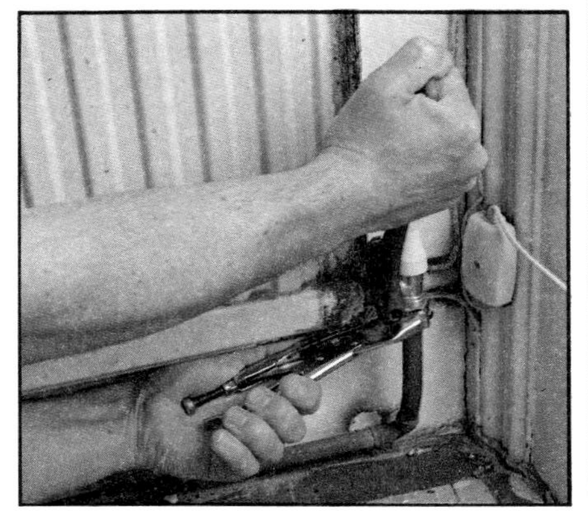

**2** *Hold the lock-shield valve body with a wrench so you don't bend the pipework, and undo the valve coupling carefully with an adjustable spanner.*

**3** *Open the air-bleed valve, pull the coupling away and allow the radiator to drain into a convenient container. Have rags and a larger bowl handy too.*

**4** *Having drained most of the water, undo the other coupling, lift the radiator off its brackets and drain out the dregs. Then remove the old brackets.*

turned fully on, remains uncomfortably chilly.

However, one way of increasing heat output, while retaining the same sized radiator, is to install a double-panel radiator. This is, literally, an ordinary radiator with two panels for the hot water to fill instead of the usual one and therefore has virtually double the heat output. So, while a single panel radiator 675mm x 750mm (27in x 30in) will have a heat output of 0.68kW, a double panel one of the same size will be rated at 1.15kW.

Although modern radiators are likely to provide more heat than the older variety, they do have one drawback. Because of the thinness of their metal, they are more prone to internal corrosion and this will ultimately produce leaks.

### Dealing with internal corrosion

Internal corrosion in modern radiators arises from an electrolytic reaction between the steel of the radiators and the copper circulating pipes of the central heating system. This results in the production of a corrosive black iron oxide sludge (magnetite) and hydrogen gas. In a similar fashion, if the original installation of your heating system was somewhat messily done, then copper swarf, produced when the pipes were cut, could have been retained within the circulating pipes. This will also corrode the steel at any point where the two come in contact – usually within a radiator. Because the raw material from which the sludge is produced is the metal of the radiators, eventually they will leak and need to be replaced. And as the sludge is also attracted by the magnetic field of the circulating pump, its abrasive qualities are a common cause of early pump failure.

Early indications of serious internal corrosion are a need to vent one or more radiators at regular intervals, and cold spots on their

## Ready Reference

### HOW RADIATORS WORK

A radiator works by convection. It heats up the air in direct contact with its surface. This becomes lighter, rises and is replaced by cooler, heavier air from floor level. So, gradually, the whole room is warmed.

### POSITIONING A RADIATOR

A radiator is most effective if positioned under a window. That way it kills the convection down-draught produced when warm air comes into contact with the cooler glass, and so increases comfort.

### CLEARING AIR LOCKS

You might find air locks in your existing radiators or your new one. In that case you'll have to vent the radiator. You should

- obtain a square-ended bleed key from a plumbing or hardware shop
- insert the key into the air-bleed valve and turn in an anti-clockwise direction
- hold a cloth or container under the valve to catch water
- tighten the valve once all the air is displaced and water emerges.

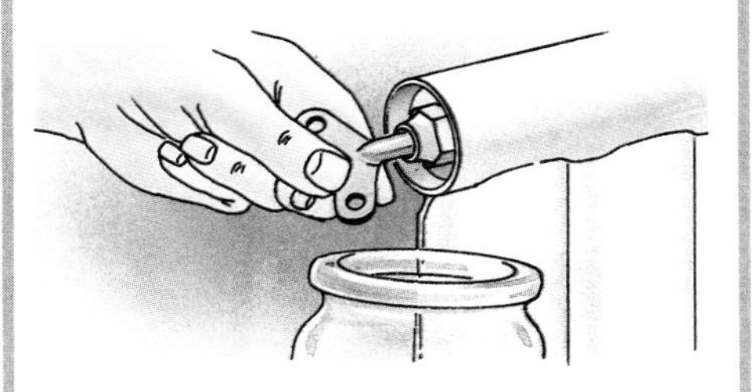

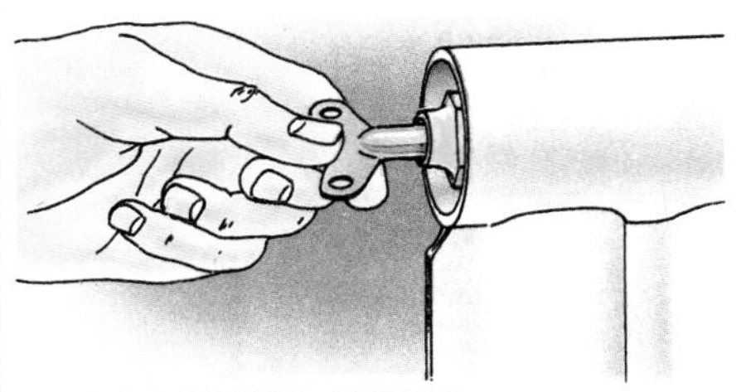

### DECORATING YOUR RADIATORS

Your new radiator will be finished in white factory-applied primer. Paint it with special radiator paint or gloss before you fix it to the wall, otherwise you won't be able to reach the back. Once the radiator is in place you can touch up any parts scratched during installation.

### TIP: FIXING A FOIL REFLECTOR

Before fitting a replacement radiator against an outside wall it's a good idea to fit reflective foil against the wall. That way you'll help to cut down on heat losses.

surfaces. If in doubt, the diagnosis can be confirmed by applying a flame to the escaping gas when the radiator is being vented. If it burns with a blue and yellow flame, you can be sure that hydrogen is in the system and will have been produced by the chemical reaction of the two metals. Once you've confirmed that corrosion is present within the system, you'll have to flush it through and introduce a reliable corrosion preventative chemical into the feed and expansion tank as you refill the system. That way you should be able to prevent further corrosion and so save your system.

### Removing the old radiator

One of the great deterrents to anyone wanting to remove a radiator is the prospect of having to drain the whole system. However, this won't be necessary provided the radiator to be replaced has a valve at both the hot water inlet and the outlet. Once these are closed, you'll be able to keep virtually all the system's water isolated in other parts.

At the inlet end you're likely to find the hand-valve which is the control by which you open and close the radiator. At the outlet end you'll find what is termed the lock-shield valve. When you come to inspect your radiator, don't worry if their positions are reversed – they will still be equally effective.

The first thing to do when removing a radiator is to close these valves. The hand-valve is straightforward, but you'll have to remove the cover to get at the lock-shield valve. You'll be able to close this valve using a spanner or an adjustable wrench with which to grip its spindle.

As you turn it, it's a good idea to note carefully how many turns it takes to close. And you'll find this task slightly easier if you mark the turning nut with a piece of chalk before you begin. The reason for all this is to maintain the balance of the system. After it was first installed, your system would have been balanced. The lock-shield valves of all the radiators were adjusted to give an equal level of water through-flow so that they were all heating up equally. So, by noting the number of turns taken to close the lock-shield, when you come to fit the new radiator you can simply open it up by the same amount – so avoiding the somewhat tedious task of re-balancing the whole system.

Once you've closed both valves, you can unscrew the nuts which connect the valves to the radiator inlet and outlet. Do these one at a time after having placed a low dish under each end to collect the water and protect the floor. Use an adjustable wrench to undo the coupling nuts. It's wise to hold the circulating pipe securely in place with another wrench. Otherwise, if you apply too much pressure to the coupling nut you risk fracturing the flowpipe, and this would cause

## FITTING THE NEW RADIATOR

**1** *To ensure watertight connections to the new radiator, wrap PTFE tape round all threaded fittings and then smear on some jointing compound.*

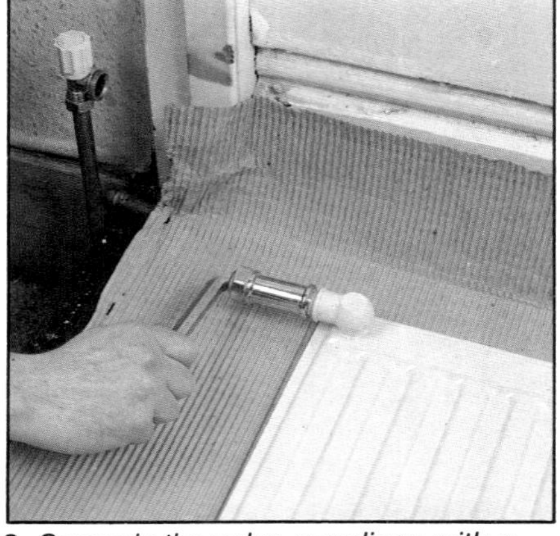

**2** *Screw in the valve couplings with a hexagonal radiator spanner. Use extension pieces if the new radiator is slightly narrower than the old one.*

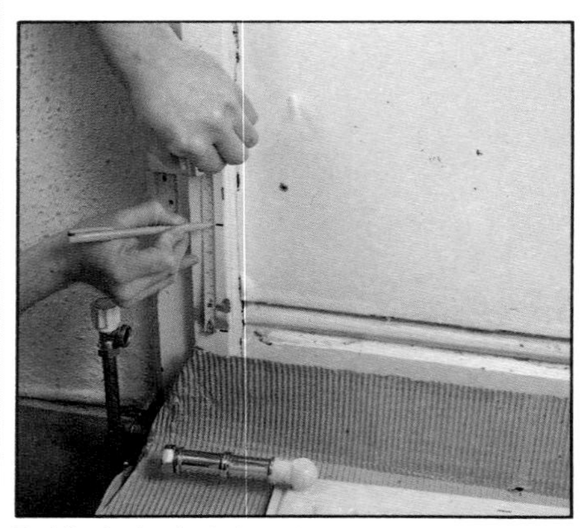

**5** *Mark the height taken in* **4** *on the wall above each valve, and join up the marks at each end with a pencil line. This marks the level of the new brackets.*

**6** *Transfer the measurements taken in* **3** *to the wall to indicate the vertical position of each bracket. Accuracy is not so vital here as in* **5**.

**9** *Lift the radiator into place on its brackets. You can move it slightly from side to side to align the valve couplings with the inlet and outlet valves.*

**10** *Wrap the coupling threads in PTFE tape and jointing compound, and do up the couplings. Again, use a wrench to support the valve body and prevent strain.*

**3** *Lay the radiator down in line with the two valves, and measure the distance from each valve coupling to the centre of the nearest bracket mounting.*

**4** *Next, measure the height of the base of the radiator brackets from a line joining the centres of the inlet and outlet valves.*

**7** *Hold the bracket against the wall in line with the vertical and horizontal marks you've made, and draw in the positions for the fixing screws.*

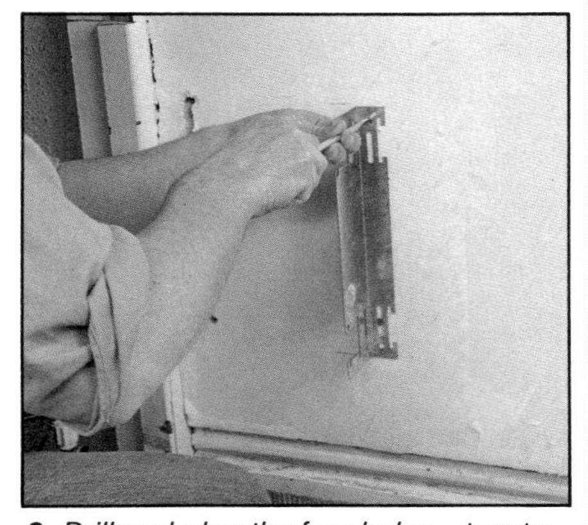

**8** *Drill and plug the four holes – two to each bracket – and fix the brackets in position. Make sure the wallplug is well below the plaster to avoid cracking.*

**11** *After connecting up the couplings, use a bleed key to open the air-bleed valve slightly so that air can escape as the radiator fills with water.*

**12** *Open the inlet valve, allow the radiator to fill and then close the air-bleed valve. Finally open the lock-shield valve by as many turns as you took to close it.*

you a lot of extra work and expense to mend – as well as causing quite a mess. As you unscrew each nut, the water from the radiator will flow out. If the system has been previously treated with corrosion proofer, it's well worth saving the water. That way you can pour it back into the feed-and-expansion tank when the job is complete.

Once the water has drained out, remove the tail pieces and coupling nuts from each end. Then block up each hole with a rag and lift the radiator from the brackets that hold it to the wall. It's a good idea to get the radiator out of your home as soon as possible – just in case it leaks any remaining dirty water on to your carpet.

### Fitting a new radiator

Your new radiator will probably have four holes or tappings – one at each corner – and each one will have a female screwed thread. How you connect the radiator up to your system depends on the way in which the old one was fitted. Nowadays it is usual for the flow and return connections to be made to the bottom two holes but, of course, if your system had the flow pipe at a higher level then you'll have to reconnect it in the same way.

Fit an air-valve into one of the top tappings. First wrap PTFE thread sealing tape anti-clockwise round the male thread of the valve and then use a radiator key that grips inside the body of the valve to screw it home. Unless your radiator has a top inlet the other top tapping must be plugged with a blanking off plug. This should also be wrapped with PTFE tape and screwed home in the same way as the air vent.

You'll then have to fit tail pieces and coupling screws (either new ones, or the ones from the original radiator if you can remove them) on to the new one. Again wrap each thread with PTFE tape before fitting them. It's a good idea to buy new wall brackets for your replacement radiator. After all, you can't be sure the old ones will be suitable. You should drill and plug the wall and then fix the brackets in place. Fit the radiator so that the air vent end is fractionally higher than the outlet valve. This will make venting easier. You can now fix the radiator in place and connect the coupling nuts to the hand-valve and lock-shield valve and screw them up tightly.

You'll have to open the air-valve at the top of the radiator so that the air in it can be displaced as it fills with water. All you do is slowly open the hand-valve and allow the radiator to fill. When water starts to flow from the air-valve you'll know all the air has been displaced and you should immediately close the valve. Finally, open the lock-shield valve by the same number of turns and part turns it took originally to close it.

# INSULATING TANKS AND PIPEWORK

**Worried by the thought of your next heating bill? Concerned by the prospect of your pipes freezing in winter? Proper insulation could well be the answer – and what's more it's cheap and easy to install.**

Insulation is important because it reduces heat loss, and when properly applied to your water system it benefits you in a number of ways. Firstly, it saves you money by slowing down the rate at which heat is lost from the pipes and tanks of your hot water system. Secondly, by reducing the heat loss from your cold water system (and even the coldest water contains *some* heat) it tends to keep your cold water warmer in winter, thereby minimising the risk of frozen pipes. Warmer cold water in winter also means that it takes less energy to heat it up to the desired temperature when it enters your hot water tank. In this respect, too, insulation saves you money.

So for all the above reasons you should consider properly insulating your pipes and tanks. The cost of the materials you will need is small and the potential savings great. And if you have already insulated your loft floor then this is one job you really must attend to. It has to be done because the temperature of your loft in winter will now be only marginally higher than that of the air outside, which means that the danger of any exposed pipework freezing in cold weather is greatly increased. Ideally you should therefore insulate your pipes and tanks before you tackle the loft floor. And don't forget that the risk of frozen pipes also applies to pipes in the cellar, and anywhere else where they might be subject to extremes of cold.

Before purchasing the insulation material for your pipes and tanks, work out how much you are likely to need. Most tanks will have their capacity and/or their dimensions marked on them somewhere – if yours don't then measure them yourself. You will also need to calculate the combined length of the pipes you intend insulating and establish what their diameter is – though this last measurement is only important if you plan to use split sleeve insulation (see below). As you'll want the insulation on your tanks to overlap that which you fit to any pipes that run into them, it's best to start by insulating your pipework.

## Insulating pipes

Two types of pipe insulation are commonly available. The first is made out of a glass fibre or mineral wool material similar to that used for insulating loft floors, but supplied in bandage form (75 to 100mm/3 to 4in wide and 10mm/3⁄8in thick) generally with a flimsy plastic backing. The second type comes in the form of split sleeves which are made from some sort of foamed material – usually plastic. Both types of pipe insulation have their advantages and disadvantages (see below) and both types are cheap. And since there is no reason why they can't be used side by side on the same pipe system, you'll almost certainly find that the easiest way to insulate your pipework is by using lengths of both.

## Fitting bandage insulation

The bandage type is fitted by wrapping it around the pipe in a spiral, with each turn overlapping the previous one by at least 10mm (3⁄8in). It doesn't matter which way round the plastic backing goes. Make sure that the bandage is sufficiently tight to prevent air circulating between the turns, but don't pull it too tight or you will reduce its effectiveness. When starting or finishing each roll, and at regular intervals in between, hold it in place using plastic adhesive tape or string. Tape or tie the bandage, too, on vertical pipe runs and on bends as these are places where the turns are likely to separate. And don't forget to lag any stop-valves properly – only the handle should be left visible.

Apart from being rather more time consuming to install than split-sleeve insulation the main drawback with the bandage type is that it is difficult to wrap round pipes in awkward places, such as those that run under floorboards. For pipes like these you will generally find that sleeves are more suitable since once fitted they can be pushed into position.

## Fitting split-sleeve insulation

Split-sleeve insulation normally comes in 1m (3ft 3in) or 2m (6ft 6in) lengths. It is available in a variety of sizes to fit piping from 15mm (1⁄2in) to 35mm (1 1⁄2in) in diameter. The thickness of the insulating foam is generally around 12mm (1⁄2in). Make sure that you buy the right size sleeve for your pipes – if the sleeves don't fit snugly round your pipework they won't provide satisfactory insulation.

# INSULATING PIPEWORK

**1** *Start by wrapping the bandage twice round the end of the pipe next to the tank. Hold the turns in place securely with string or tape.*

**2** *Wrap the bandage round the pipe in a spiral. Make sure that each turn overlaps the previous one by at least 10mm ($^{3}/_{8}$in). Don't pull the bandage too tight.*

**3** *Whenever you finish a roll of bandage and start a new one allow a generous overlap to prevent air circulating between the turns of the join.*

**4** *Finish off the pipe in the same way that you started, with an extra turn of bandage. Lastly, check the pipe to make sure all the insulation is secure.*

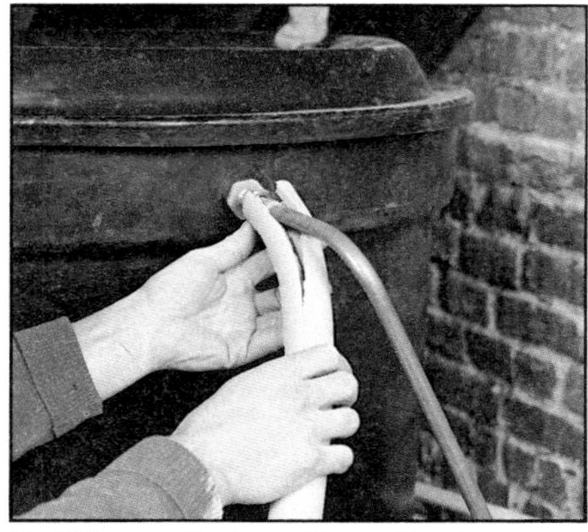

**5** *Fitting split-sleeve insulation is simple. You just prise apart the split and slip the sleeve over the pipe. Use tape to keep the sleeve in place.*

**6** *At bends, where the sleeve tends to come apart, tape the split lengthways. Tape the sleeves, too, whenever you join one to another.*

**7** *At tees, first cut a 'notch' from the main pipe sleeve. Then shape the end of the branch pipe sleeve to fit and slot it into place. Tape the join.*

**8** *Use split sleeve insulation on pipes that would be hard – or impossible – to fit with bandage. Slip the sleeve over the pipe and slide it into position.*

**9** *Sleeve and bandage insulation can – and sometimes must – be used together. A stop-valve, for example, can only be properly lagged with bandage.*

## INSULATING COLD TANKS

**1** *Proprietary jackets will fit most cold water tanks. Start by flopping the jacket over the tank and pulling it roughly into position.*

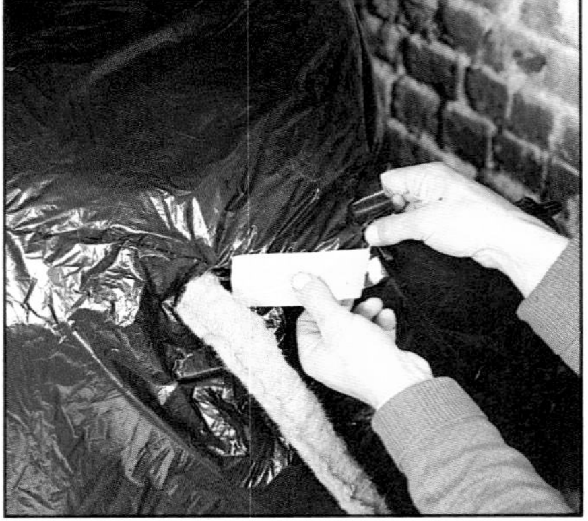

**2** *Rather than cut into the jacket's 'envelopes', try to accommodate a pipe by parting the seam between them. All cuts must be sealed with tape.*

**3** *When installing blanket insulation start with the side of the tank. If you're using glass fibre blanket wear gloves and a face mask.*

**5** *The tank must have a firm lid to prevent the water inside being polluted. Don't tie the lagging to the lid in such a way that it is impossible to undo.*

**6** *Expansion tanks need insulating too. If using sheet polystyrene, remember to cut the panels so that their ends overlap when fitted to the tank.*

**7** *Use tape, string, or glue to hold the side panels together. Fill the gaps left as a result of making cut-outs with wedges of waste polystyrene.*

Both flexible and rigid sleeves are available, but as the rigid type isn't much use for pipework that bends frequently, you'd probably be better off using the flexible variety.

Fitting the sleeves is very straightforward. You simply prise apart the slit that runs along the length of the sleeve and slip the insulation over the pipe. It's advisable to tape the sleeve at intervals, and you must do so at joins. At bends, where the sleeves will tend to come apart, you should tape the split lengthways.

Once sleeve insulation has been fitted, it can easily be slid along a length of pipe to protect a part of it that may be hard to get at. However, you should bear in mind that it won't be able to get beyond any pipe clips, very sharp bends or bulky joints it may encounter. You'll find that most flexible sleeves will readily slide round curves and even 90° bends made using soldered fittings, but whenever you run up against problems in the form of bulky compression elbows or tee connectors the sleeves will have to be cut accordingly. However, in some circumstances you might well find that bandage insulation provides the better solution.

To fit round a 90° elbow the sleeve should be cut in two and the sleeve ends then cut at an angle of 45° before being slipped over the pipe. You should then tape over the resulting join. For the most convenient method of dealing with a tee fitting see the step-by-step photographs.

### Insulating cold water storage tanks

When it comes to insulating your cold water storage tank and central heating expansion tank (if you have one), there are a number of options open to you. If your tank is circular you could cover it with a proprietary jacket consisting of a number of polythene or plastic 'envelopes' filled with insulant; or you could simply wrap it up in a layer of mineral wool or glass fibre blanket similar to – or even the same as – that which is used to insulate loft floors. If, on the other hand, your cold water tank happens to be rectangular then you could construct a 'box' for it yourself out of expanded polystyrene, or buy a proprietary one ready-made.

A proprietary jacket couldn't be easier to fit: you simply pull it into position and then tie it in place – tapes are sometimes provided by the manufacturer. If you have to cut into the jacket to accommodate a pipe, make sure that you seal it up again with plastic adhesive tape to prevent moisture getting in and the insulating material from escaping.

Expanded polystyrene kits are also extremely easy to fit. Apart from having to fix the pieces of polystyrene together with tape, string or polystyrene cement, the only work you will have to do is to make cut-outs for the pipework. More work will be required should you decide to make your tank kit out of sheet polystyrene (see step-by-step photographs)

*4 If the blanket isn't as wide as the tank is deep, a second layer, which should overlap the first, will be necessary. Use string to hold the blanket in place.*

*8 Make a lid for your tank by gluing together two panels of polystyrene. The smaller (inner) panel should just fit inside the tank.*

## HOT TANKS

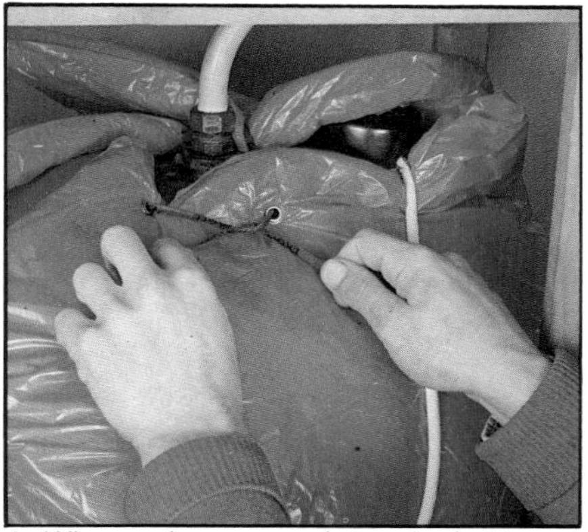

*1 When using a proprietary jacket to insulate a hot water cylinder, start by securing the polythene 'envelopes' round the hot water supply pipe.*

*2 The sides of the jacket are held in place with straps. Take care not to cover the capping and wiring of any immersion heater.*

## Ready Reference

### SLEEVING SIZES

To be effective, split-sleeve insulation must be the right size for your pipes. If they are modern – which usually means copper – most of your pipes will be 15mm (½in), though the main distribution ones are likely to be 22mm (¾in). Check any pipes that you aren't sure of.

### TIP: PROBLEM PIPES

There are two areas where you must take extra care:

- when insulating a pipe that runs close to a wall – especially an outside wall – make sure that you protect the *whole* surface. To insulate only the more accessible side of the pipe would be worse than useless: the pipe would still be exposed to the cold wall but denied the heat of your house
- if the expansion pipe of the cold water tank you are insulating stops short of the lid then you'll have to devise some means of catching any outflow. The easiest way to do this is to use a plastic funnel. Bore a hole to accommodate the funnel through the lid and the insulation material, and fix it in place with plastic adhesive tape.

### TIP: GOING AWAY

Insulation alone may not be sufficient to protect your pipes and tanks from the cold if you leave your house unoccupied for more than a few days in winter. So in your absence make sure that the heating is switched on briefly each day. If you can't trust your thermostat, ask a neighbour.

– but it would of course be a lot cheaper.

If you decide to use insulation blanket to lag your tank then try to buy the sort that is bonded with paper as you will find it much easier to handle. Buy a roll that is as wide as your tank is deep if you can, as this will save you the trouble of having to go round the side of your tank twice. The thickness of the blanket isn't critical, but blanket 50mm (2in) thick will give your tank adequate insulation and be easier to work with than a thicker one. However, it could well be that you have an odd roll or two of blanket left over from some previous insulation job; if you do, then use that rather than going to the expense of buying additional rolls.

The top of the tank to be insulated must have a firm covering to prevent the water inside being contaminated by fibres from the blanket you are fitting. So if it doesn't already have a lid, cut one out of hardboard, polystyrene or some other sheet material.

Lagging a tank with blanket insulation is simply a matter of common sense. You cut the blanket to size, drape it round the side of the tank, and having cut slits to enable the blanket to fit round the pipes, secure it with string. The lagging on the lid should overlap the side lagging by about 150mm (6in); and as you'll need to inspect the inside of your tank from time to time make sure it's easily removable.

Under normal circumstances the bottom of your tank should not be insulated, nor should the loft floor directly below. The reason for this is that it allows heat from the house to rise up through the floor and slightly increase the temperature of your cold water. The only circumstance in which you do insulate these places (and this applies regardless of what form of insulation you are using) is when, in order to increase the water pressure for a shower on the floor below, the tank has been raised more than a foot or so above the joists.

### Insulating hot water tanks

Although you could in theory lag your hot water tank by adapting any of the methods that are used for cold water tanks, in practice you will nearly always find that you have no choice but to use a proprietary jacket. The fact that most hot water tanks are situated in airing cupboards means that blanket insulation is out of the question, and unless your tank is a rectangular one (which these days are very rare) you won't be able to use polystyrene.

Proprietary jackets for hot water tanks are made of the same materials as those used on cold water tanks and are just as easy to fit. The system used to fasten the jacket to the tank varies, but basically at the top you secure the 'envelopes' round the hot water supply pipe with a loop of cord, while further down you hold them in place with straps. The base of the tank is left uninsulated, as is the capping and wiring of any immersion heater.

# CLEARING BLOCKAGES

**There are few plumbing emergencies quite as unpleasant as a blocked drain or waste pipe. However, it's usually possible to cure the problem if you know what to do when you've tracked down the blockage and you have the right equipment.**

Professional plumbers rarely relish being called out to deal with a blockage. There *are* specialist drain clearance firms, but they can't always be contacted quickly in an emergency – and their charges reflect what can sometimes be the unpleasantness of the job. Drain or waste-pipe clearance is usually well within the capacity of the householder, and there are certainly few more cost-effective do-it-yourself jobs about the house.

## Coping with blocked sinks

The outlet of the sink, usually the trap immediately beneath the sink itself, is the commonest site of waste-pipe blockage. Usually the obstruction can be cleared quickly and easily by means of a sink-waste plunger or force cup. This is a very simple plumbing tool obtainable from any do-it-yourself shop, ironmongers or household store. It consists of a rubber or plastic hemisphere, usually mounted on a wooden or plastic handle. Every household should have one.

To use it to clear a sink waste blockage, first press a damp cloth firmly into the overflow outlet, holding it securely with one hand. Then pull out the plug and lower the plunger into the flooded sink so that the cup is positioned over the waste outlet. Plunge it up and down sharply half a dozen or more times. Since water cannot be compressed, the water in the waste between the cup and the obstruction is converted into a ram to clear the blockage. The overflow outlet is sealed to prevent the force being dissipated up the overflow.

If your first efforts at plunging are unsuccessful, persevere. Each thrust may be moving the obstruction a little further along the waste pipe until it is discharged into the drain gully or the main soil and waste stack.

Should plunging prove unsuccessful you'll have to gain access to the trap. Brass and lead U-shaped traps have a screwed-in plug at the base. With plastic U-shaped and bottle traps the lower part can be unscrewed and removed – see *Ready Reference*. Before attempting this, put the plug in the sink and place a bucket under the trap; it will probably be full of water unless the blockage is immediately below the sink

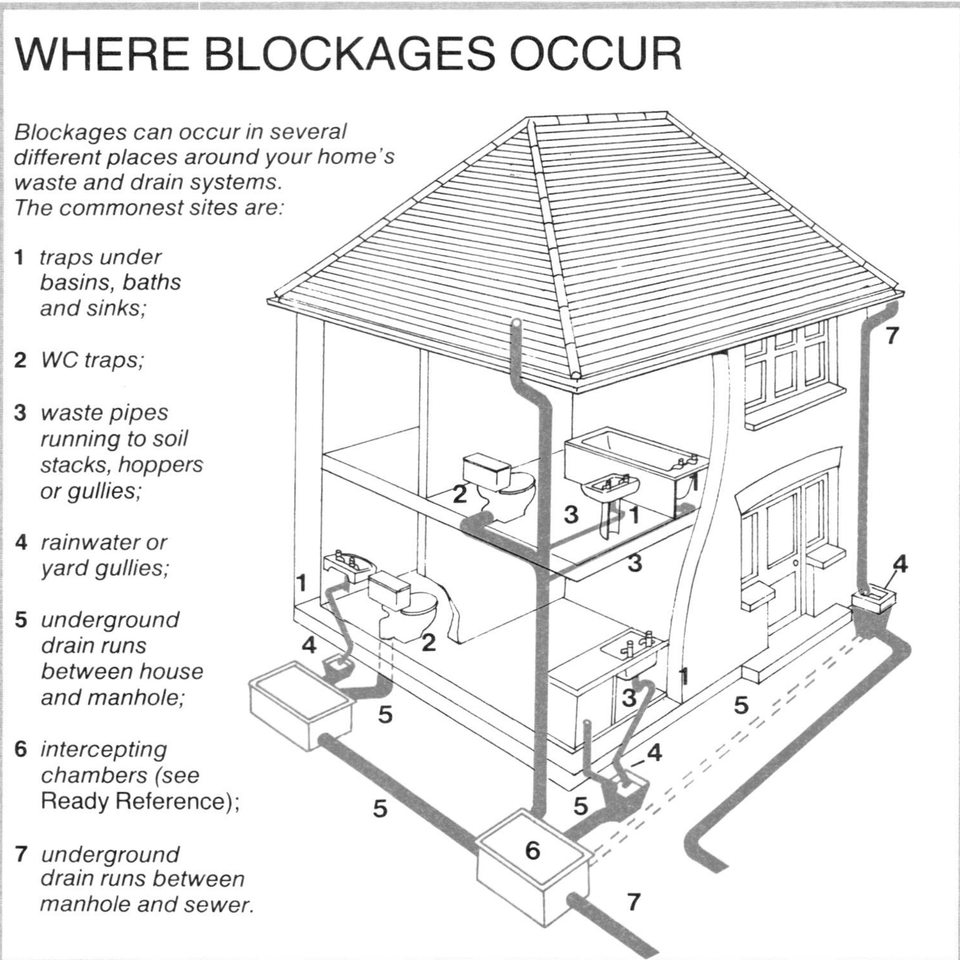

## WHERE BLOCKAGES OCCUR

*Blockages can occur in several different places around your home's waste and drain systems. The commonest sites are:*

**1** *traps under basins, baths and sinks;*

**2** *WC traps;*

**3** *waste pipes running to soil stacks, hoppers or gullies;*

**4** *rainwater or yard gullies;*

**5** *underground drain runs between house and manhole;*

**6** *intercepting chambers (see* Ready Reference*);*

**7** *underground drain runs between manhole and sewer.*

# CLEARING BLOCKED TRAPS

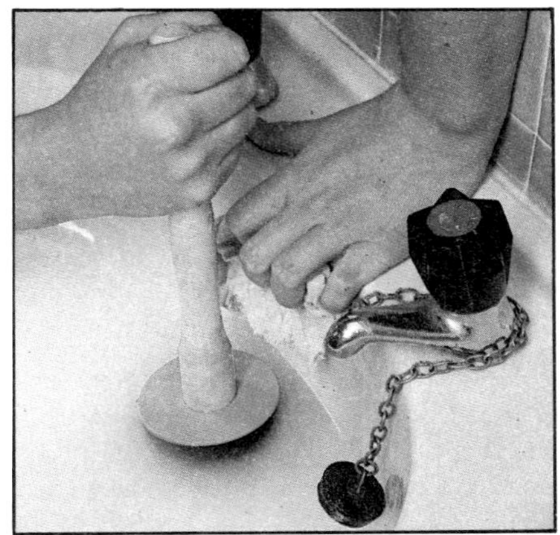

*1 Try using a plunger to clear blocked sinks, basins, baths or WCs. Cover the overflow with a damp cloth, then push the plunger down sharply several times.*

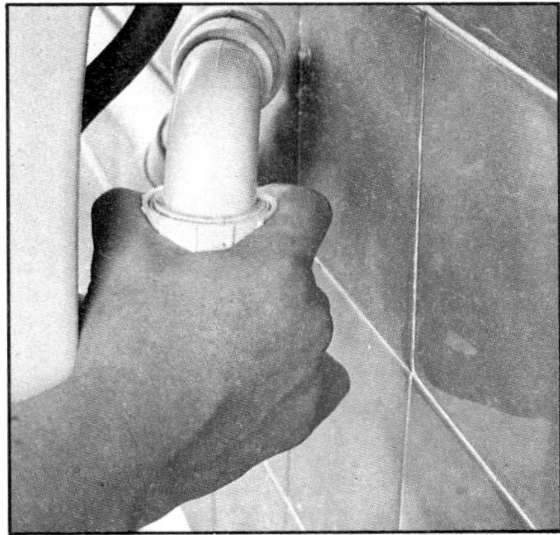

*2 If the blockage persists, you will have to open up the trap. Put the plug in the basin and have a bucket handy to catch the trap contents.*

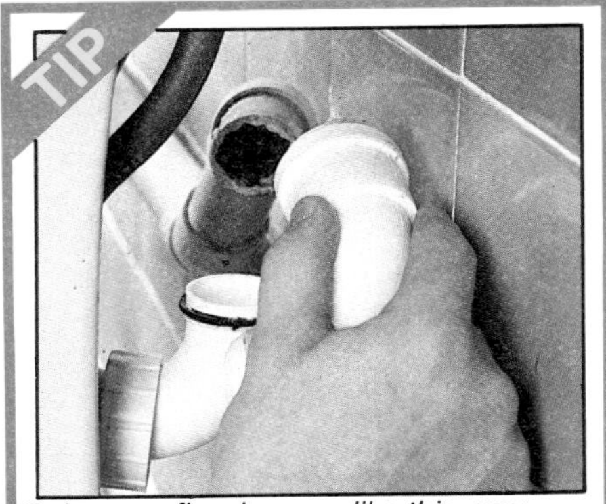


*3 In a confined space like this, you may find it easier to remove the next push-fit elbow before tackling the connection to the waste outlet itself.*

*4 With the trap fully dismantled, wash each component thoroughly to remove the blockage and any scum clinging to the pipe sides. Leave the plug in.*

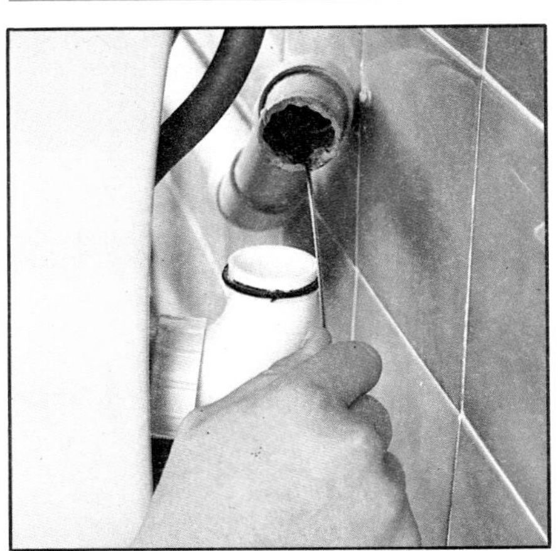

*5 Before reassembling the trap fully, check that the next section of the waste pipe is clear by poking a length of wire down it as far as you can reach.*

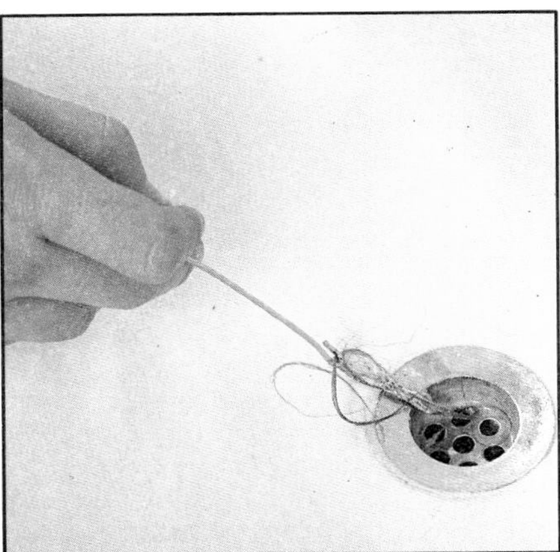

*6 A build-up of hair and scum can often block basin wastes just below the outlet. Fish out as much as possible with a slim wire hook passed through the grating.*

## Ready Reference

### TYPES OF TRAP

On old plumbing systems you may still come across lead traps, which have a removable rodding eye in the base. On more modern systems plastic traps will have been installed, and it is easy to unscrew part of the trap to clear a blockage.

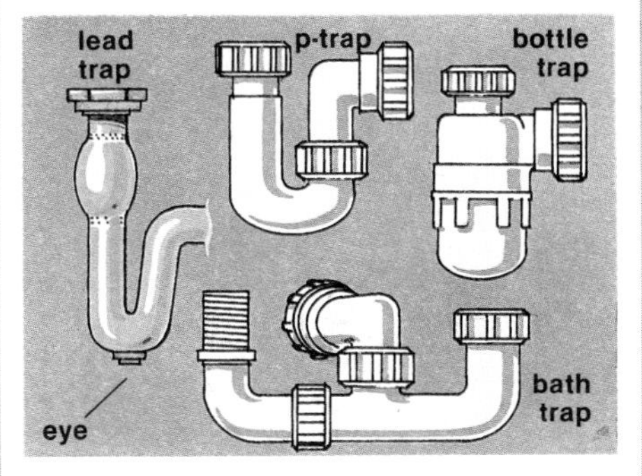


### TIP: SUPPORT LEAD TRAPS

Lead traps are very soft, and may bend or split if you use force to open the rodding eye. To avoid this:

- insert a piece of scrap wood into the U-bend of the trap
- undo the rodding eye with a spanner, turning it in the direction shown while bracing the trap with the scrap wood
- reverse the procedure to replace it.

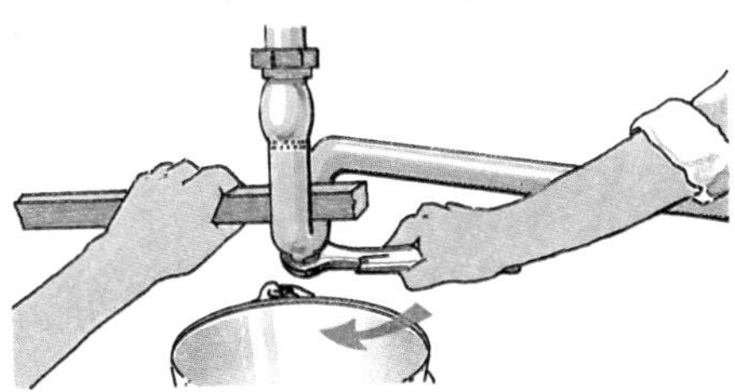

### RODDING INTERCEPTING TRAPS

The manhole nearest the main sewer may be an intercepting trap, designed to keep sewer gases out of the house drains. To clear a blockage between it and the sewer,

feed your rods into the rodding arm. To prevent the stoneware plug from being dislodged and causing a blockage, cement a glass disc in its place.

outlet, and the chances are that opening the trap will release it. Having done so, probe into the trap, and into the waste pipe itself. You can buy purpose-made sink waste augers for this purpose, but you'll find that a piece of expanding curtain wire, with a hook on the end, can be equally effective.

### Blocked baths and basins

Basin and bath wastes are less likely to be totally blocked than sink wastes but, when blockages do occur, they can usually be cleared in the same way. They are, however, very subject to partial blockage. The waste water is often found to run from the bath or basin ever more slowly. This may be due to a build-up of scum, scale and hair on the inside of the waste pipe, and the use of a proprietary drain-clearing chemical will usually clear it. These frequently have a caustic soda base, so they should be kept away from children and handled with care, strictly in accordance with the manufacturer's instructions. Before spooning them into the bath or basin waste outlet it is wise to smear petroleum jelly over the rim of the outlet to protect the chromium finish, especially with plastic baths or fittings.

Partial blockage of a wash basin waste may often be caused by hair suspended from the grid of the outlet. This may be all but invisible from above, but probing with a piece of wire (the old standby of a straightened-out wire coathanger is useful) can often produce festoons. If you can't clear the hair by this means, unscrew the nut that connects the threaded waste outlet to the trap and pull the trap to one side. Now use a pair of pliers to pull the hair away from beneath the grid.

### Overflows from gullies

Where waste pipes and downpipes discharge into gullies, the first signs of trouble may be when the gully overflows and the surrounding area is flooded as a result. The gully trap has probably become blocked, either by blown leaves or other debris, or by a build-up of grease and scum on the sides of the trap. Raise the gully grid if one is fitted (and get a new one if it's broken or missing). Then scoop out any debris with a rubber-gloved hand or an improvised scoop, scrub the gully out with caustic soda and flush it through with plenty of clean water before replacing the grid.

### Blockages below ground

A blockage in the underground drains may be shown up by a WC which, when flushed, fills with water almost to the rim and then very slowly subsides, or by dirty water seeping from under a manhole cover. You'll need a set of drain rods to clear any underground blockage. It is best to hire these from a local tool hire firm if and when the emergency arises. A drain that blocks sufficiently frequently to justify the purchase of a set of rods undoubtedly has a major defect that needs professional advice and attention.

Raising the manhole covers will give you an indication of the position of the blockage. If, for instance, the manhole near your front boundary is empty, but the one beside the house into which the soil pipe and yard gully discharges is flooded, then the blockage must be between these two manholes. Screw two or three lengths of drain-rod together, add the appropriate accessory to one end and then lower it into the flooded manhole. Feel for the drain half-channel at its base and push the rod end along it and into the drain towards the obstruction. Screw on extra rods as necessary until you reach and clear the blockage. You may find it easier to push the rods into the drain – and to extract them again – if you twist them as you do so. *Always* twist in a clockwise direction. If you twist anti-clockwise the rods will unscrew and one or more lengths will be left irretrievably in the drain.

Many older houses have intercepting traps. These traps, which were intended to keep sewer gases out of the house drains, are the commonest site of drain blockage. You can see if your drains have an intercepting trap by raising the cover of the manhole nearest to your property boundary before trouble occurs and looking inside. If there is an intercepting trap the half-channel of the gully will fall into what appears to be a hole at the end of the manhole; actually it is the inlet to the trap. Immediately above this hole will be a stoneware stopper. This closes the rodding arm giving access to the length of drain between the intercepting trap and the sewer.

A blockage in the intercepting trap is

## CLEARING BLOCKED GULLIES

**1** *Both surface-water and yard gullies are easily blocked by wind-blown debris such as waste paper and dead leaves. First lift off the gully grating.*

**2** *Try to scoop out as much debris as possible from the gully trap, either by hand or with an improvised scoop such as an old tin can.*

**3** *If the blockage is cleared and the water flows away, scrub out the sides of the gully with detergent or caustic soda. Clean the gully grating too.*

**4** *Finally, hose the gully out thoroughly with running water. If you are unable to clear the blockage, you may have to rod the drain run from a nearby manhole.*

## RODDING BLOCKED DRAINS

*1 Raise manhole covers carefully. If the hand grips are missing, use an old brick bolster to lift one edge, and then slide in a piece of wood.*

*2 With the wood supporting one end of the cover, grasp it securely and lift it to one side. Bend from the knees so you don't strain your back.*

*3 Select one of the drain rod heads (a rubber disc is being fitted here) and screw it securely onto the threaded end of the first drain rod.*

*4 Screw a second rod onto the end of the first, and lower the head into the half-channel in the bottom of the chamber. Push the rods towards the blockage.*

*5 Screw on further rods as necessary and work the head in and out to clear the blockage. Never turn the rods anticlockwise, or they may unscrew and be lost.*

*6 When you have cleared the blockage, hose down the sides and base of the manhole with running water, and let water run through the drain for a while.*

indicated when all the drain inspection chambers are flooded. It can usually be cleared quite easily by plunging. To do this, screw a drain plunger (a 100mm or 4in diameter rubber disc) onto the end of a drain rod. Screw on one or two other rods as necessary and lower the plunger into the flooded manhole. Feel for the half-channel at its base and move the plunger along until you reach the inlet of the intercepting trap. Plunge down sharply three or four times and, unless you are very unlucky, there will be a gurgle and the water level in the manhole will quickly fall.

Very occasionally, there may be a blockage between the intercepting trap and the sewer, and the point must be made that this length of drain is the householder's responsibility, even though much of it may lie under the public highway. To clear such a blockage the stoneware cap must be knocked out of the inlet to the rodding arm (this can be done with the drain rods but it isn't the easiest of jobs) and the rods passed down the rodding arm towards the sewer.

Intercepting traps are also subject to a kind of partial blockage that may go unnoticed for weeks or even months. An increase in pressure on the sewer side of the trap – due to a surge of storm water, for instance – may push the stopper out of the rodding arm. It will fall into the trap below and cause an almost immediate stoppage. However this will not be noticed because sewage will now be able to escape down the open rodding arm to the sewer. The householder usually becomes aware of a partial blockage of this kind as a result of an unpleasant smell, caused by the decomposition of the sewage in the base of the manhole.

The remedy is, of course, to remove the stopper and to replace it. Where the trouble recurs it is best to discard the stopper and to lightly cement a glass or slate disc in its place. In the very unusual event of a stoppage between the intercepting trap and the sewer, this disc can be broken with a crowbar and replaced after the drain has been cleared – see *Ready Reference*.

After any drain clearance the manhole walls should be washed down with a hot soda solution and a garden hose should be used to flush the drain through thoroughly.

### Blocked gutters

Roof rainwater gutters may become obstructed by leaves or other objects. An overflowing gutter isn't an instant catastrophe but, if neglected, it will cause dampness to the house walls. An inspection, removal of debris and a hose down of gutters should be a routine part of every householder's preparations for winter.

# EMERGENCY PIPE REPAIRS

**A leaking pipe is no joke. First you have to stop the water – so you need to know where to turn if off – and then to make some kind of emergency repair, even if it's just a holding operation.**

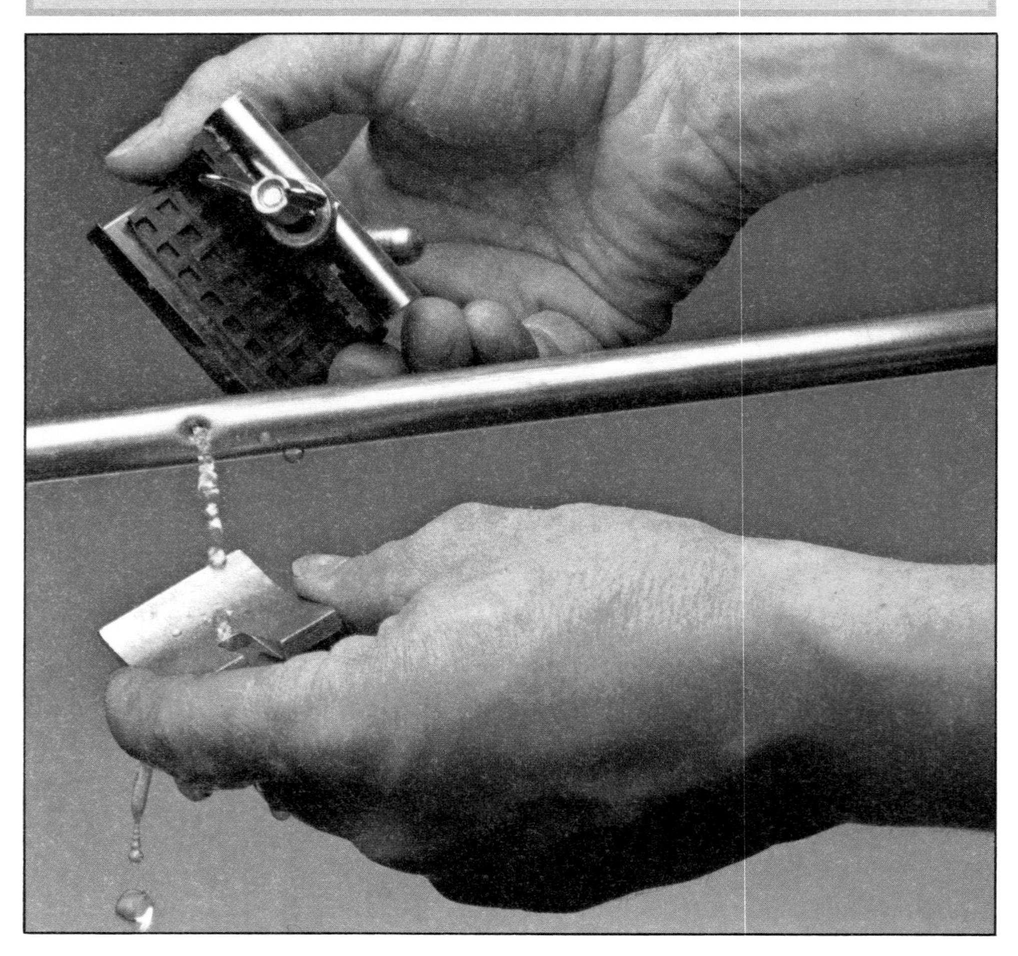

Leaks in domestic plumbing systems have a nasty habit of happening at the most inconvenient of times, often when it isn't possible to carry out a proper permanent repair. What you need is a plumbing emergency first aid kit, and there are now several proprietary products available that will at least enable you to make a temporary repair and get the water flowing again.

With any leak, the vital first step is to stop the flow of water. Even a small leak can create a surprisingly large pool of water in no time. Stopping the flow in any pipe is relatively easy provided that you know the locations of the various stop-taps or valves that isolate parts of your water system, or cut it off completely from the mains supply.

Water comes into the house through a pipe known as the rising main, and because water in this pipe (and others leading from it) is under mains pressure, leaks from it will be particularly serious. It enters the house underground, and from there leads either to all the cold taps and a water heating system, or to just the cold tap in the kitchen and to a cold water storage tank.

Leaks can result from a number of causes. Pipework may have been forced or strained at some point, resulting in a leak at one of the fittings connecting the lengths of pipe together, or in a fracture at a bend.

Corrosion within pipes may lead to pinholes in pipe lengths, while frost damage can lead to bursts and splits in pipes and to leaks at fittings caused by ice forcing the fitting open. Whatever the cause, cutting off the water supply to the affected pipe is the first vital step.

## Where to turn off the water

**1 Cold water supply pipes connected directly to the mains:** in the UK these pipes usually only supply the kitchen cold tap, the cold water storage tank and sometimes instantaneous water heaters. In many other countries, the pipes may supply *all* cold water taps and the hot water storage cylinder. The simple way of deciding whether any pipe or tap is supplied directly by the mains is by the pressure – taps supplied from a tank are what's known as gravity-fed and the pressure of water is relatively low compared to mains pressure.

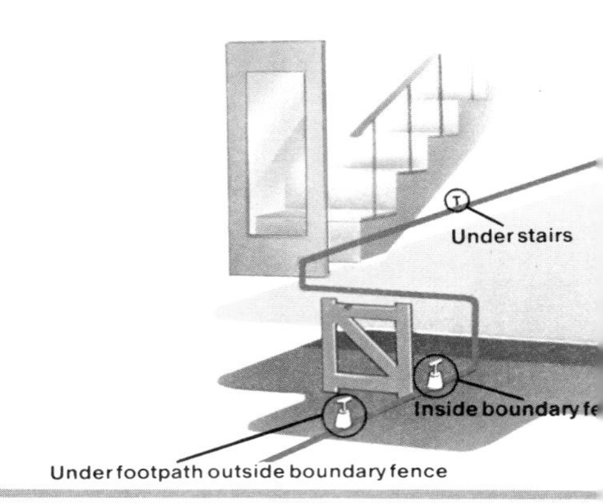


**2 Cold water supply pipes from a cold water storage tank:** in the UK these pipes usually supply the bathroom cold taps, the WC cistern and the hot water cylinder.

To close off the water supply in these pipes there's often a stop-valve immediately alongside the cold water tank where the pipe exits. Turn this off first and then open all cold water taps. They'll run dry almost immediately. If there isn't a stop-valve, you have to drain the whole tank. So first you stop water entering the tank by either turning off the mains (as above) or by tying up the ball-valve in the tank so that it remains closed. Then you open all the taps in the house.

**3 Hot water pipes:** these are all supplied from a hot water cylinder, which in turn gets its cold water either from the cold tank or from the mains.

Since hot water leaves the hot water storage cylinder from the top, it's only the pressure of water going in at the bottom of the cylinder that forces the water out. Turn off the supply of cold water (either at the cold water tank, or at the mains) and you stop the flow. In this sort of situation the hot water cylinder remains full. If for any reason you need to drain this as well, use the drain cock near the bottom. It's essential in this case to turn off either the immersion heater or boiler.

To turn off the water, look for the mains stop-valves. There may, in fact, be two: one inside the house where the mains pipe enters (under the kitchen sink, in the utility room, or even under the stairs); the other outside – either just inside the boundary of the property (near to a water meter, if you have one), or under the footpath outside the garden fence. Outdoor stop-valves may be set as much as a metre (3 ft) down beneath a hinged cover or metal plate, and you may need a special 'key' which is really just a long rod with a square socket on the end which fits over the tap to turn it. In most cases, however, it's simply a matter of reaching down to turn it off by hand or with a wrench. Some outdoor stop-valves also control a neighbour's water supply, so do warn them if you're turning it off.

The stop-valve inside will either be a wheel type or an ordinary T-shaped type. The only possible complication is if it hasn't been touched for years and is stuck fast. A little penetrating oil and tapping it with a hammer will usually loosen it sufficiently. (It's worth closing the stop-valve now and again to see that it doesn't get stuck.)

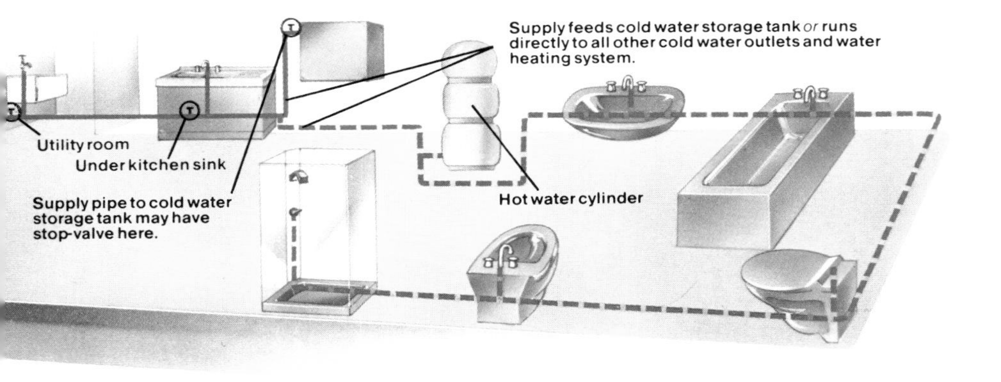


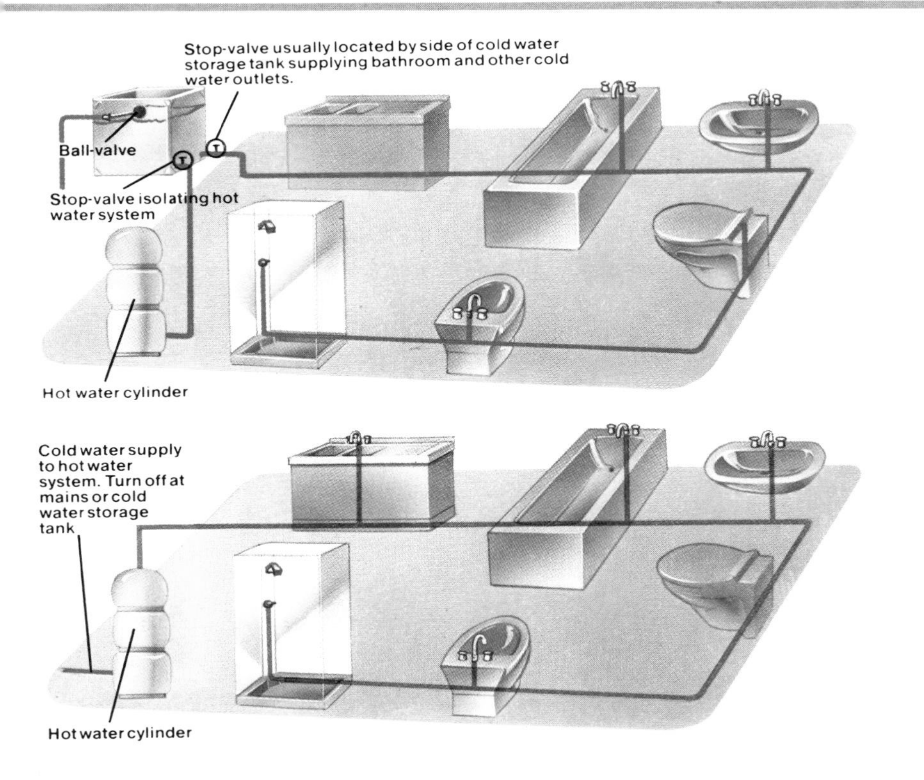


## Ready Reference

### TURNING OFF THE STOP TAP

Make sure the family knows where the mains stop tap is.

- do not force the handle if it has seized up – it could break off
- use a hammer or wrench to tap the fitting while pouring penetrating oil down spindle.
- if you can't free it call the water authority emergency service — they can turn the water off where your supply pipe leaves the mains.
- don't reopen stop valve fully when turning on the supply until a permanent pipe repair is made. This reduces water pressure on a temporary seal.

### TIP: MAKESHIFT REPAIRS

If you don't have the right materials to hand (see next page) try this:

- bandage insulating tape round the pipe and hole
- cover with a 150mm (6in) piece of garden hosepipe slit along its length and tie with wire at each end, twisting ends of wire together with pliers
- wrap more tape tightly over this

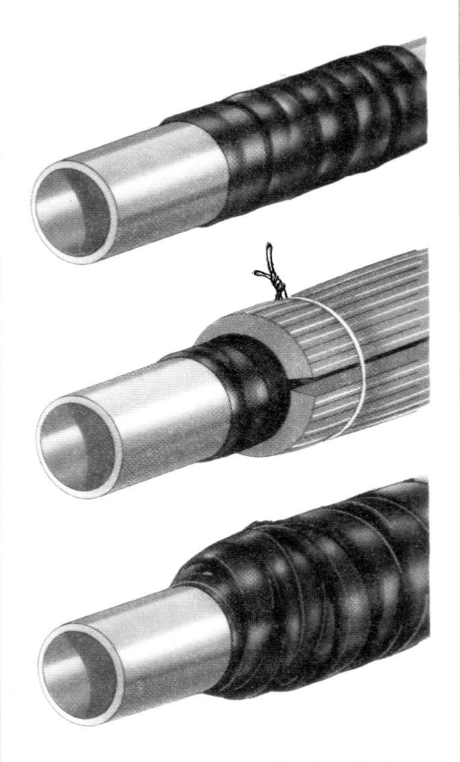

**For permanent repairs of leaks at joints in copper pipe see pages 20 to 24.**

# EMERGENCY REPAIRS

● One type of repair kit is based on a two-part **epoxy resin plastic putty** supplied as two strips of differently-coloured putty in an airtight pack. When the strips are thoroughly kneaded together the putty is packed firmly round the pipe, where it will harden to form a seal. However, this hardening process takes up to 24 hours and the water supply will have to remain off for this period. (If you don't need to use all the pack in one go, reseal it immediately).

Equal amounts of putty should always be used and mixed together thoroughly until a uniform colour results, otherwise it won't harden properly. It's also essential that the pipe or joint is scrupulously rubbed down and cleaned with methylated spirit or nail polish remover. This will ensure a good bond between the putty and the metal.

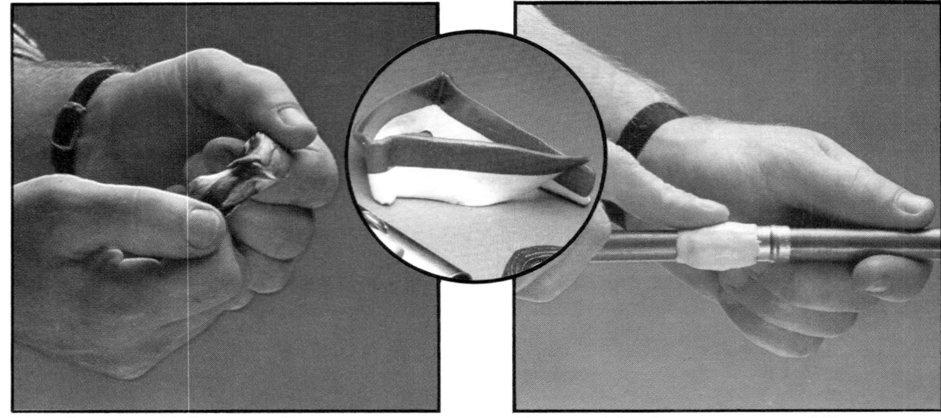

**Plastic putty** *Using your fingers, mix together equal amounts of the two putty strips. It's ready for use when the colour is even all through.*

*Thoroughly clean area round the leaking pipe, then pack putty round fitting. It can be sanded smooth when it's completely hard.*

● One of the most valuable aids is a multi-size **pipe repair clamp** which has the added advantage of being reusable. It consists of a rubber pad which fits over the hole (for this repair it's not necessary to turn off the water) and a metal clamp which draws the rubber tightly against the pipe when it is screwed in place.

Position the pad and one side of the clamp over the hole, and link the two parts of the clamp together, making sure that the pad is still in place. Tighten the wing nut fully. If the position of the hole makes this difficult, use blocks of wood to hold the pipe away from the wall. This method of repair cannot, of course, be used to mend leaks occurring at fittings.

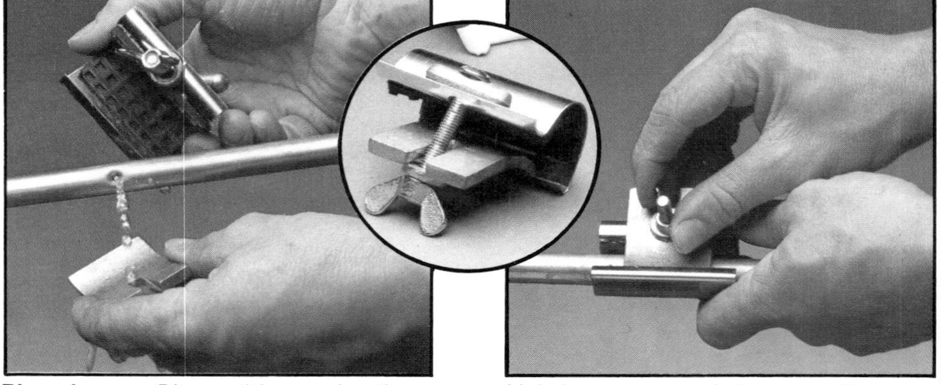

**Pipe clamp** *Place rubber pad and one side of metal clamp directly over leak in pipe. There's no need to turn off the water with this type of repair.*

*Link the two parts of clamp together, being careful to keep it in position. Screw down wing nut to secure rubber pad against pipe.*

● Another proprietary product uses a two-part **sticky tape** system which builds up waterproof layers over the leak — in the true sense this does form an instant repair. The area round the leak should be dried and cleaned and then the first of the tapes is wrapped tightly round the pipe, covering the leak and 25mm (1in) either side of it. Then 150mm (6in) strips of the second tape, with the backing film removed, are stuck to the pipe and stretched as they are wound round, each turn overlapping the previous one by about half the width of the tape. This covering should extend 25mm (1in) beyond either end of the first layer of tape. The job is completed by wrapping the first tape over all the repair.

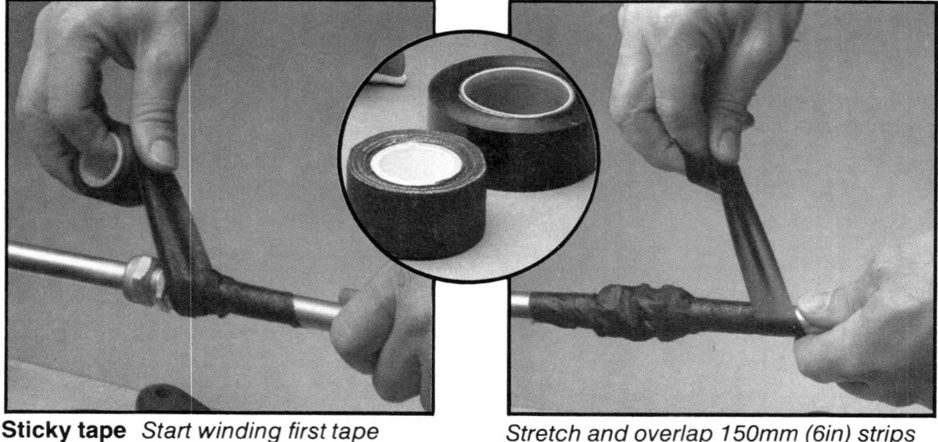

**Sticky tape** *Start winding first tape round pipe about 25mm (1in) from the leaking fitting. Continue over the joint and for 25mm on other side.*

*Stretch and overlap 150mm (6in) strips of second tape round pipe. Continue 25mm (1in) either side of first tape. Finish off with layer of first tape.*

## CHAPTER 4

# PLUMBING JOBS IN THE KITCHEN

**Water is essential in the kitchen – for drinking, food preparation, washing cooking utensils and crockery and in many homes for washing clothes, too, unless there is a separate laundry room.**

# INSTALLING A SINK UNIT

**The sink is a highly important item of kitchen equipment, and replacing an old model is usually one of the first priorities for anyone modernising their kitchen. In this article we consider the range available and how to fit them.**

If your house was built in the 1930s or 1940s, and the kitchen has never been modernised, the chances are that it contains the original deep white glazed stoneware 'Belfast pattern' sink, supported by heavy cast-iron brackets built into the wall. It will incorporate a weir overflow and will probably have a detachable wooden draining board. A deep sink of this kind was regarded as the height of domestic luxury in the pre-war and early post-war years. An even older property might have a shallow yellow 'London pattern' sink, probably supported by brick pillars. In either case the water will very likely come from brass bib-taps (taps with horizontal inlets) projecting from a tiled splash-back fixed to the wall behind the sink. Old London pattern sinks were sometimes installed with an untrapped waste that passed through the kitchen wall to discharge over an outside gully drain. More recent sinks would have a lead or brass U-trap screwed to the waste outlet from which a branch waste pipe would discharge over the gully.

## Sink units

Because these old stoneware sinks were certain death to crockery dropped into them, and looked increasingly dated, they were gradually replaced by sink units with one-piece sink tops. The sink tops were made of enamelled pressed steel or stainless steel, and the units into which they were fixed became the starting point for complete kitchen ranges incorporating continuous work surfaces. The early enamelled pressed steel sink tops had the disadvantage that the enamel was vulnerable to accidental damage. Dropping any hard object onto them could easily chip or crack the enamel. The stainless steel sink therefore became the most important innovation.

## Taps and traps

It was usual, when replacing an old stoneware sink with a stainless steel or an enamelled pressed-steel sink, to get rid of the old bib-taps projecting from the wall, and to replace them with chromium-plated brass pillar taps or a mixer fitted into the

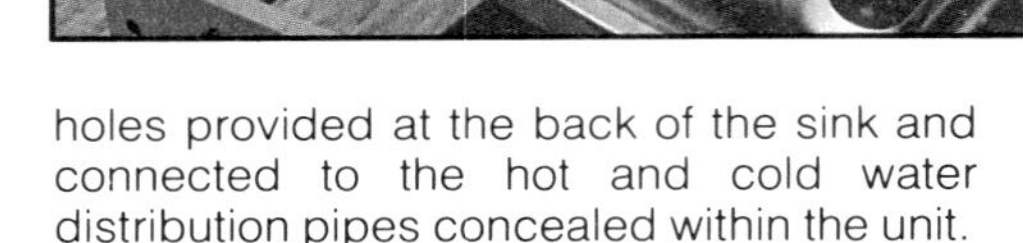

holes provided at the back of the sink and connected to the hot and cold water distribution pipes concealed within the unit.

Early sinks of this kind were provided with traps, also concealed within the unit. The trap might still be of brass with a copper waste pipe, but plastic was soon introduced, connected to a plastic waste pipe by means of ring-seal push-fit connectors. Bottle traps, as distinct from the traditional U-traps, became increasingly popular. They were neater in appearance, space saving and easy to dismantle in case of a blockage, although their discharge rate was not as great. Modern ground floor sinks often still discharge over a yard gully, but the waste pipe outlet should be taken to below the gully grid either through a slotted grid or by the use of a back or side-inlet gully.

## Overflows

Early sink tops had a built-in overflow consisting of a unit welded to the back of the sink. But these inevitably leaked after a time, and nowadays they have been replaced by a flexible overflow pipe. This is like the overflow pipe from a bath which is taken from the sink's overflow outlet to connect, by means of a sleeve or 'banjo' fitting, to the slotted waste pipe, before its connection to the trap. Householders who possess a sink of the older pattern with a leaking built-in overflow, will find that if the sink is dismounted and turned upside down, the overflow unit can be sawn off and replaced with one of the more modern waste and overflow fittings. But, of course, it may be better to replace the the sink.

## New developments

Nowadays, there is no question of being restricted to a single sink with either right or left-hand drainer. Double sinks, one for washing the crockery and cutlery and the other for a hot rinse before air drying, have become more and more popular. The two sinks may be of equal size, around 450mm (18in) in width, or one may be smaller than the other for use in food preparation. A second sink like this might be only 240mm (10in) in width. There are also sinks with double drainers, though these are rather less in demand as they take up a lot of space; they are usually around 2m (6ft 6in) long. Overall sizes of rectangular sinks and drainer units range from about 900mm (3ft) to 1500mm (5ft) in length, and usually measure 500 or 600mm (20 to 24in) deep, to fit metric base units. Some sink tops are still available in the 21in (533mm) size to match old imperial base units. There are also many intermediate sizes, and bowl depths may range between 130 and 180mm (5 and 7in).

Early glass-reinforced plastic sink tops and drainers proved to be a complete disaster. They were incapable of standing up to the very heavy use to which sinks are subjected, their colours faded and they cracked, and crazed. Considerable advances have since been made, and modern plastic sinks and sink tops seem well able to stand up to everything that is required of them.

Ceramic sinks are making a come back, though they are very different from the old Belfast and London pattern sinks. Modern ranges include tough inset sinks and tops in an attractive range of colours. There are inset round bowls 450mm (18in) in diameter with an accompanying but separate round drainer 380mm (15in) in diameter. Then there is a conventional rectangular double sink and drainer – all of ceramic ware – in an overall size of 1125 x 505mm (45 x 20in). There is also a conventional rectangular single sink and drainer and round double sinks and drainer in one unit. A feature of these new ceramic units is their extreme toughness.

The waste and overflow of the new ceramic sinks are arranged in exactly the same way as those of the old Belfast models. A built-in overflow connects to the slot in a slotted waste outlet that is bedded on mastic in the outlet hole. Stainless steel sinks are provided with the flexible overflow already referred to, which connects to the slotted waste below the sink but above the trap. Double sinks have only one trap. This is fitted into the outlet of the sink nearest to the drain outlet, the waste from the other sink being connected to it above the level of the single trap.

### Mixers

Individual sink pillar taps are still freely available, but the choice nowadays is more likely to be a sink mixer. A mixer with a swivel spout is an essential where a double sink is installed.

Sink mixers differ from bath and basin mixers in one important respect. The latter are simply two taps with a single spout. The hot and cold streams of water mix within the body of the mixer unit. Sink mixers have separate channels for the hot and cold streams of water which mix in the air as they leave the spout. The reason for this is that the cold water supply to the kitchen sink (the household's supply of water for drinking and cooking) comes direct from the rising main. The hot supply usually comes from a cylinder storage hot water system, fed with water from a main cold water storage cistern. It is illegal to mix, in one fitting, water from the main and water from a storage cistern.

Everybody is familiar with the conventional sink mixer, made of chromium-plated brass with 'shrouded' cross-top handles of plastic and a long swivel spout. Nowadays, though, there are some exciting new designs available. With some the mixer unit is fitted into just one hole at the back of the sink. The other hole may be blanked off or may be used to accommodate a rinsing brush, supplied with hot water by a flexible tube connected to the hot water supply pipe.

### Putting in the sink top

When you come to install your new sink it's a good idea to make the first job fitting the taps or mixer, waste and overflow to it. This will avoid unnecessary interruption to the rest of the plumbing services. Start by putting in the combined waste and overflow unit, then attach the taps or mixer. If the sink is made of stainless steel the shanks of the taps will protrude through the holes so you won't be able to screw up the back-nuts tight. Use 'top hat' washers or spacers to accommodate the shanks.

When the sink is in position the tap tails will usually be fairly inaccessible, so it may be a good idea to attach purpose-made extension pieces to bring them to a level below the sink basin where they will be accessible.

When you've got the new sink top ready, you'll have to turn off the main stop-valve and drain the hot and cold water pipes which supply the existing sink. Then you can disconnect the waste outlet, and use a cold chisel and hammer to chip away any seal between the back of the sink and the wall. You can remove the old sink (remember, it's going to be very heavy) and saw off the heavy cantilevered brackets that supported the old sink flush with the wall.

The hot and cold water supply pipes to the bib-taps over the old sink will probably be chased (inset) into the wall, so you'll have to unscrew and remove the old taps, excavate the pipes from the wall and pull them forward so that they can be connected to the tails of new taps.

With the new sink unit in position, the next job is to cut the water supply pipes to the correct length to connect to the tails of the taps. The sink top simply rests on the sink unit, so the tails of the taps can now be connected to the water supply pipes. If the trap of the old sink will connect to the new waste it can be reused.

## Ready Reference

### TRADITIONAL SINKS

The traditional Belfast sink, made of fireclay and enamelled after baking is still sometimes installed, fixed on cantilevered brackets or on leg supports.

Most modern sinks are made of stainless steel, stamped out of sheet metal, which gives a functional, streamlined finish and is easy to clean. Modern sinks come as either sink tops or as inset sinks.

### SINK TOPS

Sink tops fit on top of a sink unit of the same size. While sink units started off as an alternative to the cantilevered support Belfast sink, they are now often made part of a work surface. As nearly all sink units are now designed on a modular basis, the sizes of sink tops correspond to the module sizes.

### INSET SINKS

An inset sink is inset into a continuous work surface into which an aperture has been cut or built. As they are not required to form the top of a kitchen unit they can be positioned with greater flexibility provided that there is sufficient space underneath for a bowl and plumbing pipes.

## THE PLUMBING CONNECTIONS

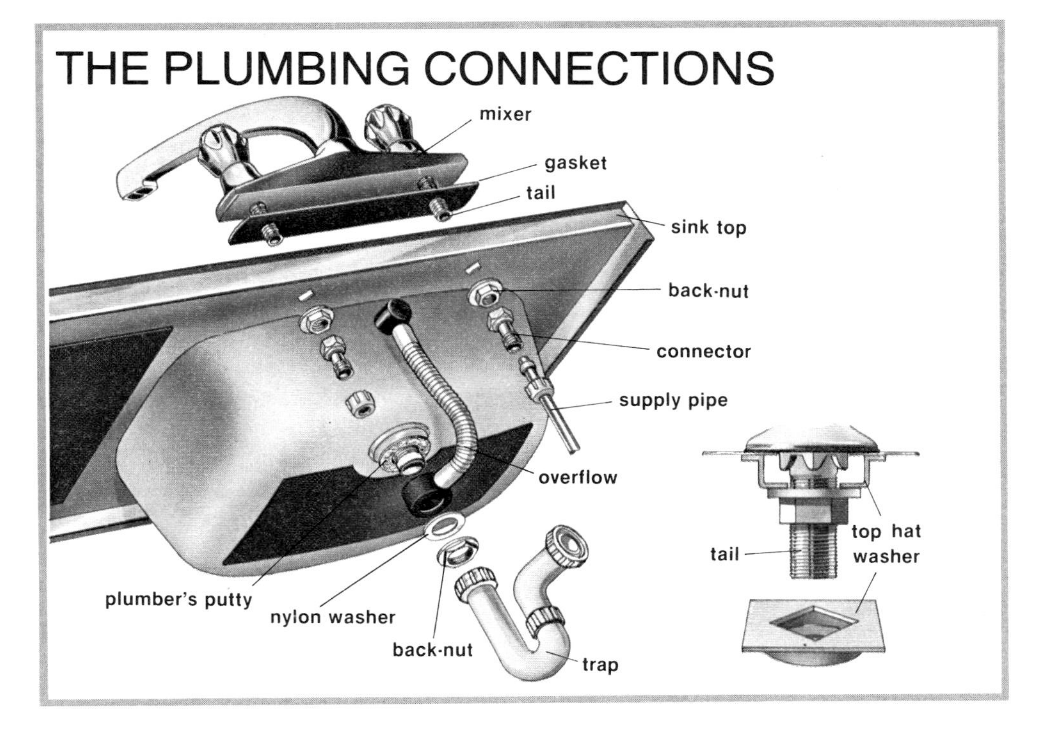

# INSTALLING A SINK TOP

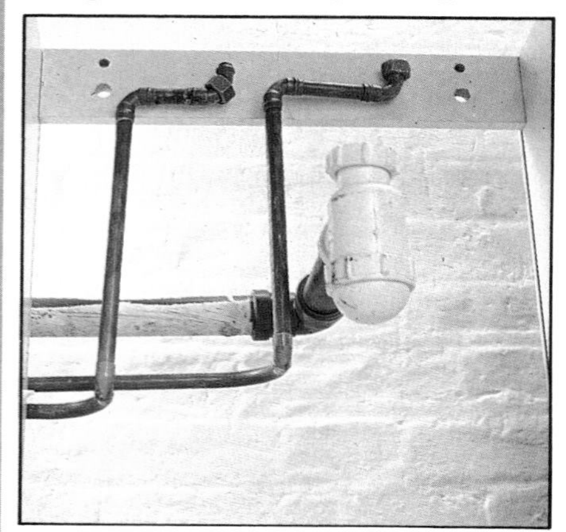

**1** *Take out your old sink top and check that the existing plumbing connections are undamaged. Replace as necessary.*

**2** *Place your new sink top downwards on the floor. Take the waste outlet and press plumber's putty around the top of the screw.*

**3** *Press the outlet firmly into position in the sink outlet aperture, at the same time squeezing out excess putty. Then put on the plastic washer.*

**6** *Place the outlet collar of the banjo unit firmly on top of the plastic washer and support it with one hand before putting on the back-nut.*

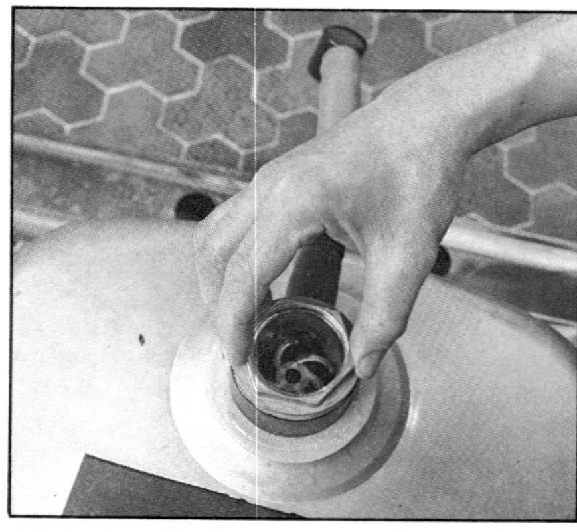

**7** *Put on the back-nut and screw it up tightly against the banjo unit collar, making sure it runs straight towards the sink outlet hole.*

**8** *Screw up the overflow rose to the banjo unit overflow pipe. To help get it tight, hold the back of the outlet with a pair of pliers.*

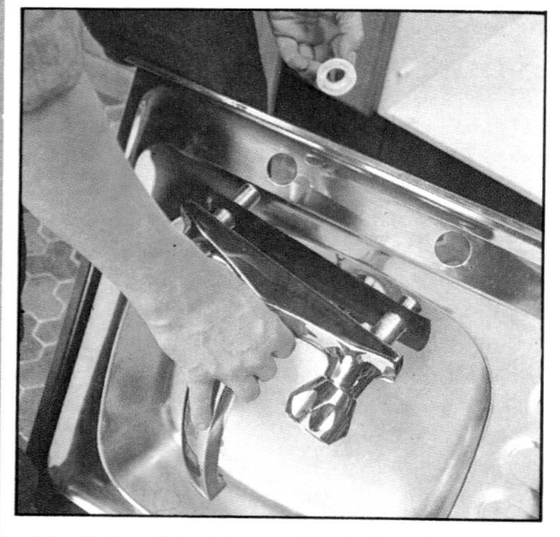

**11** *Take the mixer unit and ensure that the rubber gasket has no grit on it; then place the inlet tails into the holes and press the unit into position.*

**12** *Screw on the inlet tail back-nuts and tighten them, making sure the gasket remains flat. You don't need to use any plumber's putty.*

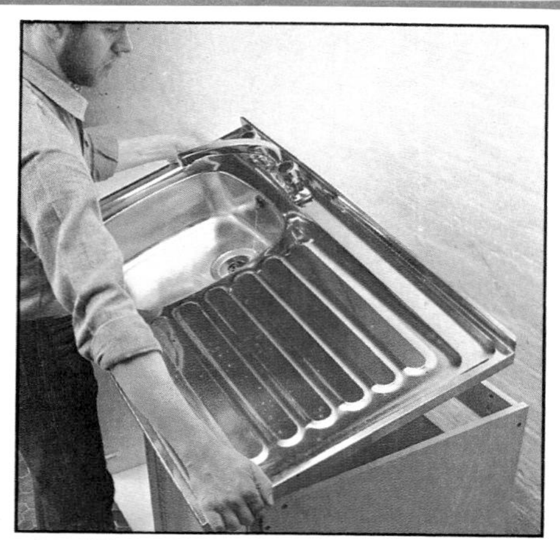

**13** *When the outlet and mixer installation is complete, lift the sink top into its correct position and screw it to the kitchen unit.*

**4** *With the plastic washer pushed firmly home, take a roll of PTFE tape and run it around the thread right up to the end of the outlet.*

**5** *Before putting on the banjo unit run a thick film of pipe-jointing compound around the uppermost surface of the plastic washer.*

**9** *Run a knife around the edge of the plumber's putty squeezed out from around the outlet flange. Be careful not to score the metal.*

**10** *Peel away the surplus putty and check that the outlet flange is tightly held into the sink. If not, tighten the back-nut further.*

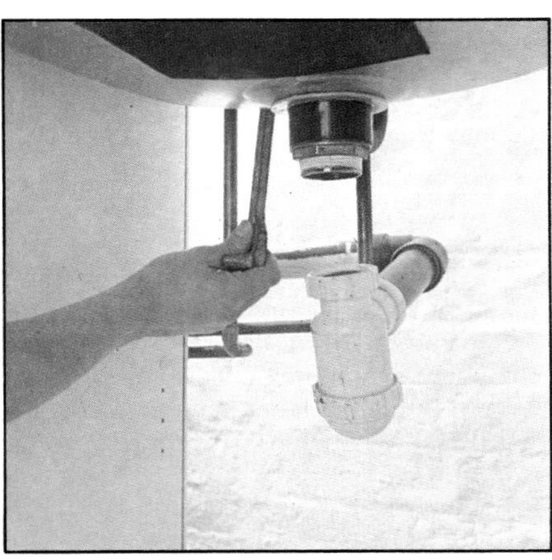
**14** *Attach the inlet pipes to the mixer tails and tighten the nuts with a crowsfoot spanner, which helps you reach them.*

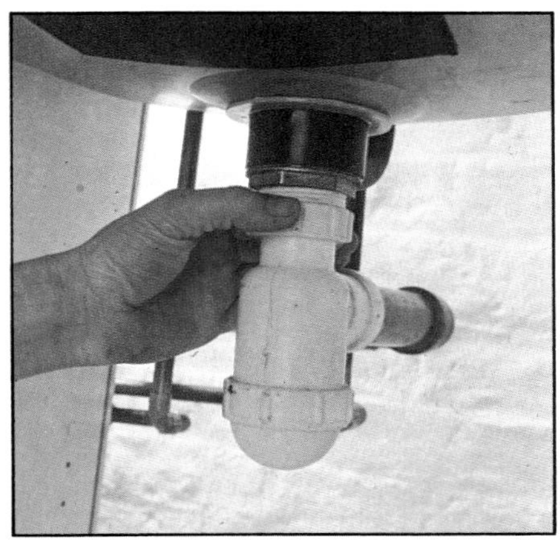
**15** *Check that the old trap is clear and screw it up tightly to the outlet pipe; then turn on the taps to check that there are no leaks.*

# Ready Reference

## SINK DESIGNS

Sink designs come in several different variations particularly in the inset range. Think carefully about what you use your sink for, and what space you have available before deciding on size and design.

## TYPICAL SINK SIZES

S=single, D=double, Si=sink, Dr=drainer

| | Tops | Inset |
|---|---|---|
| SDrSSi | 42x31in<br>1000x500mm<br>1000x600mm<br>1200x600mm | 37x19in<br>940x485mm |
| DDrSSi | 63x21in<br>1500x500mm<br>1500x600mm | 55x19in<br>1395x485mm |
| SDrDSi | 63x21in<br>1500x600mm | 55x19in<br>1395x485mm |
| DDrDSi | 84x21in<br>2000x600mm | 74x19in<br>1850x485mm |

## TYPICAL DESIGNS

If you don't have a dishwasher a double bowl is useful – one for washing and one for rinsing.

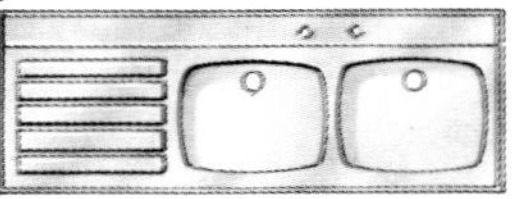
**double bowl**

A double drainer will give you a greater working area at the sink but will cut down on the remainder of your work surface.

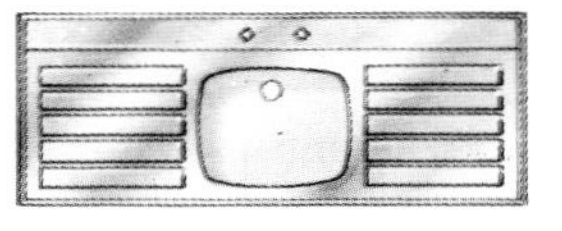
**double drainer**

If you're short of space you may dispense with the drainer altogether and use an inset bowl only. There are also units with small subsidiary bowls specially incorporated to house a waste disposal unit. These may also be supplied with trays which fit in or over the bowl, facilitating such tasks as salad preparation.

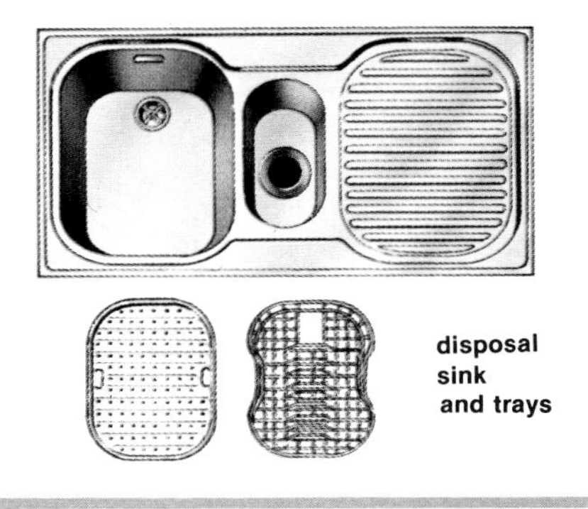
**disposal sink and trays**

# INSTALLING AN INSET SINK

**If you're fitting a new kitchen, or modernising an old one, one job you'll almost certainly have to carry out is to install an inset sink into a worktop.**

Not so long ago, an assortment of cupboards, work surfaces and a kitchen sink unit formed the framework of the average kitchen. It was not a particularly efficient arrangement, but because few appliances had to be fitted in it didn't matter too much if a little space was wasted. However, as more and more homes acquired washing machines, tumble dryers, refrigerators and the like, some way had to be found of fitting these appliances into what was often a relatively small area.

What resulted from this was the 'integral' kitchen which housed all this equipment under roomy and well-lit worktops. And hand in hand with this development went the introduction of the inset sink.

The old enamelled and stainless steel sit-on sinks, with their single or double drainers, completely covered their base units. From a functional point of view they were ideal because the one-piece top meant that it was virtually impossible for water to seep into the cupboard below. Yet the kitchen sink remained a conspicuous, and somewhat unattractive, feature, divorced from other kitchen surfaces. And because of the space it took up, the unit was restricted to only one or two positions in the room. Consequently, many kitchens had to be planned around it, which naturally limited the ways in which they could be made more labour-saving and pleasant to work in.

However, once the move to creating uninterrupted work surfaces took hold, the benefits of installing a 'built-into-the-worktop' sink became readily apparent. For the first time it meant that a sink could be fitted into an overall design, which could still retain a clean, streamlined look. It didn't have to be fitted directly over a base unit, which gave far more flexibility as to where it could be positioned. However, there still had to be sufficient clearance under the worktop to take the bowl, and the plumbing supply and waste runs still had to make sense.

In fact, the idea for inset sinks stemmed from bathroom and bedroom vanity units, where a washbasin was let into the surface of a small cupboard. The surrounding melamine-finished surface was easy to clean and provided a standing area for bottles, cosmetics and the like. It was only a matter of time before the idea was adopted in the kitchen.

## Choosing an inset sink

Whether you're revamping your kitchen, or just modernising the existing sink, there are a number of points to take into account before buying a new inset model.

The first is to decide what exactly the sink has to handle, because this will give you a fair guide as to the size you'll need, and whether two bowls would be better instead of just one. Indeed, there are a number of advantages in installing two or even two-and-a-half bowls (the 'half' being specifically for cutlery) not the least being that you'll still have access to the taps even if one bowl is occupied. And the amount of extra plumbing you'll have to carry out is quite small. All it entails is slightly extending the waste run. If you install a mixer tap with a swivel spout this can be used to fill both bowls so there's no additional work on the water supply side.

As with sit-on sinks, there is a wide range of bowl/drainer combinations. There are also individual round bowls which don't have an attached drainer, although there are separate drainers available that you have to let into the worktop nearby.

Round bowls do look attractive and they are increasing in popularity, but they have a couple of disadvantages. They tend to be shallower than the traditional rectangular shape – generally, the deeper the bowl the better – and their shape sometimes makes it awkward to submerge large pans and grill trays when they're being washed.

## Which material to go for?

The other main consideration when choosing a sink is the material it's made of. Nowadays there is a far wider choice than ever before.

Stainless steel has retained its popularity, principally because it is relatively cheap and there is a wide range of styles available. Yet while it is heat-resistant and hard wearing, it can suffer at the hands of scourers and abrasive cleaners which leave minute surface scratches. You may also find this material somewhat clinical in appearance. However, if you do there are alternatives.

Don't shy away from plastic, for example. Admittedly the early glass-reinforced plastic tops proved to be a disaster: they simply weren't sturdy enough to cope with the use – and misuse – a kitchen sink is subjected to. But the ones on sale now are vastly different. These are made of impact-resistant modified polycarbonate in a range of attractive colours that extend right through the material. You can buy double as well as single sinks with round or rectangular bowls. As far as temperature resistance is concerned these sinks are very tough, and to prove it they are put through some remarkably nasty tests. One manufacturer, for example, has tested such sinks in hot water at up to 95°C for 40 days, in boiling water at five different levels of water hardness for 50 hours and by placing hot

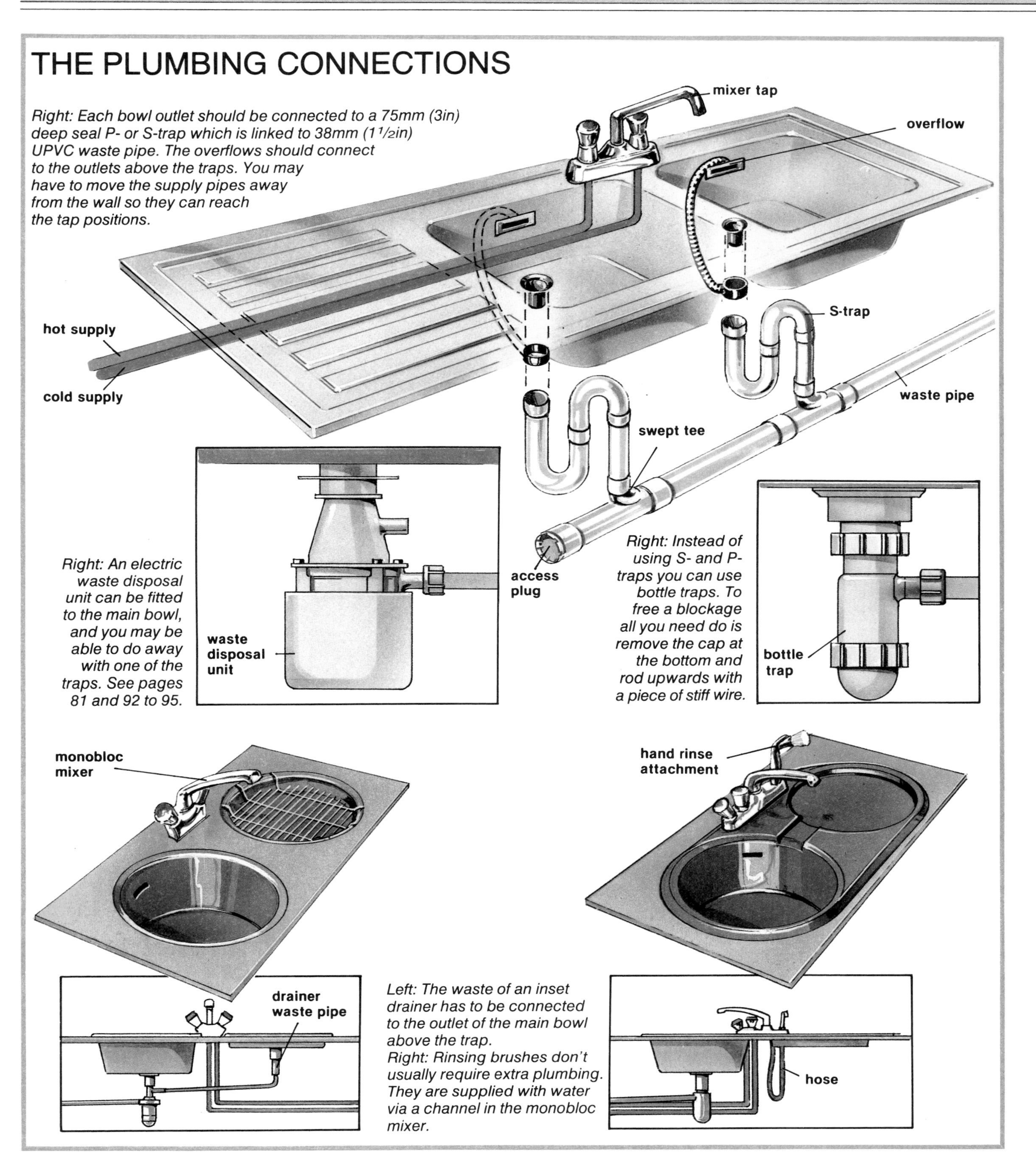


## THE PLUMBING CONNECTIONS

*Right: Each bowl outlet should be connected to a 75mm (3in) deep seal P- or S-trap which is linked to 38mm (1 1/2in) UPVC waste pipe. The overflows should connect to the outlets above the traps. You may have to move the supply pipes away from the wall so they can reach the tap positions.*

*Right: An electric waste disposal unit can be fitted to the main bowl, and you may be able to do away with one of the traps. See pages 81 and 92 to 95.*

*Right: Instead of using S- and P-traps you can use bottle traps. To free a blockage all you need do is remove the cap at the bottom and rod upwards with a piece of stiff wire.*

*Left: The waste of an inset drainer has to be connected to the outlet of the main bowl above the trap.*
*Right: Rinsing brushes don't usually require extra plumbing. They are supplied with water via a channel in the monobloc mixer.*

## INSTALLING AN INSET SINK

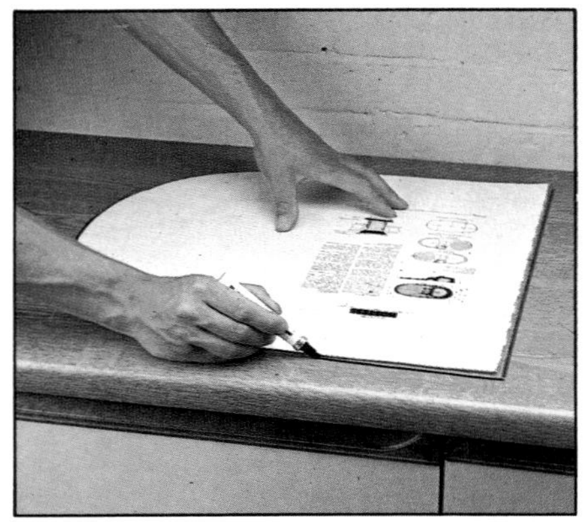

**1** *If space is limited and the worktop is fixed in position, check underneath that there is clearance for the bowls and then mark round the template.*

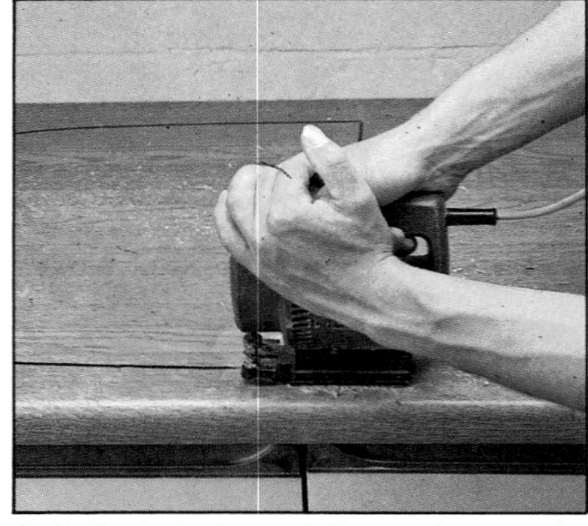

**2** *Drill a hole through the worktop on the waste side of the cut-out. Insert the jigsaw and cut out the hole, supporting the waste on the underside.*

**3** *Test fit the sink in the hole, wriggling it a little to get it to drop down flush with the top. If it sticks, file back the area where it catches.*

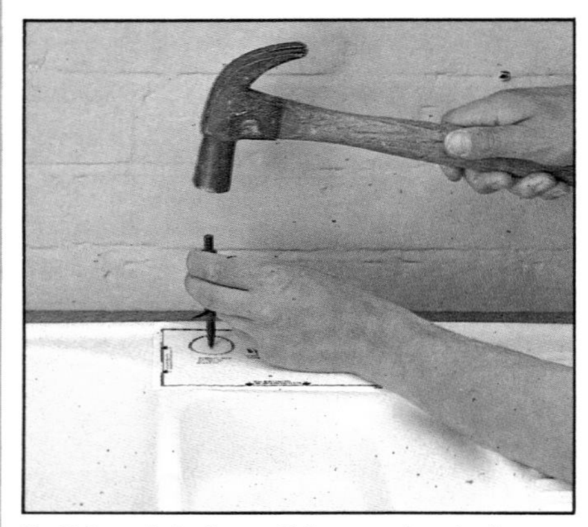

**6** *If the sink doesn't have a tap hole punched, place the special template over the knockout and gently use a hammer and punch to make one.*

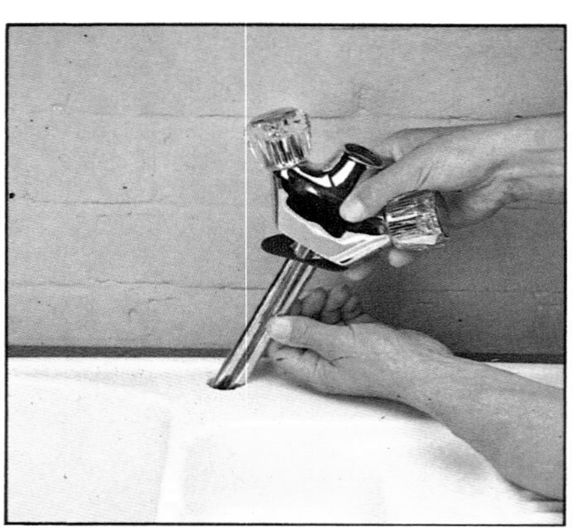

**7** *Insert the monobloc mixer, making sure that it sits on a rubber gasket. Then use a spanner to tighten the back-nut underneath the sink.*

**8** *Make up the outlets for the main and half bowls and the overflow. Some outlets are bedded on plumber's putty while others sit on special plastic washers.*

saucepans on them for short periods at temperatures up to 180°C. No domestic sink is likely to experience anything like that amount of misuse; even so the sinks weathered the punishment.

Ceramic sinks are once more on the market and are becoming increasingly popular. Again, they are very different from their early counterparts, but one thing hasn't changed. They spell certain death to any piece of crockery dropped into them. It's a point that should perhaps be borne in mind when choosing a sink top. Having said this, these sinks are available in an attractive range of colours (you can even get a mixer tap to match), and as with plastic and stainless steel models some versions have integral drainers. Once installed these sinks are highly resistant to being damaged. However, if you do plump for a ceramic sink and you want to install a waste disposal unit check that the two are compatible, because it's impossible to widen the outlet as you can do with a stainless steel top.

### Choosing the taps

Apart from all the other considerations it's important to choose an inset sink with the taps in mind.

If you go for a two or two-and-a-half bowl top then you're going to need some form of swivel mixer. Some sinks will only take a monobloc mixer because there is only one access hole for the hot and cold supply pipes. Others take conventional mixers. Alternatively, you could use separate pillar taps.

Some sink tops are reversible, in that depending on which way round you fit them they can have a left-hand or right-hand drainer. Obviously you can't have tap holes on both sides of the bowl, so to get round the problem usually there are knockouts in the potential tap sites and you just remove those you want to use.

Sometimes no provision is made for taps. In this case you'll have to install bib taps coming out of the wall or drill holes through the worktop itself and fit the taps to these.

### How to install an inset sink

Installing an inset sink presents no special difficulties. As with conventional sinks, and indeed most other plumbing fittings, it's best to carry out as much work as possible before putting the worktop in position. But if the worktop is fixed, rather than remove it work in situ instead. First, fit the taps. With a mixer you'll need a flat washer between the base and the sink top. And for a plastic or stainless steel sink, you'll probably need to use top hat or spacer washers over the tap tails to accommodate the protruding shanks before screwing on the back-nuts.

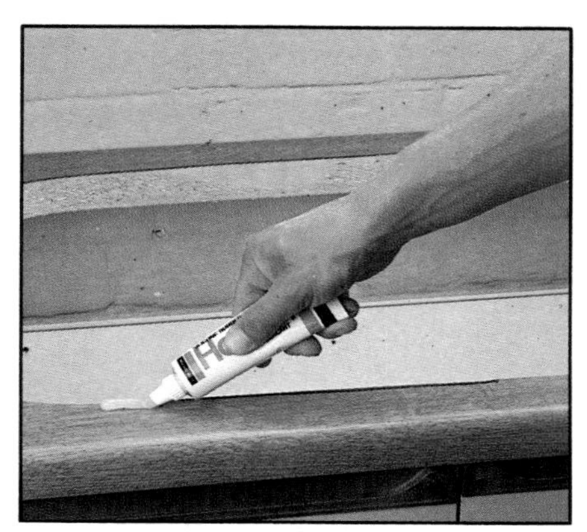

**4** *Some sinks are bedded on a rubber or plastic seal. If not, run silicone rubber or non-setting mastic round the edge of the hole before fitting the sink.*

**5** *Lower the inset sink into the hole and then fasten it in position underneath using the clips provided. Clean away any sealant that oozes from the edges.*

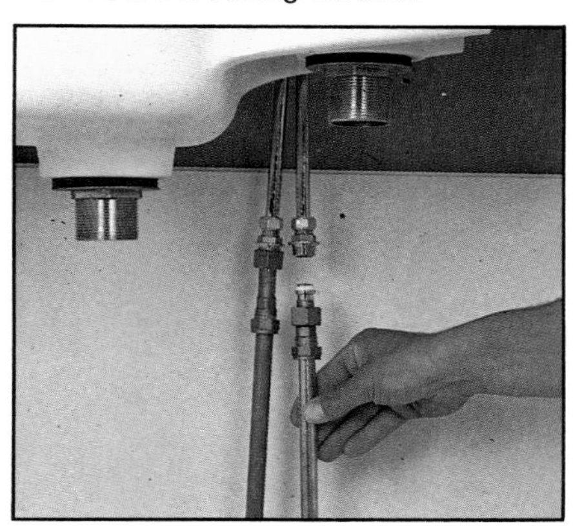

**9** *Use tap connectors and special reducers to connect the 15mm (1/2in) hot and cold supply runs to the tap tails, which on this model are slightly narrower.*

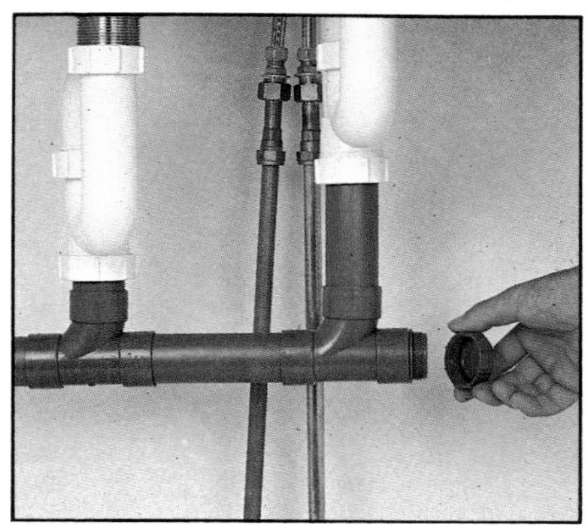

**10** *Use S-traps and swept tees to connect the 38mm (1 1/2in) wastes to a common waste run. An inspection eye at the end of the run aids blockage removal.*

The tap tails will be difficult to get to once the sink is in position, particularly if the unit you are fitting over has a back to it. Therefore it's best to fit a small run of pipe, or lengths of corrugated flexible pipe, to each of the tap tails at this stage.

The waste and overflow unit is usually supplied with the sink. Don't forget to bed the outlet on a layer of mastic, and as you tighten up the back-nut make sure the slot in the shank points in the direction of the overflow. Next, screw the overflow to the outlet point at the top of the sink bowl and then slip the 'banjo' connector at the other end of the flexible hose over the slotted waste. This is held in place by another back-nut.

As far as marking out the work surface is concerned, most sink manufacturers supply a template indicating the area of worktop to be removed. Needless to say this must be done with care and accuracy, and for this reason it's best to work on the top surface and not the underside so there's no risk of getting the sink in the wrong place.

Drill a hole through the waste side of the cut-out and then use a jigsaw to cut the hole. You can then fit the retaining brackets or rim round the underside edge. The fixing clips on the sink are secured to these when it's set in its final position.

Usually, inset sinks are provided with a rubber seal or gasket so that when fitted there's a watertight seal between the bowl and drainer and the worktop. If there isn't one, run a continuous bead of non-setting mastic round the perimeter and bed the top firmly onto this.

Once you've lowered the sink into position and clipped it in place all that then remains is to set the worktop in position on top of the unit and to connect the waste pipe and the hot and cold supply runs.

## Ready Reference

### CHECK UNDERSURFACE CLEARANCE

You've got considerable flexibility as to where you position an inset sink – it need not necessarily be directly over a base unit. But wherever you propose to site it make sure there is sufficient depth under the worktop to accommodate the bowls.

### WHICH SINK TO CHOOSE

Inset sinks can have one, two or two and a half bowls. Some incorporate drainers, but with individual bowls separate drainers have to be installed alongside.

Many inset sinks are made of stainless steel, but if you choose a plastic or ceramic sink you have the added option of a wide range of colours.

### TIP: CARE WITH HOT PANS

Whatever material your sink is made of it will withstand all likely treatment. If you've a plastic sink it's advisable not to put frying pans that have just been used for frying hot meat, dry cooked foods and hot oil directly in the sink. First allow the pan to cool briefly.

### TIP: FITTING A WASTE DISPOSER

If you're installing a ceramic sink and you also want a waste disposal unit, make sure the outlet of the sink is compatible with the inlet on the disposer. Ceramic sinks can't be cut, so the two must match exactly.

### BOWL ACCESSORIES

There are various accessories you can fit over the bowl of the sink such as a draining tray (A) and a chopping board (B). Ideally, use the chopping board over the sink with a waste disposer so that any vegetable matter can be hygienically flushed away.

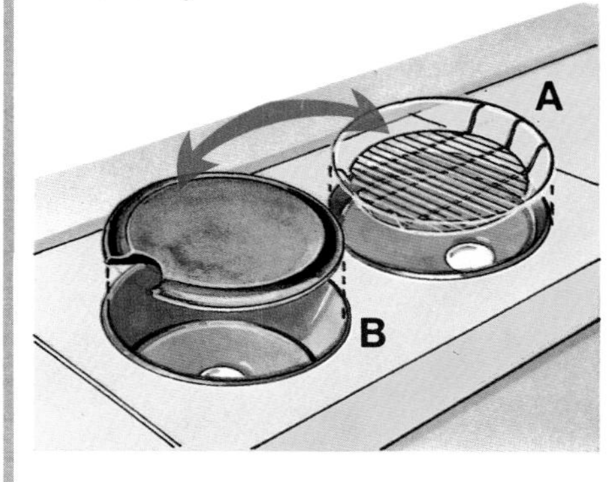

# PLUMBING IN KITCHEN APPLIANCES

**Washing machines and dishwashers can be a great boon in the house. They are best plumbed into a water supply and the waste outlet, otherwise you'll find they don't save as much time as they should.**

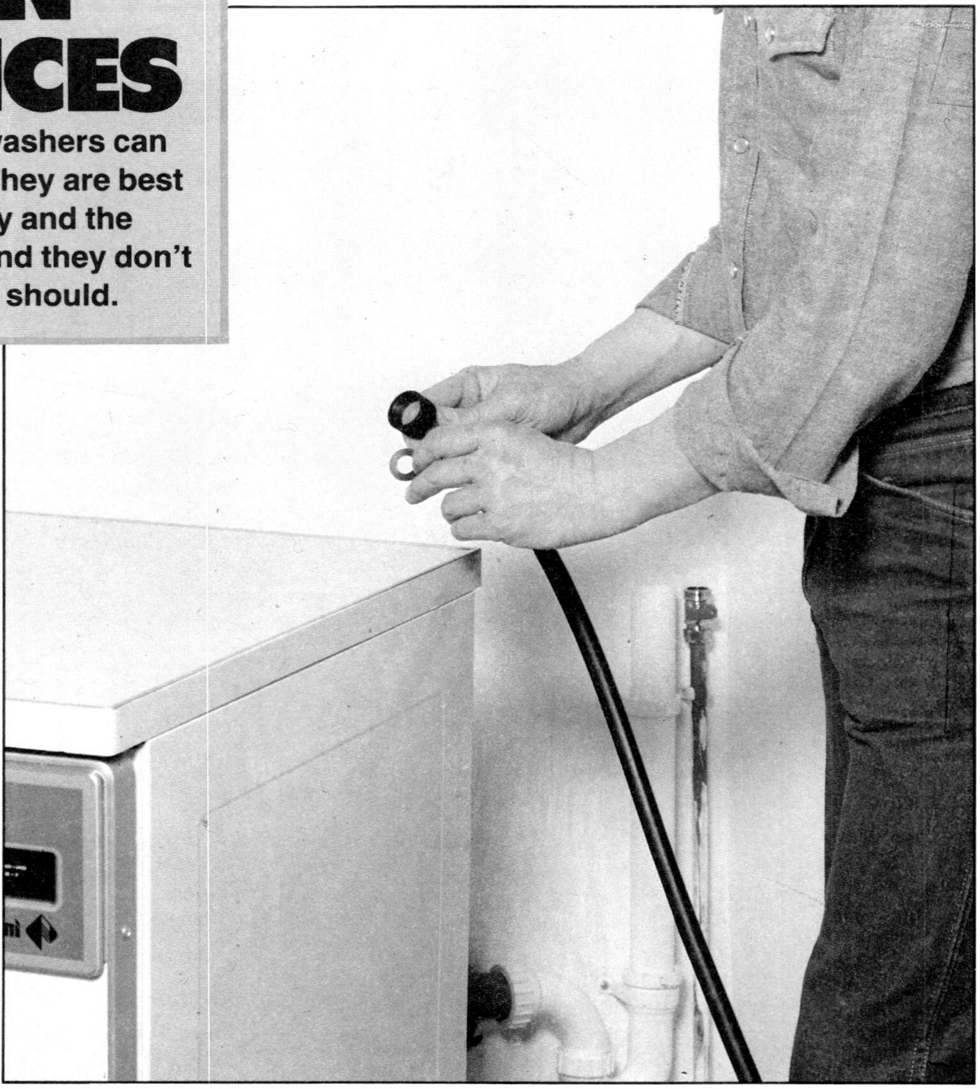

These days you'll probably opt for an automatic washing machine that fills and empties itself according to a pre-set programme, and so can be left unattended. There is a choice between top loaders and front loaders, although the latter are by far the more common. Obviously top loaders can't fit under a work surface, but drum-type top loaders tend to be narrower and this may suit your particular space requirements.

Dishwashers are almost always automatic, except for some small, cheaper sink-top models. They, too, are available as top or front loaders, though again front loaders are by far the more popular. They are also easier to load and unload, as with top loaders it's easy for crockery and cutlery to slip to the bottom of the machines.

Washing machines have become almost a necessity in busy family homes, especially where there are young children. Dishwashers are far less common, but sales are developing rapidly as more and more people wake up to their advantages. It's a simple matter to stack a dishwasher with dirty crockery direct from the meal table and then turn it on before going to bed at night. Again, for a family the labour saving is considerable.

Some washing machines don't have to be plumbed in. The inlets can be attached to the kitchen taps when the sink isn't being used, and the outlet can be hooked over the edge of the sink. The same goes for dishwashers, which usually require only a cold water feed. But to keep things really neat and tidy as well as more practical, it is best to create permanent connections for both the water supply and the waste outlet. In most kitchens this should be a fairly easy task, provided you have room for the machines in the first place.

As far as the capacities of washing machines and dishwashers go, you don't really have much choice. Washing machines have a capacity of about 4-5kg (9-11lb) and dishwashers will function quite happily provided you stack them up within the obvious tray limitations. It's important to follow the manufacturers' instructions for day-to-day maintenance. Many washing machines need their outlet filter cleaned regularly, as do dishwashers. They may also need regular doses of salts, not to mention rinse aids.

## Water supply

There are a number of ways in which you can arrange the water supply. One of them is sure to suit your plumbing system or the layout of your kitchen or utility room. A washing machine may need a hot and cold supply; dishwashers and some cheaper washing machines need only a cold supply.

Let's first consider the conventional means of plumbing in – the means that a professional plumber would almost certainly adopt if you called him in to do the job for you. It is likely to be most satisfactory where the machine is to be positioned in the immediate vicinity of the kitchen sink and the 15mm (½in) hot and cold supply pipes to the sink taps are readily accessible and in close proximity to each other.

The technique is to cut into these two pipes at a convenient level, after cutting off the water supply and draining the pipes, and to insert into them 15mm compression tees. From the outlets of the tees lengths of 15mm (½in) copper tube are run to terminate, against the wall, in a position immediately adjacent to the machine. Onto the ends of these lengths of pipe are fitted purpose-made stop-cocks. These are usually provided with back-plates that can be screwed to the wall after it has been drilled and plugged. The outlets of the stop-cocks are designed for connection to the machine's inlet hose or hoses.

As an alternative, which is best used where the hot and cold water pipes in the kitchen are in close proximity to the position of the machine, you can use a special patent valve. This is a 'tee' with a valve outlet designed for direct connection to the washing machine hose. There are compression joints at each end of the tee and the valve is particularly

## PLUMBING IN A WASHING MACHINE

Plumbing in a washing machine shouldn't present too many problems. Normally it's sited next to an existing sink, so you'll know that the water supply pipes and drainage facilities are close at hand.

Most machines are run off separate 15mm (½in) hot and cold supplies (1 & 2) taken from tees (3) inserted in the pipe runs to the sink. You should also insert some form of stop-valve (4) into the pipes so the machine can be isolated for repairs. You'll have to use female/male connections (5) to join the copper pipes to the machine's rubber inlet hoses (6).

When the water has been used, it's fed into a rubber drain hose (7) which should be loosely inserted into the top of the stand-pipe (8). This in turn connects to a 75mm (3in) trap and from here the waste water is taken in 38mm (1½in) pipe to discharge in the gully outside below the grille.

***Dealing with single-stack drainage***

From the trap at the bottom of the stand-pipe (11) the waste water is conducted to the main drainage stack (12) where the pipe is connected via a fitting known as a strap boss(13).

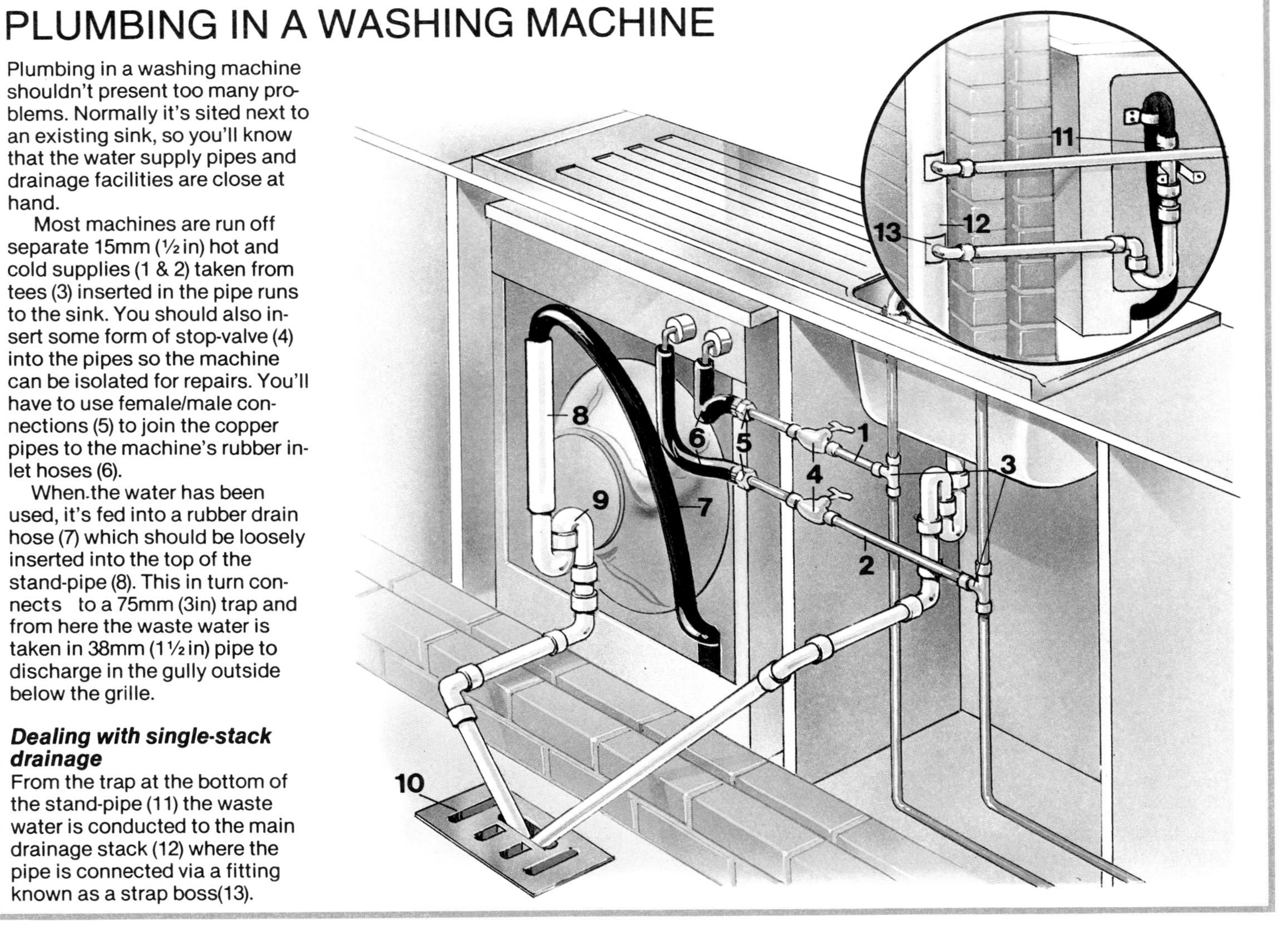


easily fitted because there is no tube-stop in one of these joints. This cuts out the difficult business of 'springing' the cut ends of the pipe into the tee.

Then there are valves which can be connected without cutting a section out of the water supply pipes. With one such valve the pipe is drained and is then drilled with a 8mm (5⁄16in) bit. A back-plate is then fitted to the wall behind it and a front-plate, with a short projecting pipe and a rubber seal that fits into the hole in the pipe, is clamped to it. The washing machine valve then screws into this front-plate.

Yet another valve is self-tapping and screws its own hole in the water pipe. This, so the makers claim, can be done without cutting off the water supply and draining the pipe.

A valve which depends upon drilling the water supply pipe will not permit the same flow of water as one in which the pipe is cut and a tee inserted. It must be said, though, that this seems to make very little difference in practice, but obviously in the former case the tightening of the connection must be more than sufficient for it to work properly.

### Putting in drainage

The simplest method is undoubtedly to hook the machine's outlet hose over the rim of the kitchen or utility room sink when required. However, this method isn't always convenient and is certainly untidy. An alternative is to provide an open-ended stand-pipe fixed to the kitchen wall into which the outlet hose of the machine can be permanently hooked. The open end of the stand-pipe should be at least 600mm (24in) above floor level and should have an internal diameter of at least 35mm (1⅜in). A deep seal (75mm/3in) trap should be provided at its base and a branch waste pipe taken from its outlet to an exterior gully, if on the ground floor, or to the main soil and waste stack of a single stack system if on an upper floor. As with all connections to a single soil and waste stack this should be done only under the supervision of the district or borough council's Building Control Officer. Manufacturers of plastic drainage systems include suitable drainage stand-pipes and accessories in their range of equipment (the trap and pipe being sold as one unit).

It is sometimes possible to deal with washing machine or dishwasher drainage by taking the waste pipe to connect directly to the trap of the kitchen sink and this course of action may be suggested at DIY centres and by builders' merchants staff. But it must be stressed that this is not recommended by the manufacturers of washing machines, who consider that it involves a considerable risk of back-siphonage. This could lead to waste water from the sink siphoning back into the machine. In the case of a washing machine this could mean considerable problems.

## PLUMBING IN A DISHWASHER

1 *Start by working out how to run the waste outlet. This will often mean making a hole in the wall using a club hammer and cold chisel.*

2 *Measure up the run on the inside, then cut a suitable length of 38mm (1½in) PVC plastic waste pipe and push it through the hole you have made.*

3 *Make up the outside pipe run dry, to ensure it all fits, then solvent weld it. It's useful to put in an inspection elbow in case of blockages.*

6 *Carry on assembling the run on the inside using standard waste pipe fittings. Try to keep the run close to the wall for a neat appearance.*

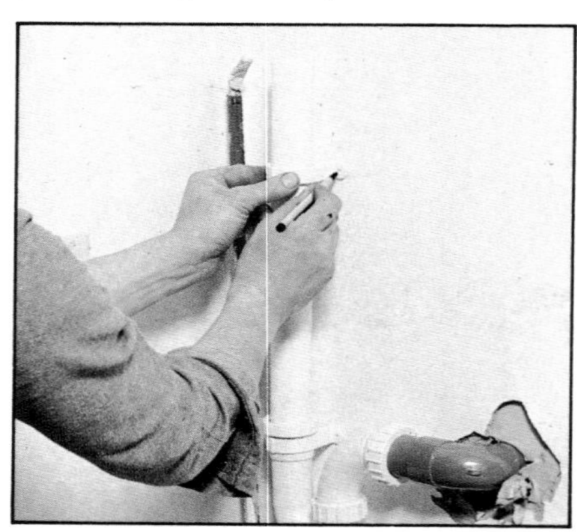

7 *Take the trap and stand-pipe, which you can buy as a standard fitting or make up yourself, and mark the bracket positions on the wall.*

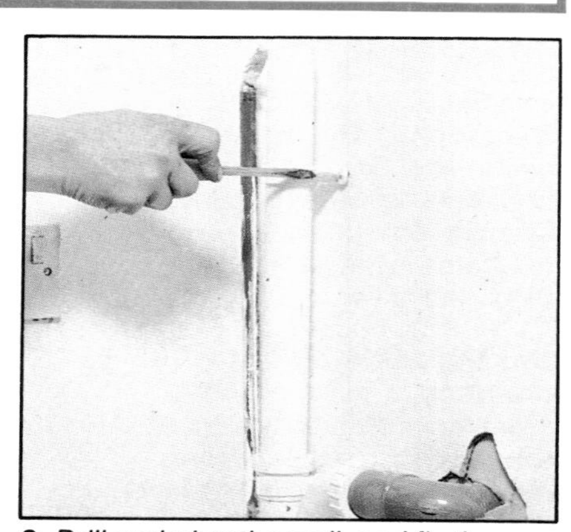

8 *Drill and plug the wall, and fix the stand-pipe in position. Make sure that it is fully supported and vertical and the trap is screwed tight.*

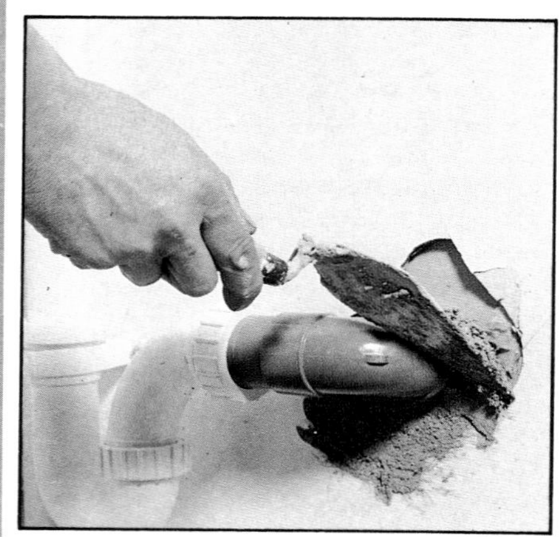

11 *Make good the damage to the wall both on the inside and out; the plastic pipe will be held firmly in place by the mortar and plaster.*

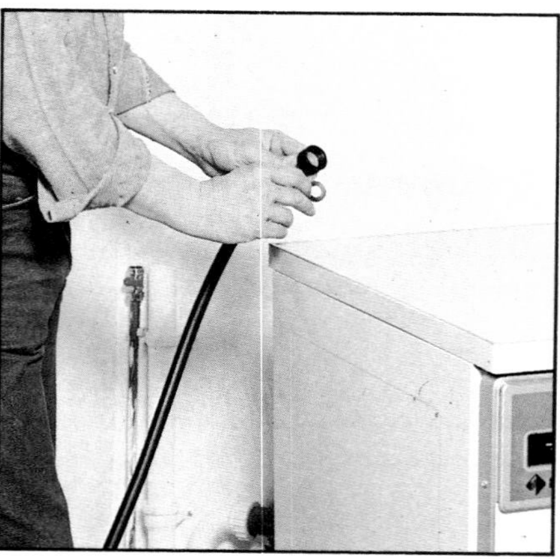

12 *You can now move the machine into position and connect it up. The inlet hose has a female screwed connector, which must have a washer in it.*

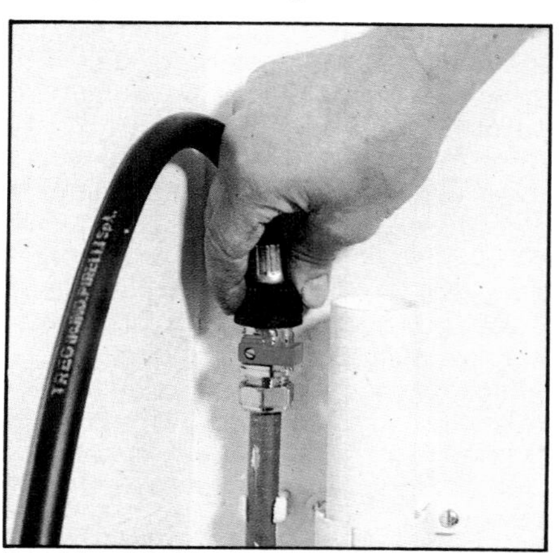

13 *With the washer in place, screw up the connector to the tap on the inlet pipe; it's enough to hand-tighten this connection.*

**4** *If the run terminates in a gully drain, then make sure that you fit the pipe so that the end is situated below the level of the water.*

**5** *When you have completed the outside waste run, replace the grid. Cut away as much of it as necessary to fit round the pipe, using a hacksaw.*

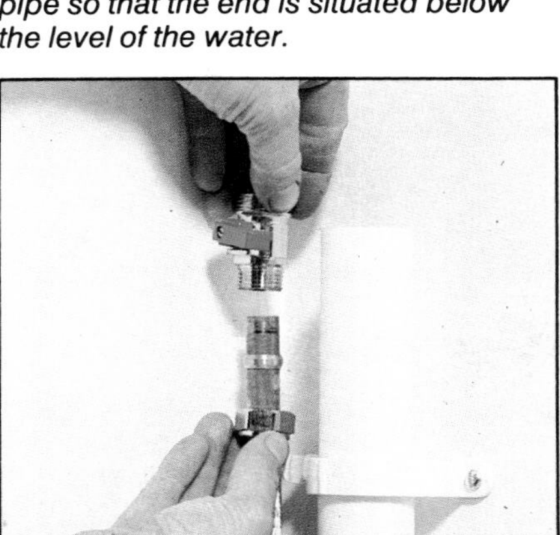

**9** *Run the cold water supply using 15mm (1/2in) pipe via a tee cut into the domestic cold supply, and attach a running tap to the end.*

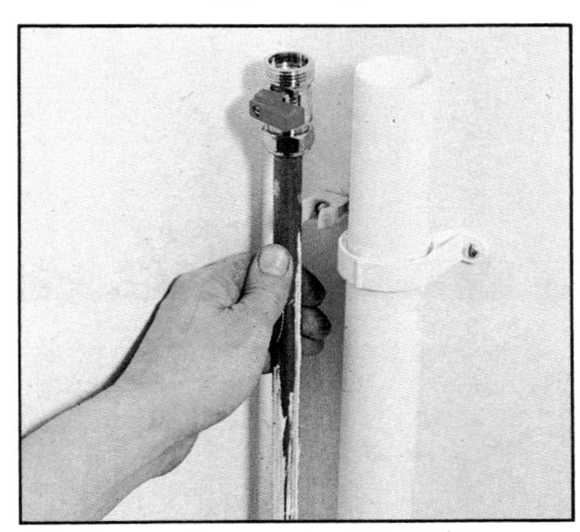

**10** *Secure the supply pipe to the wall using pipe brackets, then go back and make sure that all your connections are sound.*

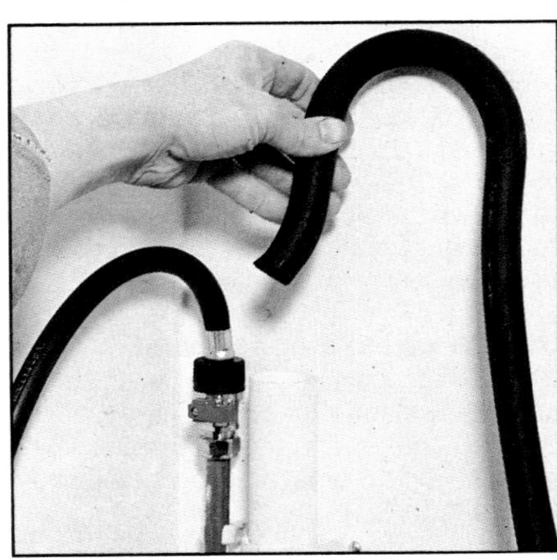

**14** *Take the outlet hose from the machine and place it in the top of the stand-pipe.You should not attempt to make the connection airtight.*

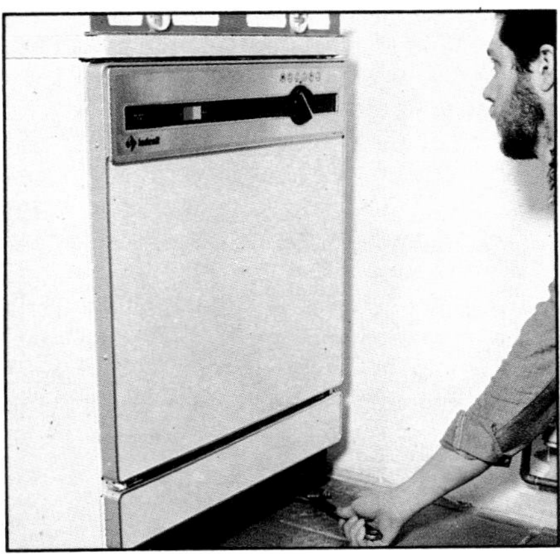

**15** *Move the machine exactly into position and check that it is level; if not, adjust the feet. Then turn on the water and test the machine.*

# Ready Reference

## INSTALLATION CHECKLIST

When installing a washing machine or dishwasher, remember that:

- it's usual to take the water supply from the domestic cold water system; if you want to use the mains you may need a pressure reducer, so check with the manufacturer's literature
- if the machine takes a hot and cold supply you will have to ensure that there is sufficient pressure in the hot supply and that this is the same as that from the cold
- to operate at maximum efficiency, the machine should stand on a level surface and this should be firm; washing machines in particular are extremely heavy when full of water.

## BATHROOM REGULATIONS

If you want to put your washing machine in the bathroom then there are electrical rules that must be obeyed:

- it must be permanently wired in
- you must not be able to touch the controls when you're in the bath or shower.

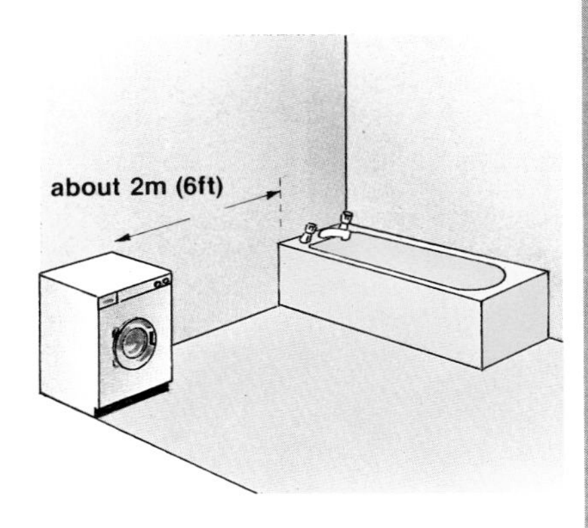


## TIP: CHECK DIMENSIONS

If the machine is going to be put between existing units or under a work surface you'll have to measure up carefully before you buy. Make sure there is enough space behind for the plumbing work.

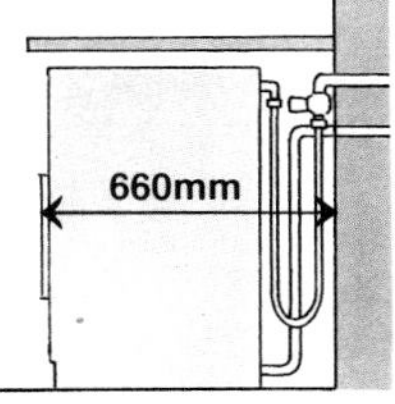


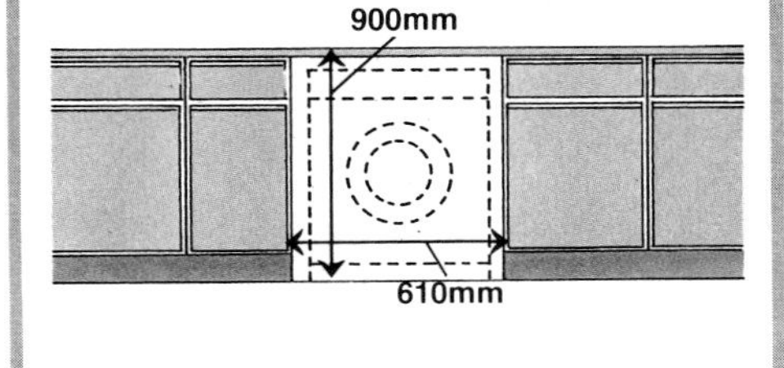

# FITTING A WASTE DISPOSAL UNIT

**Unwanted food – everything from potato peelings to leftovers – usually ends up in a smelly kitchen bin. It can be got rid of more quickly and hygienically with a waste disposal unit.**

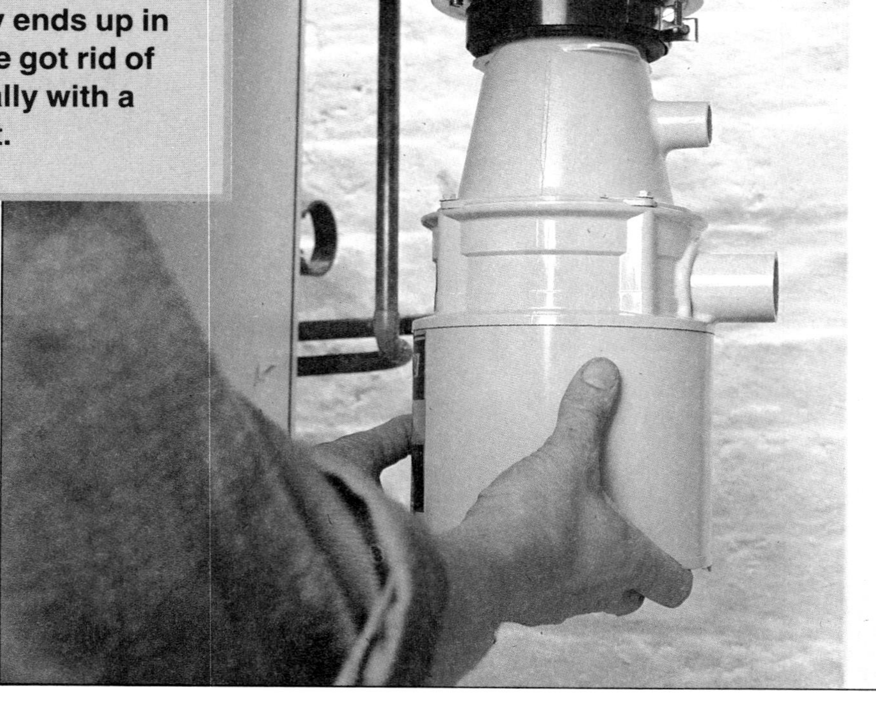

Waste disposal units are an excellent means of getting rid of waste food and the like. Potato and vegetable peelings, cabbage stalks and outer leaves, food scraps, apple cores, tea leaves, dead flowers and so on are simply washed down the kitchen sink, ground to a slurry and flushed into the drainage system. Disposal is instant and hygienic, so it removes the need for constantly emptying smelly bins of rotting food. Whether you live in a house, flat or apartment, one of these units can be a tremendous labour-saving device which makes keeping the kitchen clean that much easier.

Of course there are limitations to what a waste disposal unit can do: it can't deal with all household waste. Broken china, tin cans, bottle caps and large bones will only clog and possibly damage the appliance, so you must be careful not to put them in with other waste. Indeed, jamming is the most common problem with these units, and it usually occurs as a result of misuse. Many modern units have a reversible action motor which enables the jammed material to be cleared by flicking the reversing switch and restarting the motor. Jamming is likely to cause overheating and may operate a thermal cut-out, automatically turning off the motor. In a case like this, it may take some five minutes for the motor to cool sufficiently for it to be restarted. Models without a reversible motor are usually supplied with a key to free the jammed unit. But remember, the electricity supply must be cut off before using it.

When waste disposal units were first introduced, the sewage authorities were concerned that the slurry produced by them could result in sewers becoming choked with silt. Although these fears have proved unfounded, you must make sure that any sediment produced is flushed safely through the household drainage system. It's therefore important to leave the cold tap running while the unit is in operation. This will also help to prevent jamming.

### Installation requirements

Waste disposal units have to be plumbed permanently into the waste outlet of the kitchen sink. They are driven by a relatively powerful motor which turns a set of steel blades. It's these blades that grind the waste into the slurry that's washed into the drainage system.

In order to operate effectively the unit needs to be connected to an 89mm (3½in) diameter sink waste outlet instead of the usual 38mm (1½in) hole, although some models can be adapted to fit this size. You can usually buy a sink with this larger sized opening, but if you already have a stainless steel sink the outlet can be enlarged using a special cutting tool which is rather like a hacksaw with a saw file as a blade.

If you have a sink top made of ceramic or plastic material, or enamelled pressed steel, you can't fit a waste disposal unit unless you're prepared to renew the sink top at the same time.

The outlet from the unit itself is 38mm (1½in) diameter and, like any other waste outlet, must be connected to a trap to prevent smells from the yard gully or the main soil and waste stack entering the kitchen. It's best to use a simple tubular P-trap which will allow the waste and slurry to pass through without leaving any sediment behind. Bottle traps should not be used as they are more likely to block and they also discharge more slowly.

Where the waste pipe from a waste disposal unit situated on the ground floor of a house is taken to a yard gully, it is particularly important that the waste pipe should discharge into the gully above the water level but below the level of the gully grid. In this way the grid will not become fouled by the slurry and, more importantly, the full force of the water discharged from the sink waste will be available to ensure that the slurry will be flushed through the gully and then out into the sewer.

Back or side inlet gullies are available and these are to be preferred when a new drainage system is being installed. However, there are also slotted gully grids on the market and these are highly suitable for converting existing drainage systems. The branch waste pipe from the kitchen sink is simply extended to discharge just below the slot in the gully.

### Fitting a waste disposal unit

An existing stainless steel sink can be adapted by using a special cutting tool, after removing the existing waste outlet. When you are trying to remove the outlet, use a pair of pliers to hold the waste grid while turning the back-nut with a wrench. If this proves difficult, try heating it with a blow-torch. If this still doesn't do the trick, try burning out the washer between the base of the sink and the back-nut with your blow-torch and cutting through the old waste with a hacksaw. When

# MAKING A NEW WASTE OUTLET

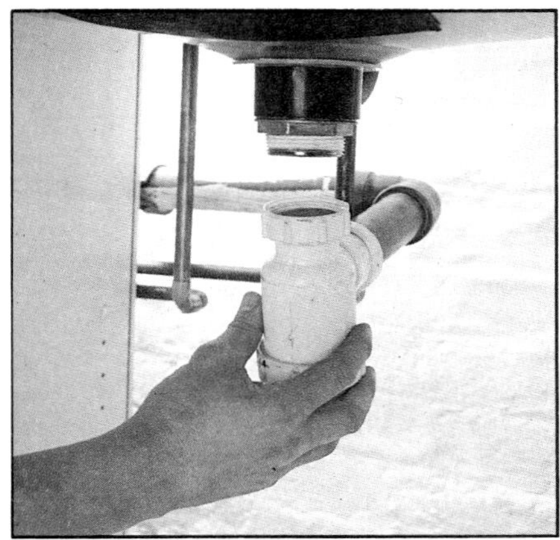

**1** *Disconnect the waste trap from your waste outlet. If the trap is plastic this should be easy; for metal traps a little more effort may be required.*

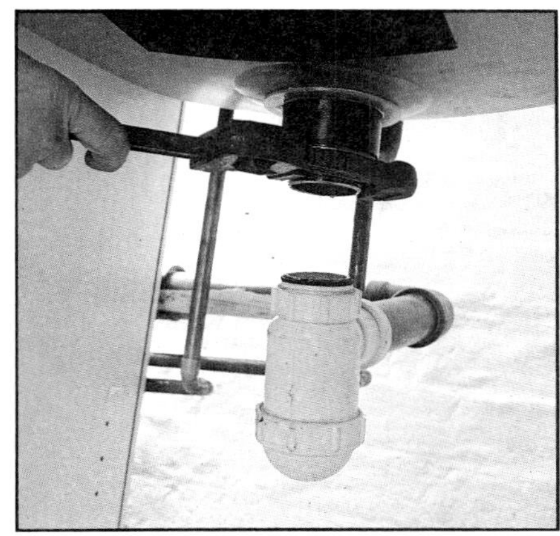

**2** *When you have detached the waste trap, use a wrench to unscrew the back-nut which holds the outlet in position. Remove it and the washer.*

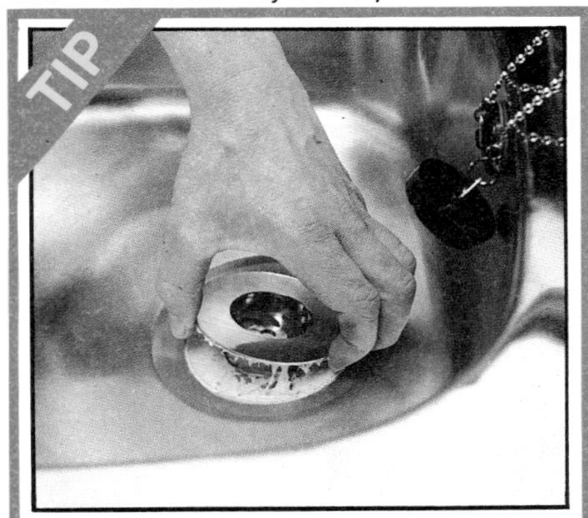


**3** *Pull out the outlet when you have detached the back-nut. If the mastic or putty holds it tightly in position, lever it out with a screwdriver.*

**4** *When you have removed the waste outlet, measure the hole you need, mark it out in the sink and cut it with a saw file cutting tool.*

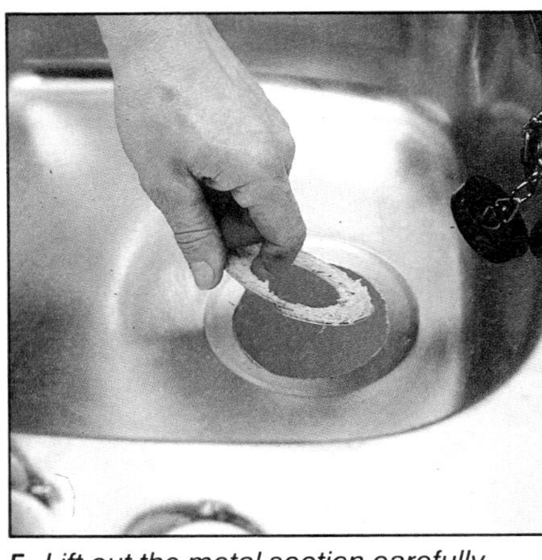

**5** *Lift out the metal section carefully as it will be ragged and sharp where you have cut it. Check that the hole is the right size.*

**6** *Take the new outlet flange supplied with the unit and put a bead of plumber's putty underneath it before placing it in the opening.*

## Ready Reference

### OPERATING A DISPOSAL UNIT

**ALWAYS**

- grind food waste with a strong flow of cold water
- grind all soft waste including paper napkins, paper towels, cigar and cigarette butts, tea bags provided they don't have strings, and also small bones such as chicken bones
- flush the unit regularly to aid thorough cleaning
- turn the power switch off before attempting to clear a jam or remove an object from the disposer
- use a long piece of wood to clear jams
- leave the outlet cover in place to reduce the risk of objects falling into it when not in use
- make sure the unit is earthed.

**NEVER**

- put your fingers or hands into the unit to clear a jam
- let children operate the unit
- use hot water when grinding waste – but you can drain it out between grinding periods
- feed in large quantities of fibrous waste at once – instead, this should be well mixed with other waste and fed in gradually
- grind cans, bottles, bottle caps, glass, china, leather, cloth, rubber, string, feathers, newsprint, or large bones
- pour any drain-cleaning chemicals through the unit
- turn off the motor or water until grinding is completed (ie, only when you can hear the motor running freely).

**FAULT FINDING**

Problems may occur with your unit:

- if there is a water leak round the sink flange: the seal will have to be remade
- if the water drains slowly when the unit is in operation and the waste is clogging up the outlet: keep on grinding and flushing through
- if the disposer won't start. There may be an electrical fault or the motor may have been overloaded: check the cut-out and reset if necessary
- if the unit doesn't function properly immediately after installation. It is likely that the drain line is blocked or can't cope with the outlet discharge – unless there is a problem with the unit itself
- if there are loud noises from the unit when it's in operation: switch off and check for foreign bodies
- if the unit jams: turn it off and follow the manufacturer's instructions for clearing blockages.

## INSTALLING THE WASTE DISPOSAL UNIT

**1** *Take the basic flange components supplied and check the assembly order. There will be a gasket ring, a spacer ring, and a protector ring.*

**2** *Hold the sink flange down, slide the assembly into place, and tighten the screws evenly to make sure there is a watertight seal.*

**3** *Lubricate the inner lip of the rubber flange on the top of the unit with a small amount of petroleum jelly or household oil.*

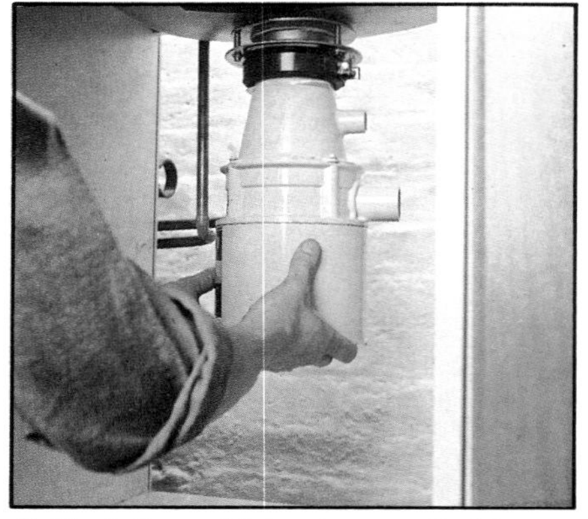

**4** *Push the unit into place so that the rubber lip engages the sink flange and is held in place by it, leaving the unit hanging by itself.*

**5** *Rotate the unit to align it with the waste outlet and tighten the screw clamp evenly all round to hold the whole assembly firmly in position.*

**6** *Fix on the waste outlet elbow and attach a P-trap 38mm (1 1/2in) in diameter. Check that the trap is tight and connect it to the waste pipe.*

the outlet has been removed, check the size of the enlarged hole you need with the new outlet as a guide, then use the cutting tool to cut it out.

With your aperture cut, or with your new sink, bed down the new waste outlet with plumber's putty, and screw up the back-nut and washer. Then attach the suspension plate for the unit, and finally the unit itself. The manufacturer should provide full instructions for the whole operation; follow them carefully.

A tubular P-trap should be attached to the unit via pipe connections which will be supplied. If there is no convenient way of attaching a sink overflow to a disposal unit, you can either seal it off or pipe it down to a socket fitted above the trap in the waste outlet.

## PARTS OF A WASTE DISPOSAL UNIT

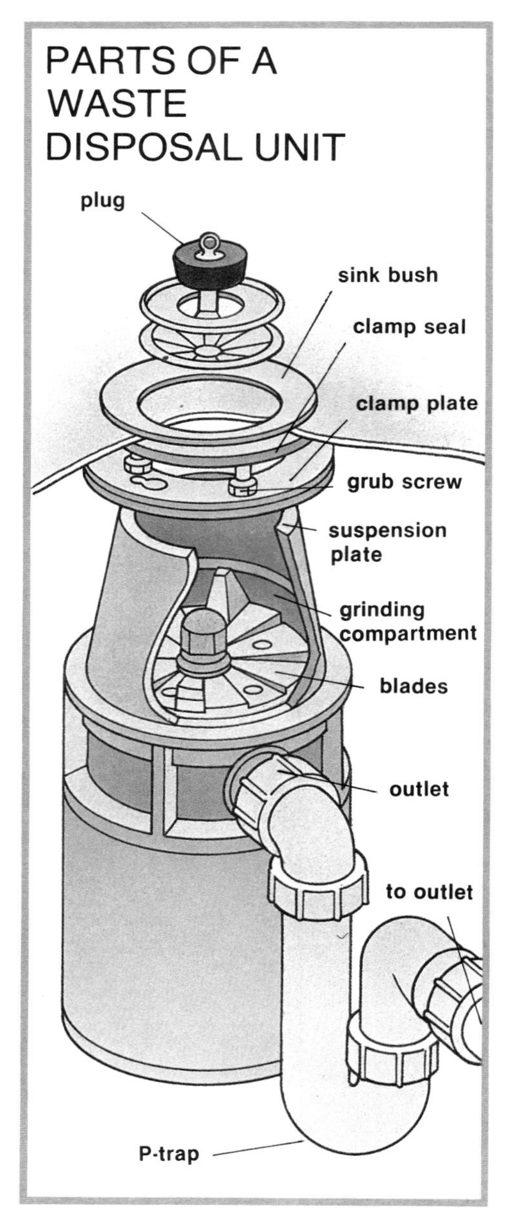

## WIRING UP THE UNIT

***Providing power for a waste disposal unit is simple. You can plug it directly into a 13A socket outlet, but it's better to run a spur and use a connection unit.***

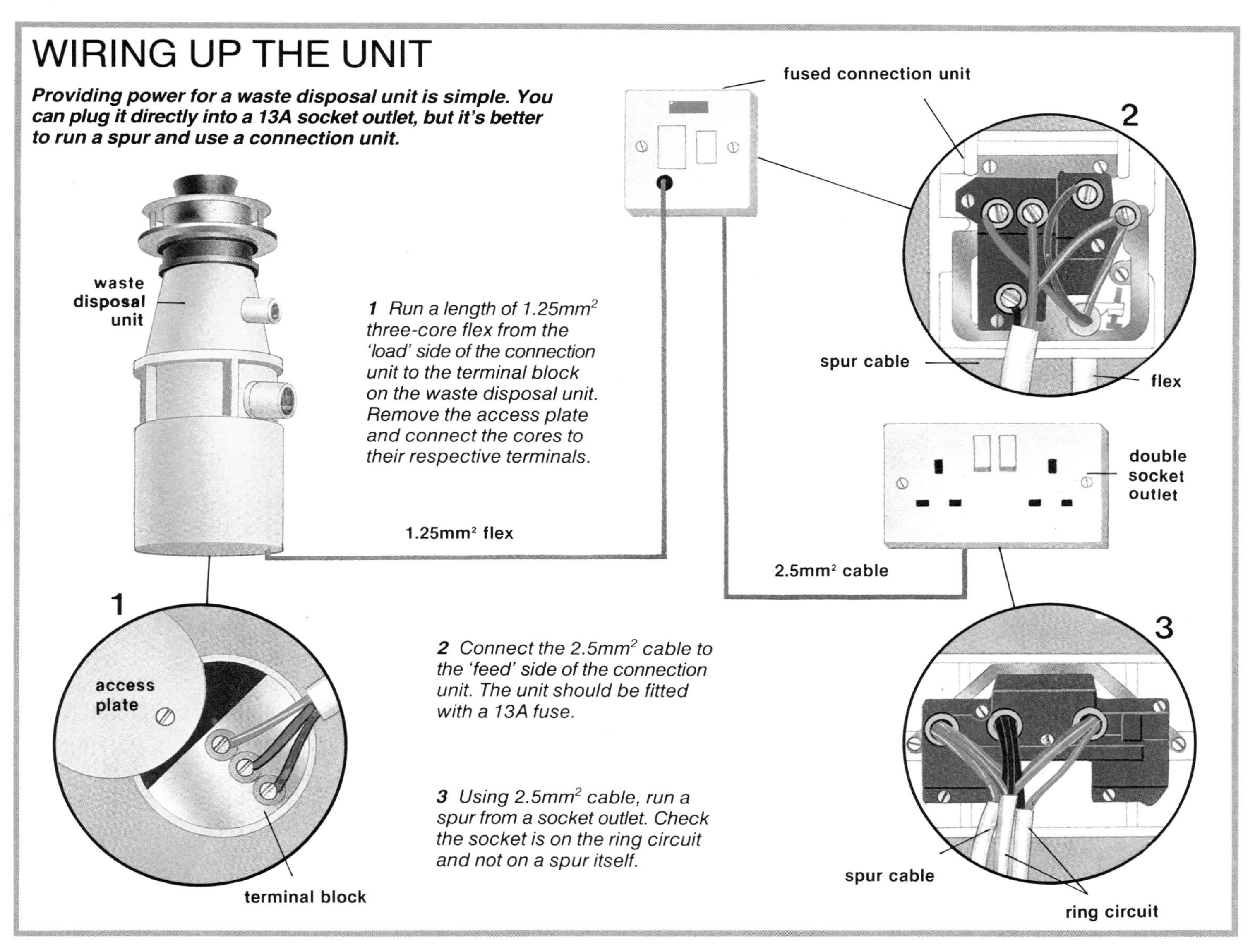


*1 Run a length of 1.25mm² three-core flex from the 'load' side of the connection unit to the terminal block on the waste disposal unit. Remove the access plate and connect the cores to their respective terminals.*

*2 Connect the 2.5mm² cable to the 'feed' side of the connection unit. The unit should be fitted with a 13A fuse.*

*3 Using 2.5mm² cable, run a spur from a socket outlet. Check the socket is on the ring circuit and not on a spur itself.*

### Wiring up the unit

Most waste disposal units are powered by an electric induction motor. This sort of motor is constructed differently to the motor found in most other home electrical appliances. It starts immediately on full load, the starting current needed being much less than that of other types of electric motor. As a result a waste disposal unit needs only a 13A electricity supply, which can conveniently be provided from a nearby circuit.

There are a number of models on the market, and the differences between them can affect the electric wiring you have to provide. The principal difference is whether the unit has reversing facilities or not. The simplest type has no reversing facilities – it runs in one direction only. Should the unit become jammed the electricity supply must be switched off before a release key is inserted to engage the impeller and release the jam. Such one-way motors are protected from the overloading a jam causes by a thermal cut-out; after clearing the jam you will have to reset this by depressing a button on the motor frame before the motor can be restarted.

Other versions have special switch-gear which reverses the direction of the electric motor every time it is switched on. With these types the reversing controller, which incorporates a double-pole switch and 13A fuse, is either mounted integral with the unit or fixed to the wall in the kitchen some 300mm (12in) above the work surface.

A waste disposal unit should ideally be connected to a 13A switched fused connection unit (once called a fused spur unit). This unit has the required double-pole isolating switch and 13A cartridge fuse; it might be best to choose the version with a neon indicator light.

A possible alternative outlet is a 13A fused plug and switched socket outlet, but as the switch is only single-pole it is always necessary to remove the plug to isolate the unit and there is also a likelihood that the socket may be used temporarily for other appliances. The circuit wiring required to supply a waste disposal unit is simply a spur cable branching off the ring circuit cable. The connection at the ring circuit is usually more conveniently made at an existing 13A socket outlet than at a junction box inserted into the ring cable. You should use 2.5mm² two-core and earth cable and run it from the socket to the point where you intend to fix the switched fused connection unit or special reversing controller.

Connect a length of 1.25mm² three-core flex to the 'load' side of the connection unit and run it to the terminal block of the waste disposal unit. The brown core should then be connected to the 'L' terminal, the blue to the 'N' and finally the green/yellow to the 'E' terminal.

# INSTALLING A WATER SOFTENER

**Hard water is more than just a nuisance causing fur in kettles – scale can even affect the efficiency of a plumbing system. But if you install a water softener you can prevent most of these problems occurring.**

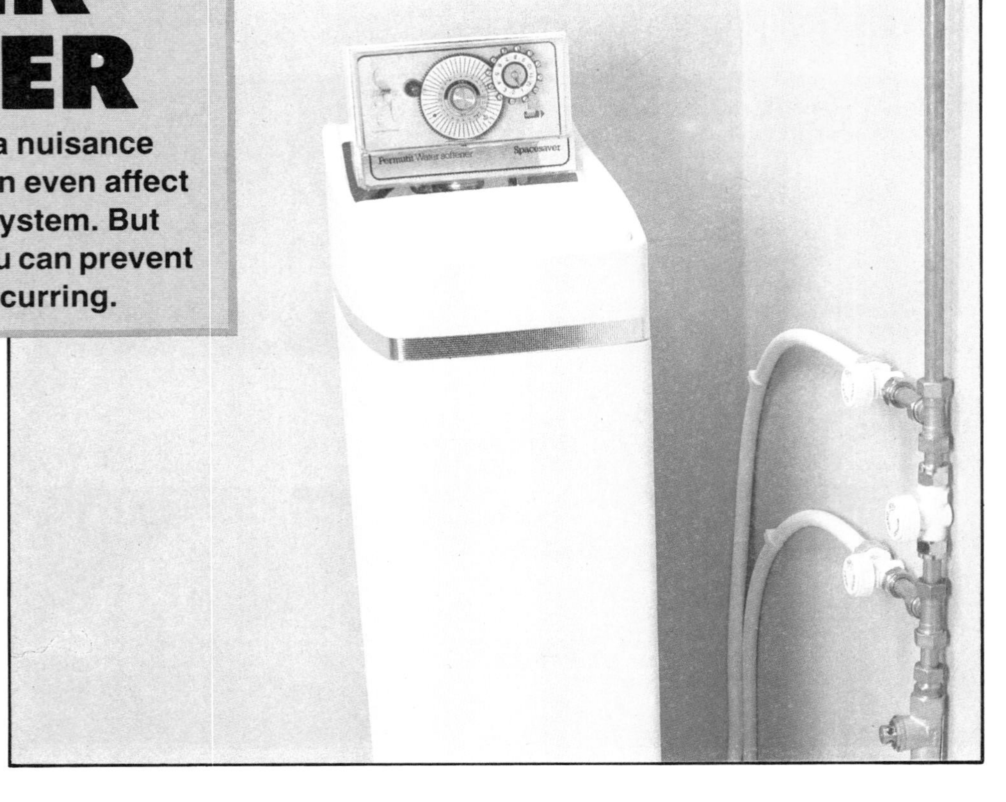

Wherever you are in the country, one glass of water looks virtually the same as a glass from another area. This may be stating the obvious – water is water – but there are important invisible differences which affect the chemical composition of water and therefore, in turn, its qualities. It's because of these differences that water can be described as being 'hard' or 'soft' (see below). And if you live in an area which has hard water you'll know all too well what that means. When you're washing, for example, the soap will form an insoluble curd – scum – instead of a cleansing lather. Woollens mat in the wash, hair washing becomes a misery, and a dirty tidemark is left round baths and basins which has to be laboriously wiped away. There are few things as unpleasant in a kitchen than 'fur' on the inside of a kettle (an instant sign of hard water). And if this is allowed to build up, eventually it will affect the taste of the water (as well as shortening the life of the heating element). Furthermore, hard water scale clogs ball-valves and taps, leaving an unsightly deposit round the spout.

As you can see, if the build up of scale is left unchecked it can seriously affect the efficiency of your plumbing system. A coating of scale on the element of an immersion heater, for instance, means the element has to become even hotter to get the water to the required temperature. Apart from using up expensive electricity to do this, it will soon burn itself out. The build-up of scale on the inside of pipes or a boiler will have a similar effect.

### Causes of hard water

Most of our domestic water supply starts its life as rainfall. As each droplet falls, it absorbs gases in the atmosphere such as oxygen, sulphur dioxide and carbon dioxide. It is because of the absorption of the last gas in particular that rainwater is in fact very weakly acidic. This process of absorbing or carrying impurities in suspension continues once the rain reaches the ground, and it dramatically affects the overall qualities of the water.

For example, if rainwater falls on moorland peat or sandstone the water becomes more acidic and is said to be 'soft'. However, water

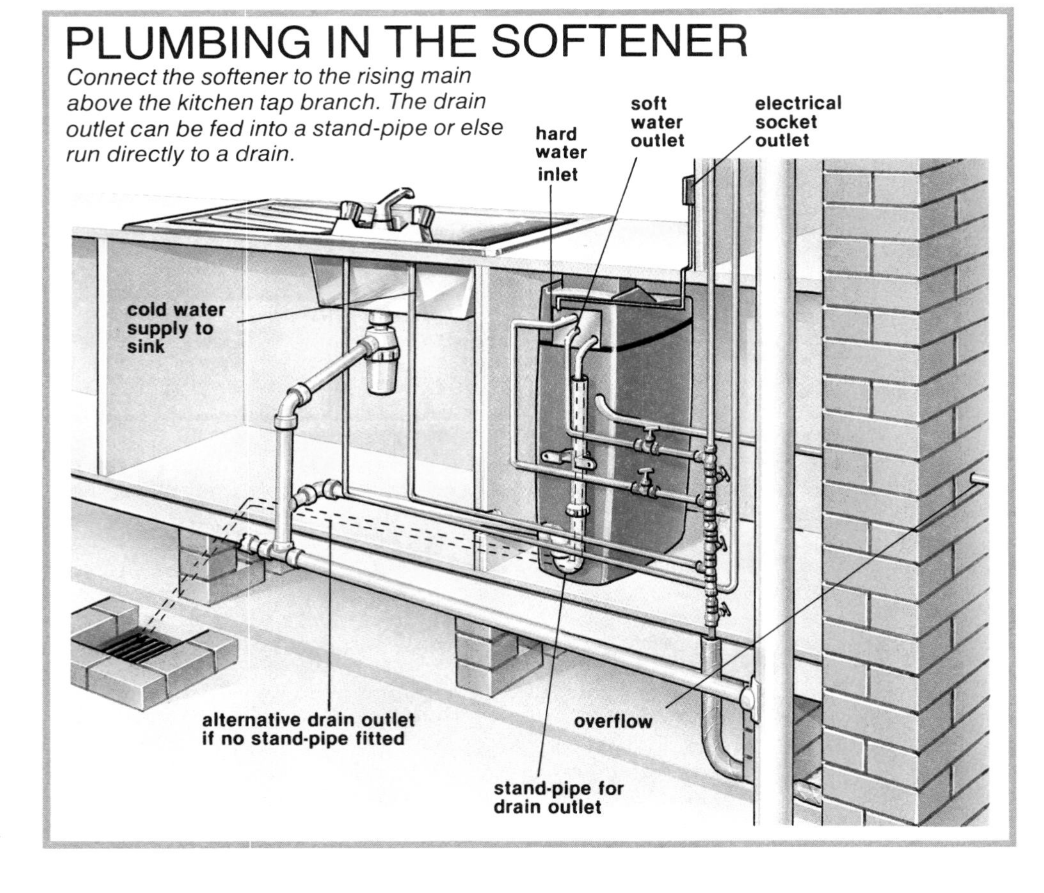


## PLUMBING IN THE SOFTENER

*Connect the softener to the rising main above the kitchen tap branch. The drain outlet can be fed into a stand-pipe or else run directly to a drain.*

# CONNECTING INTO THE MAINS

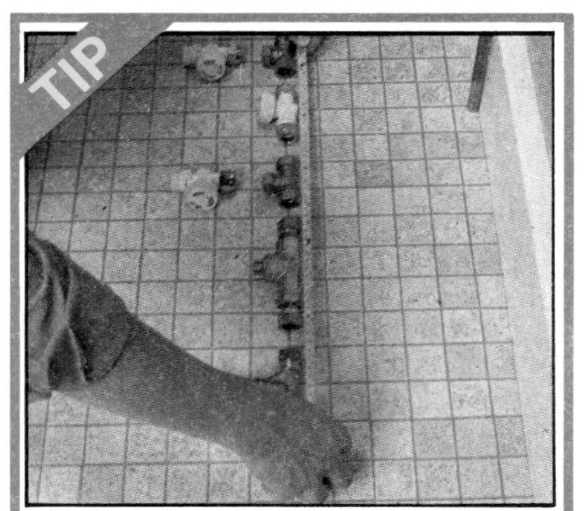


**1** *Lay out the fittings in the order they have to be assembled (see* Ready Reference*). Remember to allow for short stubs of pipe linking the fittings.*

**2** *Mark off the overall measurement of the length of fittings on the relevant section of rising main. Then turn off the water supply and drain the pipe.*

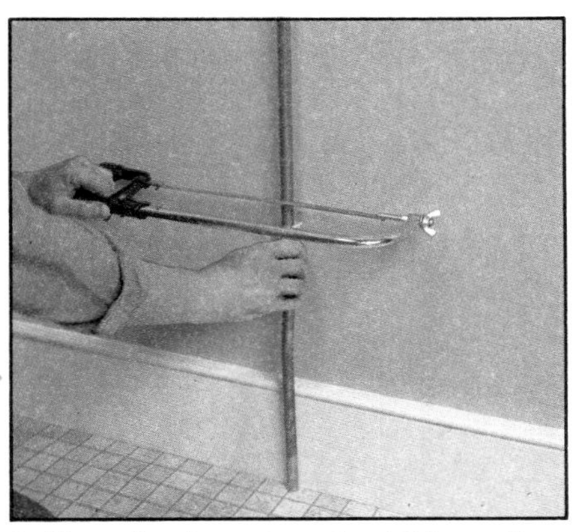

**3** *Use a hacksaw to cut out this section of pipe. Make sure you support the rising main with your free hand to reduce damaging any joints on the run.*

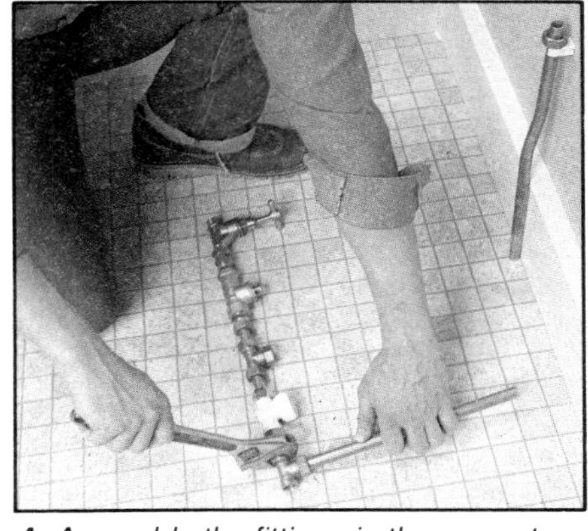

**4** *Assemble the fittings in the correct order, but leave them finger-tight. The final tightening will be done when everything is in position.*

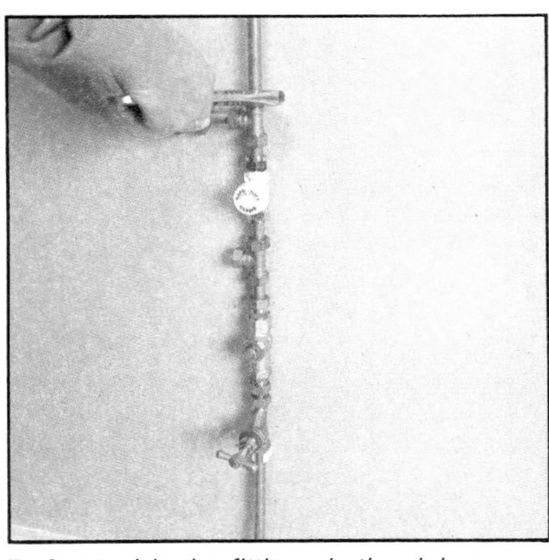

**5** *Assemble the fittings in the rising main, making sure that the compression tees are parallel to the wall. Then tighten all the joins.*

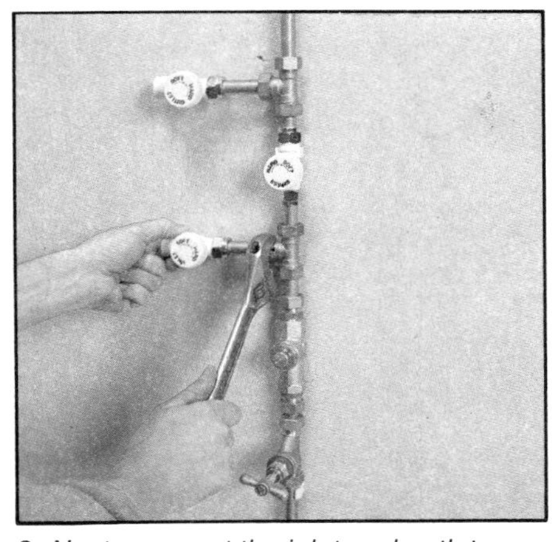

**6** *Next, connect the inlet and outlet valves to the tees (the inlet valve goes at the bottom). Turn these valves 'off' and restore the water supply.*

## Ready Reference

### DO YOU NEED A SOFTENER?

If you live in the South or East of England, or in the Midlands, you'll almost certainly have a hard water supply. Elsewhere – in the Scottish Highlands, the West Country or Wales, for instance – the water supply may be soft, but there are also pockets of hard water in these areas.

### TYPES OF HARD WATER

Hard water can either be 'temporary' or 'permanent':

- temporary hardness can be removed by boiling the water. This causes scale to be deposited which furs up kettles and hot water systems
- permanent hardness can't be removed by heating. It doesn't affect hot water systems but the other effects remain.

### TIP: PREVENT SCALE

- Scale builds up when the water temperature exceeds 60°C, so in hard water areas turn boiler thermostats down to this level. In soft water areas it can be set at 70°C.
- Convert a direct to an indirect hot water system
- Add chemical softeners to the water to prevent scale building up.

### HOW A SOFTENER WORKS

The softener has to be connected into the rising main. Water is passed through a resin where the chemicals which cause hardness – calcium and magnesium bicarbonates, sulphates and chlorides – are exchanged for sodium salts.

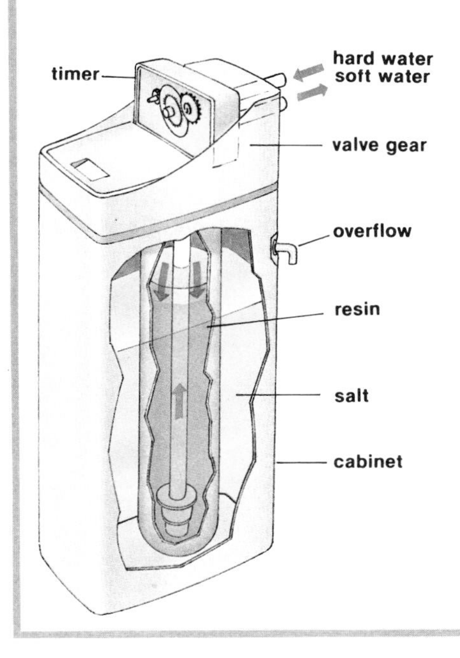

## CONNECTING UP THE WATER SOFTENER

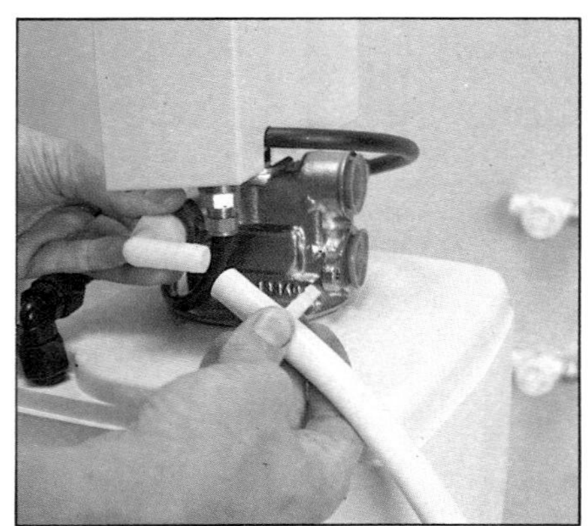

**1** *Measure the length of drain hose to run from the appliance to an outside drain. Push the end over the drain spigot and secure with a clip.*

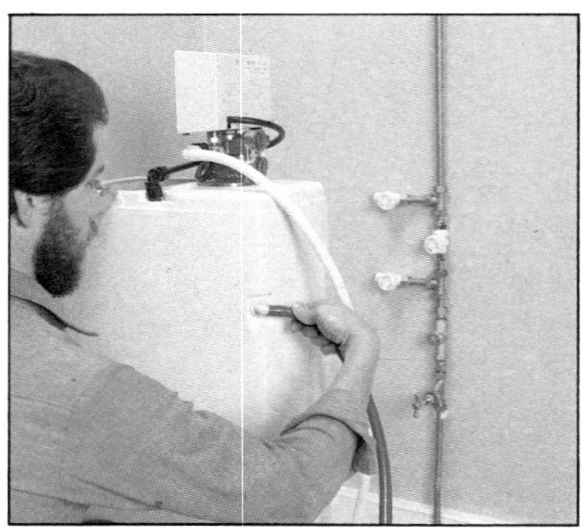

**2** *Similarly, fix a length of hose to the overflow spigot and then run it to an outside wall where you can easily see any water discharging from it.*

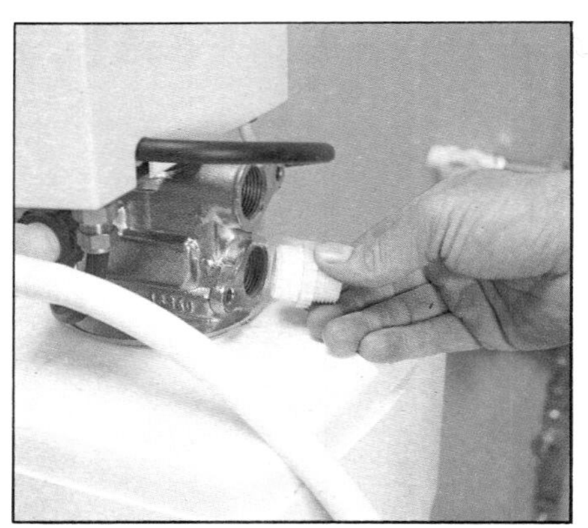

**3** *Next connect the plastic nipples to the inlet and outlet of the appliance. First wind PTFE tape round the thread and screw in the outlet nipple.*

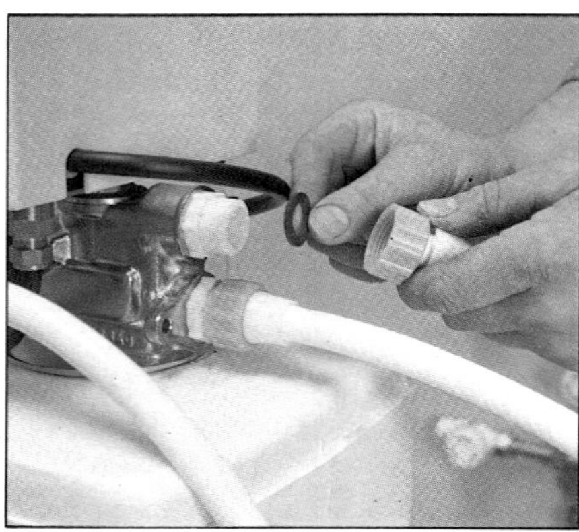

**6** *Insert a rubber washer into the end of the connector. Screw the outlet hose into position and then add the inlet hose above it.*

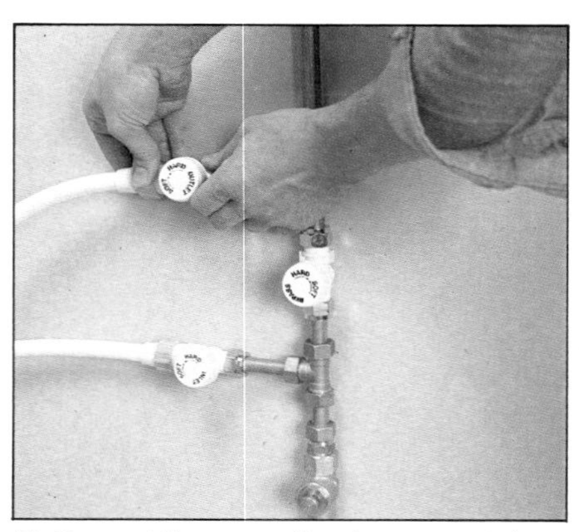

**7** *Repeat the operation to connect the hoses to the valves next to the rising main. You can use an adjustable spanner, but be careful not to overtighten the nuts.*

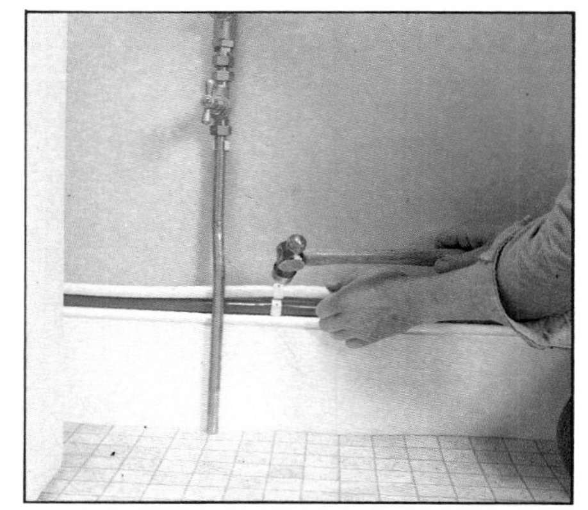

**8** *Once all the connections have been made, set the appliance in the correct position and clip the hoses neatly to the wall and skirting.*

falling on limestone (or chalk) loses its dissolved carbon dioxide as it begins to erode the rock. Such water is also likely to contain bicarbonates, sulphates and chlorides of calcium and magnesium – the chemicals that produce hardness.

### The problems of soft water

Despite the catalogue of problems associated with hard water, soft water also has some drawbacks. In particular, because soft water is acidic its corrosive properties are increased; some metals, notably iron, rust more quickly when they come into contact with it. So if you have iron pipes or tanks in a soft water area then you could expect problems as they start to corrode. The answer, obviously, is to use parts made from PVC, polythene, copper, asbestos cement or glass fibre – in other words materials not prone to this form of corrosive attack.

One other thing worth noting is that in areas where there is soft water more people are prone to cardio-vascular diseases – strokes and similar conditions – than in hard water areas. No one is really sure of the reason for this. It could be that the chemicals in hard water provide some form of natural protection. Another possible explanation is that soft water is much more likely to dissolve the metal of the pipes it flows through than hard water is – so the dissolved impurities could contribute to the diseases.

### Dealing with hard water

There are a number of ways in which the annoying effects of hard water can be reduced. Boiler scale, for instance, may be reduced or eliminated by controlling the temperature of the water or by using a chemical scale inhibitor. The most disruptive solution is to install an indirect hot water system, if you haven't already got one. Small quantities of hard water can be softened by the addition of water-softening chemicals (sold commercially as Calgon) which neutralise the dissolved salts causing the hardness. The most radical solution, though, is to install a mains water softener which can reduce to 'zero hardness' every drop of water that passes through it.

### How a mains water softener works

Mains water softeners work on a chemical principle that used to be called 'base exchange' but is now more commonly known as 'ion exchange'. The principle was discovered by observing hard water as it filtered through beds of natural sand. The water became soft. So these sands were used in the early water softeners. Now synthetic resins are used to produce the same effect. The hard water is passed through the

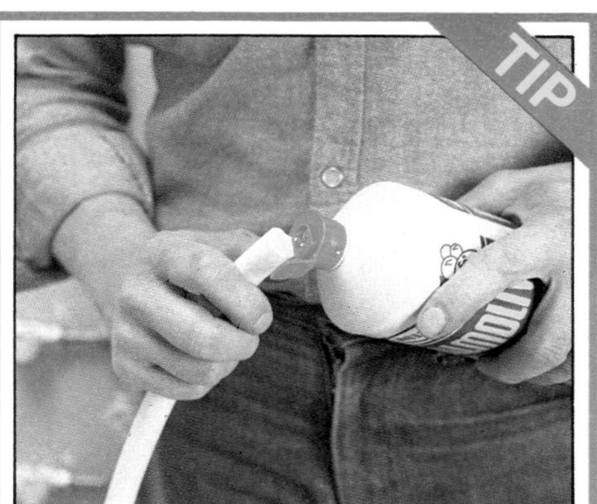

4 *Cut the feed and return hoses to length. Then lubricate the ends with washing-up liquid to make it easier to slip them over the hose connectors.*

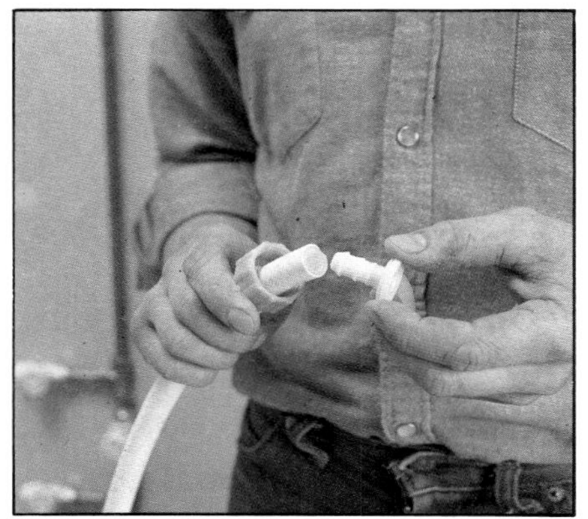

5 *Slip a nut and collar over the end of the hose, then push the end over the connector so that it butts against the shoulder.*

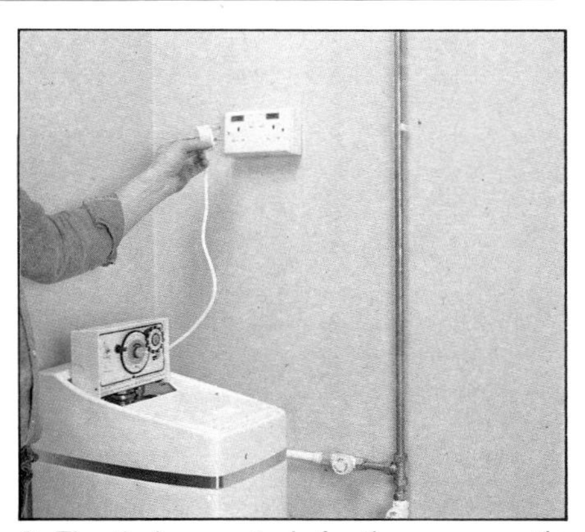

9 *The timing controls for the regeneration process have to be plugged into a convenient socket or linked to a fused connection unit.*

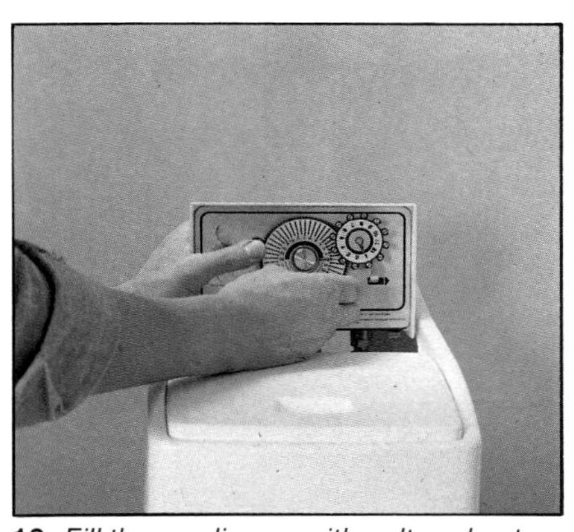

10 *Fill the appliance with salt and set the timer. The inlet and outlet valves can be opened and the bypass valve closed; the machine is then operational.*

## Ready Reference

### THE PLUMBING CONNECTIONS

Water softeners for DIY installation come with all the necessary fittings. You may also need to buy a new screw-down stop-valve. Arrange the fittings in the rising main in the following order:

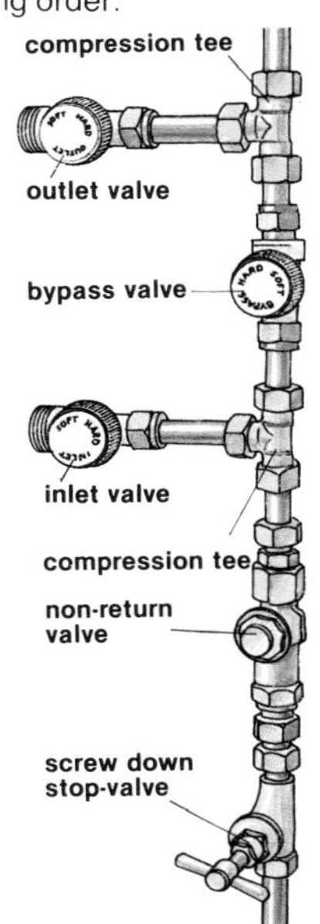


### TIP: CHECK THE STORAGE CISTERN

Fitting a water softener may reduce the pressure at the ball-valve supplying the cold water storage cistern. You may need to replace the valve with an equilibrium model.

appliance and the chemicals in the water literally 'exchange atoms' with the chemicals in the resin. The result is that dissolved *calcium* bicarbonate, for example, is replaced by dissolved *sodium* bicarbonate which does not cause hardness.

After a while, however, the softening qualities of the resin are exhausted, but they can be restored (regenerated) by passing a strong solution of sodium chloride (common salt) through the softener. The cycle of regeneration must be undertaken at regular intervals, perhaps once a week in a household with average water consumption. The resin is first backwashed to loosen up the resin bed and to remove any debris. The water is then run to waste. Next the salt solution is passed through the resin, followed by a final rinse of ordinary water to wash any surplus brine from the resin bed before the softener is brought back into use.

With early water softeners you had to carry out this regeneration process mechanically every week – a process which could become quite a chore. But now water softeners have a large salt reservoir capable of supplying brine for 25 or more regenerations. These take place automatically (usually at about 2 o'clock in the morning when everyone is asleep). The process can be started by a time clock, by a device that measures the volume of water that passes through the softener or by a sensor which can detect when the resin is beginning to lose its softening capacity. All you have to do is to replenish the salt reservoir perhaps once or twice a year.

### Installing a water softener

A mains water softener has to be plumbed in to the rising main at any convenient point, and can be used to soften every drop of water flowing into the house. However, for health reasons it's best to retain a cold supply of hard water over the kitchen sink and there's no need to soften the water supplying an outside tap. Therefore hard water remains available for drinking and cooking while soft water is used for baths, laundry and (through the hot tap over the kitchen sink) for washing up.

Once you've decided on the make and capacity of the water softener, read the installation instructions carefully and consult your local water authority before you begin. You may have to install a pressure-reducing valve as part of the installation and the authority will almost certainly demand that a non-return valve is fitted to prevent any risk of contamination of the mains supply. The step-by-step photographs show how one of these appliances is plumbed in. The provision of inlet, outlet and bypass valves means the softeners can be isolated from the mains for any maintenance that's required.

## CHAPTER 5

# PLUMBING JOBS IN THE BATHROOM

**There are many reasons why you might want to carry out plumbing work in the bathroom – to improve or increase the facilities offered or to make more efficient use of the available space by rearranging the position of fittings.**

# REPLACING A WASHBASIN

**Replacing a washbasin is fairly straightforward. It's a job you'll have to undertake if the basin is cracked – but you may also want to change the basin if you're redesigning your bathroom and adding some up-to-date fittings.**

Apart from replacing a cracked basin, which you should do immediately, the most common time to install a new basin is when you're improving a bathroom or decorating a separate WC. The chances are that the basin you'll be removing will be one of the older ceramic types, wall-hung, a pedestal model or built into a vanity unit.

The main advantage of a wall-hung basin is that it doesn't take up any floor space and because of this it is very useful in a small bathroom, WC or cloakroom. You can also set the basin at a comfortable height, unlike a pedestal basin the height of which is fixed by the height of the pedestal. However, it's usual to fit a wall-hung basin with the rim 800mm (32in) above the floor.

Vanity units are now increasing in popularity. In fact they're the descendents of the Edwardian wash-stand, with its marble top, bowl and large water jug. The unit is simply a storage cupboard with a ceramic, enamelled pressed steel or plastic basin set flush in the top. The advantage of vanity units is that you have a counter surface round the basin on which to stand toiletries. There is rarely, if ever, sufficient room for these items behind or above conventional wall-hung or pedestal basins. Usually the top has some form of plastic covering or can be tiled for easy cleaning.

### Fittings for basins

It's a good idea to choose the taps and waste fittings at the same time you select the basin, so everything matches. You could perhaps re-use the taps from the old basin, but it's doubtful if these will be in keeping with the design of the new appliance. As an alternative to shrouded head or pillar taps, you could fit a mixer, provided the holes at the back of the basin are suitably spaced to take the tap tails. But remember that because of the design of most basin mixers, you shouldn't use them if the cold water supply is directly from the mains.

Ceramic basins normally have a built-in overflow channel which in most appliances connects into the main outlet above the trap. So if you accidentally let the basin overfill you reduce the risk of water spillage.

## PUTTING IN A NEW BASIN

*You should have little trouble installing a new washbasin in the same place as the old one. It's also a good opportunity to check the pipe runs. If they're made of lead it's a good idea to replace them.*

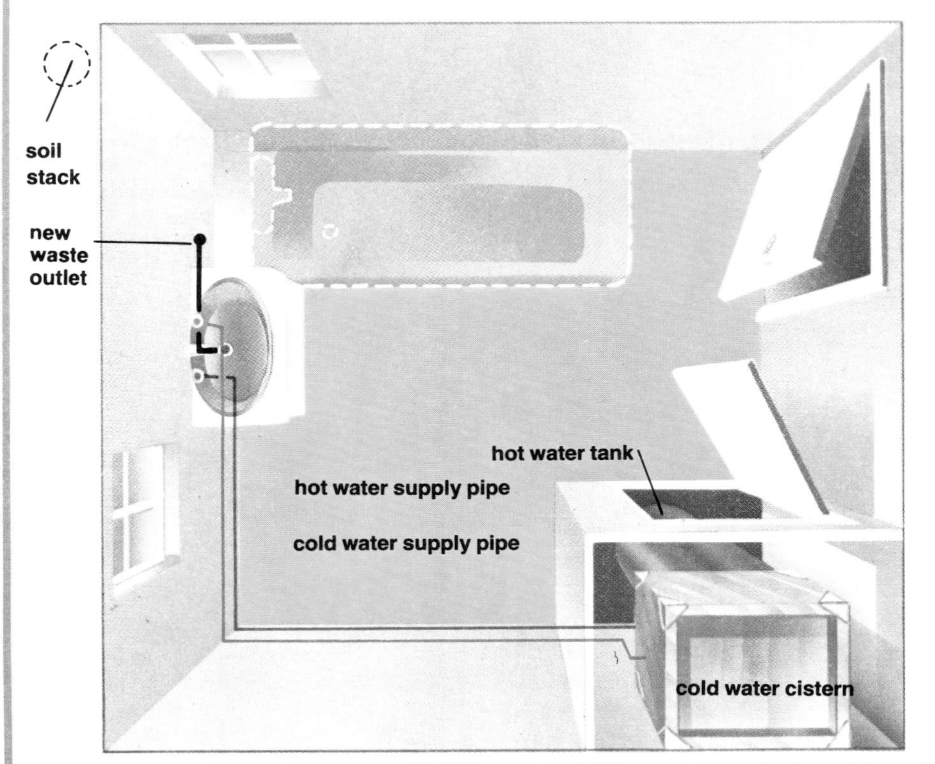

Vanity unit basins are usually sold complete with a waste and overflow unit which resembles that of a modern stainless steel sink. A flexible tube connects the overflow outlet of the basin with a sleeve or 'banjo' unit which fits tightly round a slotted waste fitting.

With both types of basin the flange of the waste outlet has to be bedded into the hole provided for it in the basin on a layer of plumber's putty. The thread of the screwed waste must also be smeared with jointing compound to ensure a watertight seal where the 'banjo' connects to it.

### Traps

The outlet of the waste must, of course, connect to a trap and branch waste pipe. At one time it was the practice to use 'shallow seal' traps with a 50mm (2in) depth of seal for two-pipe drainage systems, and 'deep seal' traps with a 75mm (3in) depth of seal for single stack systems. Today, however, deep seal traps are always fitted.

Of course, the modern bottle trap is one of the most common types used. It's neater looking and requires less space than a traditional U-trap. Where it's concealed behind a pedestal or in a vanity unit you can use one made of plastic, but there are chromium-plated and brass types if you have a wall-hung basin where trap and waste will be clearly visible. The one drawback with bottle traps is that they discharge water more slowly than a U-trap. You can now also buy traps with telescopic inlets that make it easy to provide a push-fit connection to an existing copper or plastic branch waste pipe (see page 18).

### Connecting up the water supply

It's unlikely that you'll be able to take out the old basin and install a new one without making some modification to the pipework. It's almost certain that the tap holes will be in a different position. To complicate matters further, taps are now made with shorter tails so you'll probably have to extend the supply pipes by a short length.

If you're installing new supply pipes, how you run them will depend on the type of basin you're putting in. With a wall-hung basin or the pedestal type, the hot and cold pipes are usually run neatly together up the back wall and then bent round to the tap tails. But as a vanity unit will conceal the plumbing there's no need to run the pipes together.

You might find it difficult to bend the required angles, so an easy way round the problem is to use flexible corrugated copper pipe which you can bend by hand to the shape you need. You can buy the pipe with a swivel tap connector at one end and a plain connector, on which you can use capillary or

## FITTING A VANITY UNIT

**1** *Cut a hole in the vanity unit with the help of the template provided or, if the hole is precut, check the measurement against that of the sink.*

**2** *Prop the basin up while you install the mixer unit. Start with the outlet spout which is fixed with a brass nut and packing washers.*

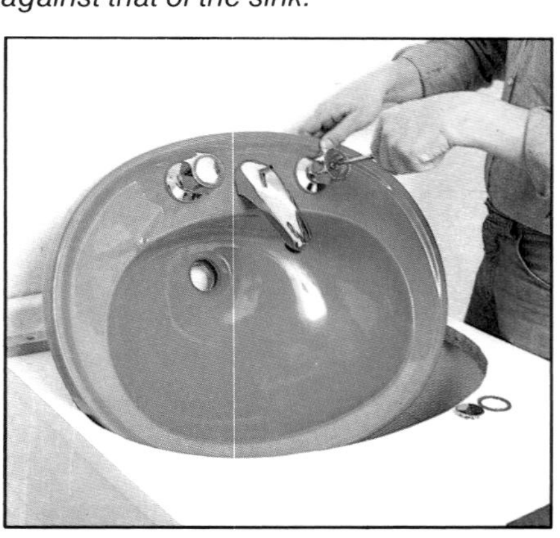

**5** *Now complete the tap heads by first sliding on the flange which covers up the securing nut; next put on the headwork and tighten the retaining nut.*

**6** *Finish off the tap assembly by fitting the coloured markers into place (red for hot is usually on the left), and gently pressing home the chrome cap.*

**9** *Before you put the basin into its final position put a strip of mastic around the opening in the vanity unit to ensure a watertight seal.*

**10** *Press the basin gently into position and fix it to the underside of the top of the vanity unit. Attach the waste plug to its keeper.*

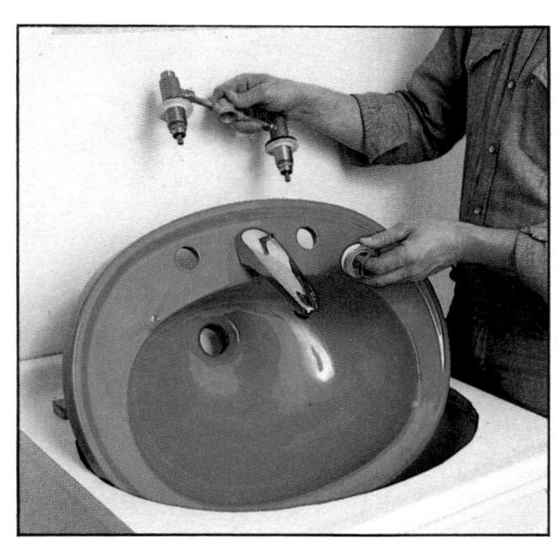

**3** *Now take the water inlet assembly and check that the hot and cold spur pipes are the right length so that the tap sub-assemblies are correctly positioned.*

**4** *Fix the assembly in position with the brass nuts supplied by the manufacturer. Make sure that all the washers are included otherwise the fitting won't be secure.*

**7** *Now insert the waste outlet. Make sure the rubber flange is fitted properly and seats comfortably into the basin surround.*

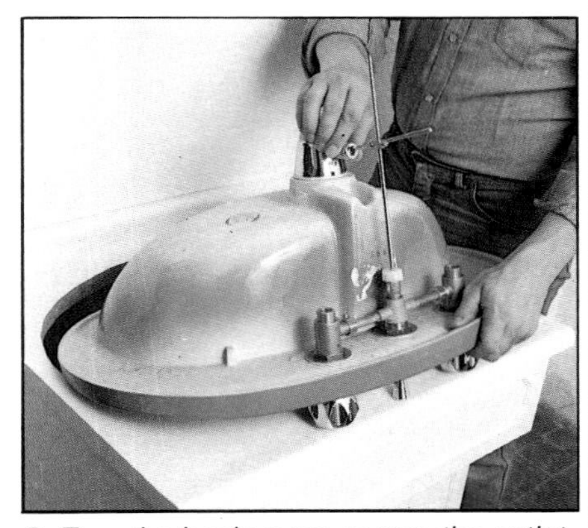

**8** *Turn the basin over; secure the outlet and the pop-up waste control rods. These may need shortening depending on clearance inside the vanity unit.*

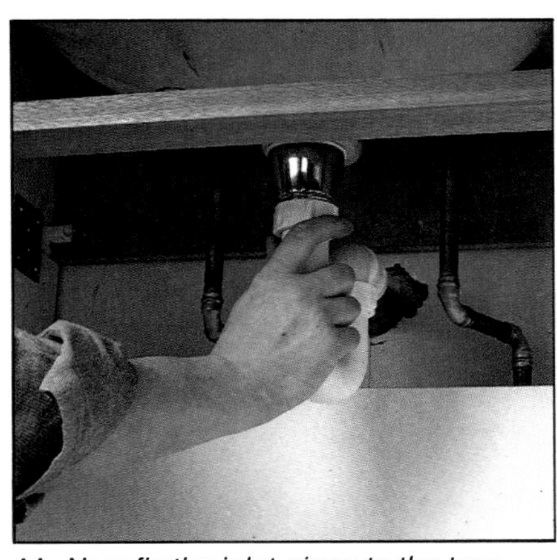

**11** *Now fix the inlet pipes to the two mixer connections and screw on the waste trap. Take the doors off the vanity unit to make access easier.*

**12** *Turn the water back on and check for leaks. Check the pop-up waste system works, then put the doors of the vanity unit back on.*

# Ready Reference

## BASIN SIZES

On basins, the dimension from side to side is specified as the length, and that from back to front as the width.

Most standard sized basins are between 550 and 700mm (22 and 28in) long, and 450 to 500mm (18 to 20in) wide.

## BASIN COMPONENTS

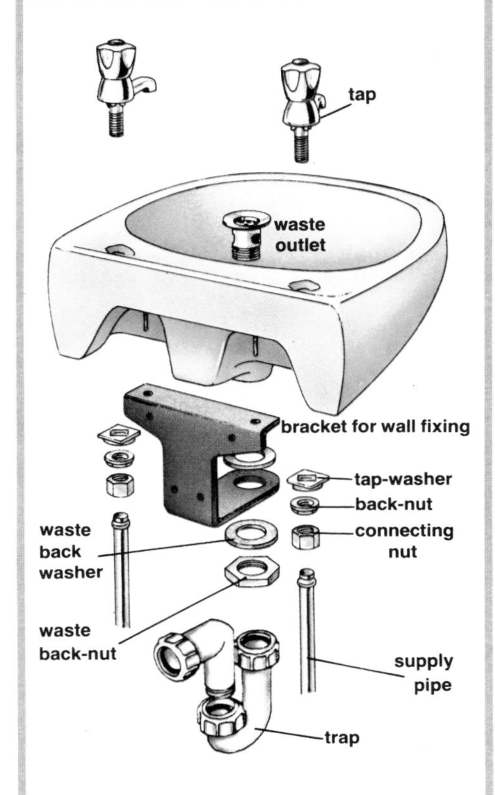


## THE SPACE YOU'LL NEED

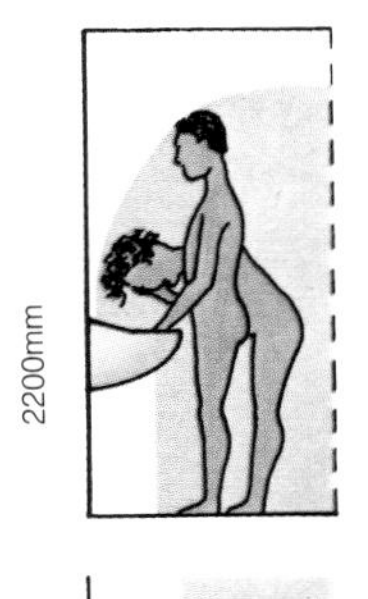


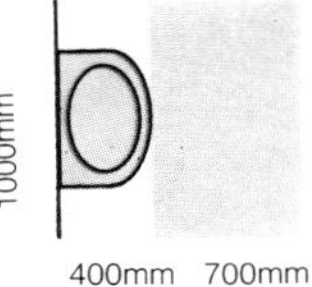


Think about the space around your basin particularly if you are installing a new one. You not only need elbow room when you are bending over it, such as when you are washing your hair, but also room in front to stand back – especially if you put a mirror above it. Here are the recommended dimensions for the area around your basin.

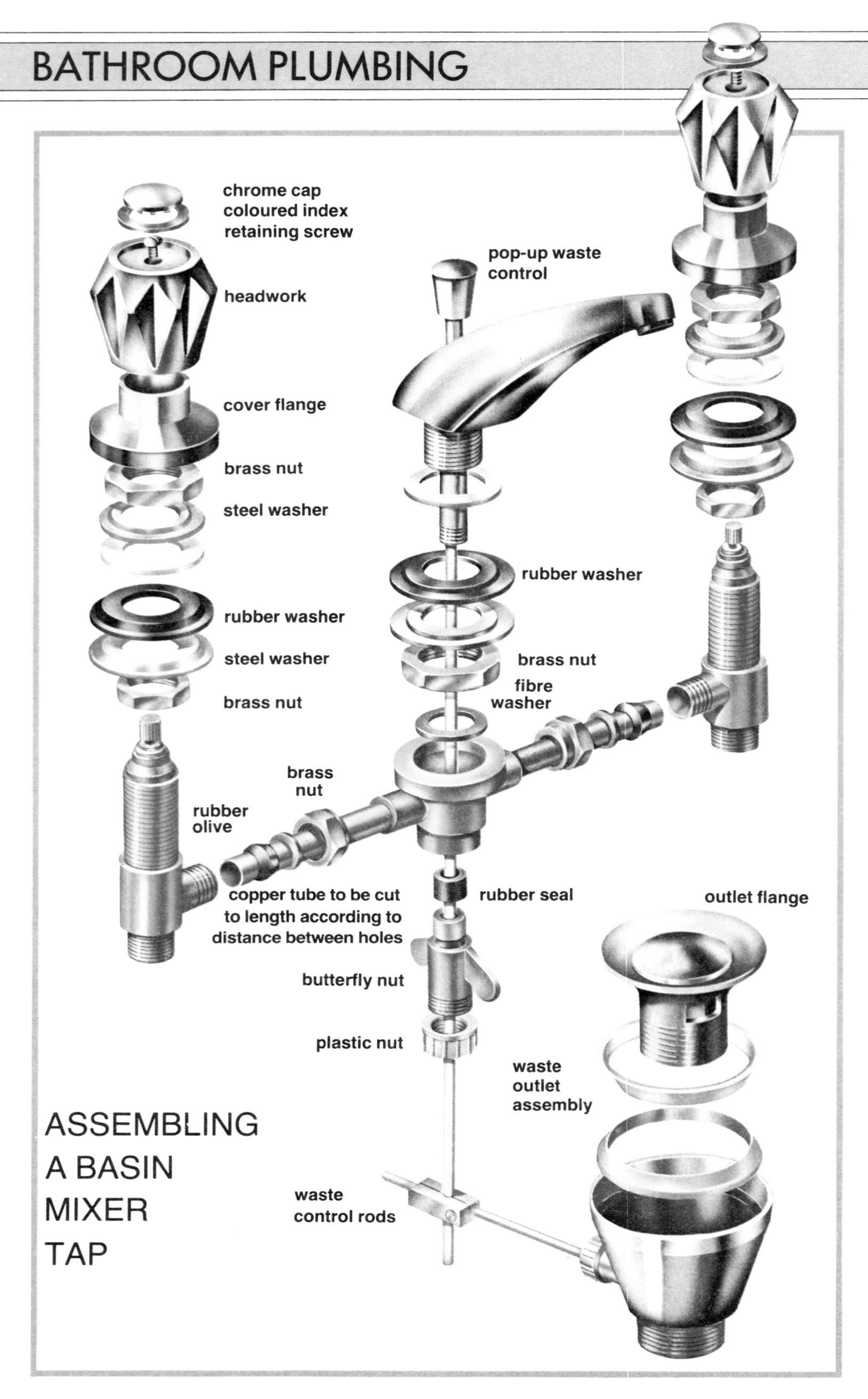


ASSEMBLING A BASIN MIXER TAP

compression fittings at the other. If you're using ordinary copper pipe, the easiest way to start is by bending the pipe to the correct angle first, and then cutting the pipe to the right length at each end afterwards. See pages 25 to 27.

### Preparing the basin

Before you fix the basin in position, you'll need to fit the taps (or mixer) and the waste. It's much easier to do this at this stage than later when the basin is against the wall because you will have more room to manoeuvre in.

When fitting the taps all you have to do is to remove the back-nuts and slip flat plastic washers over the tails (if they aren't there already). The taps can then be positioned in the holes in the basin. When this has been done more plastic washers (or top hat washers) have to be slipped over the tails before the back-nuts are replaced. It's important not to overtighten these as it's quite easy to damage a ceramic basin.

Because some vanity unit basins are made of a thinner material, you may find that the shanks of the taps fitted into them will protrude below the under-surface of the basin. The result is that when the back-nut is fully tightened, it still isn't tight against the underside of the basin. To get round the problem you have to fit a top hat washer over the shank so the back-nut can be screwed up against it.

Mixers usually have one large washer or gasket between the base of the mixer and the top of the basin and you fix them in exactly the same way.

When you've fitted the taps you can then fit the waste. With a ceramic basin you'll have to use a slotted waste to enable water from the overlfow to escape into the drainage pipe. Getting this in place means first removing the back-nut so you can slip it through the outlet hole in the basin – which itself should be coated with a generous layer of plumber's putty. It's essential to make sure that the slot in the waste fitting coincides with the outlet of the basin's built-in overflow. You'll then have to smear jointing compound on the protruding screw thread of the tail, slip on a plastic washer and replace and tighten the back-nut. As you do this the waste flange will probably try to turn on its seating, but you can prevent this by holding the grid with pliers as you tighten the back-nut.

Finally, any excess putty that is squeezed out as the flange is tightened against the basin should be wiped away.

A vanity unit will probably be supplied with a combined waste and overflow unit. This is a flexible hose that has to be fitted (unlike a ceramic basin, where it's an integral part of the appliance). The slotted waste is bedded in exactly the same way as a waste on a ceramic basin. You then have to fit one end of the overflow to the basin outlet and slip the 'banjo' outlet on the other end over the tail of the waste to cover the slot. It's held in position by a washer and back-nut.

### Fitting the basin

Once the taps and waste have been fixed in position on the new basin, you should be ready to remove the old basin and fit the new one in its place. First you need to cut off the water supply to the basin, either by turning off the main stop-valve (or any gate valve on the distribution pipes) or by tying up the ball-valve supplying the main cold water storage cistern. Then open the taps and leave them until the water ceases to flow. If the existing basin is a pedestal model you'll have to remove the pedestal which may be screwed to the floor. Take off the nut that connects the basin trap to the threaded waste outlet and unscrew the nuts that connect the water supply pipes to the tails of the taps. These will either be swivel tap connectors or cap and lining joints. You'll need to be able to lift the basin clear and then remove the brackets or hangers on which it rests.

You'll probably need some help when installing the new basin as it's much easier to mark the fixing holes if someone else is holding the basin against the wall. With a pedestal basin, the pedestal will determine the level of the basin. The same applies with a vanity unit. But if the basin is set on hangers or brackets, you can adjust the height for convenience.

Once the fixing holes have been drilled and plugged, the basin can be screwed into position and you can deal with the plumbing. Before you make the connections to the water supply pipes you may have to cut or lengthen them to meet the tap tails. If you need to lengthen them you'll find it easier to use corrugated copper pipe. The actual connection between pipe and tail is made with a swivel tap connector – a form of compression fitting.

Finally you have to connect the trap. You may be able to re-use the old one, but it's more likely you'll want to fit a new one. And if its position doesn't coincide with the old one, you can use a bottle trap with an adjustable telescopic inlet.

## FITTING A PEDESTAL BASIN

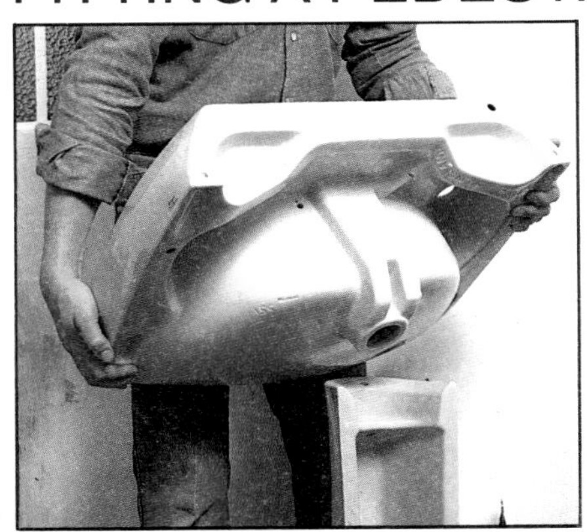

**1** *Stand the basin on the pedestal to check the height of the water supply pipe runs and the outlet. Measure the height of the wall fixing points.*

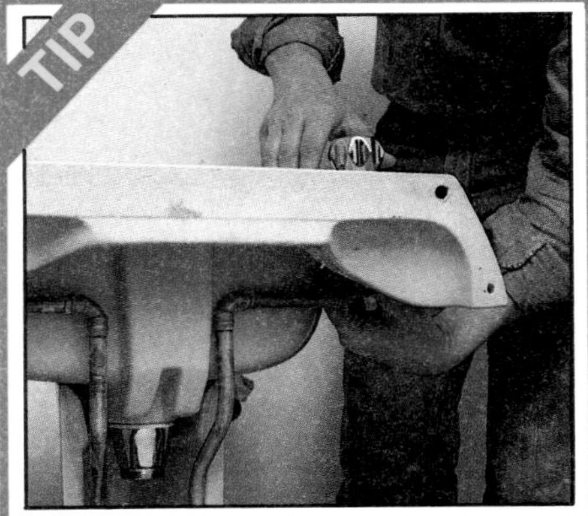


**2** *When you're making up the pipe run to connect to the tap tails, plan it so the pipes are neatly concealed within the body of the pedestal.*

**3** *Line up the piped waste outlet and fix the trap to the basin outlet. A telescopic trap may be useful here to adjust for a varying level.*

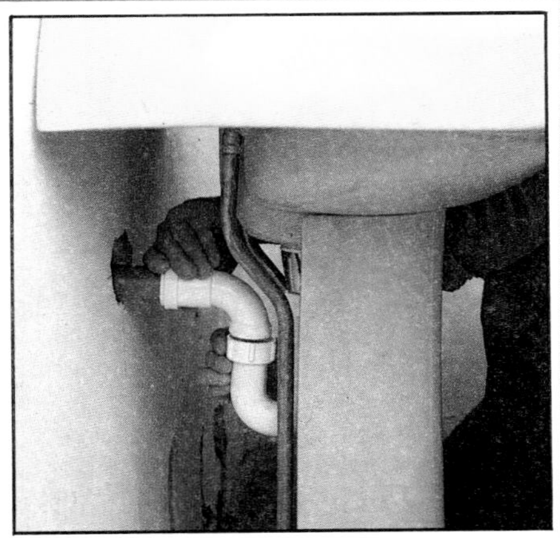

**4** *Move the whole unit into its final position, screw the basin to the wall, connect the waste trap to the outlet, and connect up the supply pipes.*

## Ready Reference

### TYPES OF BASIN

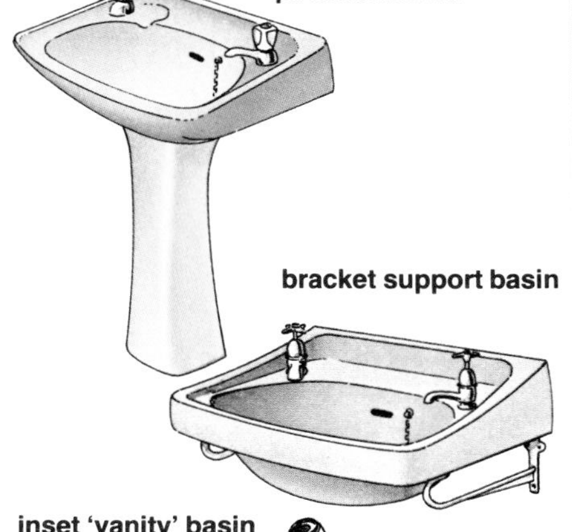

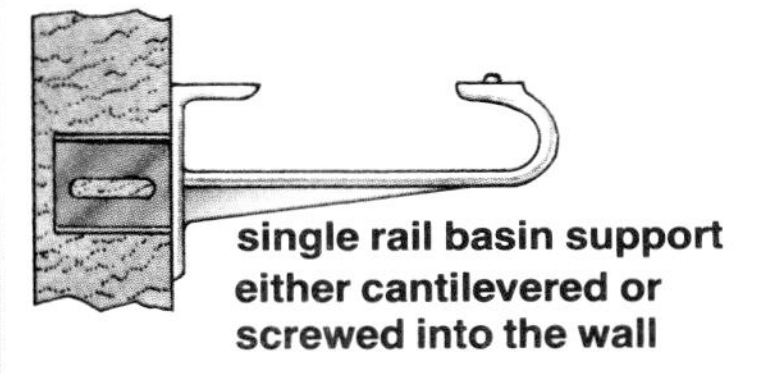


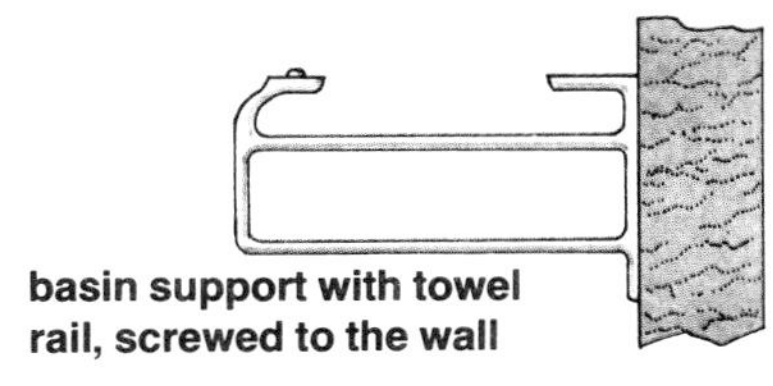


### FITTING A VANITY BASIN

When you buy a vanity basin it should be supplied with a template to guide you in cutting your work surface or vanity unit. This should also include fitting instructions, and necessary fixing screws and mastic strip. It may look like this.

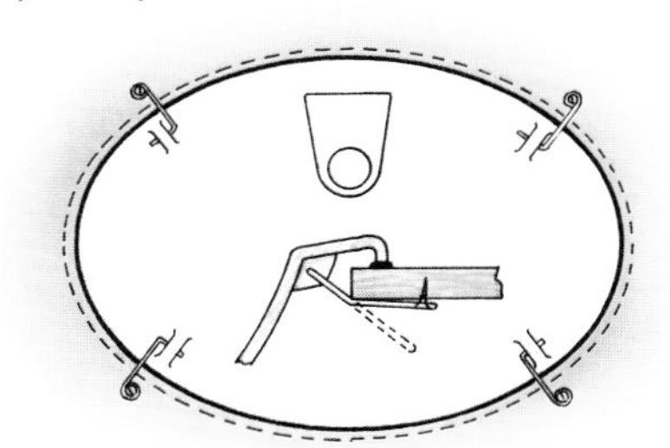

# PLUMBING IN A BATH

**Replacing a bath may seem to be an ambitious do-it-yourself project but it is well within the capabilities of the determined home handyman prepared to tackle the job carefully and logically. Here is what is involved.**

As with many other plumbing projects the most difficult part is likely to be the removal of the old fitting rather than the installation of the new one.

The old bath will almost certainly be made of enamelled cast iron. The once-white enamel may be discoloured and wearing away, and may even reveal rusting bare metal underneath. Green or brown coloured stains beneath the taps indicate a long-neglected need for rewashering. The taps may look out of date and have worn chromium plating. The finish of the bath may be old and unattractive and the bath itself not panelled in.

## Checking it out

First have a look at the existing bath. If there are side or end panels, strip them off and examine, with the aid of an electric torch, the water supply pipes and the waste and the overflow arrangements in the cramped and badly lit space between the foot of the bath and the wall. You will see that the water supply pipes connect the threaded tails of the taps by means of brass 'swivel tap connectors' or 'cap and lining joints'.

Check whether the water supply pipes are made of copper or lead by scraping their surface with the blade of a pocket knife. If this reveals the characteristic grey sheen of lead you should think of replacing the piping. If you *do* want to retain the lead piping you will have to call in a qualified plumber – it's not an easy task. If the pipes are of copper you should be able to tackle the entire project without professional aid.

The overflow from a modern bath is taken, by means of a flexible pipe, to the waste trap. In the past, the overflow pipe often simply led through the external wall, and was the source of incurable bathroom draughts. If your bath's overflow is like this, you'll have to cut it off flush with the wall.

If the bath has adjustable feet, apply some penetrating oil to the screws. Once they begin to move, lowering the level of the bath before you attempt to remove it can help to prevent damage to the wall tiling.

## The alternatives

It is possible to replace your cast iron bath with a new one made of the same material, but more modern in styling. However, these baths are expensive and very heavy indeed. Carrying one into the bathroom and fitting it requires considerable strength (you'd need at least one strong helper) as well as care. There are other snags about enamelled cast iron baths. They normally have a slippery base that can make them dangerous to use – particularly by the very young and the elderly, though some are available with a non-slip surface. Furthermore, the material of which they are made rapidly conducts the heat away from the water and while this didn't matter too much in the days when energy was plentiful and cheap, large amounts of hot water cost rather more today.

One economical alternative is an enamelled pressed steel bath. This is lighter and cheaper than enamelled cast iron but can be more easily damaged in storage or installation.

For do-it-yourself installation a plastic bath is the obvious choice. These are made of acrylic plastic sheet, sometimes reinforced with glass fibre. They are available in a number of attractive colours and, as the colour extends right through the material of which they are made, any surface scratches can be easily polished out. They are light in weight and one man can quite easily carry one upstairs for installation. The plastic of which they are made is a poor conductor of heat which means that they are both comfortable and economical to use. Many of them have a non-slip base to make them safe.

But plastic baths do have their snags. They are easily damaged by extreme heat. You should be beware of using a blow torch in proximity to one and a lighted cigarette should never be rested, even momentarily, on the rim. A fault of early plastic baths was their tendency to creak and sag when filled with hot water and, sometimes, when you got into them. This has now been overcome by the manufacturers who provide substantial frames or cradles for support; but these frames must be assembled and fixed exactly as recommended. Some come already attached to the bath.

A combined plastic waste and overflow assembly is likely to be the choice nowadays for any bath, and is obligatory with a plastic bath. If a rigid metal trap is used with a plastic bath, the material of the bath could be damaged as hot water causes unequal expansion.

You obviously won't want to re-use the old bath taps and will probably opt for either individual modern ¾in bath pillar taps or a bath mixer. A mixer should be chosen only if the cold water supply is taken from the same cold

## REPOSITIONING A BATH

*In many bathrooms, a new bath simply takes the place of an existing one; there's no room for manoeuvre. But in some cases moving the bath to another position in the room can lead to a more practical arrangement and better use of the available space. In this bathroom the new bath was installed at the other side of the room, so that the space it had formerly occupied could house a shower cubicle and a WC. Moving the bath to this position involved extending the existing hot and cold water supply pipes, but brought it nearer the soil stack on the outside wall and meant that the waste pipe was short and simple to connect up outside.*

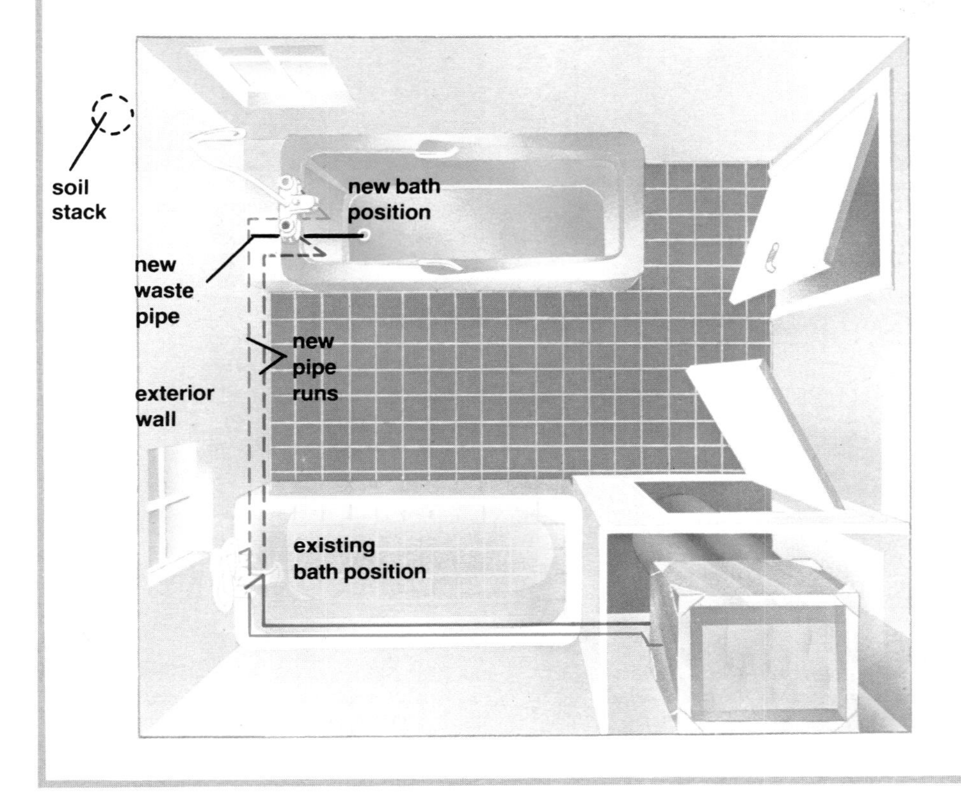


water storage cistern that supplies the hot water system. It should not be used where the cold water supply to the bathroom comes directly from the mains supply.

### How to proceed

To avoid too long a disruption of the domestic hot and cold water supplies you can fit the taps, waste and trap into the new bath before removing the old one.

Slip a flat plastic washer over the tail of each tap and insert the tails through the holes provided for them. A mixer usually has one large flat washer or gasket with two holes — one for each tap tail. Beneath the rim of the bath, slip 'top hat' or 'spacer' washers over the tails to accommodate the protruding shanks of the taps. Screw on the back-nuts and tighten them. For details, see pages 57 to 59.

Bed the waste flange onto plumber's putty or non-setting mastic, secure the back-nut and connect up the trap. Then connect up the overflow pipe.

Removing the old bath may well be the most difficult part of the procedure. Turn off the hot and cold water supplies and drain the distribution pipes from the bath taps. If you haven't done so already, remove the bath panel to give access to the plumbing at the foot of the bath. You can try to unscrew the back-nuts holding the taps in position, but it's generally easier to undo the nuts that connect the distribution pipes to the tails of the taps. In order to reach the one nearest the wall you may have to dismantle the overflow, either by unscrewing it or, if it is taken through the wall, by cutting it off flush with the wall. Then undo the waste connection.

The bath is now disconnected from the water supply pipes and from the branch waste pipe and can be pulled away from the wall. Unless you particularly want to save the old bath and

## Ready Reference

### EQUIPMENT ROUND-UP

To replace a bath, you're likely to need the following tools:

- crowsfoot wrench
- adjustable spanner
- adjustable wrench
- hacksaw (possibly)
- spirit level

You'll also need:

- new bath — measure up carefully before you buy it to make sure it fits. It should come complete with supports, carcase and side panels, otherwise you'll need these as well
- new overflow connection, waste outlet and PVC trap
- taps/mixer and new inlet pipe if you are replacing them
- plumber's putty

### KNOW YOUR BATH

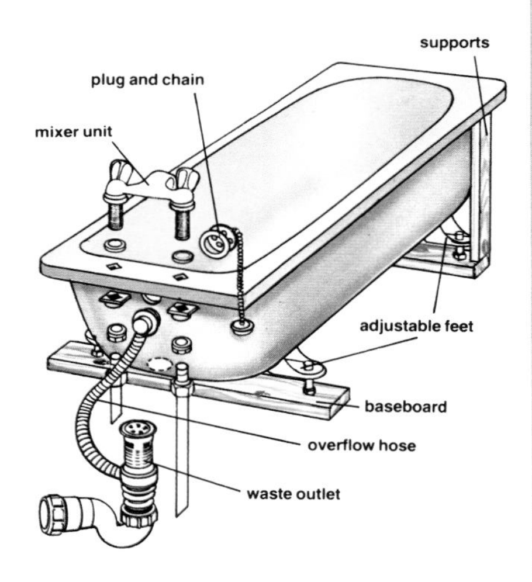


### THE SPACE YOU NEED

You need a minimum amount of space around a bath (below) and also a minimum ceiling height above it (right).

2200mm
1100mm
700mm
700mm
1700mm

have some strong helpers, do not attempt to remove it from the room or the house in one piece. It is very heavy. The best course of action is to break it into manageable pieces. Drape an old blanket over it to prevent flying chips of enamel and wear goggles to protect the eyes. Then, with a club hammer, break the bath up into pieces that you can easily carry away.

Place the new plastic bath in position and assemble the cradle or other support exactly as recommended by the manufacturer. It is most unlikely that the tails of the new taps will coincide with the position of the tap connectors of the old distribution pipes. If they don't, the easiest way of making the connections is by means of bendable copper pipe. This is corrugated copper tubing – easily bent by hand. It is obtainable in 15mm and 22mm sizes and either with two plain ends for connection to soldered capillary or compression joints, or with one plain end and a swivel tap connector at the other. For this particular job two lengths of 22mm corrugated copper pipe will be required, each with one end plain and one end fitted with a swivel tap connector.

Offer the corrugated pipe lengths up to the tap tails and cut back the distribution pipes to the length required for connection to the plain ends. Leave these pipes slightly too long rather than too short. The corrugated pipe can be bent to accommodate a little extra length. Now connect the plain ends to the cut distribution pipes using either soldered capillary or Type 'A' compression couplings.

The chances are that the distribution pipes will be ¾in imperial size. If you use compression fittings an adaptor — probably simply a larger olive — will be needed for connection to a 22mm coupling. If you use soldered capillary fittings, special ¾in to 22mm couplings must be used. Remember to keep the blowtorch flame well away from the plastic of the bath. Connect up the swivel tap connectors of the corrugated pipe and the overflow of the bath. Do this in a logical order. First connect the tap connector to the further tap. A fibre washer inside the nut of the tap connector will ensure a watertight joint. Then connect up the flexible overflow pipe of the combined waste-and-overflow fitting to the bath's overflow outlet. Finally connect the nearer tap to the nearer tap connector.

If you have installed new pipework then you can install the entire trap, waste and water supply pipe spurs before moving the bath into position. Whatever you have decided upon, finish making all the connections, then reinstate the water supply and check for leaks.

The level of the positioned bath should now be checked using a spirit level, and adjustments made (you'll need a spanner to set the adjustable feet). When all is level, fit the side and end panels in position and the job is finished.

## TAKING OUT THE OLD BATH

*1 Think about how you're going to get the old bath out before you begin. The connections are likely to be inaccessible, old and corroded.*

*2 Start by trying to detach the waste trap using an adjustable wrench and, if necessary, penetrating oil.*

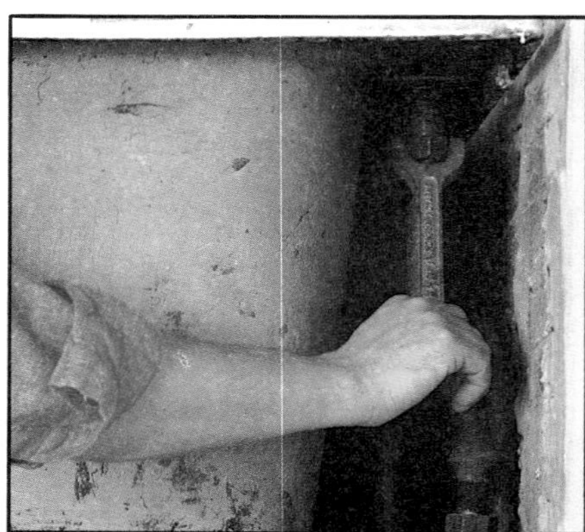

*3 Undo the back-nuts underneath the taps or mixer. These are likely to be more difficult to undo than the trap; use a crowsfoot wrench.*

*4 If the back-nuts won't undo you may have to detach the supply pipes at another joint. Use an adjustable spanner to undo the nut.*

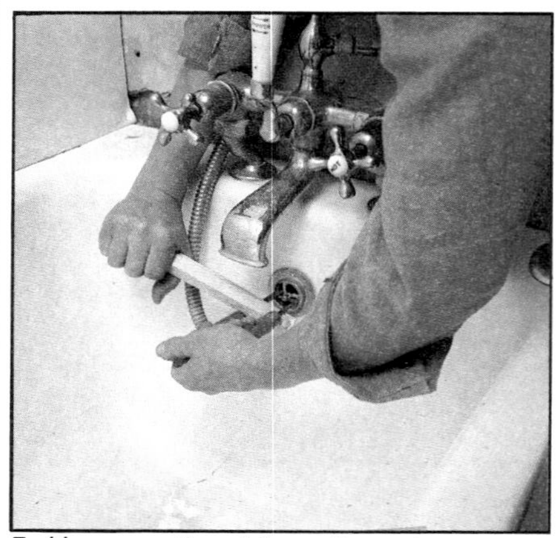

*5 Unscrew the old overflow pipe. Alternatively you can simply saw off both supply and overflow pipes — but you'll need to install new ones.*

*6 When the bath is free, drag it out of position. You'll need at least one other person to help you get a cast iron bath out unless you break it up first.*

## ATTACHING THE NEW FITTINGS

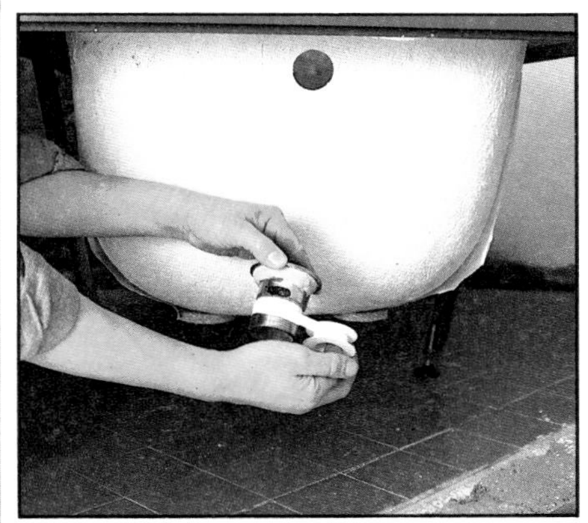

**1** *Start to assemble the new plumbing. Wind PTFE tape around the screw thread of the waste outlet and spread some plumber's putty underneath the rim.*

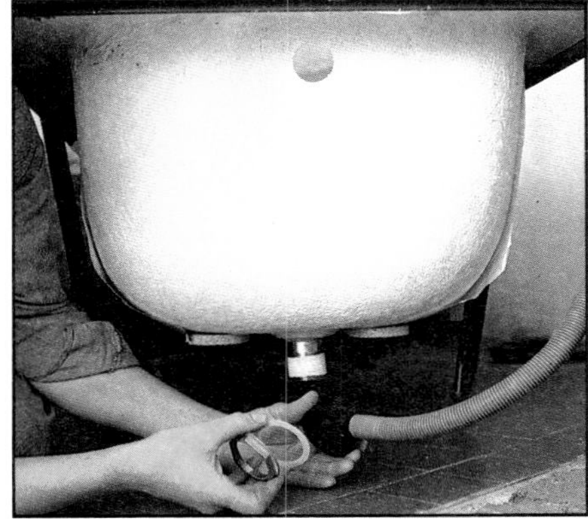

**2** *Put the waste outlet in position and make sure that it is firmly seated. These days the overflow will be made of plastic and connects to the waste outlet.*

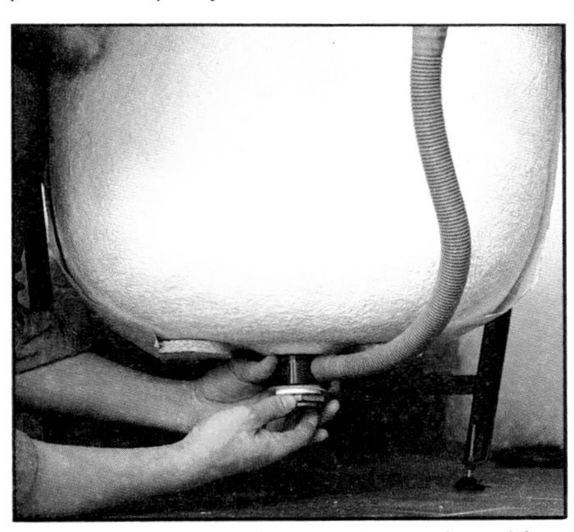

**3** *Attach the overflow to the outlet with a locking nut and a plastic O ring, which is inserted between them. Screw up the nut and tighten gently.*

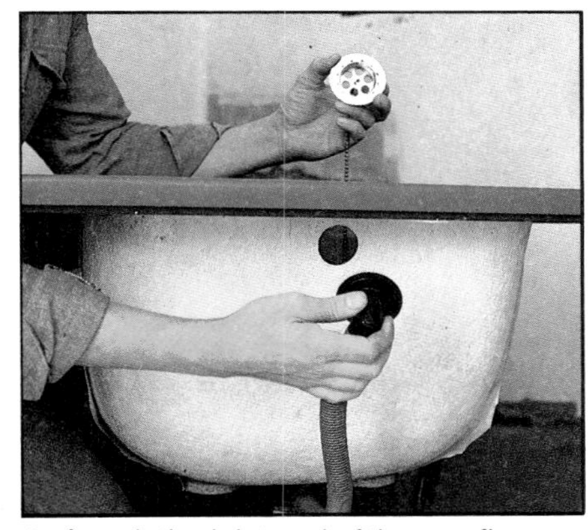

**4** *Attach the inlet end of the overflow which will have the plug and chain attached to it. Screw it into the pipe connector and tighten it up.*

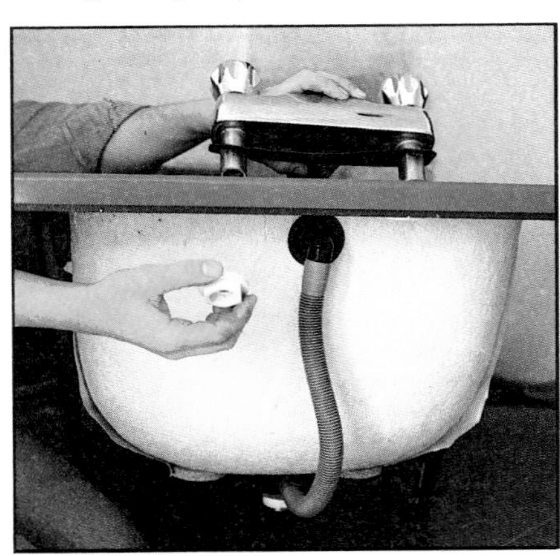

**5** *Take the mixer and check that the rubber gasket is in position between the unit and the bath, and also that it is clean and free from bits of grit.*

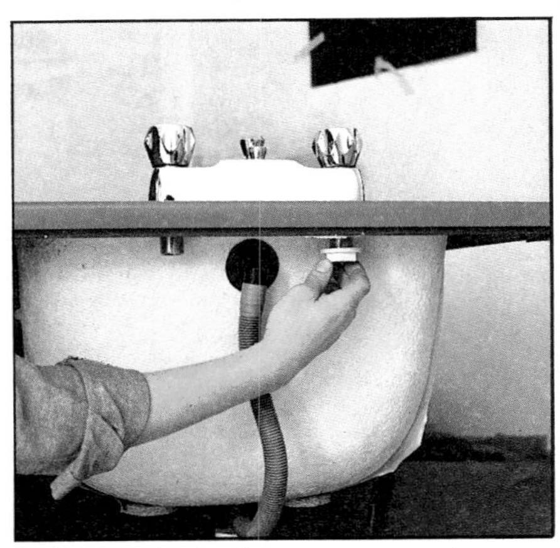

**6** *Screw the back-nuts up onto the trap and tighten them. Insert a flat plastic washer or top hat washer between the nut and the bath.*

## Ready Reference

### BATH TYPES

Most baths sold today have outside dimensions of about 1675mm (66in) long, 750mm (30in) wide, and 550mm (21in) high. Shorter baths are available for particularly small bathrooms and these are roughly 1525mm (60in) and 1375mm (54in) long. Other baths may be up to 1825mm (72in) long and 1100mm (43in) wide. They also come in different bottom mouldings to make them safe and often have handles to help the less active get in and out. Although most are basically rectangular inside and out some are oval-shaped and designed to fit into corners. There are also special baths for the disabled which are much shorter and formed in the shape of a seat.

**Plain traditional rectangular**

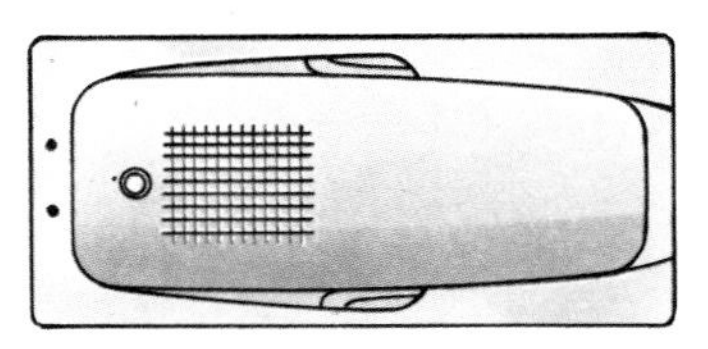

**Off-rectangular with handles**

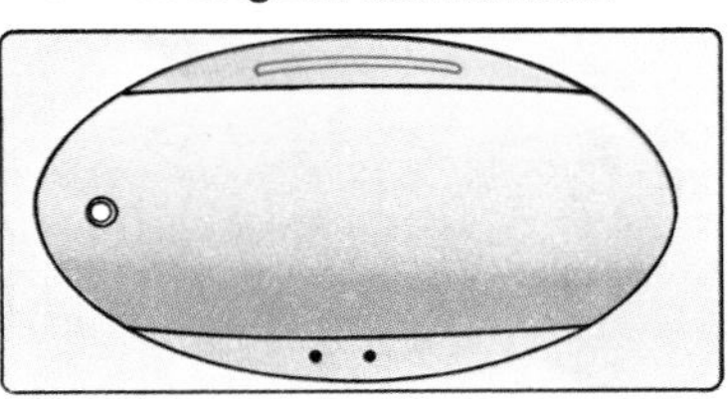

**Large oval with side plumbing**

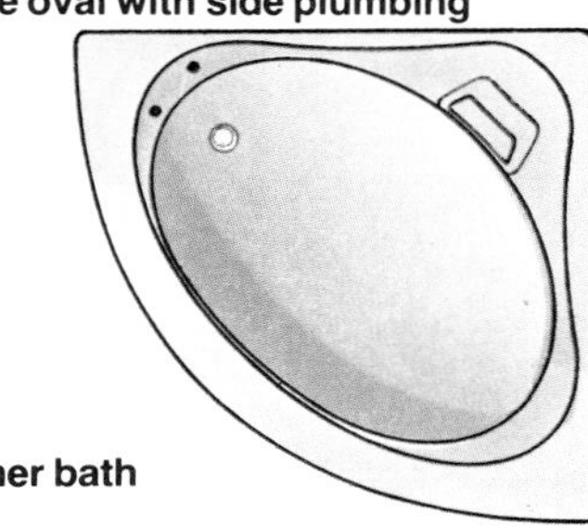

**Corner bath**

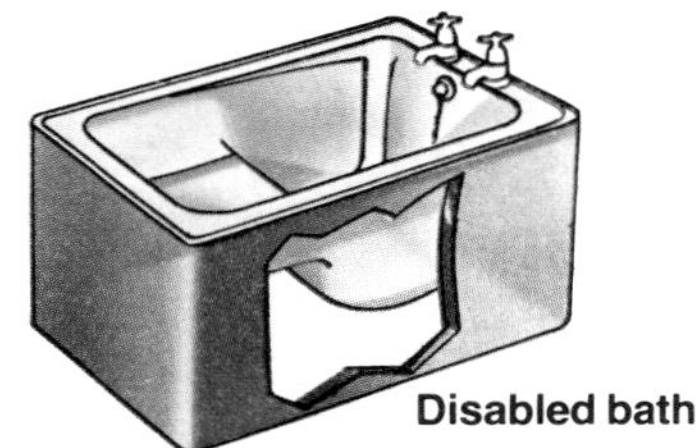

**Disabled bath**

# INSTALLING THE NEW BATH

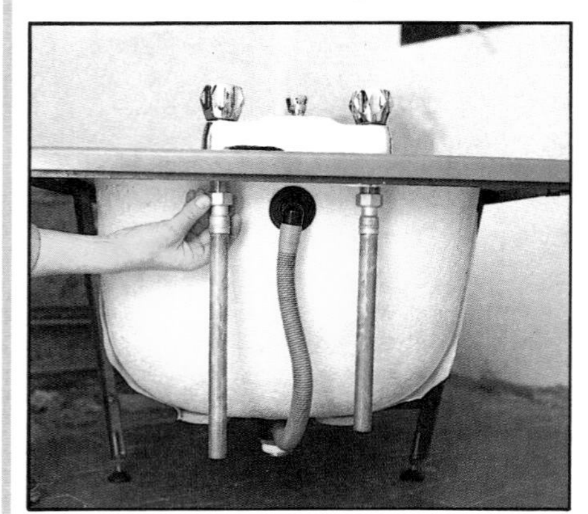

**1** *If you have installed new pipework, you should attach inlet spurs to the taps before you have to install the bath in its final position.*

**2** *Put the bath into position. You may want to stand it away from the wall at the front end so that you can build in a shelf. Connect the inlet pipes.*

**3** *Fit the waste trap and attach it to the waste pipe. When all the pipework is connected up, turn on the water and check for leaks.*

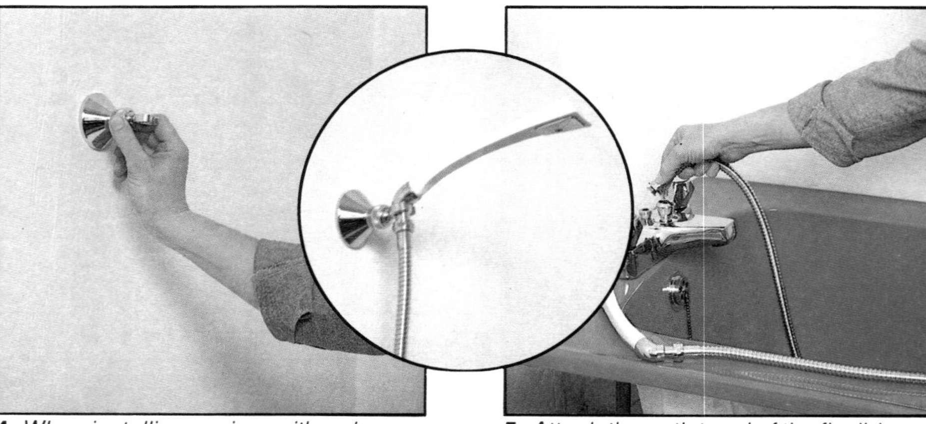

**4** *When installing a mixer with a shower attachment, fix the shower head bracket to the wall and fit the shower head into the bracket (inset).*

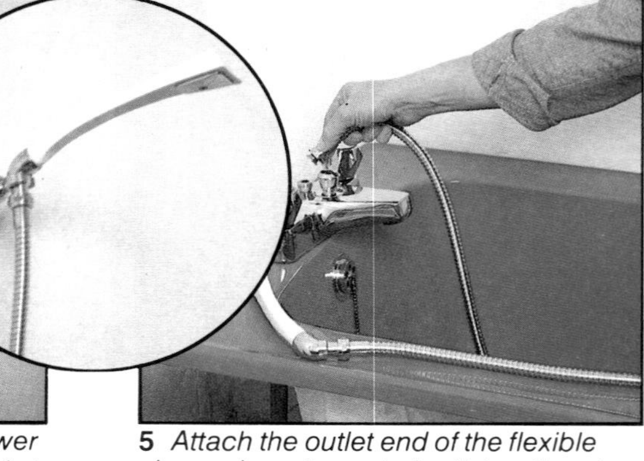

**5** *Attach the outlet end of the flexible shower hose to central outlet on the mixer unit. It should plug in and click into position with a slight turn.*

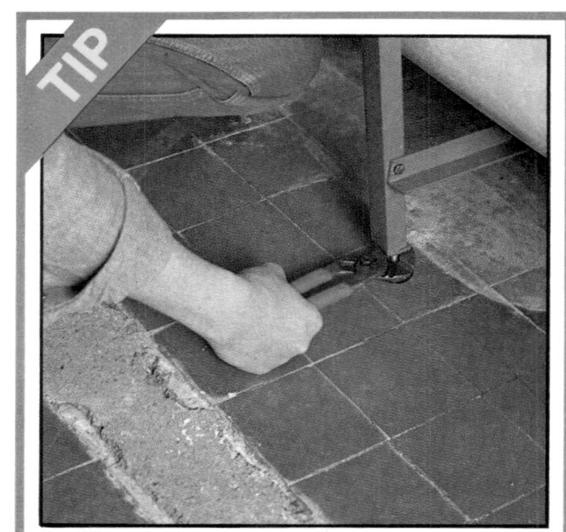


**6** *Check that the bath is level both lengthways and widthways with a spirit level. Adjust the screwed-on feet to get the level right.*

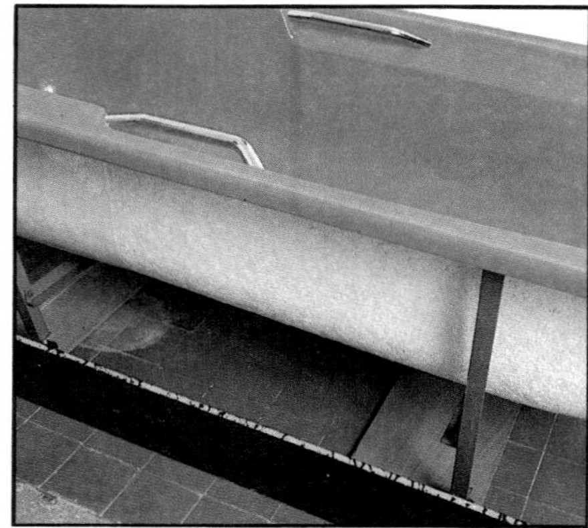

**7** *Fix the bath panels in position by screwing them to the wooden carcase which surrounds the bath and is supplied by the manufacturer.*

**8** *Screw the panels on carefully. They will usually be made of moulded high impact polystyrene which is easily chipped around the screw holes.*

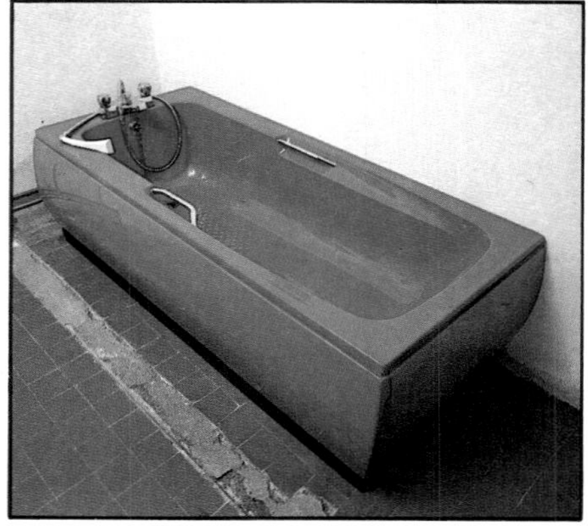

**9** *When all the bath work is complete you will have to make good the décor. If possible tile around the bath and box in the pipework.*

# INSTALLING A SHOWER

**Showers have become a part of the modern home, whether fitted over the bath or in a separate cubicle. They save time, space and energy and are quite easy to install once the design is right.**

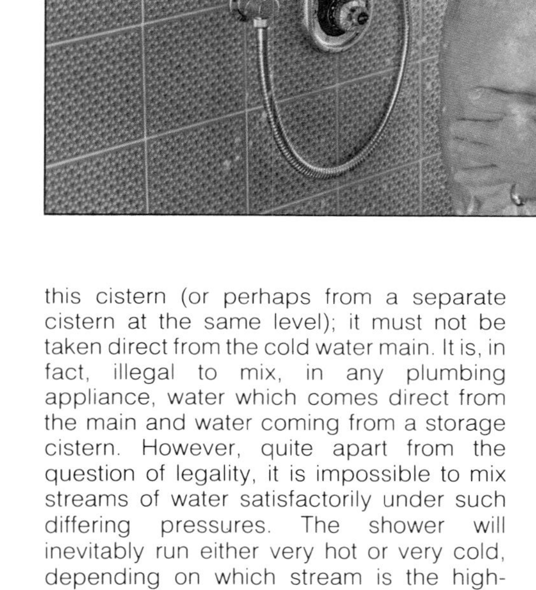

It is possible for four or five members of a family to have showers in the same time – and with the same amount of hot water – that would be needed for just one of them to have a bath. Showers, if properly installed, are safer for use by the elderly and the very young than a sit-down bath and need less cleaning. They are also more hygienic to use than a bath, as the bather isn't sitting in his own soapy and dirty water, and can rinse thoroughly in fresh water.

Where a shower is provided in its own cubicle, as distinct from over a bath, it takes up very little extra space. One can be provided in any space which is at least 900mm (36in) square, and can be put in a variety of locations such as a bedroom, on a landing, in a lobby or even in the cupboard under the stairs.

Yet shower installation can all too often prove to be a disappointment. Poorly designed systems may provide only a trickle of water at the sprinkler, or may run icy cold until the cold tap is almost turned off, and will then run scalding hot.

So, although it is possible to provide a shower in virtually any household, it is important that you match the shower equipment and your existing hot and cold water systems. If you have a cylinder storage hot water system, which is by far the commonest kind of hot water supply to be found in British homes, a conventional shower connected to the household's hot and cold water supplies is likely to be the most satisfactory and the easiest to install. But the hot and cold water systems must comply with certain quite definite design requirements if the shower is to operate safely and satisfactorily.

## Pressure

The most important requirement is that the hot and cold supply pipes to the shower must be under equal water pressure. With a cylinder storage hot water system, whether direct or indirect (described on pages 9 to 13), hot water pressure comes from the main cold water storage cistern supplying the cylinder with water. The cold water supply to the shower must therefore also come from this cistern (or perhaps from a separate cistern at the same level); it must not be taken direct from the cold water main. It is, in fact, illegal to mix, in any plumbing appliance, water which comes direct from the main and water coming from a storage cistern. However, quite apart from the question of legality, it is impossible to mix streams of water satisfactorily under such differing pressures. The shower will inevitably run either very hot or very cold, depending on which stream is the high-pressure one.

The cold water storage cistern must also be high enough above the shower sprinkler to provide a satisfactory operating pressure. Best results will be obtained if the base of the cold water storage cistern is 1.5m (5ft) or more above the sprinkler. However, provided that pipe runs are short and have only slight changes of direction, a reasonable shower can be obtained when the vertical distance between the base of the cistern and the shower sprinkler is as little as 1m (39in). The level of the hot water storage tank in relation to the shower doesn't matter in the least. It can be above, below or at the same level as the shower. It is the level of the cold water storage cistern that matters.

There is yet another design requirement for conventional shower installation which sometimes applies. This is that the cold water supply to the shower should be a separate 15mm (½in) branch direct from the cold water storage cistern, and not taken from the main bathroom distribution pipe. This is a safety precaution. If the cold supply were taken as a branch from a main distribution pipe, then flushing a lavatory cistern would reduce the pressure on the cold side of the shower causing it to run dangerously hot. For the same reason it is best for the hot supply to be taken direct from the vent pipe immediately above the hot water storage cylinder and not as a branch from another distribution pipe, though this is rather less important. A reduction in the hot water pressure would result in the shower running cold. This would be highly unpleasant, although not dangerous.

## Mixers

Showers must have some kind of mixing valve to mix the streams of hot and cold water and thus to produce a shower at the required temperature. The two handles of the bath taps provide the very simplest mixing valve, and push-on shower attachments can be cheaply obtained. Opening the bath taps then mixes the two streams of water and diverts them upwards to a wall-hung shower rose. These very simple attachments work quite satisfactorily – provided that the design requirements already referred to are met. However, it isn't always easy to adjust the tap handles to provide water at exactly the temperature required.

A bath/shower mixer provides a slightly more sophisticated alternative operating on the same principle. With one of these, the tap handles are adjusted until water is flowing through the mixer spout into the bath at the required temperature. The water is then

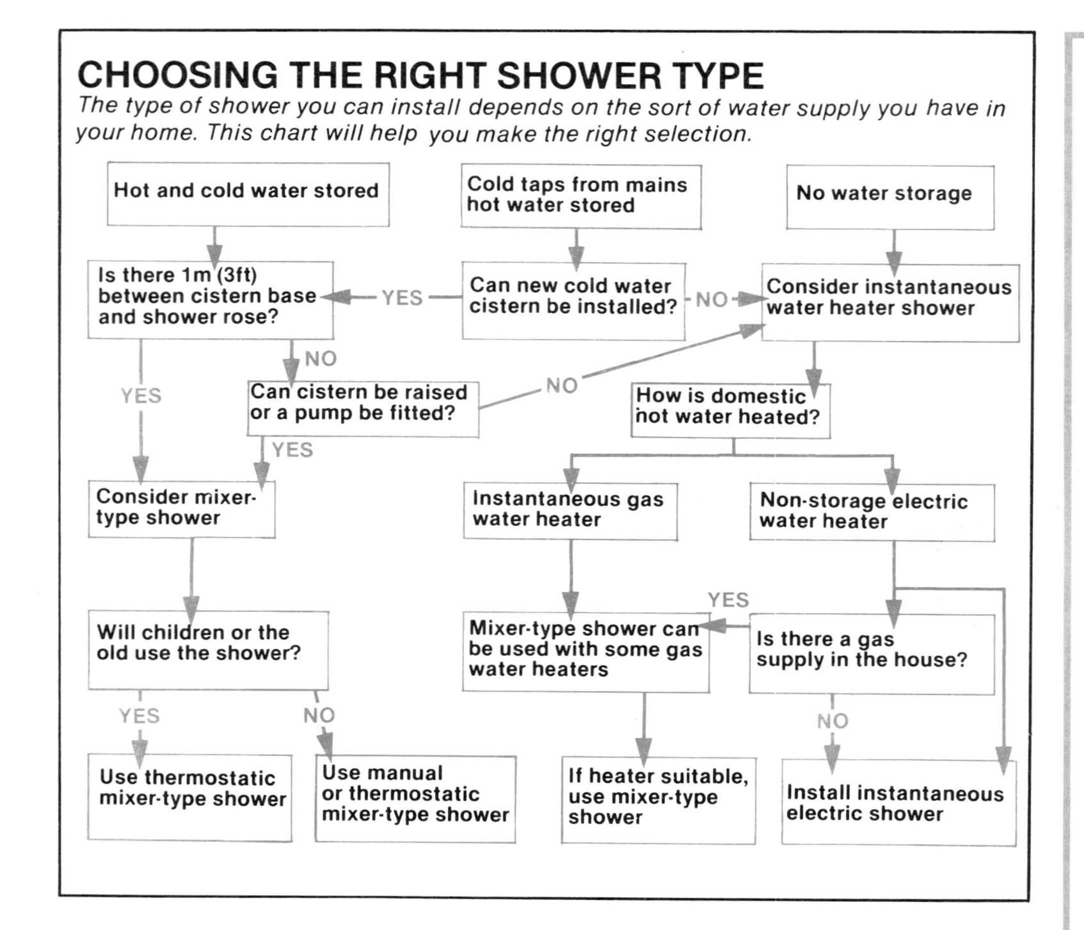


diverted up to the head by turning a valve.

Then there are manual shower mixers. These are standard equipment in independent shower cubicles and may also be used over a bath. With a manual mixer the hot and cold streams of water are mixed in a single valve. Temperature, and sometimes flow control, are obtained by turning large knurled control knobs.

Finally, there are thermostatic shower mixing valves. These may resemble manual mixers in appearance but are designed to accommodate small pressure fluctuations in either the hot or cold water supplies to the shower. They are thus very useful safety devices. But thermostatic valves cannot, even if it were legal, compensate for the very great difference of pressure between mains supply and a supply from a cold water storage cistern. Nor can they add pressure to either the hot or cold supply. If pressure falls on one side of the valve the thermostatic device will reduce flow on the other side to match it.

Thermostatic valves are more expensive but they eliminate the need to take an independent cold water supply pipe from the storage cistern to the shower and can possibly reduce the total cost of installation.

Where a shower is provided over an existing bath, steps must be taken to protect the bathroom floor from splashed water. A plastic shower curtain provides the cheapest means of doing this but a folding, glass shower screen has a much more attractive appearance and is more effective.

### Electric showers

You can run your shower independently of the existing domestic hot water system by fitting an instantaneously heated electric one. There are a number of these on the market nowadays. They need only to be connected to the rising main and to a suitable source of electricity to provide an 'instant shower'. You'll find more information about these on pages 115 to 119.

### Installing a bath/shower mixer

To install a shower above a bath, first disconnect the water supply, and drain the cistern (see pages 49 to 51). Remove the bath panel, if there is one, and disconnect the tap tails from the supply pipes. Then unscrew and remove the tap back-nuts and take the taps off.

You can now fix the new mixer in place (see pages 106 to 110). Finally, decide on the position for the shower spray bracket and fix it in place.

## Ready Reference

### WHY HAVE A SHOWER?

Showers have many advantages over baths:

- they are hygienic as you don't sit in dirty, soapy water and you get continually rinsed
- they are pleasant to use. Standing under jets of water can be immensely stimulating, especially first thing in the morning
- they use a lot less water per 'wash' than a bath, which saves energy and is also an advantage where water softeners are in use
- economy of hot water usage means that at peak traffic times there is more water to go round
- showers take less time, they don't have to be 'run', and users can't lay back and bask, monopolizing the bathroom
- easy temperature adjustment of a shower gives greater comfort for the user and lessens the risk of catching cold in a cold bathroom.

### SHOWER LOCATION

You don't have to install a shower over a bath or even in the bathroom. A bedroom is one alternative site, but landings and utility rooms are another possibility. Provided a supply of water is available, the pressure head satisfactory, and the disposal of waste water possible, a shower can provide a compact and very useful house improvement in many parts of the home.

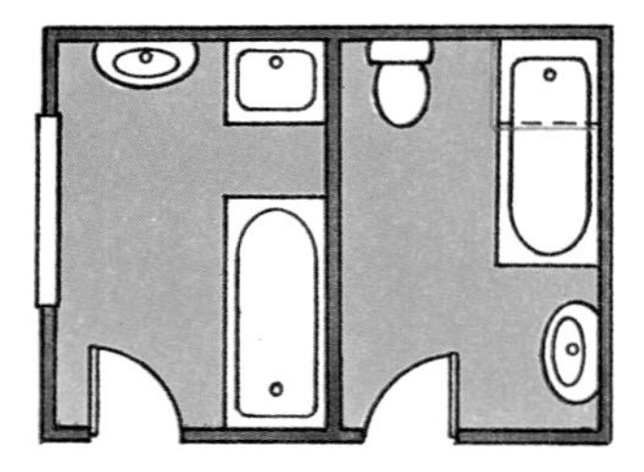

**In a bathroom** a shower will usually go over a bath, which is the easiest and most popular position. In a larger bathroom a cubicle is a good idea.

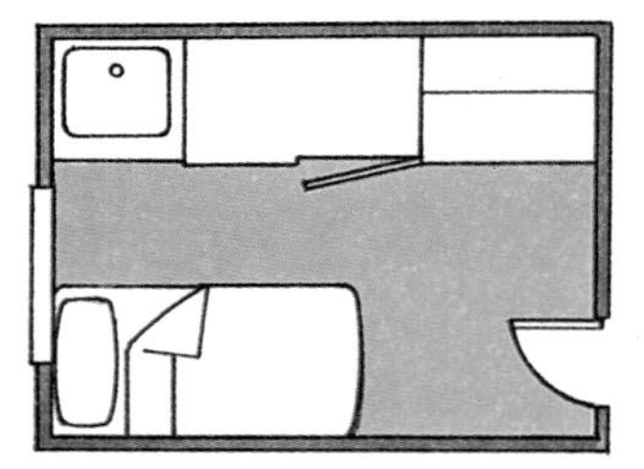

**In a bedroom** a shower can be easily fitted at the end of built-in wardrobes.

# HOW TO ADAPT YOUR SYSTEM

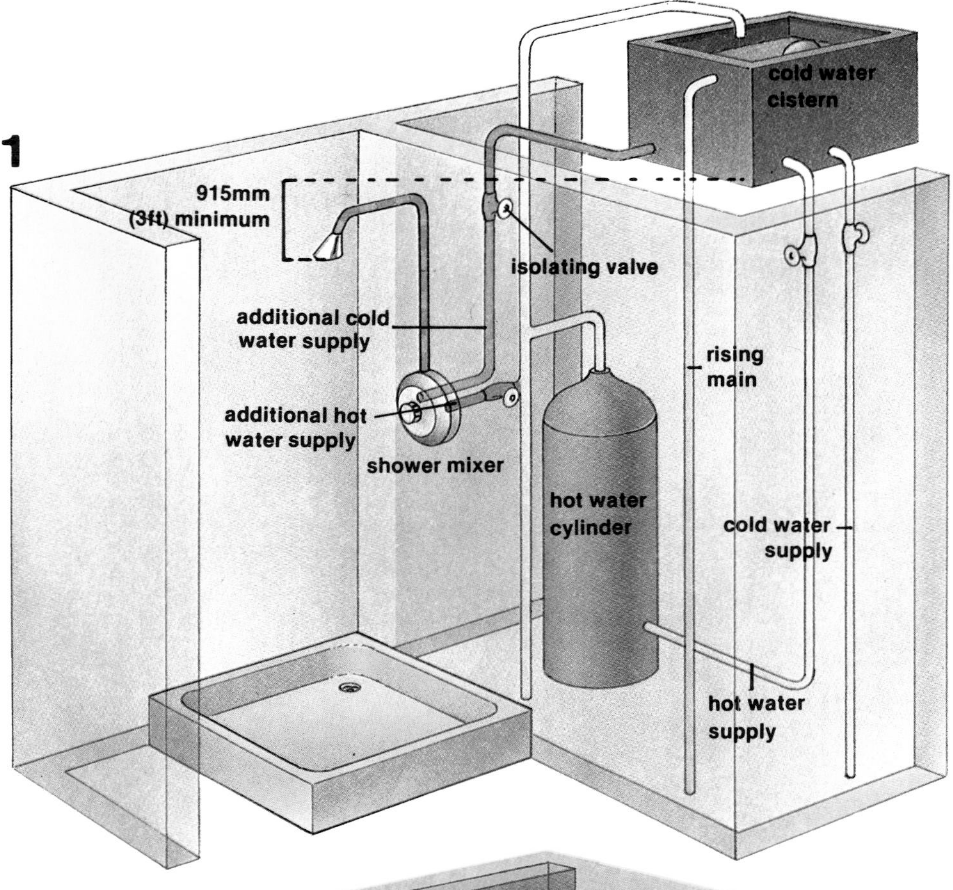


## 1 : Just add pipework

◁ *The most common domestic plumbing system has a cold water cistern in the loft which feeds a hot water tank. In this case you must check that the vertical distance from the bottom of the cold cistern to the shower outlet head is at least 915mm (3ft). To install a shower you must take a 15mm cold water supply direct from the cistern to the cold inlet of the mixer, and a 15mm (1/2in) hot water supply from the draw-off pipe, which emerges from the hot water tank, to the hot water inlet of the mixer.*

## 2 : Raise the cistern

▷ *In many older houses the cold water cistern may be in the airing cupboard immediately above the hot water tank, or in another position but still beneath ceiling height. This will usually mean that there is insufficient pressure for a mixer-type shower on the same floor. To get round this problem the cistern can be raised into the loft by extending the pipework upwards. Moving an old galvanised cistern will be rather arduous so this is a good opportunity to replace it with a modern plastic one, (see pages 156 to 159).*

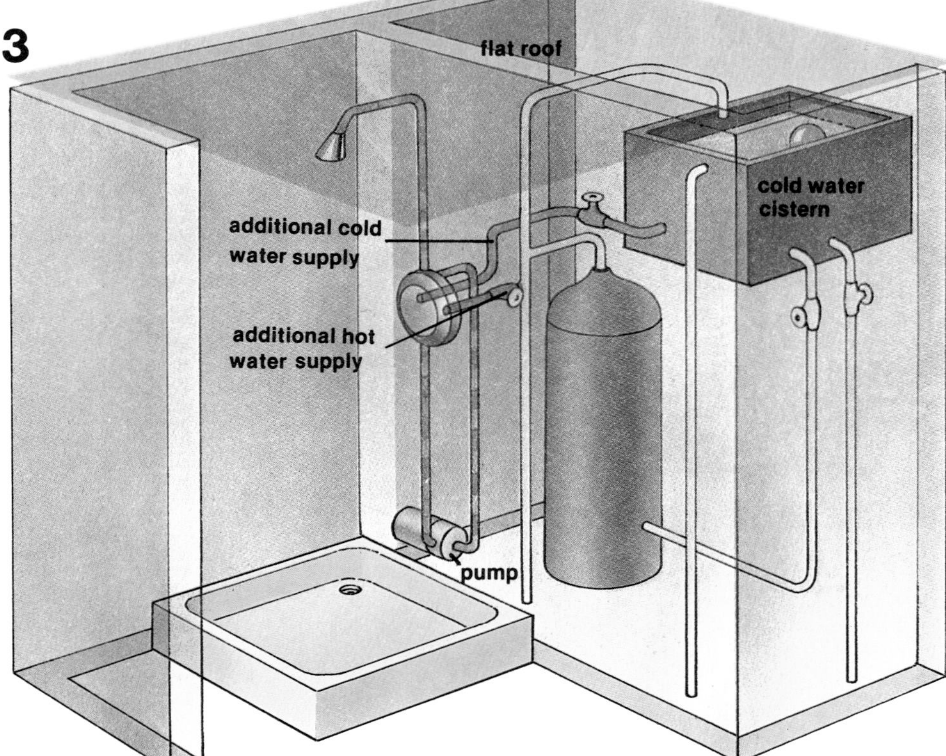


## 3 : Install a pump

◁ *In some homes which have flat roofs it is impossible to raise the cistern indoors to provide a sufficient pressure head for a shower on the same floor. While you could consider putting the cistern on top of the roof this would involve providing extensive insulation and is an unsatisfactory solution. Pump-assisted mixer showers are available which will artificially increase the pressure head when the shower is turned on and these are fairly simple to install. As they are electrically operated they should be situated outside the bathroom area.*

## 4 : Add a new cistern

▷ *Many modern houses have combination hot and cold water storage units which are supplied and installed as one unit. They have a disadvantage in that cold water capacity is about one-third of the hot water cylinder and would provide an insufficient supply for a shower. This problem can be overcome by installing a pump and a supplementary cold water storage cistern. To ensure similar hot and cold pressures at the shower the supplementary cistern must be at a comparable level with the combination unit's cold water storage.*

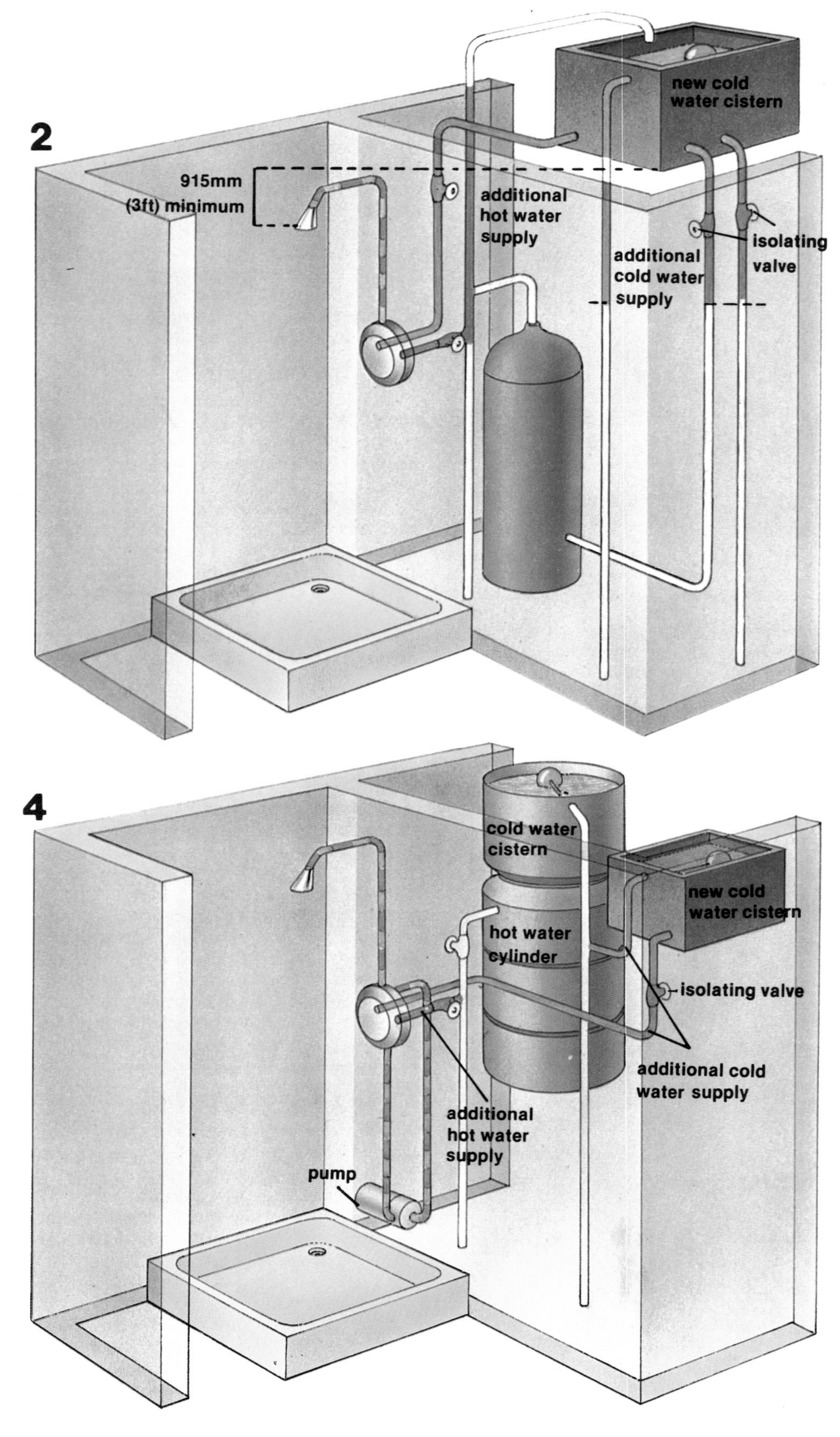


# Ready Reference

## TYPES OF SHOWER

There are two basic types of shower:

- those attached to a mixer on a bath
- those independent of the bath, discharging over their own bases, in their own cubicles.

Bath showers may be attached to a mixer head on which you have to adjust both taps, or they may simply fit over the tap outlets. The shower head in either case is detachable and may be mounted at whatever height you require.

Independent showers have fixed position heads or are adjustable. They may have a single control mixer, or a dual control which means that you can adjust the flow as well as the temperature. Thermostatic mixing valves are also available which can cope with small pressure fluctuations in the hot and cold water supply. These only reduce pressure on one side of the valve if that on the other side falls; they cannot increase the pressure unless they have already decreased it.

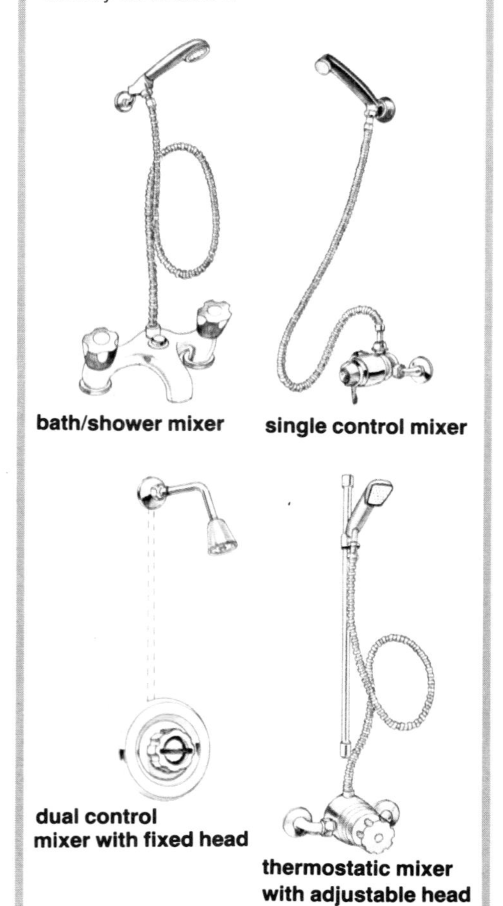

# PLUMBING IN AN ELECTRIC SHOWER

**If you would like to install a shower but think you can't because there's insufficient water pressure, you might like to consider an instantaneous electric shower. It's connected directly to the mains cold water supply, so you are guaranteed a good jet of water. And as you heat only the water you use, it's very economical to run.**

Until quite recently a properly functioning shower was all but an impossibility in many homes. Either it lacked the cylinder storage hot water system needed to supply a conventional shower, or the system that existed wouldn't permit a successful shower installation. For example, the main cold water storage cistern might have had insufficient capacity to supply the cold side of the shower mixer as well as feeding the hot water storage cylinder, or it may have been situated at too low a level to give adequate pressure at the shower rose. (For more information about the theory of shower design see previous section.)

The increasing popularity of showers has led to two new developments: the electric shower pump which increases pressure at the shower rose where this is inadequate; and the instantaneous electric shower.

## Going back to geysers

There is nothing particularly new about appliances which heat water 'instantaneously' as it flows through them. The Edwardian geyser, installed over the bath in many a turn-of-the century middle-class home, was an early example. The modern single-point or multi-point instantaneous gas water heater – which can provide hot water for the whole house – is its direct descendant. Instantaneous water heaters were designed for connection directly to the rising main so they could operate under mains pressure. They needed no cold water storage cistern or storage cylinder and they had the advantage that heat energy was expended only to heat water that was actually to be used at that time.

However, until a couple of decades ago, the only instantaneous water heating appliances that were available were – like the early geysers – gas-operated. It just wasn't possible to devise an electric appliance that could 'instantaneously' heat a sufficiently large volume of water to fill a sit-down bath, a sink or even a wash basin. It still isn't. But manufacturers have now produced electric water heaters powerful enough to provide a steady flow of hot water for spray hand-washing over a washbasin in a WC compartment and for the provision of a shower. In neither case is very hot water needed in large volumes.

An instantaneous electric water heater is a relatively compact appliance that needs only to be connected – by means of a 15mm (½in) branch water supply pipe – to the main supply, and to a suitable supply of electricity. It is normally operated by a flow-switch which ensures that electricity is switched on only when water is flowing through the appliance. As it does so, it passes over powerful electrical heating elements.

Temperature control was originally obtained solely by controlling the volume of water flowing through the heater. Opening up the tap or control valve produced a heavy flow of cool water. As the control valve was closed down and the flow diminished, warmer and warmer water was obtained from the shower spray.

The crude, early models were something of a disaster and were frowned on by water authorities and electricity boards. They rarely provided a satisfactory shower. The flow was markedly less than that from a conventional, cylinder-supplied shower. Flushing the WC or opening up any other tap in the house would reduce the pressure of the water entering the heater, so reducing the flow and raising the water temperature from the shower spray. Such unpredictable temperature changes could cause serious scalding to an unsuspecting user. Other problems arose from the hard water scale that tended to form on the heating elements.

## Instantaneous showers today

However, an unhappy experience a decade or so ago with one of the early instantaneous electric showers need not deter you from having a modern one installed today. There have been some tremendous advances in design and construction and you can be confident that a modern model will work

## WHAT'S INSIDE THE CASING

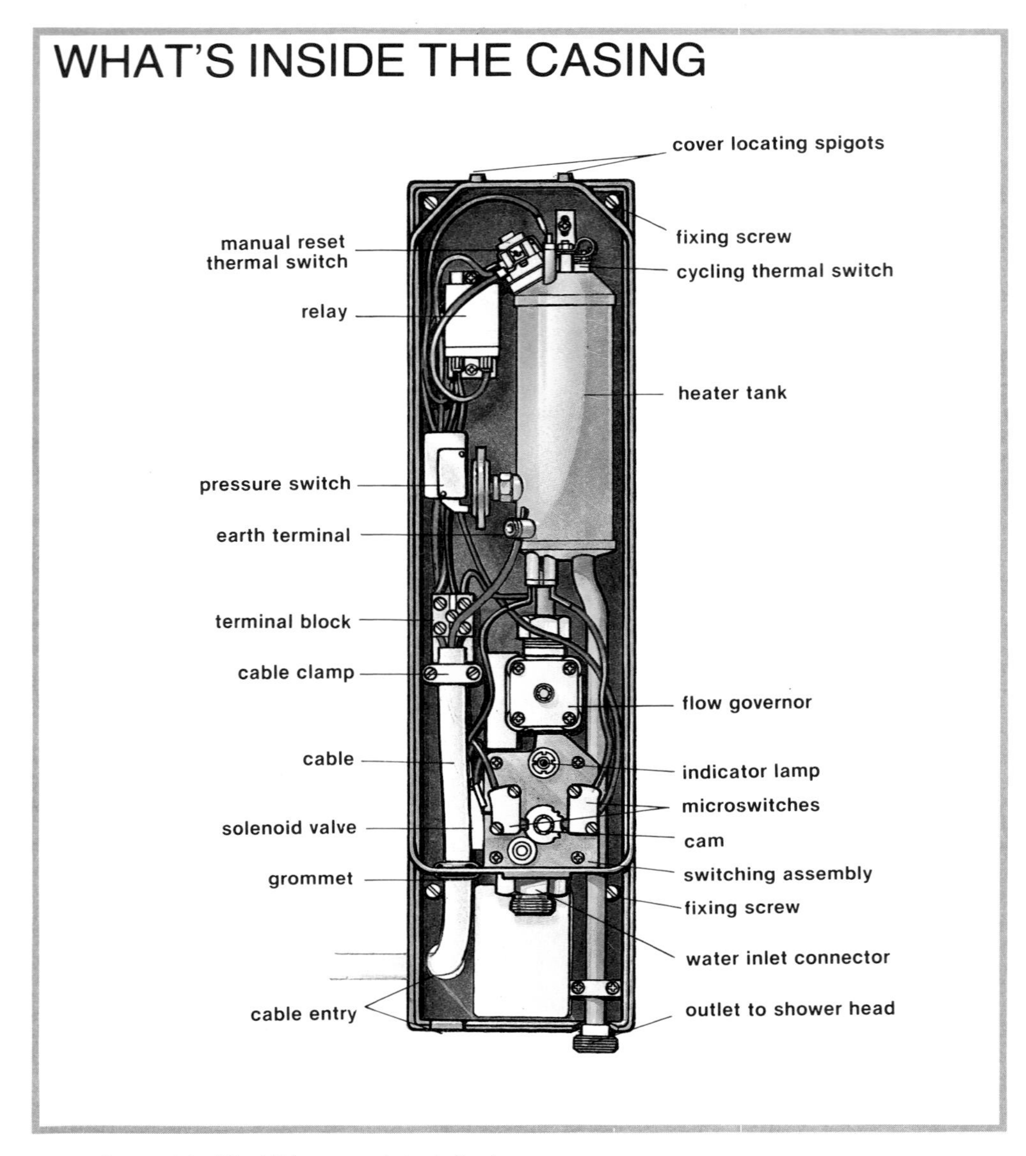


properly provided that it is properly installed according to the manufacturer's instructions.

Most instantaneous showers must be supplied with water at a minimum pressure of 1.05kg per sq cm (15lb per sq in). They are intended for connection direct to the mains supply, though they can be supplied by a cistern if it is at least 10.75m (35ft) above the level of the shower spray. In most cases mains water pressure will be adequate, but those who live in an area where mains pressure is low should check the actual pressure with their local water authority before incurring the expense of installation.

Modern electric showers usually have an electrical loading of 6kW to 7kW and it is often possible, for the sake of economy, to switch to a low setting of 3kW or 4kW during the summer months. Choose a model that incorporates a temperature stabiliser. This is an anti-scald device that maintains the water temperature at the level chosen by the user of the shower, despite any fluctuations in pressure which may result from water being drawn off from taps or by flushing the W.C. Should there be a drop in pressure beyond the capacity of the stabiliser, a safety sensor turns the shower off completely.

When choosing your instantaneous electric shower, look for evidence that it has been approved by such national safety committees as the B.E.A.B., the National Water Council and the A.N.T. (Assessment of Techniques) Committee of the Institute of Electrical Engineers.

### Fitting a shower

Although instantaneous electric showers can be fitted over a sit-down bath, they are usually installed in a separate shower cubicle which may be in a bathroom, in a bedroom or even on a landing. The shower tray must have a trapped outlet and the branch waste pipe can discharge by the same route as basin or bath wastes (see WASTE WATER SYSTEMS, pages 14 to 18).

Plumbing connections should be straightforward. It's best to connect the supply pipe to the shower heater first and then work backwards to the main supply, making this connection last of all. In this way you will interrupt the supply to the rest of the house as little as possible.

The connection to the shower may be a simple compression coupling (described on pages 20 to 24) or it may have a screwed male thread. In which case you'll need a compression fitting with a coupling at one end and a female screwed connector at the other. To connect into the rising main you should use a compression tee (as described on pages 28 to 32).

### Obtaining the power

Instantaneous showers get their power from a separate radial circuit taken from the consumer unit. As most models of shower have a loading of either 6 or 7kW they can be supplied safely by a circuit that has a current rating of 30A and is run in 6mm$^2$ two-core and earth cable. Recently, however, an 8kW shower has been introduced on the market by some manufacturers. This shouldn't pose extra problems for anyone intending to install it: provided the radial circuit originates at either a cartridge fuse or MCB – which both have the effect of uprating the circuit by one third – then a 30A circuit will be adequate. Should you decide to install one of these larger showers then it's still probably a good idea to check their requirements with the makers beforehand.

Showers should be controlled by a 30A double-pole cord-operated switch. From this a length of 6mm$^2$ two-core and earth cable will run to the shower unit. There is one type that requires a slightly different method of connecting up. If you're going to fit a shower that has a control unit already connected to a length of three-core flex then you'll have to fix a flex outlet unit on the wall near the shower unit so you can connect the flex into the circuit.

### Fitting the switch

Ceiling switches can either be surface or flush mounted. If you're going to surface mount one, you'll have to pierce a hole in the ceiling so the cables can be drawn through into a plastic mounting box. Before fixing this in position with No 8 wood screws, you should knock a thin section of plastic from the base to align with the hole in the ceiling. Ideally the box should be fitted against a joist, but if there isn't one suitably placed, you'll have to fix a support batten between the joists made from 75 x 25mm (3 x 1in) timber with a hole drilled in it big enough to let two lengths of

## INSTALLING THE SHOWER UNIT

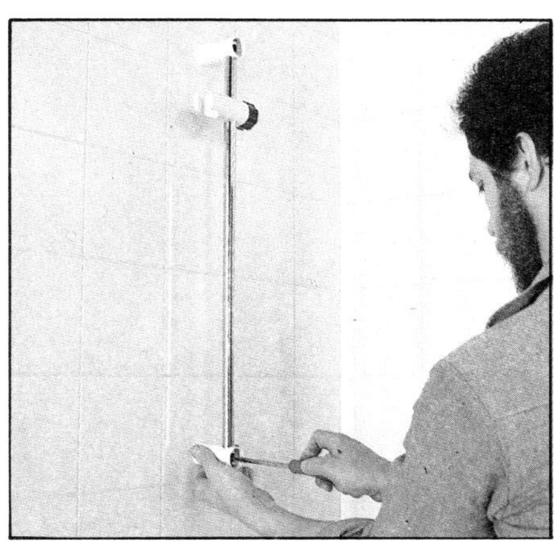

**1** *First take the shower spray support assembly and fix it to the wall. It is important to follow the manufacturer's recommendations as to height.*

**2** *Remove the control knobs and any other fittings from the shower unit to enable the faceplate to be taken off before further installation takes place.*

**3** *Carefully position the unit on the shower cubicle wall and mark the screw fitting holes, water and power channels; drill out the fixing holes.*

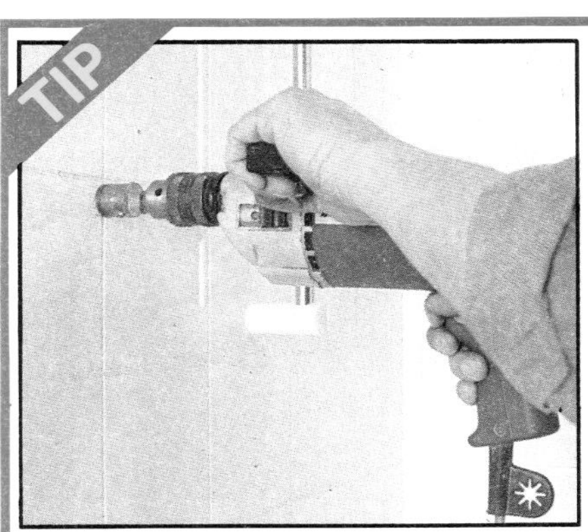


**4** *Using a hole saw attachment for your drill, cut holes in the cubicle wall for the water and power supplies, then fix the unit to the wall.*

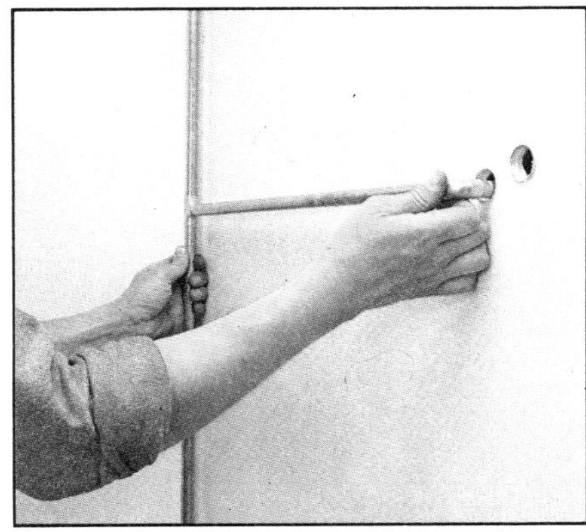

**5** *Make a tee junction with the main, and run a length of pipe to the water access; then add an elbow and length of pipe to go through the wall.*

**6** *Use a swivel tap connector to attach the cold water feed to the unit; this is linked to the inlet pipe by a soldered capillary joint.*

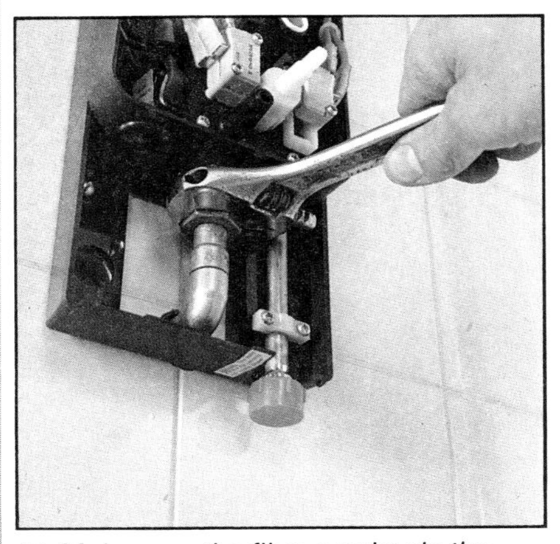

**7** *Make sure the fibre washer in the connector is in place; then screw it up and tighten. Don't use any sealant on the nylon inlet.*

**8** *Attach the shower hose to the screwed outlet, making sure that the rubber washer is in place. Then make the electrical connections (page 118).*

**9** *Turn on the water supply and also the electricity to make sure that the unit works. Finally, replace the cover and control knobs.*

$6mm^2$ cable pass through. When you're feeding the cables into the mounting box, it's a good idea to write 'mains' on the end of the circuit cable and 'shower' on the end of the shower feed cable. This could be surface mounted on the ceiling and wall, but it's neater to conceal it in the ceiling void and chase it into the wall, running it in plastic conduit.

You can now strip back the insulation and make the connections. The mains cable should go to the 'supply' side of the switch, with the red core going to the terminal marked L and the black to the one marked N, and the shower cable to the equivalent terminals on the 'load' side. Remember to sleeve the earth cores in green/yellow PVC and connect them to the earth terminal in the switch. Place the six cores neatly in the box and screw the switch to it.

If you're going to flush-mount the switch you'll have to mark the size of the mounting box on the ceiling and, using a pad saw, carefully cut out an equivalent size hole. Then cut a piece of timber to fit between the joists, lay it across the hole and mark the square on it. Knock out a blank from the base of the metal box and drill a hole in the corresponding spot in the timber. Then screw the box to the timber and fix the timber to the joists at a height above the ceiling that allows the box edge to sit flush with the ceiling surface. This can be checked by holding a straight edge across the hole in the ceiling. You should then thread in the two marked cables and make the connections. If you want to fix the switch at a point where there is a joist you can always cut away a section of it. This is best done by using a drill fitted with a 25mm (1in) wood bit to remove most of the wood and then chiselling the remainder away. That way you won't need access to the ceiling void as long as you can 'fish' the cable across the ceiling using a length of stiff wire.

### Connecting into the shower

The cable to the shower can be run down the wall on the surface, using plastic cable clips or mini-trunking, or buried in a chase chopped in the plaster. The cover of the control unit must be removed to allow you access to the terminal block, but do read fully the manufacturer's instructions before going any further. Thread in the cable and strip off some of the sheathing and insulation before connecting the red core to the L terminal and the black to the N terminal. Before connecting the earth core to the earth terminal make sure you've sleeved it in green/yellow PVC. If the unit has a cable clamp, fix the cable in it, double checking that it's the whole, sheathed cable that is held by it and not just individual cores. This is very important as it serves to protect the connections. Finally, refit the unit cover, finish off the radial circuit connections at the consumer unit, switch on at the mains and test the shower.

## CONNECTING THE POWER

**1** *After fixing the shower unit to the bathroom wall and making the connection from the rising main, thread in the circuit cable.*

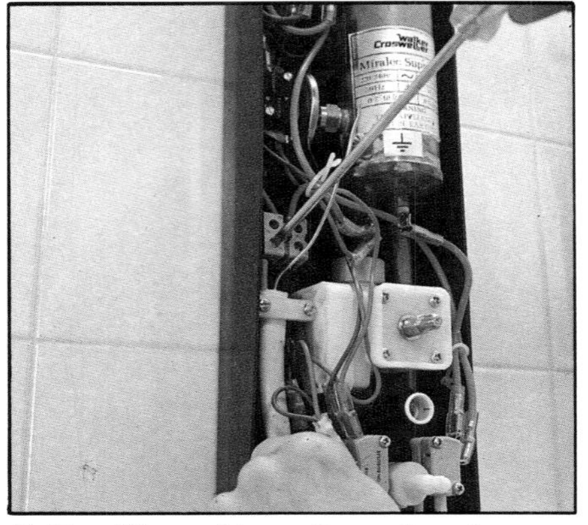

**2** *Feed the cable up the unit and strip it before connecting the red and black cores to the L and N terminals respectively.*

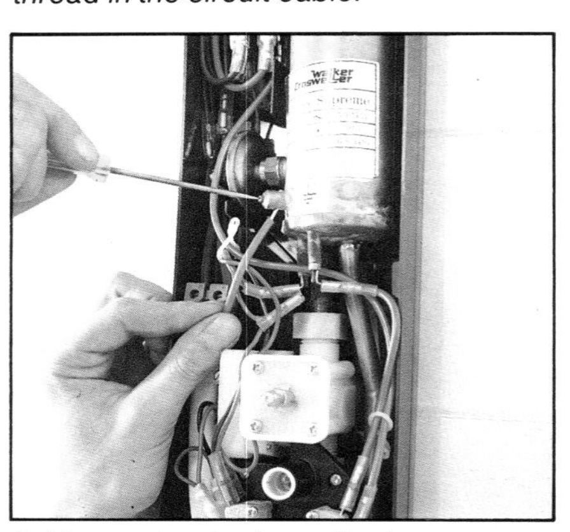

**3** *Remember to sleeve the bare earth core in green/yellow PVC before feeding it into the earth terminal and connecting it up.*

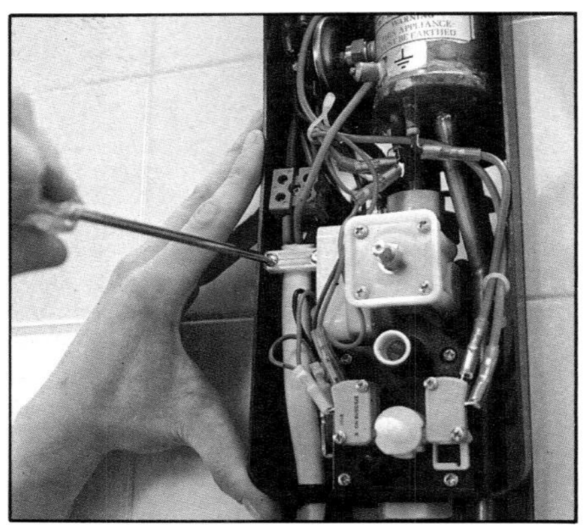

**4** *Then make sure that the clamp plate will bear down on the cable sheathing before tightening it up to protect all the connections.*

### Fitting a flex outlet plate

You'll have to use a flex outlet plate only if there is already a flex connected to the shower unit. This can be fitted on either a one-gang moulded plastic box for surface mounting, or else in a 35mm (1½in) metal box for flush mounting, in which case you'll have to chop a hole. After fixing one or other of the boxes to the wall, run the cable into it through a knockout hole, which, in the case of the metal box, should be fitted with a grommet. The unit has three banks of terminals with two terminal screws per bank and you should connect the green/yellow sleeved earth core to a terminal of the non-shielded bank marked 'E'. Then connect the red insulated core to a terminal of one of the shielded banks and the black to a terminal of the other bank.

Prepare the end of the flex by stripping off approximately 12mm (½in) of insulation from the end of each core. Remember to thread the flex through the hole in the unit's cover before you connect the flex to the unit as you won't be able to fit it after you've made the connections. Then connect the earth core, which should be already sleeved in green and yellow PVC, to the other terminal in the 'E' bank, the brown core to the bank containing the red core and the blue core to the bank containing the black circuit core. Tighten the cord clamp, again making sure that it's the flex sheath that it grips and not the unsheathed cores as this protects the connections. Lay the six cores neatly in the box and fix the unit to the box with the two screws supplied. You can then switch on the power and test the shower.

# THE ELECTRICAL CONNECTIONS

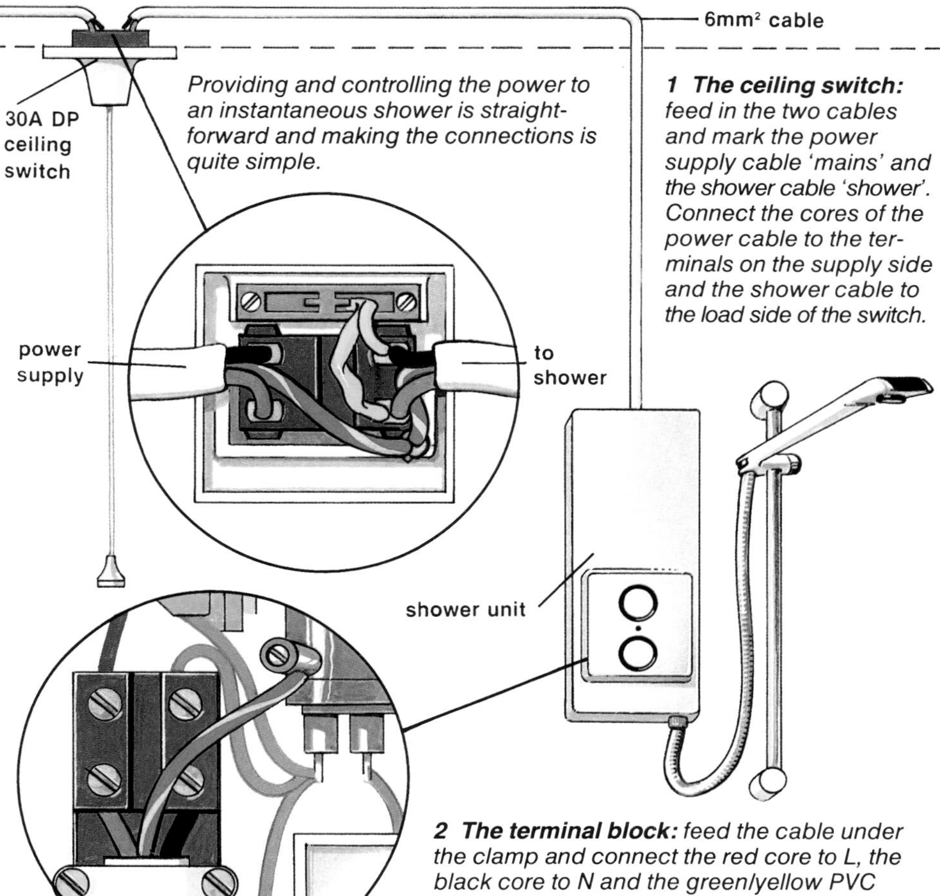


*Providing and controlling the power to an instantaneous shower is straight-forward and making the connections is quite simple.*

***1 The ceiling switch:*** *feed in the two cables and mark the power supply cable 'mains' and the shower cable 'shower'. Connect the cores of the power cable to the terminals on the supply side and the shower cable to the load side of the switch.*

***2 The terminal block:*** *feed the cable under the clamp and connect the red core to L, the black core to N and the green/yellow PVC sleeved earth core to the earth screw on the heater tank. Make sure you tighten the clamp on the cable and not individual cores.*

## FITTING A CEILING SWITCH

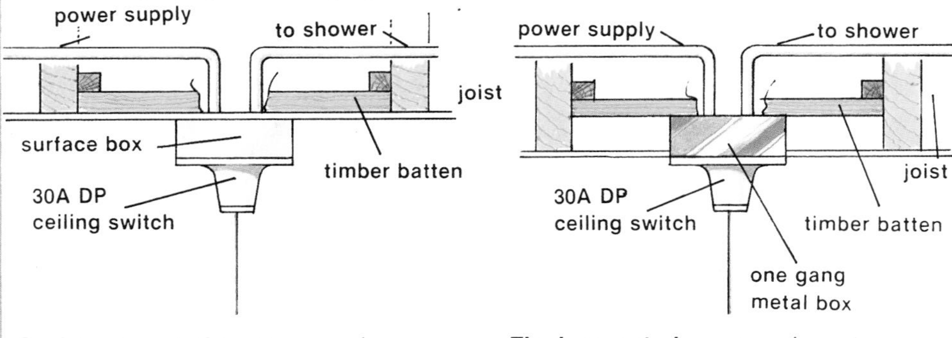


***Surface mounted:*** *try to mount the switch on a joist. If you can't, fit a timber batten. Drill holes in the batten and ceiling to admit the cables and remove a knockout from the base of the box. Fix the box to the ceiling and make the connections.*

***Flush mounted:*** *use a pad saw to cut a hole in the ceiling for the mounting box. Fix the box to a batten between the joists and set the batten so the box is flush with the ceiling. Feed the cables through and make the connections.*

## Ready Reference

### PLUMBING REQUIREMENTS

The shower unit should be connected directly to the cold water mains supply. If this isn't possible, a storage tank may be used to supply the unit; but it must be about 10.75m (35ft) above the shower spray head.

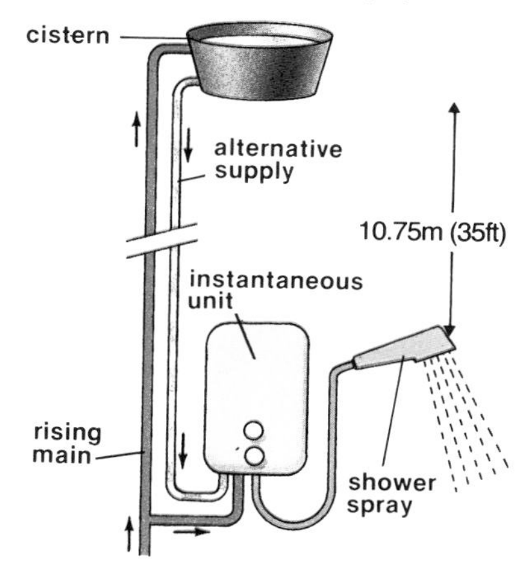


### USING THE SHOWER

After turning on the unit, you'll have to wait a short while so the water retained in the heater tank and shower fittings from the last shower is drawn off. The water temperature is controlled by the rate of flow through the heater – the slower the flow rate, the higher the temperature, and vice versa. Because the cold water supply is likely to be comparatively colder in the winter than in summer, this means in winter you may have to put up with a slower flow rate in order to get the required temperature.

### ELECTRICAL CONNECTION

When you're wiring up an instantaneous shower, you must ensure that:

- it is permanently connected to its own separate 30A power supply, and is properly earthed
- it is controlled by a 30A double-pole cord-operated switch mounted on the ceiling. An ordinary ceiling light switch is not suitable.

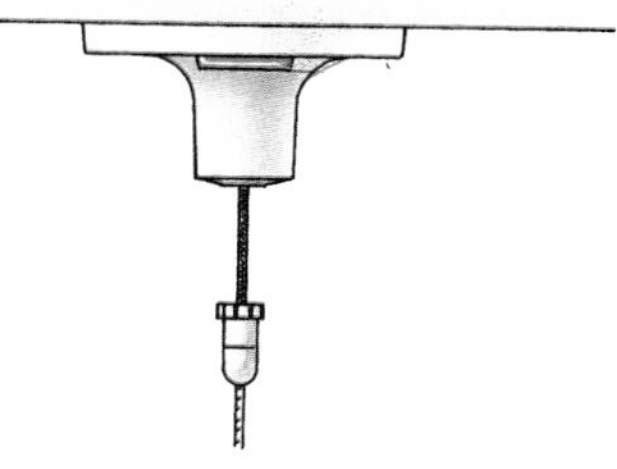

**NEVER** turn on the electricity supply until all the plumbing has been completed, including mounting the handset and hose, and the power supply and earthing connections are made.

# CONNECTING SHOWER FITTINGS

**Before you get to grips with installing a new shower cubicle, you ought to select the type of control fitting you're going to use. Your choice may affect the way you organise the plumbing.**

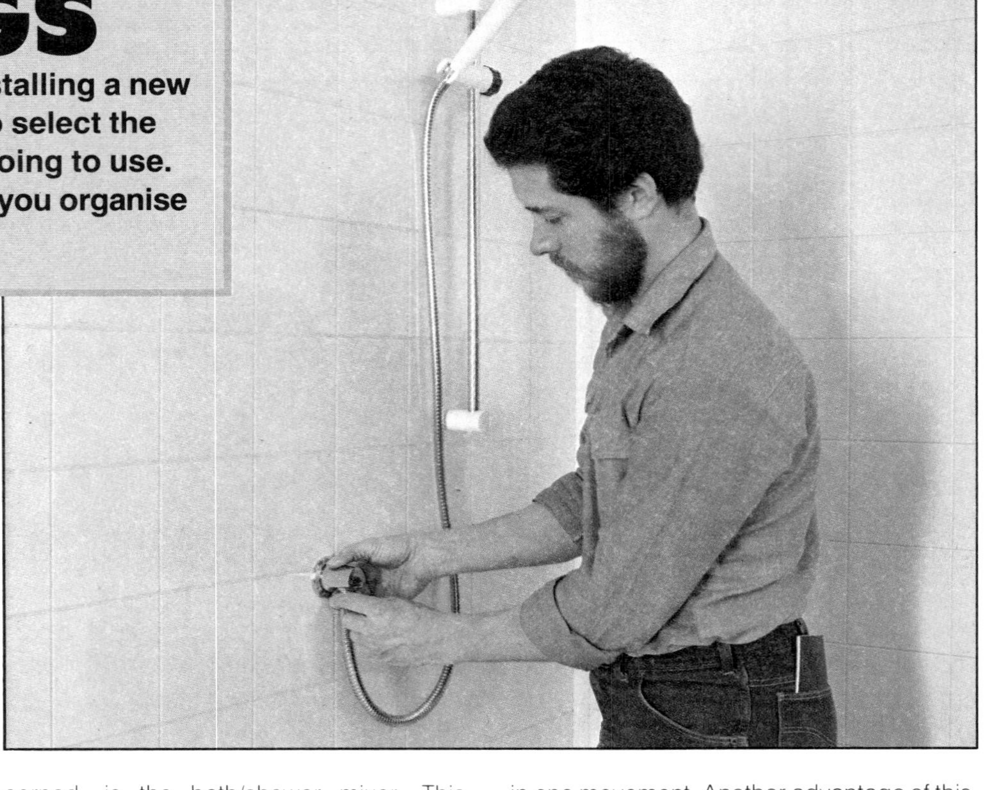

Once you've decided where you're going to site your shower – over a bath or in a separate cubicle – you'll have to determine what type of fitting you're going to use to run it. In order for the shower to work effectively, you need to be able to control the rate of flow of water and also, more importantly, it's temperature. There's nothing worse than standing under a stuttering supply of water that's hot one minute and cold the next. So it's the job of the shower fitting to provide this control fast and effectively.

Some fittings work by having individual taps to control the hot and cold water supplies, while the more sophisticated types have a simple valve or a mixer. How they are connected up to the water supply depends primarily on their design. For example, instantaneous showers (see the previous section) need only to be connected to the mains cold water supply, as they heat all the hot water required just before it comes out of the shower rose. A hot water supply is therefore unnecessary. But for all other showers, the temperature of the water is controlled by mixing together separate supplies of hot and cold water which may also be at different pressures.

## The simplest fittings

Before proper showers over a bath and separate shower cubicles became popular, it was quite common to find a rather makeshift device being used to supply a spray of water. This consisted of a length of rubber hose with a rose attached at one end and two connectors fitted at the other which slipped over the hot and cold taps on the bath. By adjusting these taps you could regulate the flow and temperature of the water. In fact the principle of this very basic mixing valve was used in early shower cubicles. Gate valves on the hot and cold distribution pipes were used to control the flow, and the two supplies were mixed at a 'tee' in the pipework before being fed in a single pipe to an overhead shower rose.

## Mixer taps

An improvement on this very simple arrangement, as far as showers over baths are concerned, is the bath/shower mixer. This resembles an ordinary mixer tap on a bath, except that a flexible metal hose rises from the centre of the mixer to a spray head which can be fixed at varying heights on the wall above the bath. Again the water is mixed by adjusting the hot and cold taps, and at this stage it will be coming out of the spout of the tap. When the required temperature has been reached you pull up a lever on the body of the tap and this diverts the water upwards to the spray head.

Nowadays, showers in cubicles normally have what's known as a manual mixing valve. This has two inlets, one for the hot and another for the cold supply; but the temperature is regulated by turning just one mixer knob. The flow may also be adjusted by turning another knob which is set round the outside of the temperature control. In this way you can control the water more quickly and positively than you could do if you had to adjust two separate taps (which tends to be a bit of a juggling act).

Shower mixers are constantly being improved so that they are more convenient and safer to use. With one modern manual mixing valve, for example, the temperature of the water is controlled by turning a knurled knob, not unlike the handle of a tap. And the flow and on/off control is worked by pushing in or pulling out this knob. You can therefore control the flow and temperature of the water in one movement. Another advantage of this kind of control is that the shower can be stopped instantly if the pressure on the cold side falls (as a result of a toilet being flushed or cold water being drawn off elsewhere in the house, for example). If this happened the shower would suddenly run very hot, but by flicking the control knob downwards the flow ceases. It's not so serious if the pressure falls on the hot side, because the shower would just run cold. But again, to prevent discomfort the flow can be stopped quickly by flicking the control knob.

However, prevention is better than cure and there are ways of organising the plumbing so that this problem can't arise. To alleviate the danger it's best to run the 15mm (½in) cold water supply pipe to the shower direct from the cold water storage cistern and not as a branch from the 22mm (¾in) distribution pipe to the bathroom. This will supply a continuous volume of cold water provided the cistern is working properly.

## Thermostatic valves

Of course it may mean too much of an upheaval to lay in a new pipe run, but instead you could install a special thermostatic mixing valve. This enables you to pre-set the temperature of the shower water and this will remain constant despite fluctuations of pressure in the hot and cold supplies. And apart from this, thermostatic mixers provide

## INSTALLING A FIXED ROSE

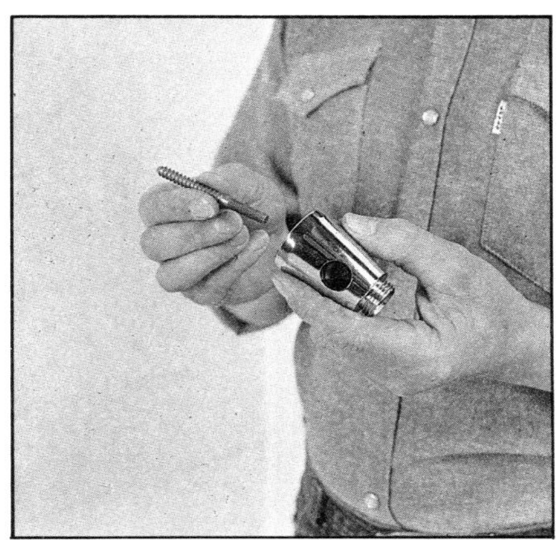
**1** *To mount the wall fixing, thread one end of the double-ended screw supplied into the hole in the base of the casting.*

**2** *With the flange in place, screw the fitting into the shower wall using a pre-drilled fixing hole. The inlet hole must point downwards.*

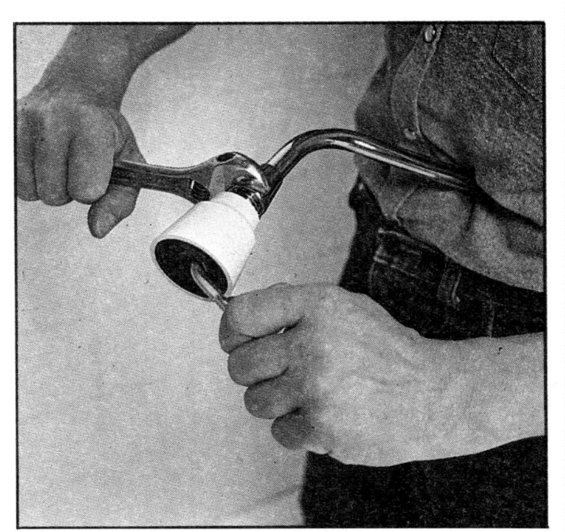
**3** *Screw the outlet rose onto the outlet pipe by removing the rose and inserting an Allen key into the recess you will find inside.*

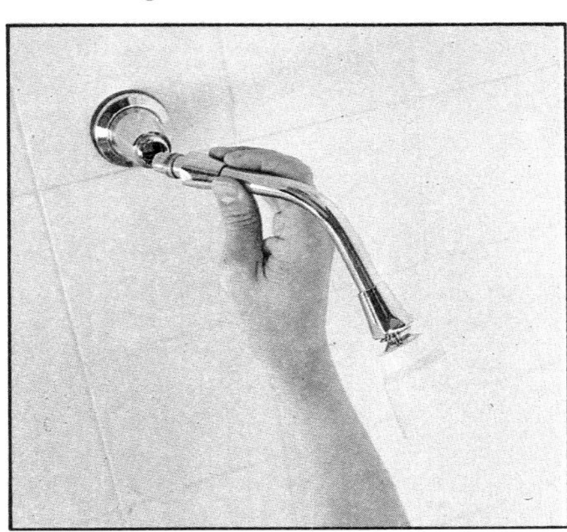
**4** *Attach the outlet fitting to the wall fixing, by tightening the fixing nut on the rose so it crushes the olive. But don't chip the chrome.*

**5** *Make sure that the outlet rose swivels firmly but freely on its ball bearing, and that it emerges at right angles to the wall.*

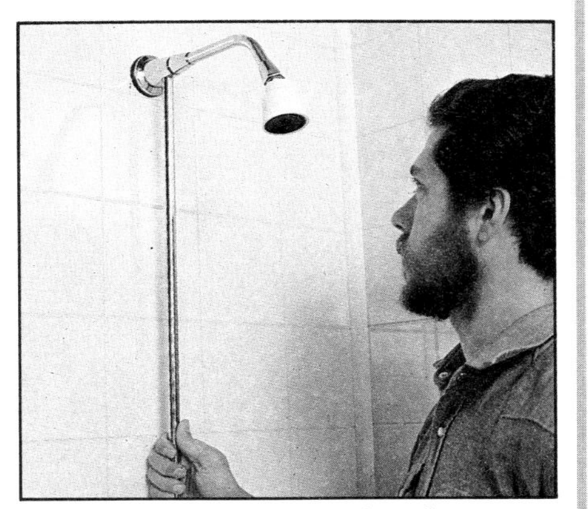
**6** *Screw the supply pipe into the outlet supply until it is tight against the washer, and check that it is truly vertical.*

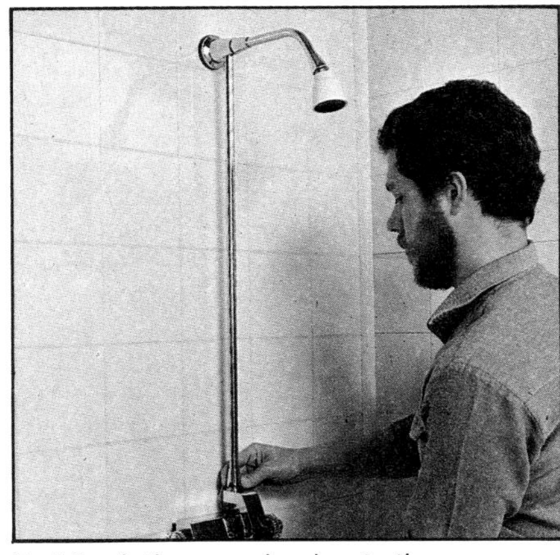
**7** *Attach the supply pipe to the thermostatic control unit and mark the position of the supply pipe holes on the shower wall.*

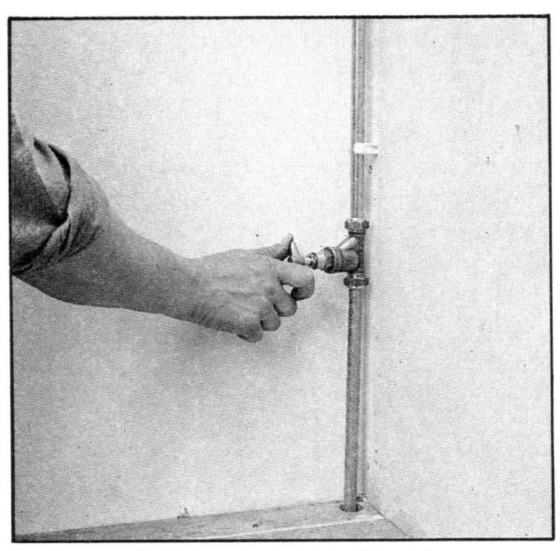
**8** *Turn off the water supplies via stop-valves, if fitted, and tee off the supply pipes to feed the hot and cold inlets of the shower mixer.*

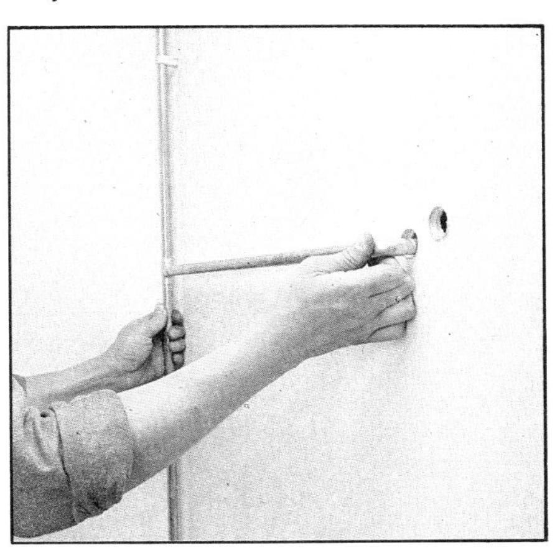
**9** *Drill holes in the shower wall so that the supply pipes can be fed through from behind and connected up to the shower mixer.*

## INSTALLING AN ADJUSTABLE ROSE

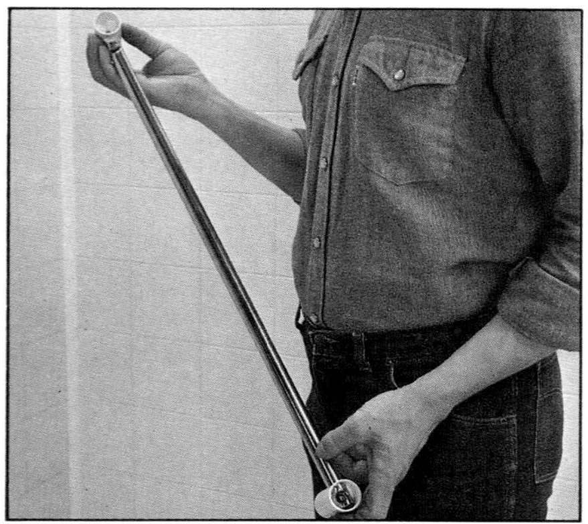

**1** *Fit the two wall fixing brackets to the end of the runner, and align them both so that they are pointing in the same direction.*

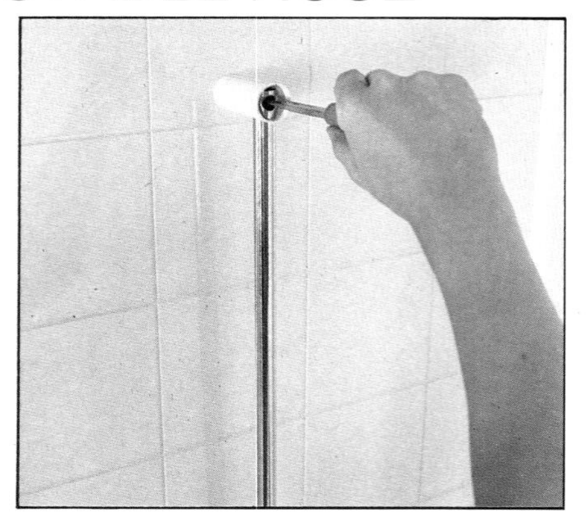

**2** *Mark the positions for the fixing screws on the shower wall, drill the holes and then proceed to screw on the uppermost bracket.*

**3** *Slide on the movable rose support and fix the lower bracket to the wall. Cover the screw entry holes with plastic caps.*

**4** *Take the one-piece shower head and rose and screw on the flexible hose, making sure that the fibre washer is correctly placed.*

**5** *Hold the wall supply point fixing in place and mark the wall for drilling. Drill the hole, making sure you don't damage the tiled surround.*

**6** *Insert the fixing and screw it up tight. Then take your chosen mixer, drill its fixing holes and plumb in the supply pipes.*

just that extra margin of safety and assurance against discomfort.

Before buying a thermostatic mixing valve, it's important that you recognise its limitations as well as its advantages. These valves can deal with relatively minor fluctuations in pressure that can result from water being drawn off from one or other of the supply pipes. They can't accommodate the great differences in pressure between a hot water supply under pressure from a storage cylinder and a cold supply taken direct from the main (in any case, you should never arrange your shower plumbing in this way). Some thermostatic valves even require a greater working 'hydraulic head' (the vertical distance between the cold water cistern and the shower rose) than the 1m (3ft) minimum that is usual for manual mixers. So it's a good idea to check on these points and on the 'head' available before you buy one of them.

### Shower pumps

An inadequate 'head' is, of course, one of the commonest reasons why a shower won't work properly. Although the minimum distance between the base of the cold water cistern and the shower rose must be 1m (3ft), for best results this distance ought to be 1.5m (5ft) or more.

However, all is not lost if you can't get this head because you can install a shower pump. They're expensive but they can make the difference between a stimulating shower and a miserable, low-pressure trickle, which isn't much good to anyone.

Different types of pump are controlled in different ways. Some have manual switches which are controlled by a pull-cord. In this case the pump is only switched on after the water has begun to flow, and is turned off before it has been stopped. Other pumps are operated automatically when the water is turned on at the shower by the movement of water in the pipes.

You can install a simple pump between the mixer and the shower rose outlet, but you may find it difficult to conceal. On the other hand, automatic pumps must be connected into the water supply before it reaches the mixer, so it's easier to choose a convenient site where the pump can be hidden from view or disguised.

Shower pumps need quite a lot of plumbing in, and if you're not careful about planning you may end up with a lot of exposed pipework. It's also worth remembering that when you wire up the electricity supply you have to connect the pump to a fused connection unit with a double-pole switch. And if the pump is situated inside the bathroom it must be protected from steam and water (except in the case of units specially designed to be inside the shower cubicle).

# THREE TYPES OF SHOWER

*There are several types of shower mixer available on the market. They fall into two types – those which simply mix the hot and cold flows, and those which make an effort to provide the mixed flows at a constant, pre-set, temperature. All of them are usually finished in chrome and the controls are made of a strong plastic which will resist most knocks and blows.*

**Surface-mounted mixer**
*Left: This is a surface-mounted mixer control with separate supply pipes emerging through the wall to supply the control which provides power over flow and temperature.*

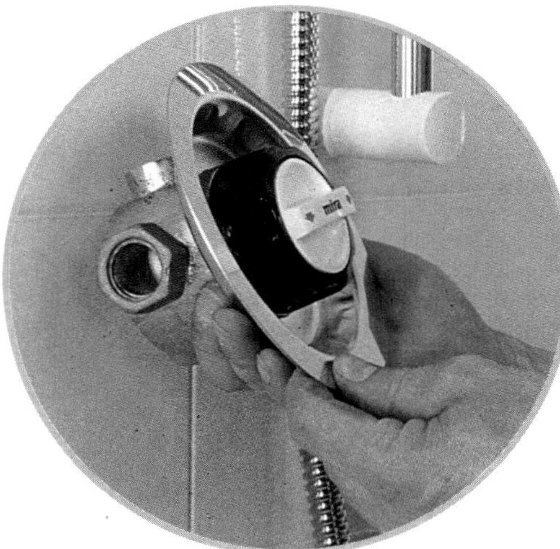

**Built-in mixer**
*Right: This built-in control is supplied from behind the shower wall so that the supply pipes are hidden. These fittings are also available in a gold finish.*

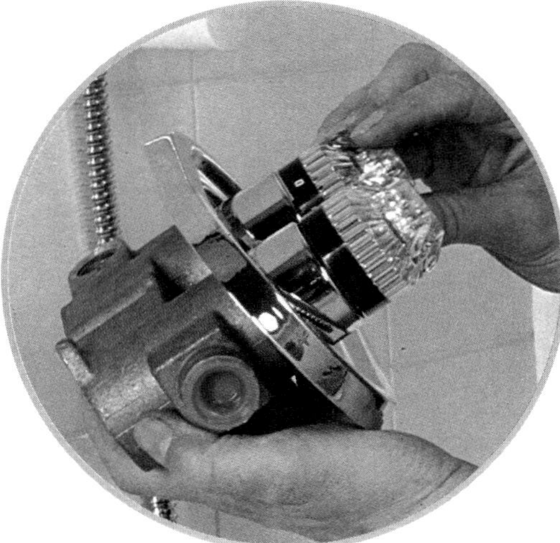

**Thermostatic mixer**
*Left: This thermostatic mixer is also supplied from behind and provides two separate controls – one for pre-setting the temperature, and one for adjusting the flow of the water once the user is inside the shower.*

## Ready Reference

### TYPES OF SUPPLY

Here is a summary of the various types of shower supply you could choose:

**Rear supply – surface mounting**
Both hot and cold supplies come through the wall behind the mixer, which is surface mounted on the cubicle wall.

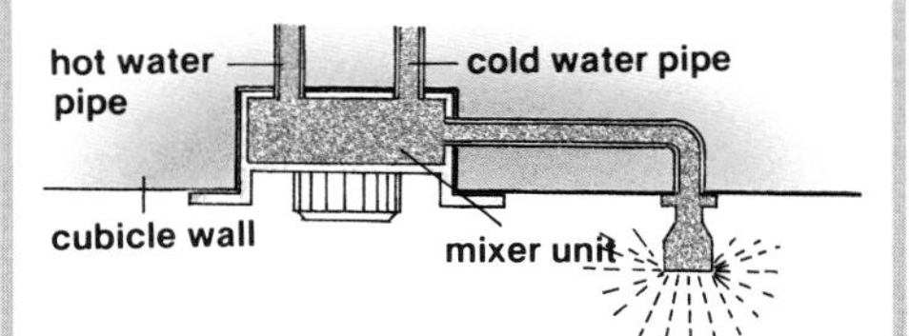


**Surface supply – surface mixing**
The hot and cold supplies come independently through the shower wall and can be seen entering the surface-mounted mixing unit.

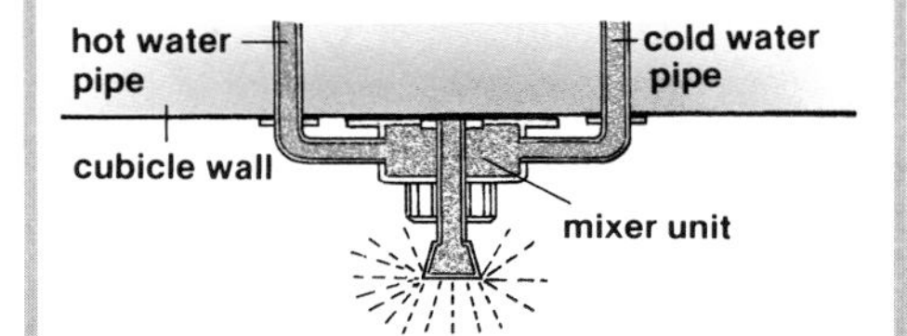


**Surface supply – thermostatic mixing**
Water supplies come through the wall into the surface-mounted unit, and then are regulated by sensitive flow and temperature controls.

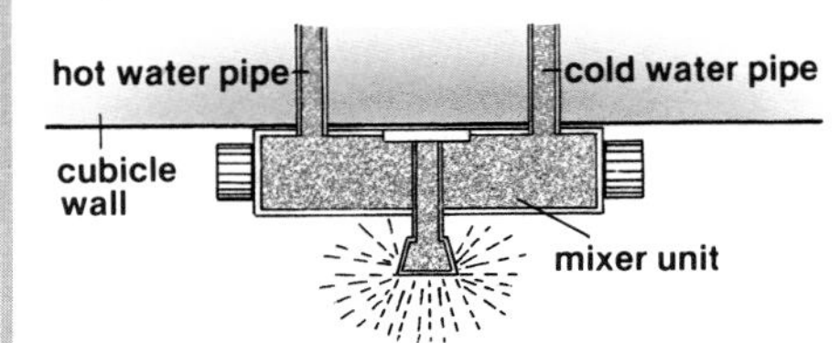


**Rear supply – instantaneous shower**
The mains (cold-water only) supply comes through or along the wall, and enters the unit for rapid heating and distribution through the rose.

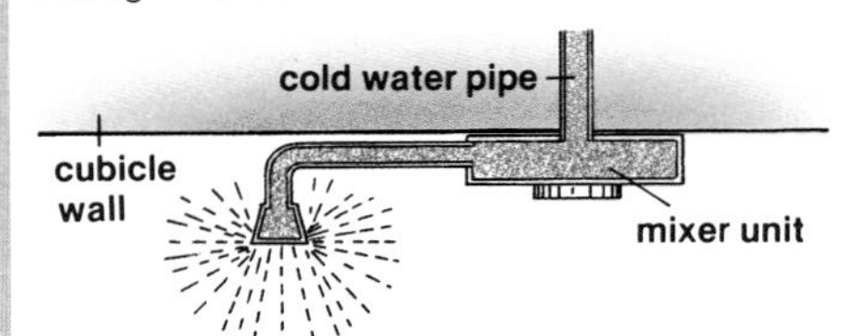


### TIP: TEST YOUR SEALS

However much purpose-built shower surround you buy – or however much you build – it must all have a waterproof seal with the tray and any solid cubicle walls. Test all joints for leaks with a hand spray, and if they do leak, make sure they are filled with a flexible non-setting mastic.

# BUILDING A SHOWER CUBICLE

**The simplest way to add showering facilities to your bathroom is to install the shower over the bath. However, building a separate cubicle is a better solution.**

When you come to install a shower in your home, the most obvious place for it is over the bath because you can make use of the bath's water supply and waste facilities. But this isn't the most advantageous site: putting a shower there does not increase your bathing facilities, it merely improves the existing ones. It's far better to have your shower as a separate cubicle, even if the cubicle is in the bathroom itself. If you can put the cubicle in another part of the home, you have as good as provided an extra bathroom.

You may think that you have no room in your home for a shower outside the bathroom, but that is not necessarily true. A shower does not require all that much space and you can make do with an area about 900mm (3ft) square. But you've got to think about how much space you need to get into and out of the shower. It isn't usually that easy or efficient to dry off inside, so you need some space to dry off at the point of exit. You will also have to take into consideration the relationship of the drying area with bathroom fittings.

You can buy a ready-made shower cubicle, or build your own from scratch. The latter course will save a lot of money, and is easier than you might think, but you've got to take care to ensure that it is properly waterproofed.

### Putting in the tray

To build a shower cubicle you start with the shower tray. Many people attempt to make one of these themselves by building a box that they cover with some impervious material – usually tiles. However, the construction is not easy because making the box absolutely waterproof can present problems, and then it is difficult to get the right gradient from every part of the tray to carry water to the waste outlet. On the whole, you would do better to buy a tray.

Normally, trays are made in acrylic plastic or glazed ceramics. The latter are dearer, but much longer-lasting, as acrylics can crack. Both types are available in standard sanitary-ware colours, so if you have a modern coloured bathroom suite, you should be able to match it. Trays come in a range of sizes, so be sure to choose one to fit the space you have, since obviously the size of tray governs the area your installation will take up. Ceramic trays can also be very heavy so it's likely you'll need help to get one into position.

The tray will have a waste outlet, and this may be in one corner, or in the middle of one side. It must be sited so that its waste pipe can discharge conveniently into a hopper of a two-pipe system, or be connected up to an existing waste pipe, or to the main stack of a single-pipe system. The waste pipe must slope downwards all the way, and it is important to get the fall right in order to drain water away efficiently. In general, the fall should be between 6 and 50mm per 300mm run of pipe (¼ to 2in per ft) depending on the length of the run (measured from the actual waste outlet). Too steep a run can produce a siphonage effect that will drain the water out of the trap, thus depriving your home of its protection from drain smells (see pages 14 to 18). It's a good idea to set a fall of 25mm (1in) per 300mm for a short run of say 600 to 900mm (2 to 3ft), but only a 12mm (½in) fall where the run will be 3 to 4.5m (10 to 15ft).

Most shower trays are square, and obviously these can be turned round to place the outlet in the most convenient position. However, for installation in a corner, triangular shaped trays, or quadrants – with two straight sides at right angles and a curved front – are on sale, but they're quite expensive.

The outlet does not have a plug, because it is never the intention that the tray should be filled up. Since there is no plug, no overflow is required. However, like all your bathroom fittings, it must have a trap. This should be 38mm (1½in) in diameter but, like a bath, does not have to be of the deep-seal variety.

Some trays are designed to have enough depth to enable the trap to be installed above floor level. Others are quite shallow, and the trap must go under the floor, a point to bear in mind if you have a concrete floor. Yet another possibility is to mount the tray on supports, to raise its height, and some manufacturers sell special supports to raise the tray off the ground. Otherwise you can use bricks or timber, suitably disguised by a plinth. It's a good idea to provide an inspection panel should you ever want to get access to the plumbing. Whatever the case, you will never have good access to the outlet plumbing after it's been installed – so be sure to make a good job of it.

### Providing a cubicle

A shower tray is best positioned in a corner, so that two sides of the shower enclosure are already provided by the shower tray itself; you can bridge the gap with timber covered with tiles set flush with the top of the tray.

# INSTALLING THE SHOWER TRAY

**1** *Press a sausage of plumber's putty around the underside of the outlet flange, then wind PTFE tape along the length of the thread.*

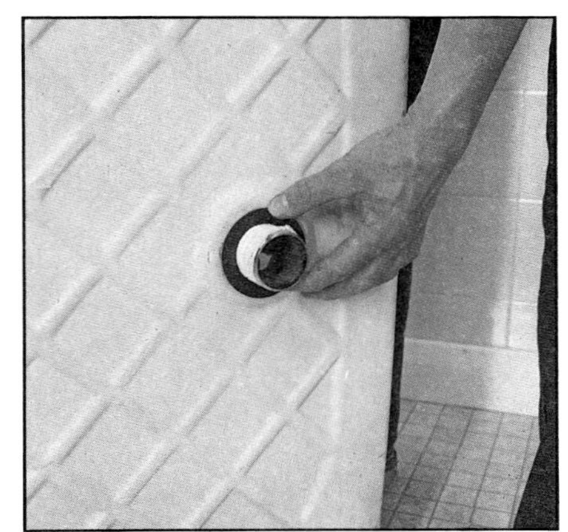

**2** *Push the flange into the waste hole in the tray, press it home until the putty squeezes out round the edge, and put on the metal washer.*

**3** *Screw on the back-nut by hand and tighten it with an adjustable wrench. This will squeeze more putty out; remove the excess neatly.*

**4** *Take the special low-seal shower trap and screw it onto the outlet flange, after first making sure that the O ring is in place.*

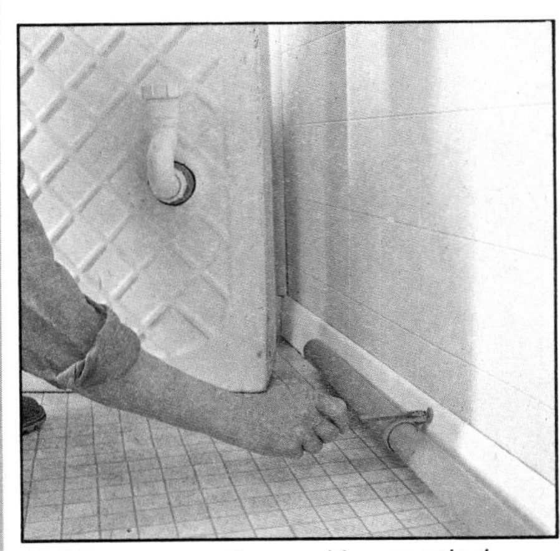

**5** *Measure up the position needed for the waste run, and install the plastic waste pipe in position ready to be connected up to the trap.*

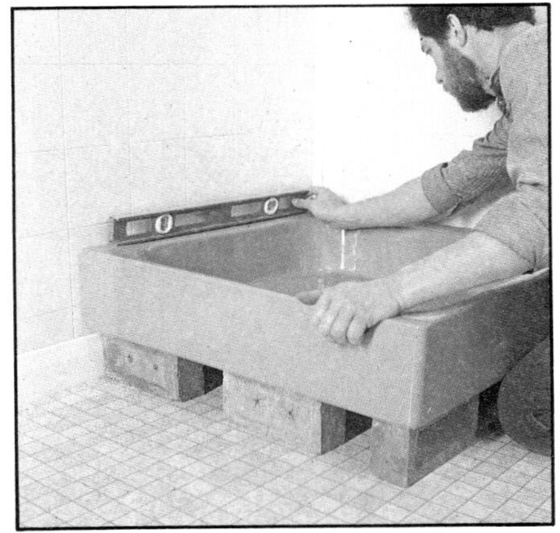

**6** *Lower the tray into place and connect up the trap to the waste pipe. Check that it is level on your prepared base.*

## Ready Reference

### WASTE OUTLET RUNS

You must provide sufficient depth underneath the shower tray to accommodate the waste trap and the outlet pipe. You can:

- support the tray on timber or bricks and face the elevation with panels

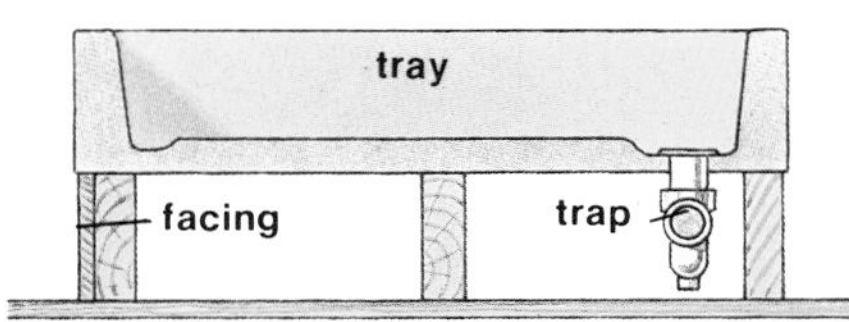


- support the tray with special supporting brackets which are usually available from shower tray manufacturers, and face the elevation with panels

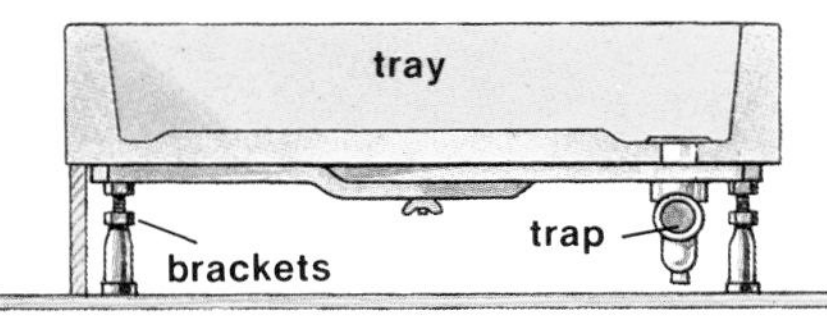


- cut a hole in the floor – if it's made of wood – and run the trap and waste above the ceiling of the room underneath. You can do this only if the joists run in the same direction as the waste pipe.

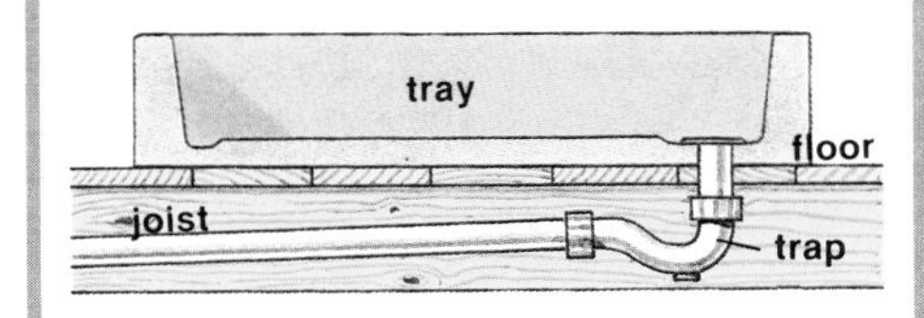


### HOW MUCH SPACE?

It's very easy to think of a shower as only occupying the same space as the tray itself. But don't forget that you will usually step out of it soaking wet and so will need sufficient area in which to dry off. If the shower is enclosed on three sides you will need more space than if it's enclosed on one side and curtained on the others.

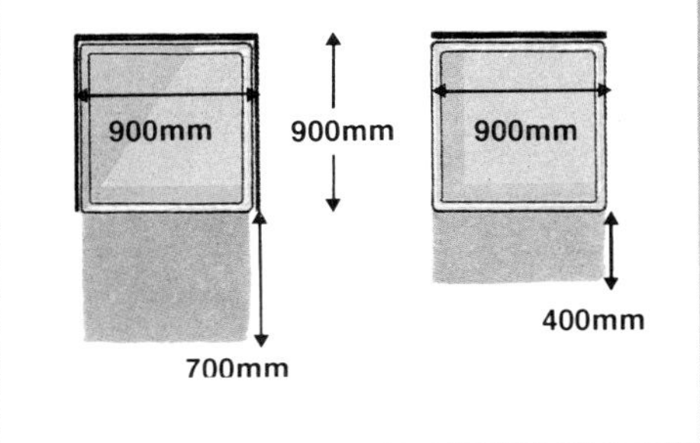

## PUTTING UP A SURROUND KIT

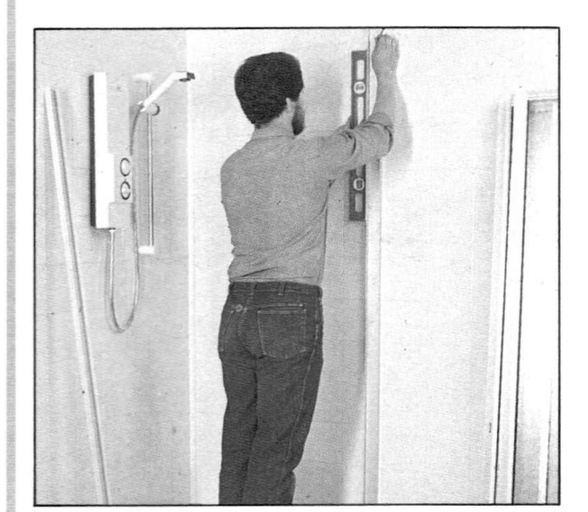

**1** *Mark the position of the wall uprights; use a spirit level to make sure that they will be truly vertical when fixed in position.*

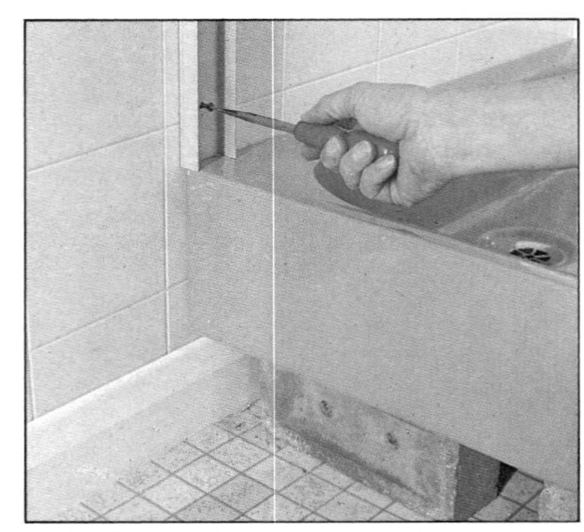

**2** *Drill holes for the upright fixings, then plug them with plastic wall plugs and screw on the uprights with the screws supplied.*

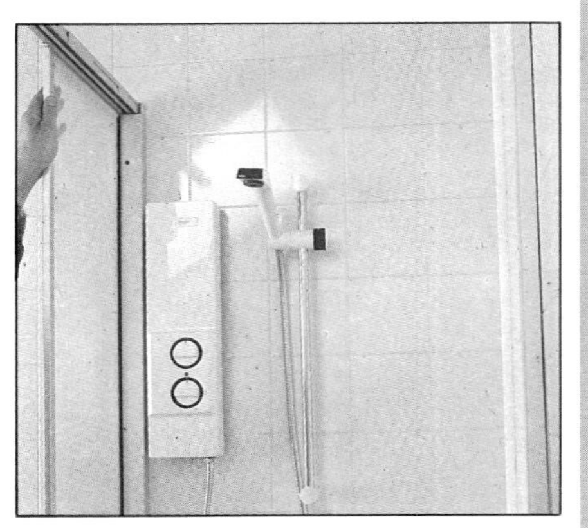

**3** *Slide the first panel into position on the wall upright and fix it; again check that the structure is in a properly vertical position.*

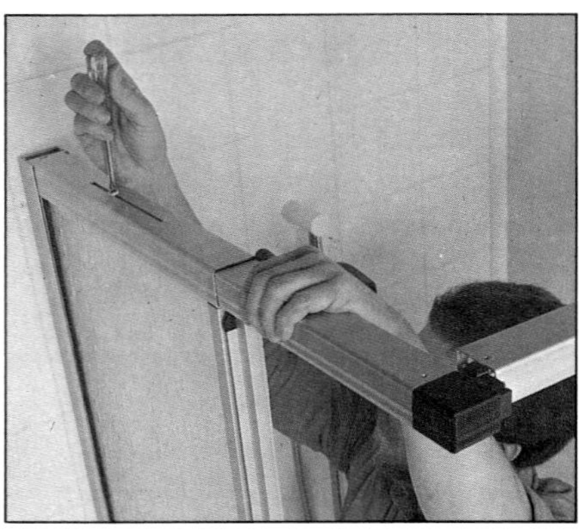

**4** *Adjust the length of the panel to fit the size of the shower tray and tighten up the screws carefully. Attach the corner bracket.*

**5** *Fix the other panel in position and adjust its length so that it mates up accurately and squarely with the corner bracket.*

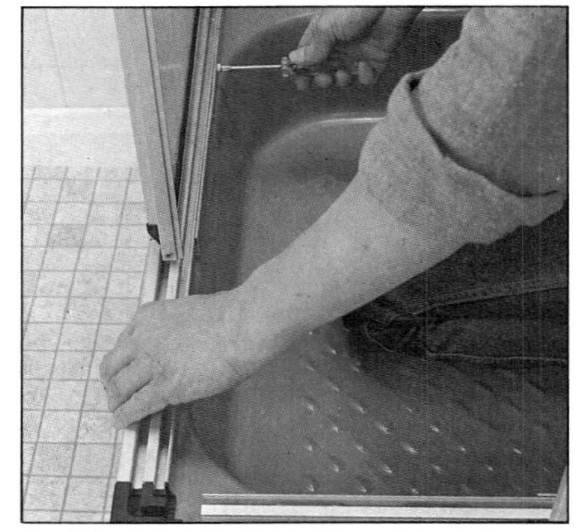

**6** *Adjust the bottom runners to the correct size so that they match up with the bottom corner bracket; check they are square to the tray.*

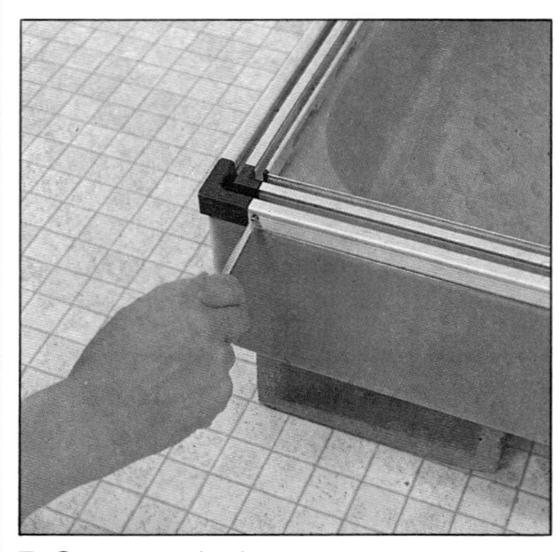

**7** *Screw up the bottom corner bracket, then check that the whole structure is firm and square and that the door opens and closes smoothly.*

**8** *Loosen the wall upright fixings and wedge up each side in turn. Squeeze sealant between the frame and the tray and refix the frame.*

**9** *Check again for alignment, then finish off the base by firmly fixing the supports in position and finally boarding in the sides of the shower.*

Existing walls forming part of the cubicle will also need tiling or covering with some laminated material – commonly waterproofed decorative wallboard, or even glass or sheet plastic over paint or wallpaper. It is obviously very important to make sure that all gaps are sealed, otherwise gradual water seepage will occur which will damage the fabric of your house.

The sides of the cubicle you have to install can be home-made or bought as kits. The simplest way to fill one or two sides is with a curtain rail and shower curtain. This works quite well with a shower in the bath, but the sides of a shower tray are much shallower than those of a bath and water is therefore quite likely to splash onto the floor. This means that curtains are really only at all suitable for the entry side of the cubicle where you might protect the floor with a bath mat, or where the floor of your bathroom is tiled and fully sealed.

You can construct any solid sides of the cubicle using a timber framework, but you will have to buy a suitable proprietary door unless you use a curtain. These doors are usually made of aluminium frames with opaque safety glass or plastic panels. They come in a wide variety of designs and colours. You can have, for example, a plain aluminium frame with clear glass, or a gold satin frame with dark smoked glass. If you plan to buy a door, check that you have calculated the size of your cubicle to fit it, and that the door comes with suitable rust-proof fittings to hang it.

The easiest (though most expensive) solution is to buy the complete surround, including a sliding or ordinary door, which will be supplied in kit form. These surrounds are made by the same manufacturers as shower doors and usually come complete with fixing instructions. They are usually adjustable to fit different shower tray sizes, and are simply fitted to the wall at each end to provide a rigid frame. Before finishing they have to be sealed where they meet the tray using a proprietary sealant, to ensure a waterproof joint. If this isn't done perfectly, water will gradually seep in and cause damp on the floor and walls of your bathroom.

### Home-made surrounds

Making your own surround will save money, and it has the advantage that you can tailor it exactly to your needs. You might, for example, want a surround which is larger than the tray itself; in which case you can install a shelf or seat next to the tray.

Begin by making a framework of 50mm (2in) square timber. You need a length on every edge, plus extra horizontal ones at 450mm (18in) centres. All should be joined with halving joints. In addition, fit any extra length needed to provide a fixing point (for the shower rose, for instance). The inside face of the partition should then be clad with 6mm (¼in) plywood. Use an exterior-grade board if the cubicle is to be tiled.

Another possibility is to use 10mm (⅜in) thick plasterboard. The framework for this should consist of a 50mm (2in) square batten on every edge, plus one extra vertical and horizontal in the middle, and any additional member needed to provide a fixing point. Fix the board with galvanised plasterboard nails driven in until the head slightly dimples the surface of the board, but without fracturing the paper liner. You can use 3mm (⅛in) hardboard to cover the outside of the cubicle framework.

Do not fix the exterior cladding for the time being. You should first clad the inside face, then fix the half-completed partition in place by driving screws through the frame members into the floor below, the wall behind and the ceiling too if it is to be a room height job.

The interior of this partition is a good place in which to conceal the supply pipes to the shower. You would then need an inspection panel, held by screws (not glued and nailed) to allow easy access to the pipework should maintenance ever be needed.

If the cubicle is not a floor-to-ceiling one, you will also need extra support at the top as you cannot leave the front top edge flapping free. This can take the form of a 75x25mm (3x1in) batten, decoratively moulded if you wish, spanning the two sides of the cubicle or fixed at one end to a block screwed to the wall, should there be only one side.

The whole interior of the shower cubicle needs to be clad with an impervious material to make sure it is waterproof. The most obvious choice is tiles, and these can be fixed to both the plywood or plasterboard cladding and the plaster of a wall. Make sure that the latter is clean and sound before tiling. Do not, however, fix the tiles direct to the timber part of the framing.

As an alternative to tiles you could use a special plastic-faced hardboard, with a tile pattern and a backing of plain hardboard. Fix the plastic-faced board by glueing and pinning with rustproof nails (if these can be lost somewhere in the pattern). Otherwise use a contact adhesive. This does not need to be spread all over the meeting surfaces. Apply it in a pattern similar to that detailed for the framework of the partitions. Adhesives applied by gun are available for this sort of work. The board on the back wall should be fixed in a similar manner.

Whatever material you use, all joins – where partitions meet the wall, or the tray – should be sealed with a silicone bath sealant. Any parts not clad with impervious material should be well painted with a three-coat system of primer, undercoat and one or two top coats.

## Ready Reference

### SHOWER SURROUNDS

**Buying a ready-made shower surround and door in kit form is the easy, but expensive, solution to enclosing the shower tray. You can use a curtain, which is less efficient, but cheaper. Surrounds can fill one, two or three sides; some of the options are illustrated below.**

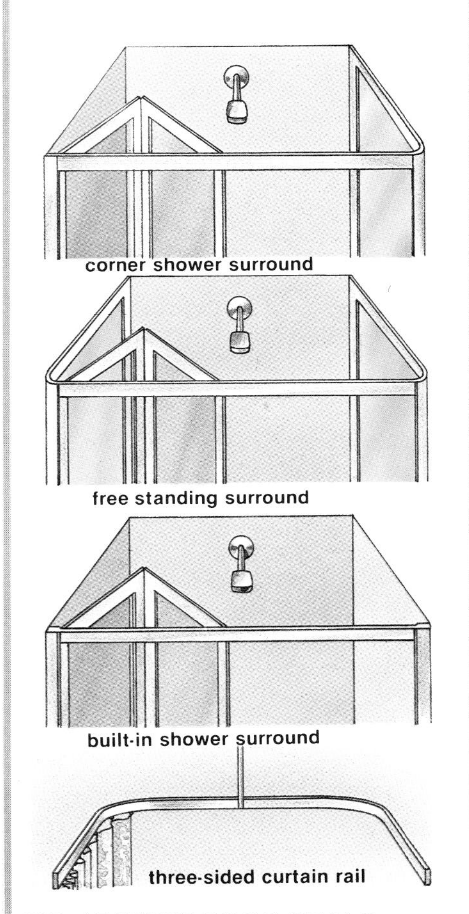


### TIP: WATERPROOF SEALS

**There's no point in fitting a surround if it's not watertight, and it is most likely to leak where the surround meets the tray. Fill this gap with non-setting mastic and then seal with any acrylic or silicone sealant to match the tray colour.**

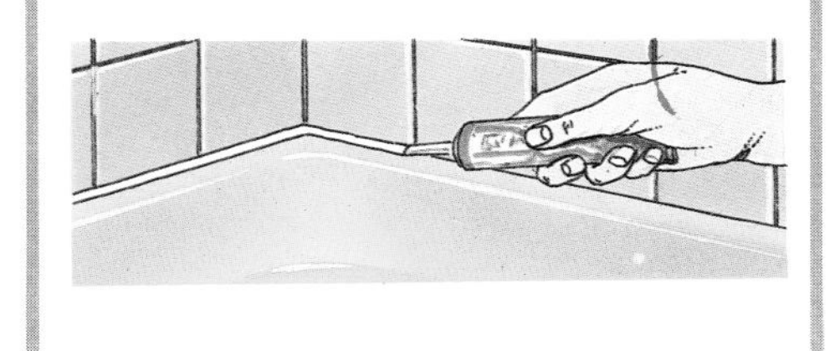

## BUILDING A CUBICLE

*If you are prepared to build one of the walls of the cubicle then the basic ingredients for the whole job are the tray itself, suitable shower fittings, a ready-made door, your other plumbing attachments and the materials for the partition.*

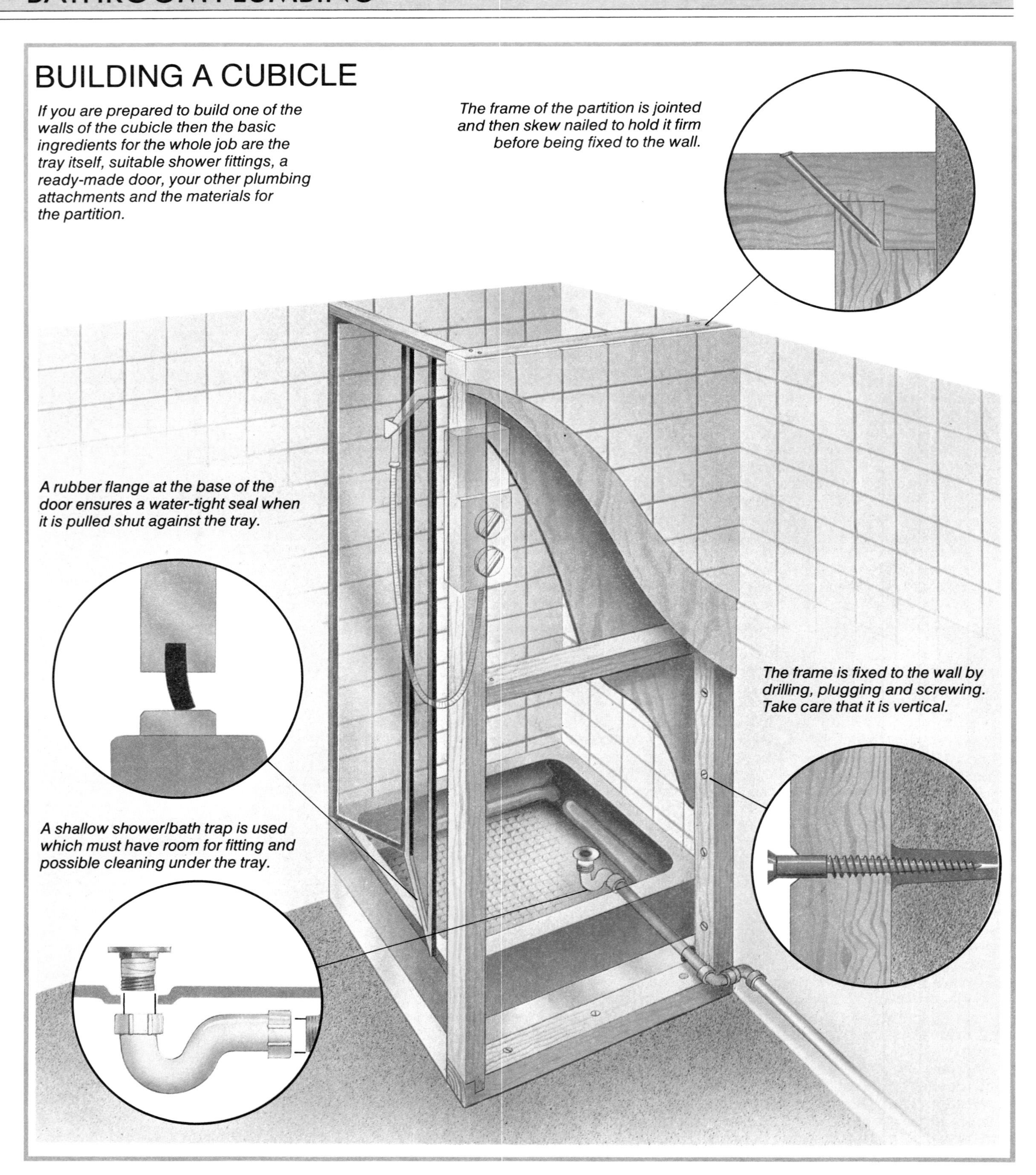

# REPLACING YOUR WC

**Replacing your WC need not be a frightening prospect provided you follow a few basic rules. It also gives you the opportunity to install a quieter and more efficient piece of equipment.**

There are several reasons why you may wish to remove and replace your WC suite. The existing pan may be cracked, in which case replacement must not be delayed, and no attempt should be made to repair it. Or the porcelain may be crazed making it unsightly, and difficult to keep clean. Most likely, however, the reason will be that your existing WC is simply old fashioned and due for replacement as part of an overall improvement plan.

## Pan or cistern?

If it's just the pan you find fault with then that's all you need to replace. Colours for sanitary-ware, as WCs are usually called by the manufacturers, are fairly standardised, and you should have no difficulty in obtaining a pan to match the existing cistern.

If, on the other hand, you want to convert an old-fashioned lavatory suite with a high-level cistern, it may be possible to replace only the flushing cistern and flush pipe (or 'flush bend' as it is often called) with a low level one, while keeping the existing pan.

However, in order to accommodate the flushing cistern, the pans of low level suites are usually positioned 25 to 50mm (1 to 2in) further from the wall behind the suite than are those of high level ones. If you overlook this point you are likely to find that the seat and cover of the pan cannot be raised properly when the new cistern is fitted.

## Slim-line cisterns

In recent years manufacturers have developed slim-line flushing cisterns or 'flush panels' only about 115mm (4¼in) deep. These can, in most cases, be used to convert a WC from high level to low level operation without moving the pan. With such a cistern the flushing inlet to the pan can be as little as 130mm (5¼in) from the wall behind, instead of the 200 to 230 (8 to 9in) required by an ordinary low level cistern. To make room for the full 9 litres (2 gal) of water needed for an adequate flush, these slimline cisterns are rather wider from side to side than conventional ones. So make sure that there is sufficient unobstructed width of wall behind the suite to accommodate it.

**PLANNING THE MOVE**

*The biggest problem concerns the position of the soil stack. In this bathroom the old soil pipe was disconnected, and a new soil pipe run was installed on the outside of the bathroom wall to link the new WC to the existing soil stack. This was much neater than running the new pipe inside the bathroom, where it would have had to be boxed in.*

*The other alteration to existing pipework involved cutting the cold feed to the cistern part-way along its run, and re-connecting it to the new cistern.*

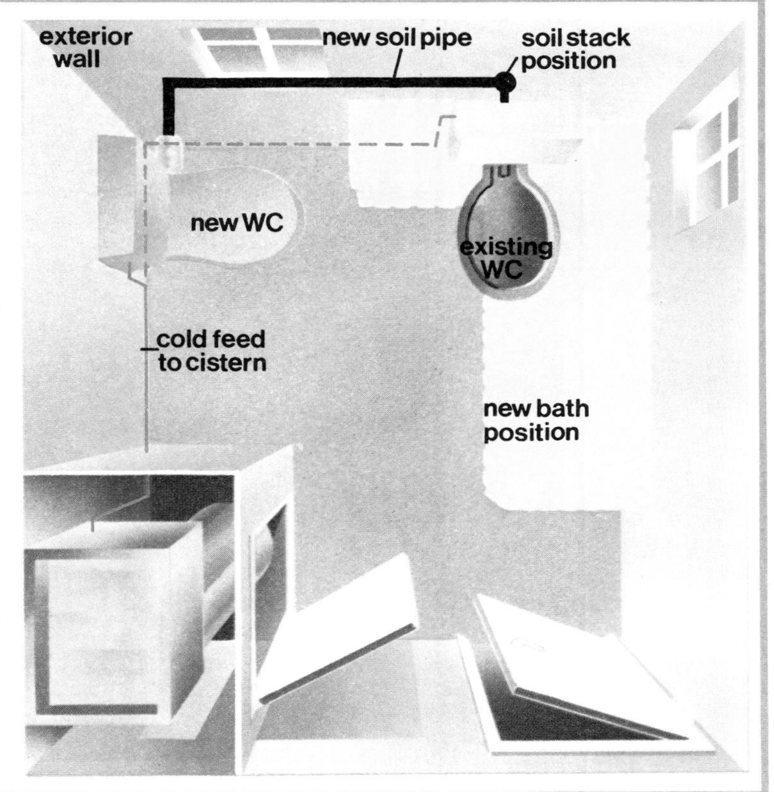

## Siphonic suites

Close-coupled lavatory suites, in which the pan and cistern form one unit without even the short flush bend of a low level cistern, are neater in appearance than the other kinds. They are particularly silent and effective where they are flushed and cleansed by siphonic action, as distinct from the 'wash down' action in which flushing simply releases the full contents of the cistern into the pan, and the weight of water carries away its contents. They also provide a larger water surface area than older pans, an important factor in maintaining the cleanliness of the pan.

There are two kinds of siphonic suite, single-trap and double-trap. The single-trap pattern is the simpler and cheaper. The outlet is first constricted and then widened to connect to the branch drain or soil pipe. When the suite is flushed, water completely fills the restricted section of the outlet and passes on, taking air with it, to create a partial vacuum. Atmospheric pressure then pushes the contents of the pan into the drain. The siphonic action is broken, often with a gurgle, as air passes under the bend of the trap.

With a double-trap siphonic suite a specially designed air pipe or 'pressure reducer' connects the air space between the two traps to the channel through which the flushing water passes. As this water flows past the pressure reducer it sucks up air from the space between the two traps, in the same way that the wind passing over the top of a chimney sucks up air from a room below. It's this that creates the partial vacuum on which siphonic action depends. Where a double-trap siphonic suite is working properly, you'll see the water level in the pan fall before the 'flush' water flows in. Although more expensive than other kinds, these suites are valuable where, as in an entrance lobby cloakroom for instance, silent operation is a prime consideration.

Just as low level WC suites normally project further from the wall behind them than high level ones, close-coupled suites project further than either. Don't forget this when considering the provision of such a suite in a small bathroom or cloakroom. You may have to change the position of the washbasin and this, in turn, could obstruct the door.

## Pan fixings

Moving an existing WC pan isn't always easy. It's likely to depend largely upon whether it is installed upstairs or on the ground floor. Upstairs WCs usually have a P-trap outlet, which is almost horizontal and is connected to a branch soil pipe by means of a putty or mortar joint. This can easily be broken with a club hammer and cold chisel once you have disconnected the pan from the floor.

Downstairs WCs usually have their bases firmly cemented to a solid floor and usually have an S-trap outlet which is vertical. This connects via a cement joint to an earthenware drain socket protruding above floor level. To remove such a pan it's necessary to break the outlet. Use a cold chisel to detach the front part of the pan from the floor, then use a cold chisel and hammer again to clear the pan outlet and the joining material from the drain socket.

Nowadays it is usual to connect both ground floor and upstairs WCs to the soil pipe using a flexible joint, usually a patent plastic push-fit joint with a spigot that is inserted into the drain and a 'finned' socket that fits over the WC pan outlet.

Such patent joins are nowadays manufactured in a range that covers virtually any WC installation. Not only are they easy to use but they help reduce the noise of a flushing lavatory. It's not considered to be good practice today to cement the base of a WC to a solid floor, as the setting of the cement can create stresses resulting in a cracked pan. It is best to remove every trace of cement from the floor and, having achieved a dead-level base, to secure the WC pan with screws driven into plugs pushed into holes drilled in the floor.

## How to start

After you have turned off the water supply and flushed the cistern to empty it, the next step is to disconnect the cistern's water supply, overflow and outlet pipes. So begin by unscrewing the cap-nut connecting the water-supply pipe to the cistern's ball-valve inlet. Then undo the back-nut retaining the cistern's overflow or warning pipe. Finally undo the large nut which secures the threaded outlet of the cistern to the flush pipe. It should now be possible to lift the old cistern off its supporting bracket or brackets.

If the WC suite is a very old one and screwed to a timber floor, unscrew and remove the pan's fixing screws. Then, taking the pan in both hands, pull it from side to side and away from the wall. If the connection to the soil pipe is made with a mastic or putty joint, the pan outlet should come easily out of its socket (which will have to be cleaned of all jointing material before the new unit is fitted). If a rigid cement joint has been used then there's usually no alternative but to use a bit of force. This means deliberately breaking the pan outlet, just behind the trap and above the pipe socket, with a club hammer. You can then prise the front part of the pan away from the floor using a cold chisel and hammer. This will separate the pan outlet from the pipe. At this point it's a

# Ready Reference

### PAN AND CISTERN POSITIONS

There are various WC suite arrangements you're likely to come across. The position of the pan in relation to the cistern is crucial, and if you're changing one without the other you must measure up carefully, to ensure that major changes of position can be avoided.

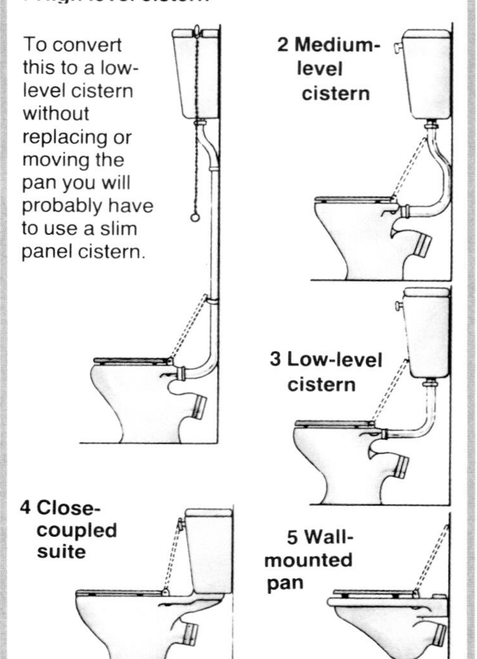


### HOW MUCH SPACE

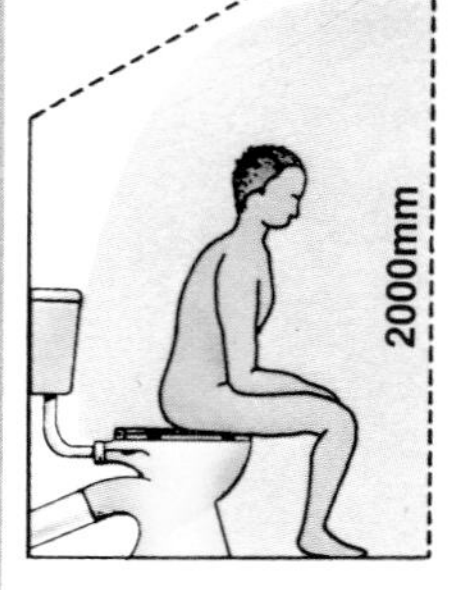


You need a minimum amount of space around a WC in order to be able to use it comfortably – above it, to each side of it and in front of it.

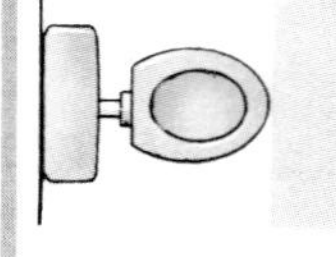

# REMOVING THE OLD PAN

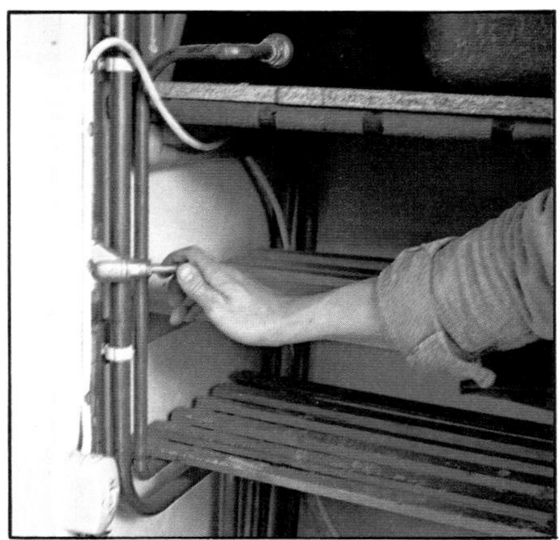

**1** *Locate the water pipe which supplies the WC cistern and completely shut off the stop valve which controls it. If no valve exists, block the cistern outlet.*

**2** *Lift the top off the cistern and then press the flush handle to empty it. No more fresh water should flow in as the ball float falls.*

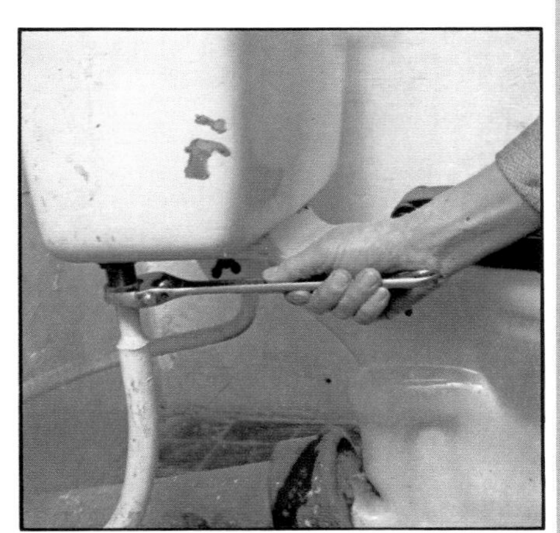

**3** *Disconnect the overflow pipe. If it is made of lead you should replace it with a PVC pipe run. Saw it off if you are repositioning the WC elsewhere.*

**4** *Disconnect the supply pipe in the same way as the overflow. If you are replacing the piping altogether, you can cut through it with a hacksaw.*

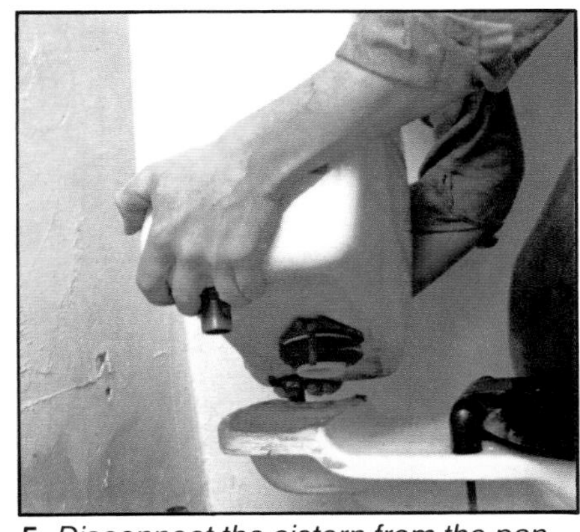

**5** *Disconnect the cistern from the pan. A close-coupled one is lifted off; with other suites you may have to disconnect the flush pipe between cistern and pan.*

**6** *Unscrew the pan from the floor, and then use a hammer and cold chisel to break the joint between the pan and the outlet, tapping gently but firmly.*

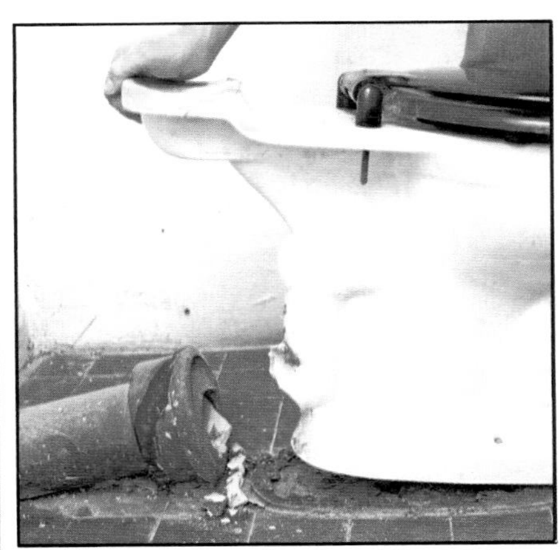

**7** *When you have fractured the joint, ease the pan away from the pipe. Even if it is bedded on mortar it should come away easily. Chip away the old mortar.*

TIP

**8** *Dispose of the pan and extract any loose bits of debris from the socket. Stuff newspaper into the opening to stop bits falling into the soil pipe.*

**9** *If you are going to use the pipe again clean it out carefully, ready to be connected up to the new WC pan with a proprietary connector.*

## INSTALLING THE NEW PAN

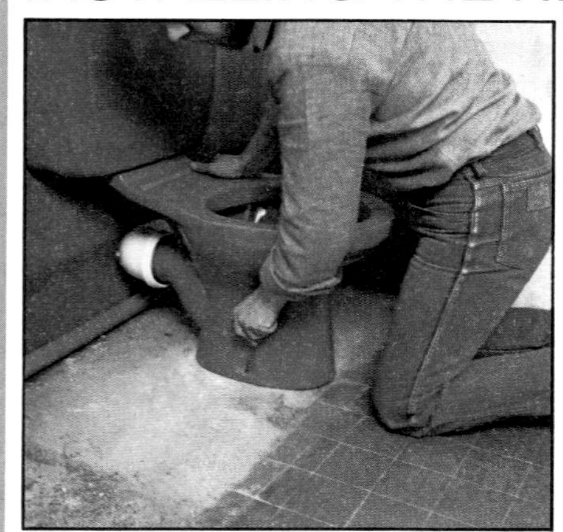

**1** *Offer up the pan to the outlet (note that here a new PVC soil pipe has been installed). When it fits snugly, mark down the positions for the fixing screws.*

**2** *Drill the holes and reposition the pan and cistern. Fit the pan outlet into the white push-fit adaptor so that it is firmly in position.*

**3** *Secure the cistern to the wall with screws and plugs. Then attach the new overflow pipe, finally tightening up the lock-nut with an adjustable spanner.*

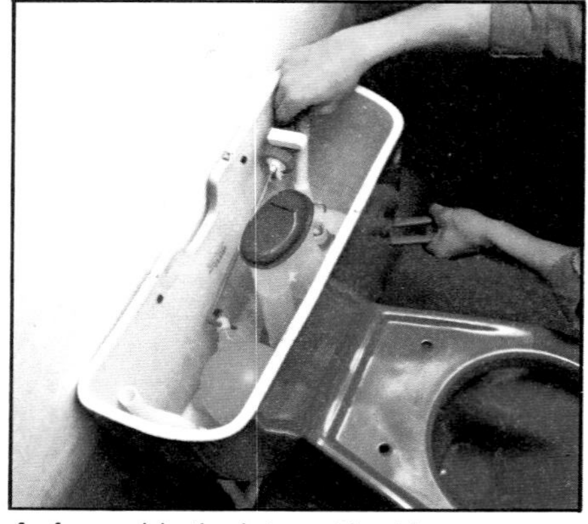

**4** *Assemble the internal flushing mechanism, see* Ready Reference. *Attach the water supply pipe and the flushing handle.*

**5** *Fit the seat assembly, making sure that the gaskets are correctly in place between the seat and the pan; screw up the nuts tightly.*

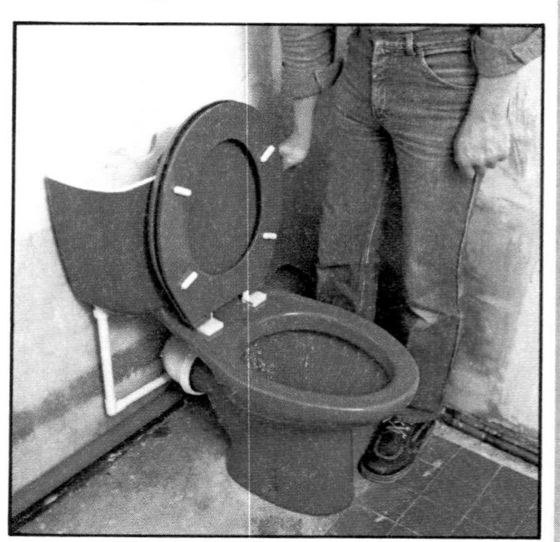

**6** *Restore the water supply. Check that the cistern fills to the correct level and adjust the ball-valve if it does not. Finally flush to fill the pan trap.*

## Ready Reference

### CISTERN MECHANISMS

There are two sorts of flushing mechanism the bell type in well-bottom cisterns and the piston type found otherwise. The latter is by far the more popular today.

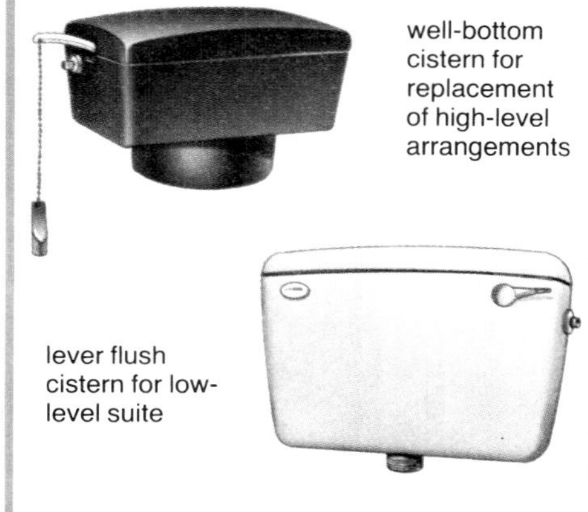

well-bottom cistern for replacement of high-level arrangements

lever flush cistern for low-level suite

slim-line flush panel where depth is restricted – usually when a high-level arrangement is converted to a low-level one

### THE FLUSH MECHANISM

You'll find you have to assemble the mechanism which is bagged up inside the new cistern. Lay out the components (A) and check them against the enclosed instruction leaflet before assembling them correctly (B).

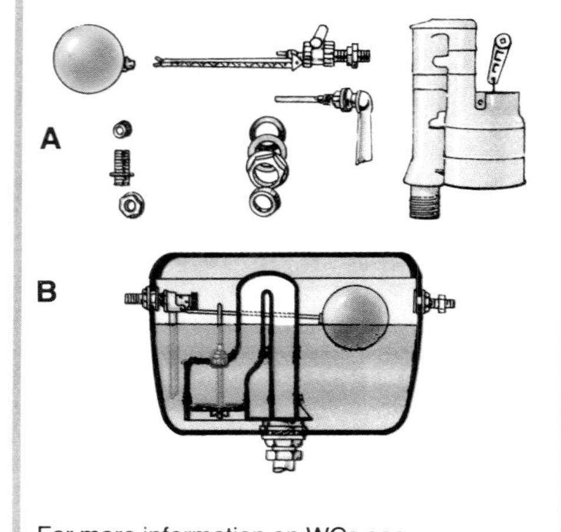


For more information on WCs see the following section.

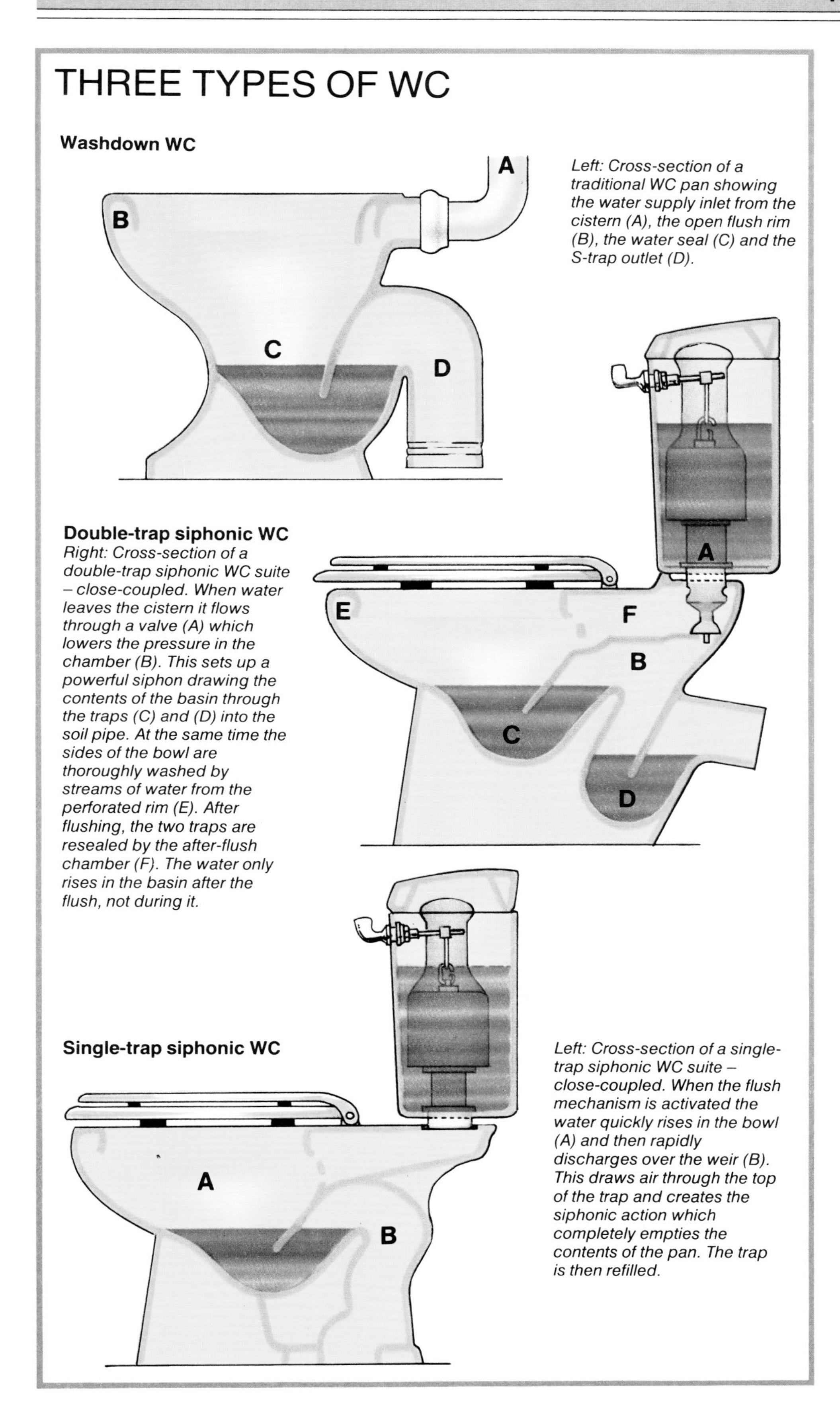


THREE TYPES OF WC

**Washdown WC**

*Left: Cross-section of a traditional WC pan showing the water supply inlet from the cistern (A), the open flush rim (B), the water seal (C) and the S-trap outlet (D).*

**Double-trap siphonic WC**

*Right: Cross-section of a double-trap siphonic WC suite – close-coupled. When water leaves the cistern it flows through a valve (A) which lowers the pressure in the chamber (B). This sets up a powerful siphon drawing the contents of the basin through the traps (C) and (D) into the soil pipe. At the same time the sides of the bowl are thoroughly washed by streams of water from the perforated rim (E). After flushing, the two traps are resealed by the after-flush chamber (F). The water only rises in the basin after the flush, not during it.*

**Single-trap siphonic WC**

*Left: Cross-section of a single-trap siphonic WC suite – close-coupled. When the flush mechanism is activated the water quickly rises in the bowl (A) and then rapidly discharges over the weir (B). This draws air through the top of the trap and creates the siphonic action which completely empties the contents of the pan. The trap is then refilled.*

good idea to stuff a bundle of rags or screwed-up newspaper into the drain socket to prevent any debris getting into the soil pipe. Next attack the socket to remove the remains of the pan's outlet. For this, use a small cold chisel and hammer but do it carefully to avoid damaging the drain socket itself – this will be used again. It's best to keep the point of the chisel pointing towards the centre of the pipe. Try to break it right down to the shoulder of the socket at one point and the rest will then come out fairly easily. Repeat the chipping process to remove all the old jointing material. Remove the bundle of rags or newspaper with the fragments of pipe and jointing material. Then with your cold chisel, remove every trace of the cement base that secured the old pan to the floor.

## Installing the new pan

Don't set the pan on a cement base – just use screws and plugs to fix it to the floor. But first you've got to get the connection to the pipe socket right. Start by positioning the patent push-fit joint in the pipe end. Then offer up the new pan to the patent push-fit socket and move the pan around until it fits snugly. To fix the pan, mark the screw positions on the floor by tapping a nail through the screw-holes, and draw round the base on the floor so that you can replace it in exactly the same position. Drill holes in the floor at the points marked and finally fit the screws. If it's a solid floor, of course, it's essential to use plastic or fibre plugs in the screw holes.

For fixing the pan, it's advisable to use brass non-corroding screws with a lead washer slipped over each one so you won't crack the pan as you tighten the screws. Screw the pan down, checking that it is exactly horizontal with the aid of a spirit level laid across the top of the bowl. If it is not dead-level, pack the lower side with thin wood or plastic strips. The latter are more suitable because thin wood rots too easily. Finally check that the outlet of the pan is firmly pushed into the connector and that you've followed any specific fitting instructions from the manufacturer.

## Fitting the cistern

Fix the new cistern to the wall at the level above the pan recommended by the manufacturer. In the case of a separate cistern, secure the upper end of the flush pipe to the cistern, usually by means of a large nut, and the lower end to the pan's flushing horn with a rubber cone connector. With a close-coupled suite, follow the manufacturer's instructions. You will now quite likely have to extend or cut back the water supply pipe to connect it to the new cistern. Complete the job by cutting and fitting a new overflow.

# REPOSITIONING YOUR WC

**Often moving a WC is the only answer to bathroom planning problems. By using plastic soil pipes the job can be made fairly straightforward, and also presents the possibility of installing an extra WC.**

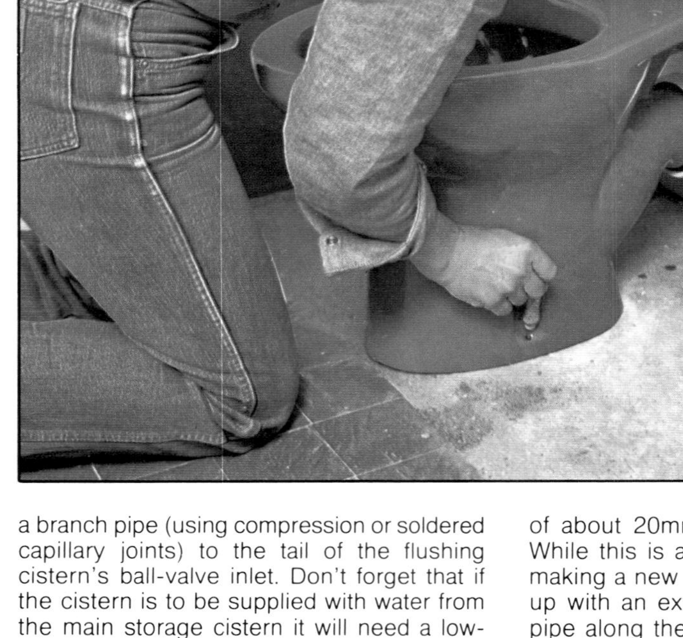

You may want to move the position of your WC because you're redesigning your bathroom. You may even want to take it out of the bathroom altogether and create a separate toilet compartment by partitioning off part of an adjoining room. This would make more space in which to install a bidet or a shower compartment. Or you may want to provide a second WC to cope with an expanding family.

### Rules and regulations

You will need to install a new WC pan and cistern as described previously. You will also have to adapt the water supply piping, provide an overflow for the new cistern and install a new soil pipe. In the case of the water supply and the soil pipe, this may mean either adapting the old pipes or putting in a new set of pipes and taking out the old redundant ones at the same time.

The adapted or replacement soil pipe must comply with the requirements of the Building Regulations as interpreted by your local authority. It's therefore essential to find out what you can and cannot do by discussing your proposals with the relevant official, who may be called the Building Inspector or Building Control Officer. The same officer must eventually approve the standard of the finished job.

If you want to put in a new WC in a separate compartment, the Regulations say that it must not have direct access to a living room or a kitchen. This may mean creating a lobby between the new compartment and the room it leads off, and installing a door in the lobby as well as one in the new compartment. However, you can have direct entry to a WC from a bedroom.

You have to think about ventilation as well. Any lavatory compartment must have an openable window in an outside wall or must be provided with an automatically-operating extractor fan (usually connected to the light switch) that is ducted to an outside wall.

### Water supply and overflow

Putting in a water supply to a new cistern is straightforward. Make a T-joint with a convenient 15mm (½in) cold water pipe and run a branch pipe (using compression or soldered capillary joints) to the tail of the flushing cistern's ball-valve inlet. Don't forget that if the cistern is to be supplied with water from the main storage cistern it will need a low-pressure ball-valve, but if it's to be connected to the rising main it will need a high-pressure one.

You will also have to connect an overflow pipe to the cistern; this goes through the outside wall and should stick out far enough to take any overflow clear of the wall surface. If the WC compartment doesn't have an outside wall the overflow pipe is usually taken to a point over the bath. The end of the pipe must be open.

### The soil pipe

If you are moving the pan a short distance, either a few feet along the bathroom wall or into the adjoining room, you can use the old connection to the outside soil pipe. You put on an angled socket and use a length of 100mm (4in) PVC soil pipe. You can do this as long as the whole length of pipe from the pan to the soil stack is not more than 6m (19ft 6in) and has a minimum gradient towards the stack of about 20mm per metre (¾in per yard). While this is a convenient and easy way of making a new soil run it means that you end up with an extended length of rather bulky pipe along the inside wall. This can be disguised by boxing it in, but it still takes up valuable space at floor level, and this might destroy the original purpose of installing it.

If you want to avoid a long inside soil pipe run or if you are installing a second WC on the same floor you can run the pipe straight through the wall and put the main pipe on the outside wall. This would mean that a new connection would have to be made to the soil stack. If the stack is made of cast iron you can't do this, and you would have to replace it with a new plastic stack (see pages 172 to 176).

An alternative is to connect the two WCs in series along one soil pipe run using swept junctions. In which case the maximum pipe run from the further WC to the soil stack can be as much as 15m (49ft) but you're not likely to need this much in an ordinary house. If the second WC is on a different floor you may be able to make a new soil pipe connection into a plastic stack, but a new groundfloor WC should be connected below ground to the underground drain via an S-trap (vertical) outlet. The operation requires considerable building work and a new entry to the underground drain, so you should employ the services of a professional builder.

### How to move the WC

Remove the existing WC pan from its outlet pipe (covered in the previous section). If this pan connection is fairly modern and has been made using a rubber or plastic collar, then it may be possible to remove it intact and install it in the new position. But if its removal means breaking the pan itself in order to detach it from the outlet, then you'll obviously have to buy a new pan.

If you are going to use the existing outlet, clean it up and fit an adaptor bend to take the new pipe run. These bends are available in a number of designs to suit the angle you need. Then fix a length of 100mm (4in) PVC pipe to the adaptor (usually a push-fit type, but see the adaptor's instructions). If possible the length of pipe should run all the way to the new WC pan site in one length, but if you have to join it there are suitable connectors available.

In fixing the pipe run you may have to make a hole in an intervening wall. To do this, mark the position of the hole with circles on each side of the wall, using the end of the pipe as a template. Drill holes all round the marked out circles and carefully chop out the hole with a club hammer and chisel. If you're tackling a timber-framed stud partition wall obviously you must avoid the vertical studs, so drill small test holes first to ensure your planned pipe run passes between them. When you've made the hole, clean up the edges and ease the pipe through.

At the other end of the pipe, fix another adaptor bend of the type which will match the outlet from the WC pan. Your supplier will tell you which one is suitable. Before you fix the pan make sure it lines up with the adaptor. You should also check that the finished pipe position has a minimum fall towards the outlet of 20mm per metre (¾in per yard). It shouldn't be any more than 30mm per metre (1¼in per yard) on long runs or else you may find that the water trap in the new pan will siphon away (see pages 14 to 18). Don't forget that the total length of pipe from the pan to the stack should be no longer than 6m (19ft 6in).

Fix the pan to the adaptor and to the floor, and attach the cistern (described on pages 129 to 133). It's best to use a P-trap pan rather

## MOVING A WC

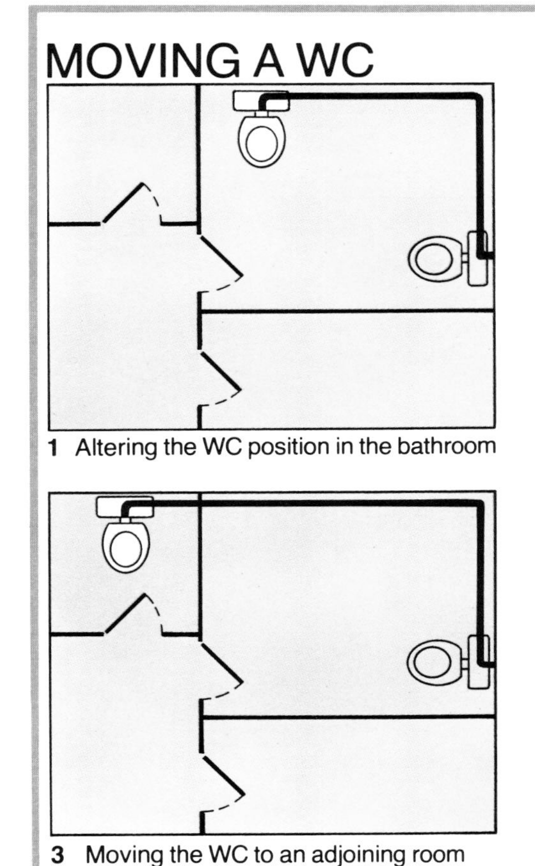

**1** Altering the WC position in the bathroom

**3** Moving the WC to an adjoining room using a longer soil pipe run

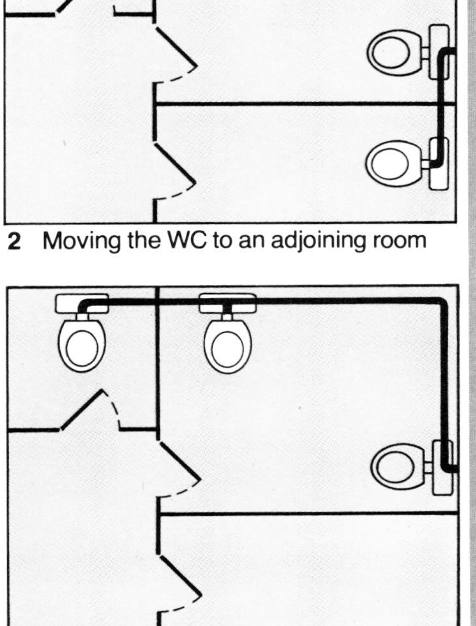

**2** Moving the WC to an adjoining room

**4** Moving inside the bathroom and installing another WC in series in an adjoining room

## Ready Reference

### CHECKING YOUR PLANS

Repositioning your WC or installing an extra one, means putting in new pipework for the water supply, the cistern overflow, and the soil pipe. Make sure that the design of the new soil pipe run conforms with the Building Regulations which include the relevant sections of the Public Health Acts. Discuss your plans with the local Building Officer before you start any installation. He must approve them and will want to inspect the finished work.

### POSITIONING THE WC

Make sure that:

- there is no direct access to a WC from a living room or kitchen, though there can be from a bedroom
- any WC compartment has either an openable window in an outside wall or a duct to an outside wall which is controlled by an automatically operating extractor fan (usually connected to the light switch)
- the soil pipe run from the pan to the stack should be no more than 6m (19ft 6in) long with a minimum gradient of 20mm per metre (¾in per yard) and slopes towards the soil stack
- any new connection of the soil pipe to the stack must be swept, as must be the connection of WCs in series to the soil run
- any ground floor WCs which are connected directly to the underground drain must be situated so that the distance between the top of the WC trap and the bottom of the bend leading into the drain is not more than 1.5m (5ft).

**Note:** To avoid direct access from a living room to a new WC compartment you may have to construct a lobby of some sort. In the case of an existing windowless bathroom, a fan and duct should already be fitted.

**Ground floor WCs**

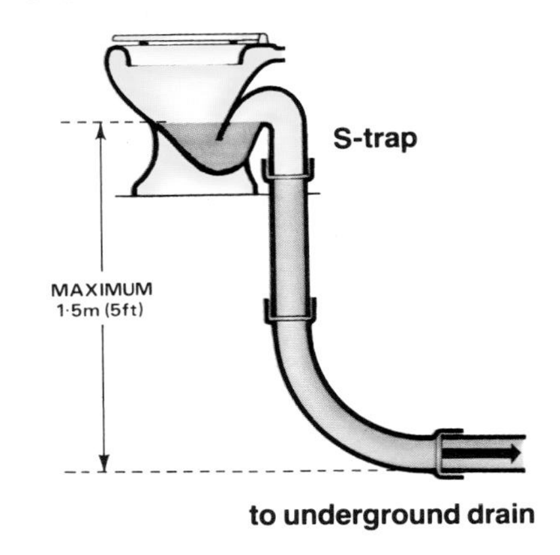

## USING THE CONNECTION

*You can connect the soil outlet of your repositioned WC to the existing soil outlet, (which is connected to the soil stack), by running new piping along the inside wall. A variety of fittings is available which makes this job comparatively easy as long as you stick to the regulations outlined in the* Ready Reference *on the previous page. This can enable you either to move your WC to a different location in the bathroom, or move it to an adjoining room.*

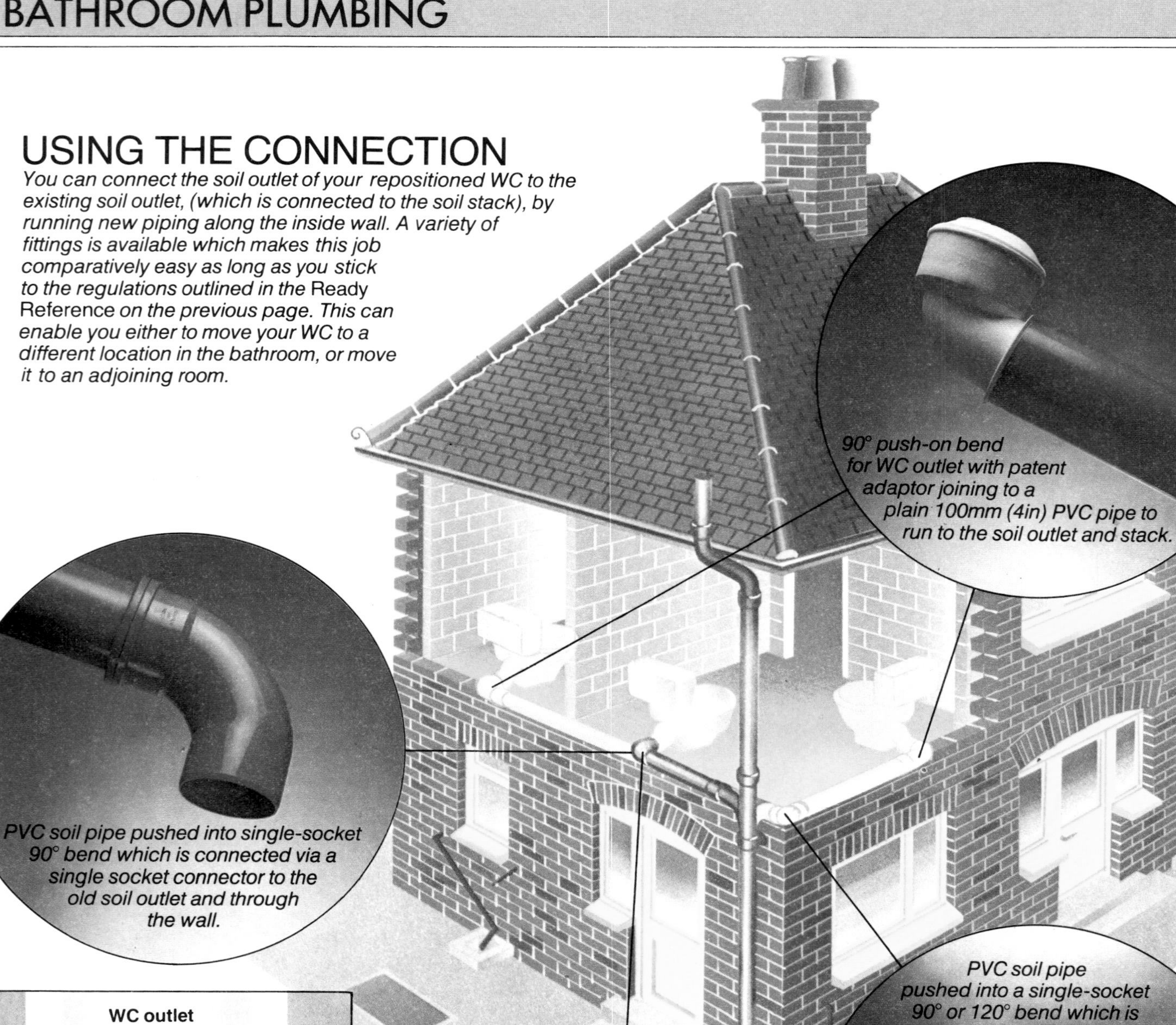

*90° push-on bend for WC outlet with patent adaptor joining to a plain 100mm (4in) PVC pipe to run to the soil outlet and stack.*

*PVC soil pipe pushed into single-socket 90° bend which is connected via a single socket connector to the old soil outlet and through the wall.*

*PVC soil pipe pushed into a single-socket 90° or 120° bend which is connected to a socketed length of PVC pipe leading to the outlet.*

*An offset connector can be used where the old outlet is larger than the new soil pipe which is to be connected to it.*

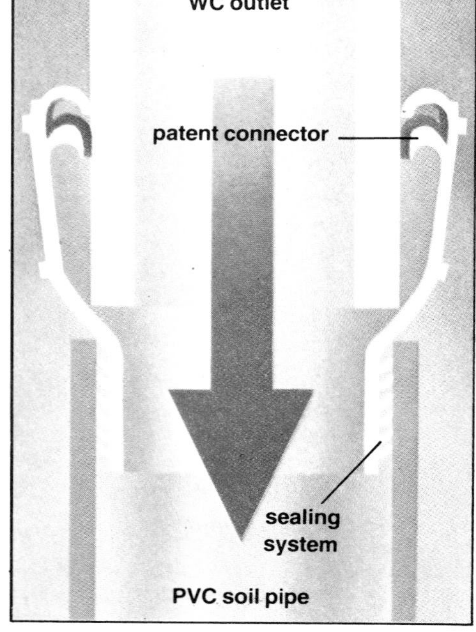

## MAKING A NEW CONNECTION

*If you want to avoid a long run of soil piping inside or want a second pan on the same floor you will have to make a new connection to the outside stack. If the stack is made of cast iron you'll need to install a new plastic stack (see pages 172 to 176).*

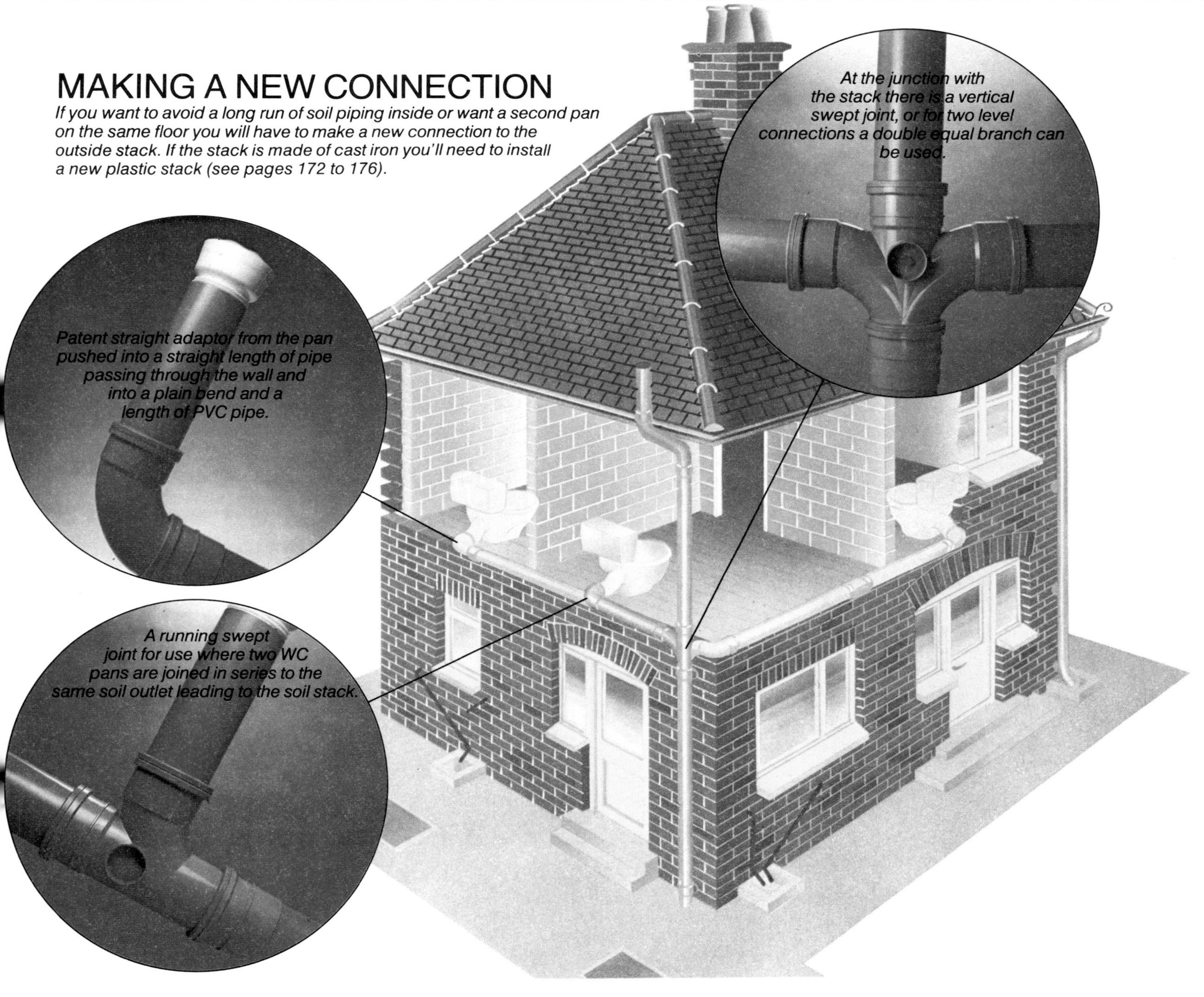


than an S-trap as otherwise you'll need another adaptor bend, and the less bends you use on soil pipe runs the better. In any case if you're draining into a single-stack system you must have a P-trap pan (see WASTE WATER SYSTEMS, pages 14 to 18).

When you've made all the connections and fitted the pan and cistern properly, flush the system and check for leaks.

### Making a new stack connection

If it's not practical to use the old soil stack connection for your new WC site, you are faced with a rather larger task – making a new connection to the soil stack somewhere else along its length. A new connection can only be made to a plastic soil pipe; if you've got a cast-iron stack you will have to replace it (as described on pages 172 to 176).

When you have removed the pan from the old position, take out the old soil connection socket and make good the wall and floor. In the new WC site mark out the hole you will need to make in the outside wall. Do this using the pan outlet as a guide. Make the hole as described above and insert a short length of PVC pipe. This should be long enough to be inserted into the pan connector at one end and into a right-angle connector positioned as close to the surface of the outside wall as possible. Link up the pan, the connector and the pipe and make good the inside of the wall.

On the outside, fix the right-angle connector and add to it a length of pipe running all the way to the stack. This pipe should be fixed to the wall using brackets supplied by the soil pipe manufacturer. At the stack a connection can be made by cutting in and inserting a swept junction.

If you want to install two WCs in series using an inside or an outside pipe the connections for the one further from the stack are the same but the junction between that nearer to the stack and the outlet pipe must be via a swept joint.

# REPLACING YOUR WC CISTERN

**If you're modernising a bathroom or separate WC, one of the most common jobs you'll have to carry out is to replace a high-level cistern with a neater-looking low-level one. Here's how it's done.**

Not very long ago every WC cistern was a high-level one set with its base about 2m (6ft) above floor-level. In better-off households there might have been a high level WC suite situated in an upstairs bathroom; but in most homes, until about 40 years ago, the WC was located in an outside cubicle.

Flushing cisterns in those days were all of the old-fashioned Burlington or 'pull-and-let-go' pattern. They were made of cast iron and had a well in the base. A stand-pipe, connected externally to the flush pipe, rose from the base of this well to terminate open-ended about 25mm (1in) or so above 'full water level'. A heavy iron bell, with lugs built onto its rim to permit water to pass freely underneath, stood over this stand-pipe with its base in the well.

The cistern was flushed by raising the bell, usually be means of a chain, and suddenly releasing it. Falling heavily into the well, the bell's 'wedge' shape forced the water contained within it up and over the rim of the stand-pipe. This water, falling through the stand-pipe and flush-pipe, carried air with it thus creating the partial vacuum that is necessary for siphonic action. Atmospheric pressure then pushed the water in the flushing cistern under the rim of the bell and down the flush-pipe to flush and cleanse the WC pan. The siphon was broken and the cistern started to refill when air passed under the bell lip.

High-level 'Burlington pattern' cisterns of this kind were efficient, tough and hard-wearing. Although they have been obsolete for years, many are still in use. Their disadvantages were, and are, a tendency to condensation, and thence to corrosion – though this could be treated by applications of anti-condensation paint – and their incurable noisiness. There was the heavy clank of the bell falling back into the cistern, the rush of the descending water and usually more rushing water as the cistern refilled.

The invention of the modern 'direct action' flushing cistern foreshadowed the end for the old high-level Burlington. These new cisterns are made of plastic or ceramic material and have a flat base. The stand-pipe does not terminate open-ended above water level, but bends over and opens out to form an open-based dome with its rim just above the base of the cistern. When the flushing mechanism is operated, a round plate is raised within this dome to throw water over the inverted U-bend into the stand-pipe and thus begin the siphonic action. The plate has a hole or holes in it to allow water to flow through freely once siphonic action has started. As the plate is raised these holes are closed by a plastic 'siphon washer' or 'flap valve'. Once it became the norm to build toilets within the house, silent operation became increasingly important and led to the almost universal provision of low-level WC suites.

## Replacing at high level

However, it cannot be denied that the cleansing effect of a flushing cistern at high level is more positive than that of a low-level cistern. There are, too, situations – such as with a supplementary outside WC – where the noisiness of a high level cistern is acceptable. When an old Burlington cistern fails in such a situation (perhaps having rusted through and sprung a leak, or as a result of the lugs at the base of the bell having worn away), you may well decide to replace it with another high-level cistern.

Although direct-action cisterns are often referred to as 'low-level cisterns' there are models which can be chain-operated from high level. One difficulty that could arise when replacing an old Burlington cistern with a direct-action one is that the latter normally has a flat base while a well is an essential feature of a Burlington cistern. At least one manufacturer has simplified the task of conversion by producing a modern, plastic, direct-action cistern with a well in its

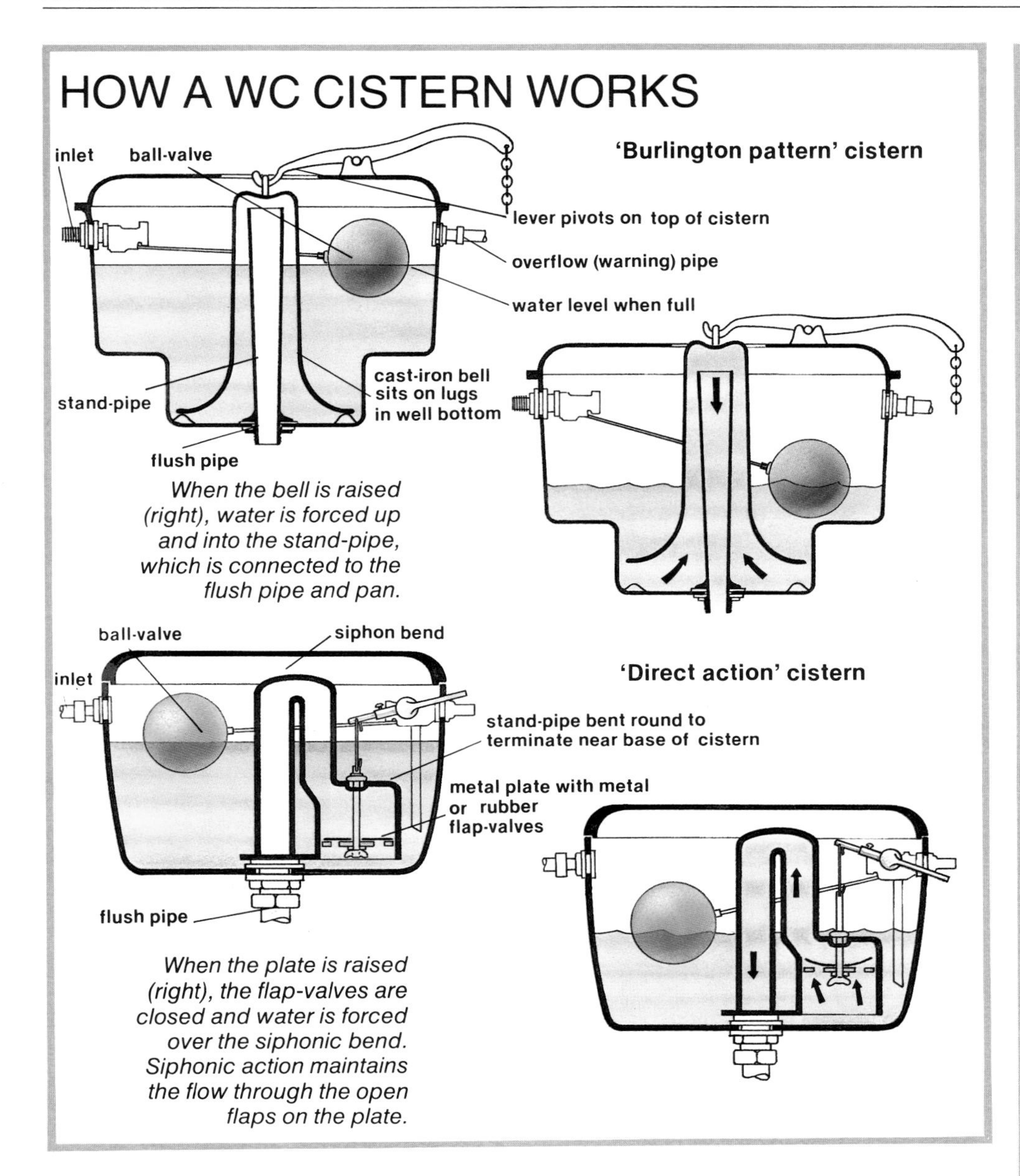


base. A cistern of this kind can be used as a replacement without adjustment to the water supply pipe, overflow or flush pipe.

### Replacing at low level

Usually, faced with the failure of an old Burlington cistern, you will decide to replace it with a more silent low-level one. This is a project that is easy enough to undertake but needs careful thought first. Many a home handyman has removed an old high-level cistern and flush-pipe and has replaced them with a low-level cistern and the slightly-larger-diameter 'flush bend' provided, only to find it impossible to raise the seat and hinged cover properly. For in order to accommodate the flushing cistern, the pan of a low-level lavatory suite is normally positioned 50 to 75mm (2 to 3in) further from the wall behind it than the pan of a high-level suite.

If the pan has a P-trap outlet and is connected to the socket of a branch soil-pipe by means of a mastic joint, an extension piece can be used without too much difficulty to bring it forward the required distance, but check that there is room to accommodate it. In some small bathrooms, moving the WC suite forward could mean having to alter the position of the washbasin and this, in turn, could make it impossible to open the door. If the pan has an S-trap outlet and is connected to a branch drain by means of a cement joint, bringing the pan forward is a daunting task.

However, it may well still be possible to convert the suite to a low-level operation without moving the pan. As an alternative to a conventional low-level flushing cistern, you could fit one of the new slim-line cisterns or 'flush panels' that have been developed in recent years to deal with this situation.

## Ready Reference

### CHECK THE PAN POSITION

You must check the position of the pan in relation to the old high-level cistern before you start work, as this may affect the sort of low-level cistern you install:

- if you intend to install an ordinary low-level cistern, check that the pan is far enough away from the wall to allow the seat to be raised freely. (With a high-level cistern, this problem will not arise as the cistern is well out of the way of the pan)
- if there's no room to move the pan forward, install a slim flush-panel cistern instead.

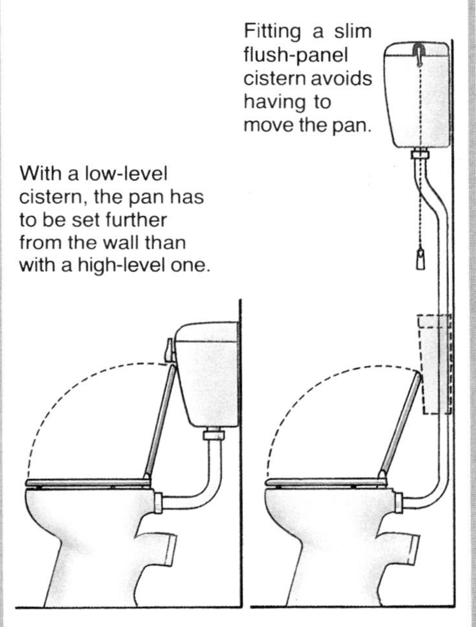


### TIP: DON'T REMOVE THE BRACKETS

If your old high-level cistern is supported on cast-iron brackets, as it probably is, don't rip them out as this will make a mess of the wall. Paint them and construct a shelf using them as supports. This can be used for storing WC supplies or for displaying plants.

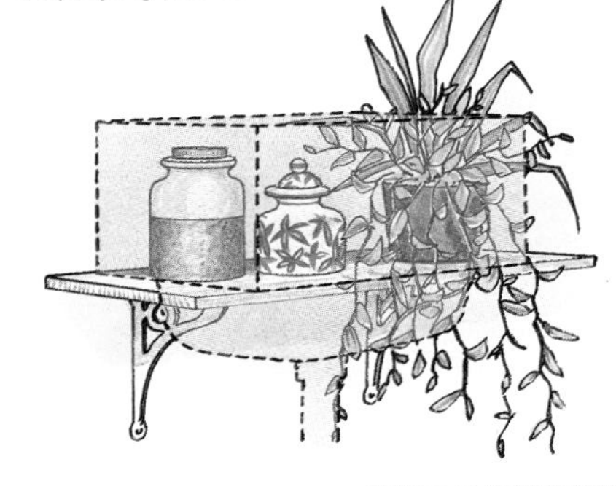

## TAKING OUT THE OLD CISTERN

**1** *Find out where you can turn off the water supply to the cistern, stop the flow and then flush the cistern to ensure that it is empty.*

**2** *Cut the old supply pipe, catching any drips which may flow out, and insert a new stop-valve for later connection to the new cistern.*

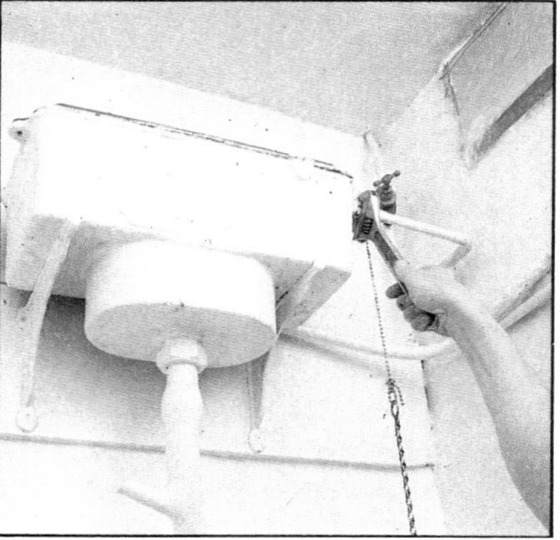

**3** *Disconnect the inlet pipe from the cistern using an adjustable spanner, and then pull the pipe right away from the cistern wall.*

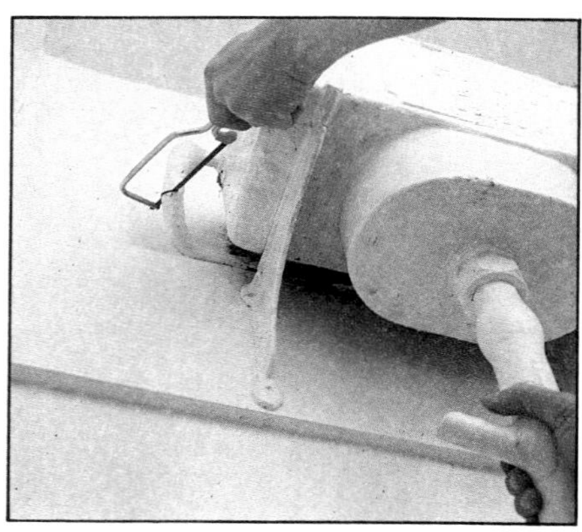

**4** *Detach the overflow in the same way, or simply cut it off with a hacksaw. It's likely to be made of lead and so will be easy to cut.*

TIP

**5** *To break the seal on the nut connecting the downpipe to the cistern, use a blow-torch to heat it up, then a wrench to turn it.*

**6** *When the cistern is completely detached from the pipework, lift off the heavy cast-iron cistern lid and place it to one side.*

**7** *Next, carefully lift the cistern off its bracket supports and lower it; it will be very heavy and will still contain some water.*

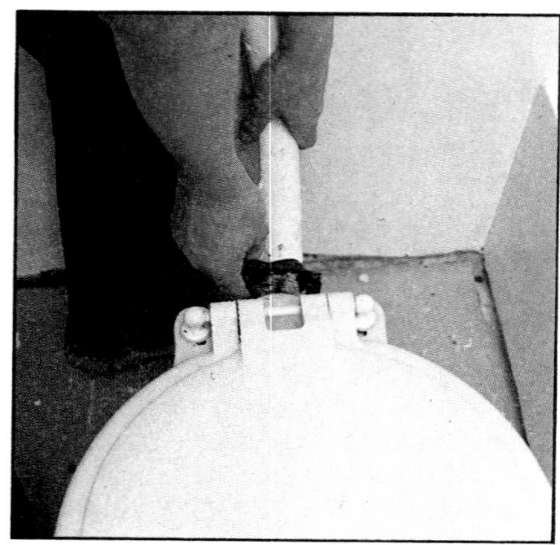

**8** *Remove the downpipe from its connection with the pan – it should come free with some gentle wiggling – and dispose of it.*

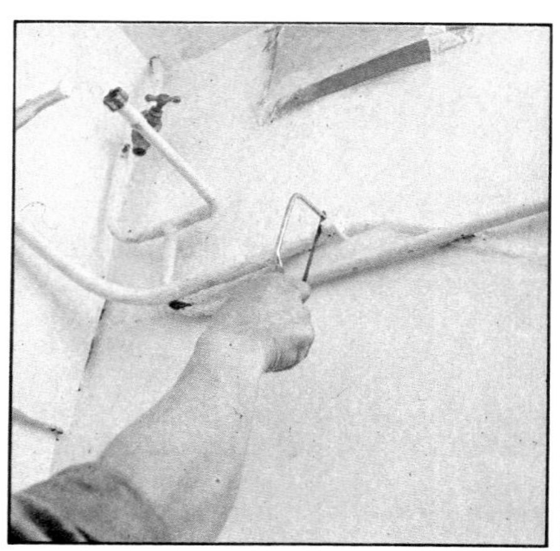

**9** *Detach any other redundant pipe-work as far as is practical; you'll probably have to find a new route for the overflow pipe.*

## PUTTING IN THE NEW CISTERN

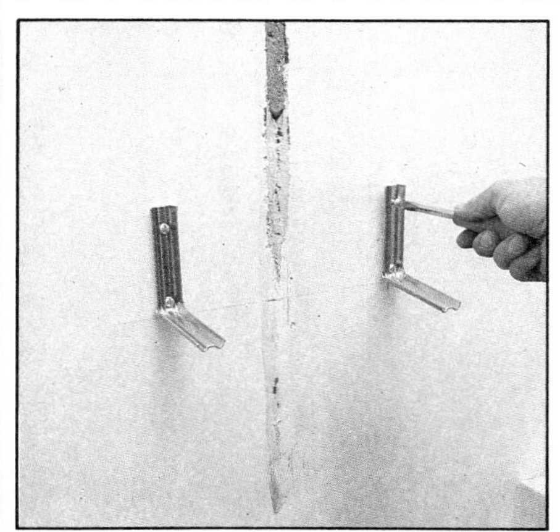

*1 Mark up the positions of the new cistern and support brackets; drill the holes, insert wallplugs and screw the brackets up.*

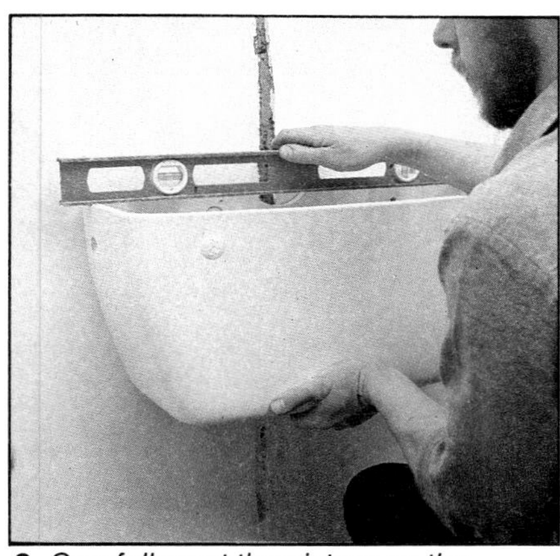

*2 Carefully rest the cistern on the brackets and check that they are holding it horizontally; if not, pack up one side or the other.*

*3 Drill and plug holes for the fixing screws, and fix the cistern in place. Pass the screwdriver through the holes in the cistern's front.*

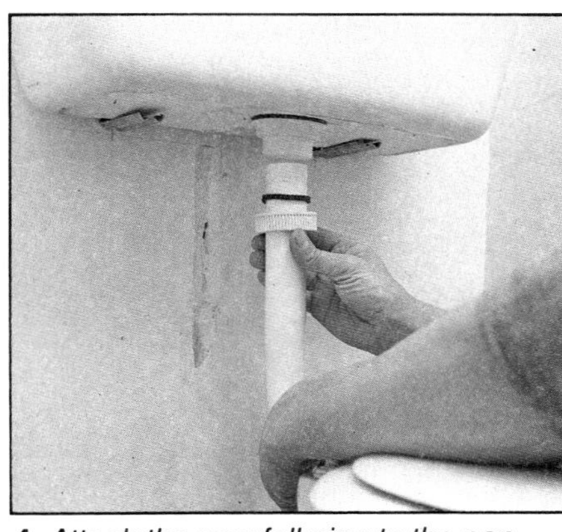

*4 Attach the new fall pipe to the pan with a rubber spigot. When connecting it to the cistern, make sure the rubber washer is in place.*

*5 With the central flushing assembly in position, you then have to screw up the inlet pipe connector to the ball-valve arm assembly.*

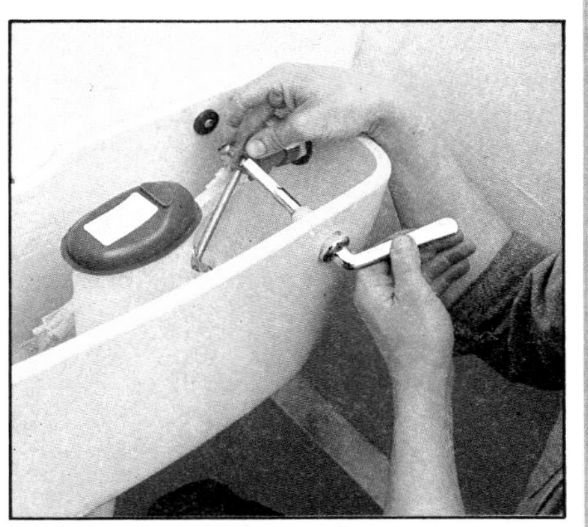

*6 Complete the internal cistern connections by making the flushing lever linkage attachments and checking that the ball arm is free.*

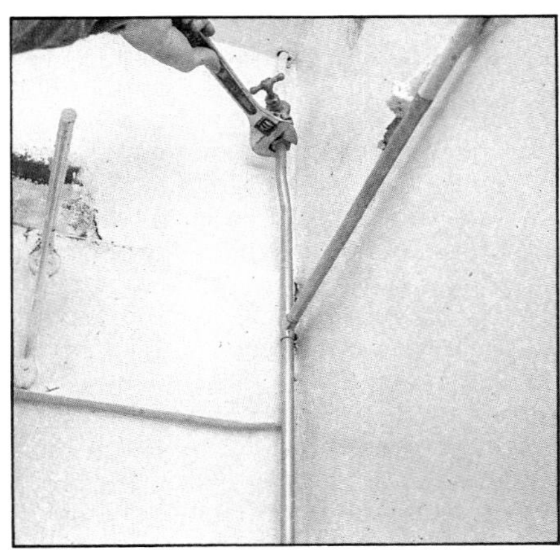

*7 Make up a new supply pipe run from the new stop-valve to the ball-valve inlet – plus a branch pipe, if needed, for a washbasin.*

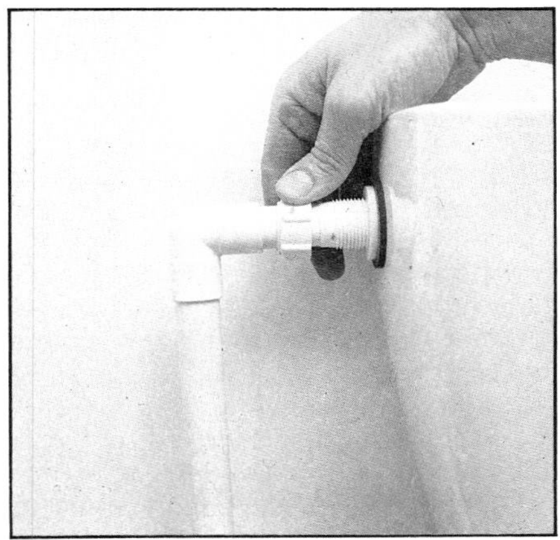

*8 Connect the overflow pipe to the cistern and either run it to a convenient outside wall or allow it to discharge to the floor waste.*

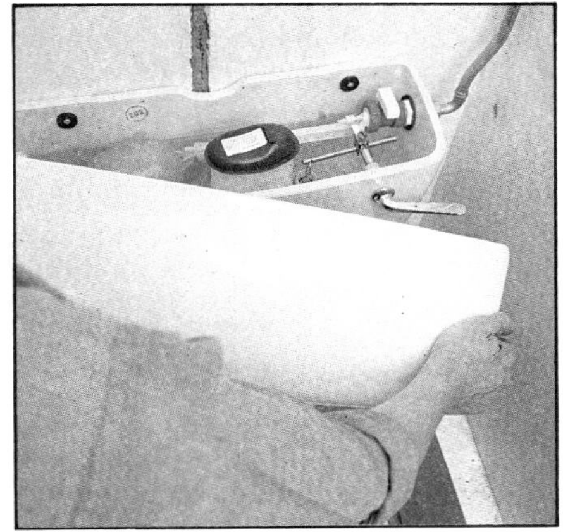

*9 Check all the connections, turn on the water, allow the cistern to fill and check that it flushes properly before putting on the lid.*

# INSTALLING A BIDET

**If you've got the room, a bidet can provide a useful addition to the bathroom. There are two types available, each of which is installed in a different way.**

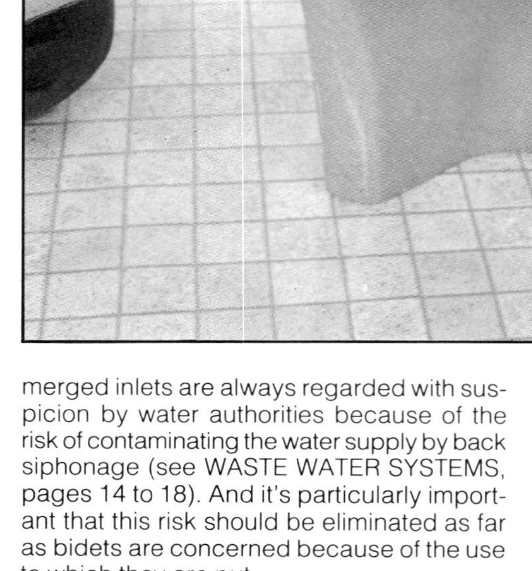

A bidet is a specially-shaped, low-level basin designed for washing between the legs – you squat on it facing the taps. In addition it can be used as a footbath, or even as a sink for soaking clothes, so it's a particularly useful appliance to have in the bathroom.

Strangely, in Britain, which has generally led in matters of hygiene and efficient plumbing, bidets are not that common. Until recently they were misguidedly seen as somewhat undesirable appliances found in the bathrooms of foreign hotels. Fortunately sense is now prevailing and the need to save space in buildings and to conserve energy means that the bidet (and the shower) are likely to increase in popularity at the expense of the traditional space-consuming bath which uses large quantities of water.

### Types of bidet

When you're buying a bidet, it's important to understand that there are in fact two types, and how you install them depends on which type you choose.

Basically the difference between the two kinds lies in the way they are supplied with hot and cold water. The simpler, cheaper and easier-to-install version is the 'over rim' bidet', sometimes referred to as a 'washbasin bidet'. It's simply a low-level washbasin supplied with hot and cold water from two basin taps, or a basin mixer, fitted in holes in the rear of the appliance.

The other kind of bidet, which seems to be the more popular type, is known as a 'rim supply bidet with ascending spray'. But it's more expensive and can be more difficult to install. A bidet of this kind has a hollow rim – not unlike the flushing rim of a lavatory pan – round which warm water first flows before entering the pan. This has the effect of warming the rim and making it more comfortable to sit on. At the flick of a control knob the warm water is diverted from the rim to a spray which is set in the bottom of the pan. The water therefore rises vertically for washing.

Because of the position of the spray outlet, it means that the rose can be submerged in water when the bidet is in use. And it's this type of inlet that can cause a few problems when you're installing such a bidet. Submerged inlets are always regarded with suspicion by water authorities because of the risk of contaminating the water supply by back siphonage (see WASTE WATER SYSTEMS, pages 14 to 18). And it's particularly important that this risk should be eliminated as far as bidets are concerned because of the use to which they are put.

Bidets are available in floor-standing and wall-mounted versions, in colours and styles that match other items of bathroom equipment.

### Connecting an over-rim bidet

When you come to install any bidet, it's best to start at the appliance end and finish by breaking into the water supply pipes. If you do this the water supply to the rest of the home will be disrupted as little as possible.

Connecting the hot and cold water supplies to this type of bidet shouldn't present any real difficulties. Because you mustn't mix water from the mains and water from a storage cistern in the same appliance, you can use a mixer only if the bathroom cold water is taken from a cold water storage cistern. The hot water will come from the hot tank, fed in turn from the same cistern. If the bathroom cold water is piped from the mains – in a direct system – then the bidet must have separate hot and cold taps.

Bidets – made, like more conventional washbasins, of ceramic material – normally have a built-in overflow discharging into the waste outlet via a slot in the waste fitting.

Once all the fittings are in place you can stand the bidet in the position where it's to be fixed so you can work out where the supply pipes and the waste outlet pipes will run. If your bathroom has modern copper or stainless steel hot and cold water distribution pipes then the task of laying in the pipes to the bidet should be fairly straightforward. You should use 15mm (½in) pipe, and the connections to the tap or mixer tails can be made using a special fitting which has a compression or capillary joint inlet on one side and a swivel tap connector or 'cap and lining joint' on the other which attaches to the tap tail (see PLUMBING FITTINGS). But since the final lengths of the supply pipes to the bidet are likely to be concealed behind the appliance, this is where two short lengths of flexible corrugated pipe with a swivel tap connector at one end can make installation that much easier.

The main bathroom water supplies are usually run in 22mm pipe, so you'll need 22mm to 15mm branch reducing tees when you come to connect your branch pipe into them. If your bathroom was installed in pre-metrication days, you'll have imperial sized ¾in pipe in place of the 22mm pipe. As you can't use 22mm fittings with this size pipe, you'll have to use some form of adaptor.

### Connecting a spray bidet

Before buying a spray bidet you should check on the regulations of your local Water Authority to make sure that the plumbing system of your home complies with these regulations, or can be made to do so. In all probability you'll need to run a separate cold water supply pipe from the cold water storage cistern to the bidet. You're not allowed to run this branch from another cold water distribution pipe, or to make a direct connection from the main. Similarly the hot water supply to the bidet must be taken by a separate distribution pipe from just above the hot water storage cylinder and not as a branch from the existing bathroom hot water supply pipe. A further requirement is likely to be that the base of the cold water storage cistern must be at least 2.75mm (9ft) above the level of the bidet inlet – a rule that could involve you in raising the position of your cistern.

While ordinary basin taps can be used for over-rim bidets, a special mixer with a diversion valve and a supply pipe to the spray must be fitted into a spray bidet. These mixers often incorporate a pop-up waste which enables the waste plug to be raised and the bidet emptied by pressing a control knob which is part of the mixer and diversion valve mechanism. This kind of bidet is normally sold with mixer, spray and pop-up waste already fitted.

### Dealing with the waste water

The waste water from a bidet must run through a trap. If your house has a single stack drainage system this should have a deep seal of 75mm (3in). With the older two-pipe drainage system a shallow seal of 50mm (2in) is permissible.

If you've got a single stack system you'll have to run the branch waste from the bidet and connect it into the main stack. And you'll have to follow the district or borough council's requirements regarding the gradient of the branch waste pipe and how the possibility of it being fouled by the discharges from the WC can be averted. (See WASTE WATER SYSTEMS, pages 14 to 18.)

If your house has a two-pipe drainage system, then it's important to remember that a bidet is a waste and not a soil appliance, so the waste water can be run into an open gully.

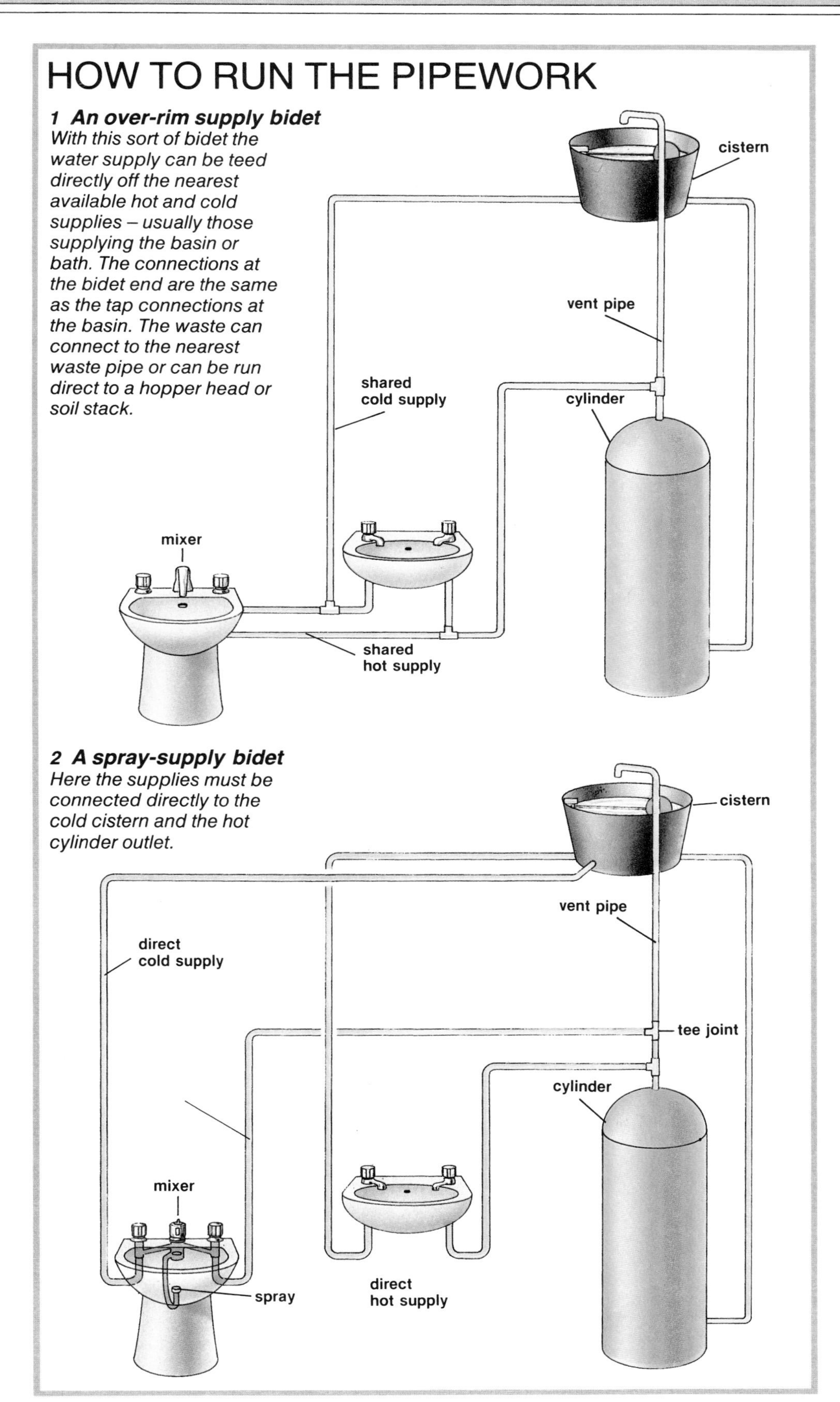


## HOW TO RUN THE PIPEWORK

***1 An over-rim supply bidet***
*With this sort of bidet the water supply can be teed directly off the nearest available hot and cold supplies – usually those supplying the basin or bath. The connections at the bidet end are the same as the tap connections at the basin. The waste can connect to the nearest waste pipe or can be run direct to a hopper head or soil stack.*

***2 A spray-supply bidet***
*Here the supplies must be connected directly to the cold cistern and the hot cylinder outlet.*

# PLUMBING IN A SPRAY BIDET

**1** *Take the rather complex plumbing assembly provided with the bidet and dismantle the central control mechanism with a screwdriver.*

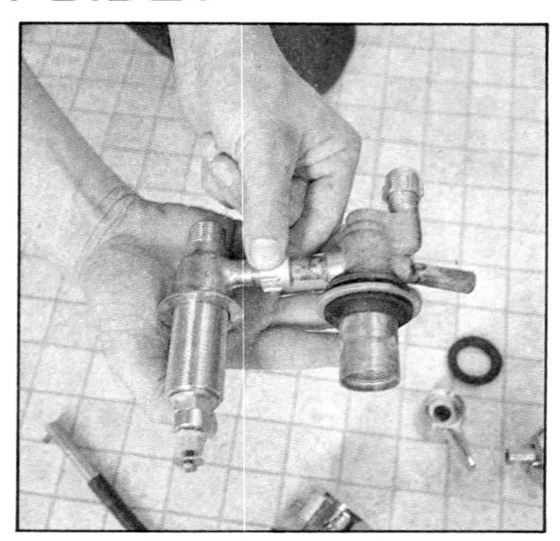

**2** *Attach the tap bodies to the wing pipes of the central unit, fixing them in the usual way with the compression fittings which are supplied.*

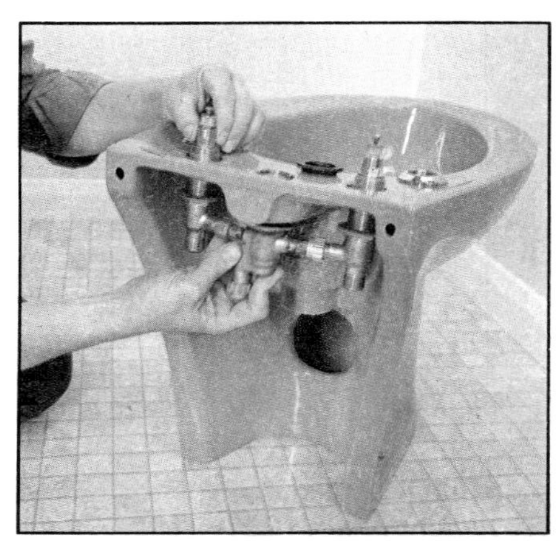

**3** *Place the back-nuts and washers over the tap bodies, insert them into the tap holes in the bidet and screw up the head nuts.*

**6** *Tighten up the back-nuts on the tap tails. These may be rather inaccessible and you will have to use any spanner or wrench that fits.*

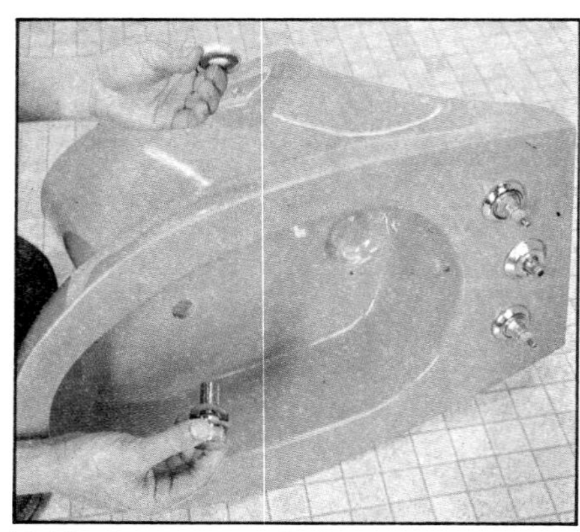

**7** *Fix the spray outlet in position at the bottom of the bowl. Make sure the rubber washers are in place, then tighten the back-nut.*

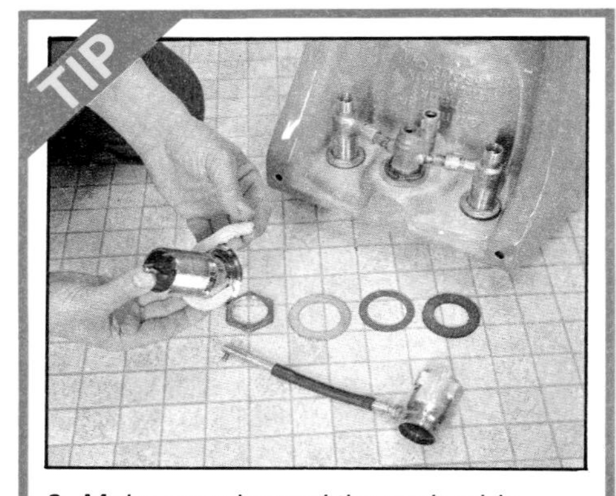


**8** *Make a seal round the underside of the outlet flange using a long sausage of plumber's putty, and bed the flange firmly into place.*

**11** *Attach the waste linkage to the waste outlet, making the connection via a split pin. You may have to shorten the control rod.*

**12** *Attach the plastic spray outlet pipe to the control unit and to the spray; both connections are made with compression fittings.*

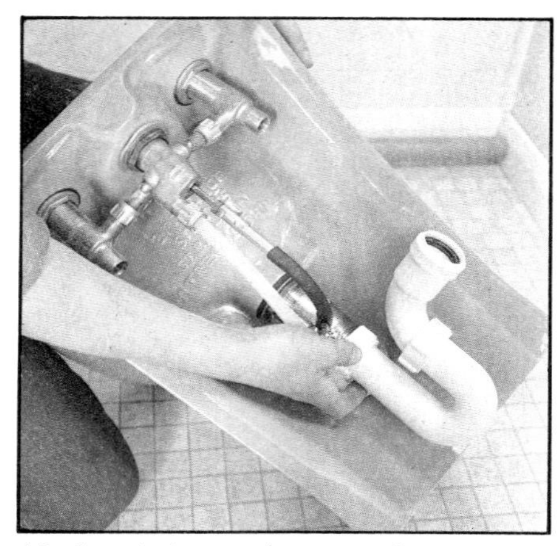

**13** *Attach the waste trap to the waste outlet pipe and check all connections for tightness. Then place the bidet in position.*

**4** *Fix the cover flanges in place over the tap heads, after putting a ring of plumber's putty round the underside of each one of them.*

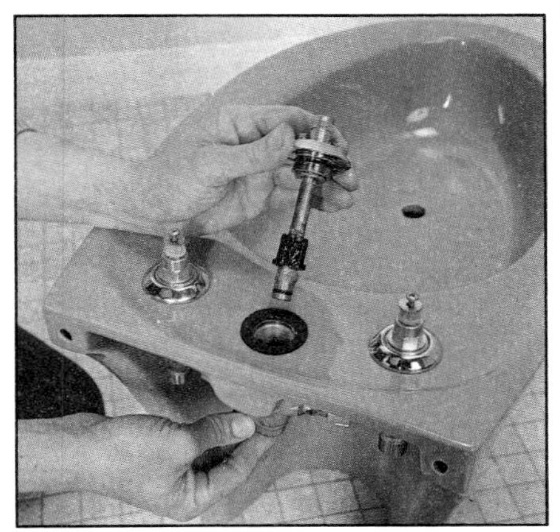

**5** *Put the central control column into position, making sure that the rubber gasket is correctly seated underneath it.*

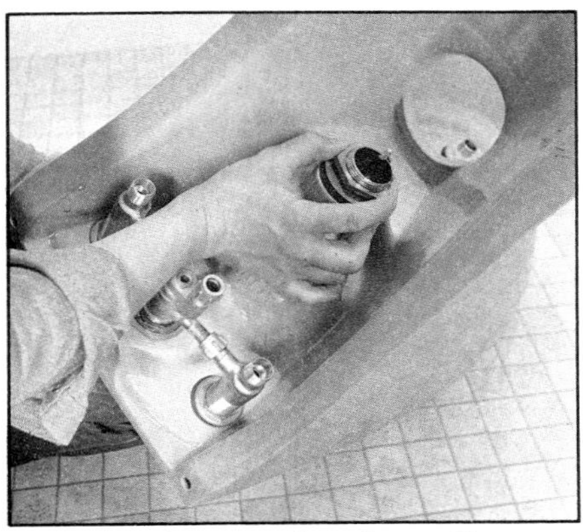

**9** *With all three washers in position, tighten the back-nut; this will squeeze out excess putty inside the bowl. Then remove the excess.*

**10** *Screw on the waste outlet extension, slip the waste control rod in through the control unit and fix the control link to the waste.*

**14** *Complete the tap head fittings by pushing on the shrouds, screwing up and pressing home the cap and index; fit the control knob too.*

**15** *Attach the waste outlet and water inlet pipes, and check for leaks. Then screw the bidet to the floor using brass screws.*

## Ready Reference

### PLUMBING CONNECTIONS

**Spray-supply bidets**

These incorporate a switch to direct water to the rim or the spray.

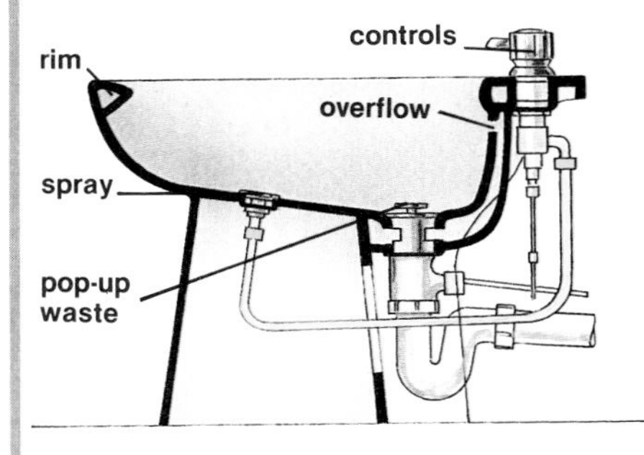


**Over rim supply bidets**

The water supply is through separate taps or a mixer unit, as for a washbasin.

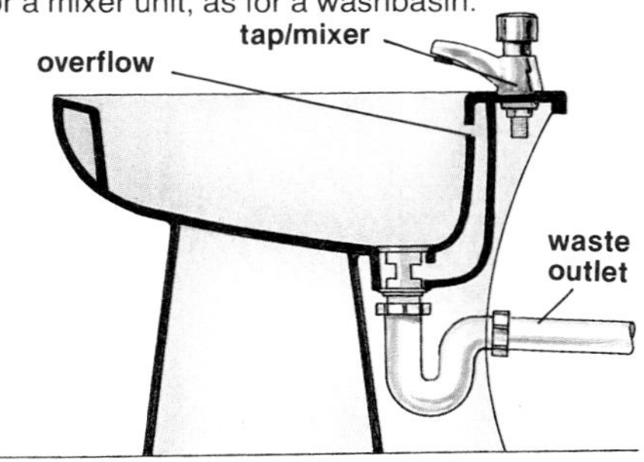


**The components**

Connecting up the supply and waste pipes simple involves assembling washers and back-nuts in the correct order to the tap tails and waste outlet. Check that you have all the necessary components before starting work.

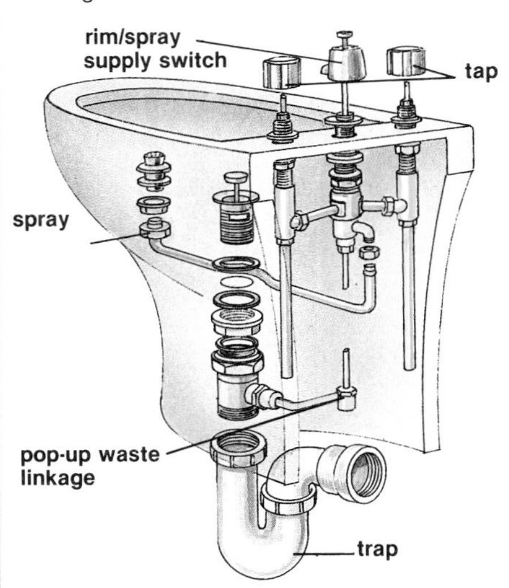

## CHAPTER 6

# TANKS AND CISTERNS

**Modern domestic hot and cold water supply systems rely on the storage of large quantities of water in the house to provide a ready supply at a constant pressure and to ensure a reserve of water should the mains supply be cut off for any reason.**

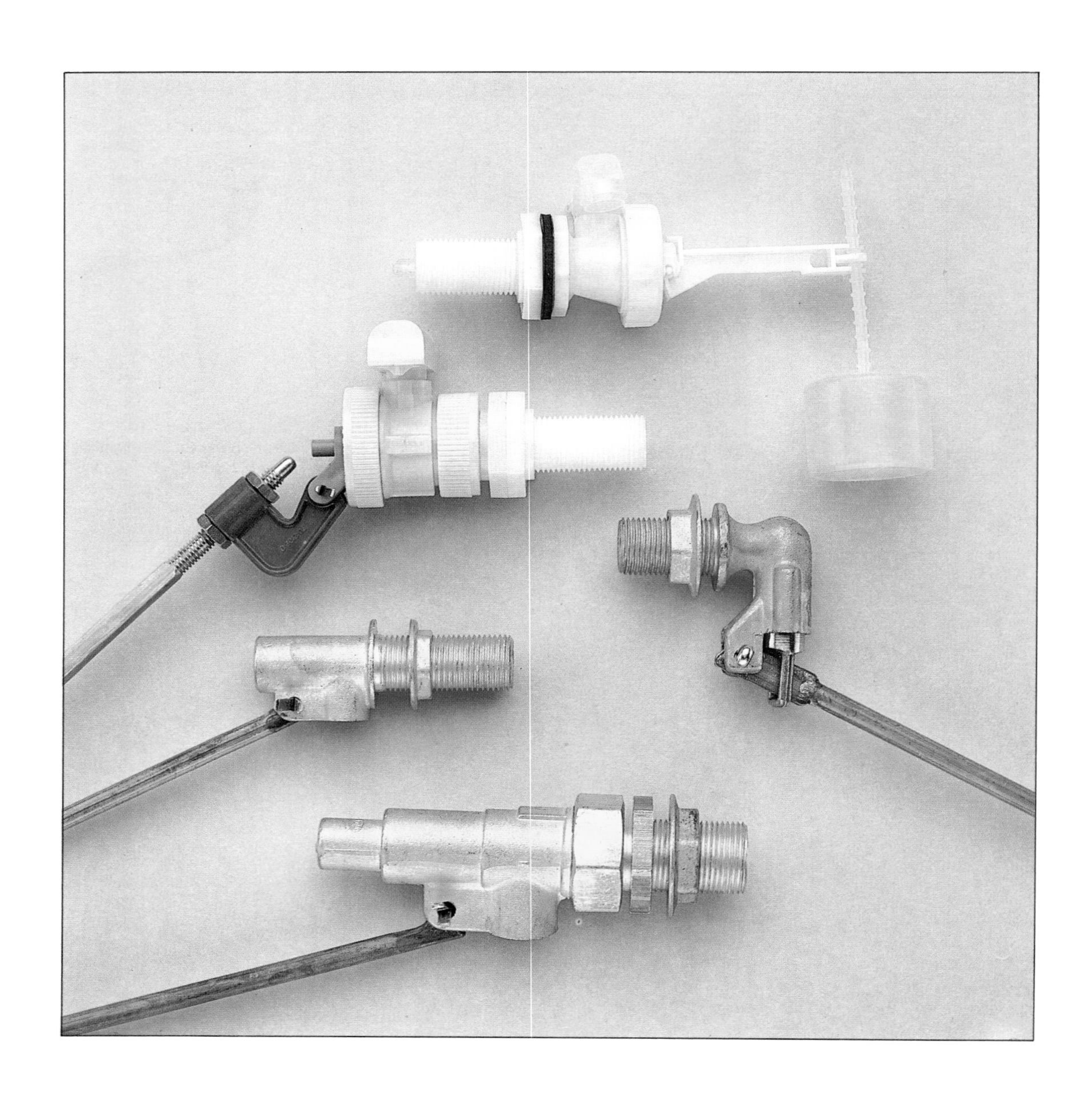

# REPLACING A HOT CYLINDER

**Copper hot water cylinders don't last for ever, and if they do spring a leak they need replacing quickly with the right type of new cylinder.**

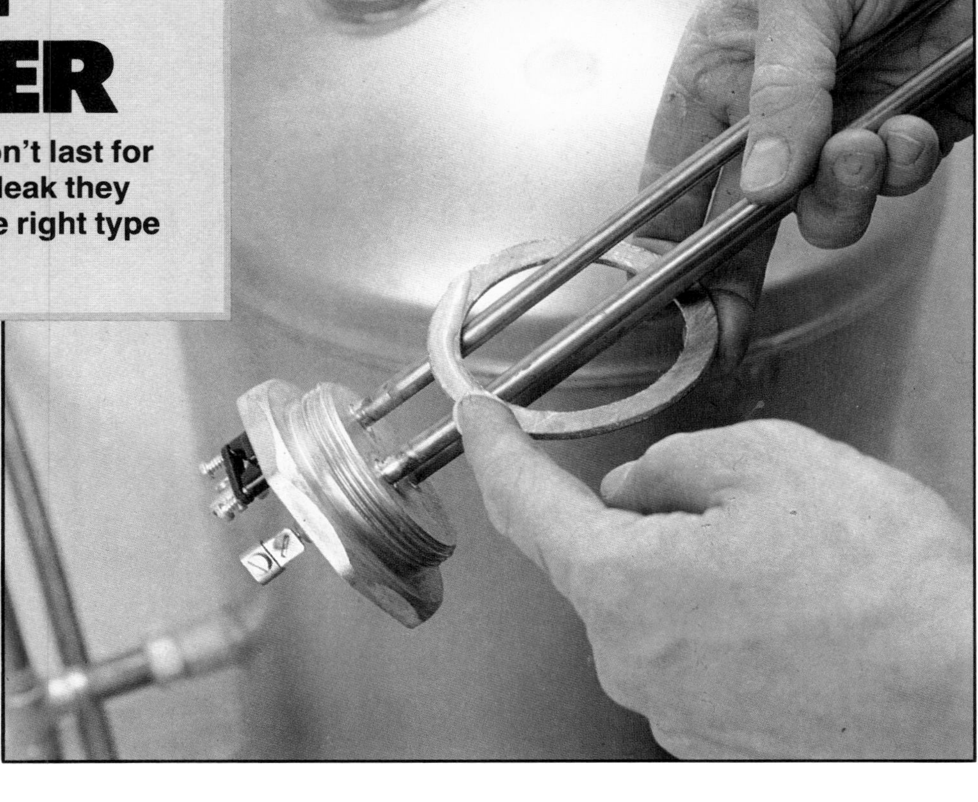

By far the most common means of hot water supply in British homes is a cylinder storage system of one kind or another. A copper cylinder of 115 to 160 litres (25 to 35 gal) capacity, usually situated in an airing cupboard, is supplied with cold water under controlled low pressure from the main cold water storage cistern, which is fitted at a higher level. The water supply enters the cylinder by a distribution pipe at least 22mm in diameter, at a tapping close to its base. A 22mm vent pipe rises from the top of the cylinder and is taken upwards and bent over to discharge, open-ended, over the cold water storage cistern. The distribution pipes supplying the kitchen and bathroom with hot water are taken from this vent pipe, via conections just above the level of the top of the cylinder.

## Heating the water

Water in the storage cylinder may be heated solely by means of a thermostatically-controlled electric immersion heater, usually fitted vertically and screwed into a special boss provided in the dome of the cylinder. Alternatively, water may be heated by a solid fuel, gas-fired or oil-fired boiler. Quite often there is a combination of immersion heater and boiler. Where the water is heated by a boiler, 28mm circulating pipes connect the upper tapping of the boiler with a tapping in the upper part of the cylinder wall, and likewise connect the return tapping of the cylinder, in the lower part of the cylinder wall, with the lower tapping of the boiler. If the water is heated by immersion heater only, the cylinder's flow and return tappings, if they exist, are blanked off.

However the cylinder is heated, the hottest water will rise to the top to be available for drawing off from the bathroom or kitchen taps. As it is drawn off, it is replaced by cold water flowing into the lower part of the cylinder from the cold water storage cistern. Surprisingly the hot and cold water 'layers' do not intermingle much, and this layer effect, with the hottest water at the top and the coldest near the base, is an essential feature of a successful cylinder storage hot water system.

## Direct and indirect systems

Where water in the cylinder is heated solely by means of an immersion heater, or where a boiler is provided only for the supply of domestic hot water, a simple direct cylinder is used. With a direct cylinder system all the water in the cylinder is heated by circulating it through the domestic boiler. As hot water is fractionally lighter than cold water, the water heated in the boiler will rise up the flow pipe to the upper part of the cylinder, while cooler water from the lower part of the cylinder flows down the return pipe and replaces it. A constant circulation will take place for as long as the boiler fire is alight.

But, where hot water supply is provided in conjunction with a central heating system, however small, an indirect cylinder system must be provided. There is also much to be said for providing an indirect system if hot water only is supplied, as it will protect the boiler, particularly in hard water areas.

With an indirect system the water stored in the cylinder does not circulate through the boiler. It is heated by means of a heat exchanger within the cylinder. Water from the boiler circulates in a closed circuit, giving up heat to the water stored in the cylinder through this heat exchanger. In this kind of system the flow and return pipes between the heat exchanger and the boiler are referred to as the primary circuit. In a conventional indirect system the primary circuit is supplied with water from its own small feed and expansion tank, usually situated in the roof space alongside the cistern, and it has its own separate vent pipe that terminates, open-ended, over this small open tank.

The water in the primary circuit cannot be drawn off from the taps. As the same water circulates over and over again there is a very small loss from evaporation, which is made up from the feed and expansion tank. Because of this, indirect systems are relatively immune to corrosion and scale formation, and this is why they must always be provided in connection with central heating installations.

Self-priming indirect cylinders don't need an expansion tank. They have a specially designed inner cylinder which serves as a heat exchanger and also has provision for the expansion of the water in the primary circuit when heated. In a conventional system this is an important function of the feed and expansion tank. When a self-priming cylinder is first filled with water from the main cold water storage system, water is able to overflow through the patent inner cylinder into the primary circuit. It is prevented from returning by an air bubble that forms an air lock within the inner cylinder.

A self-priming cylinder offers a simple and economical means of converting a cylinder hot water system from direct to indirect operation.

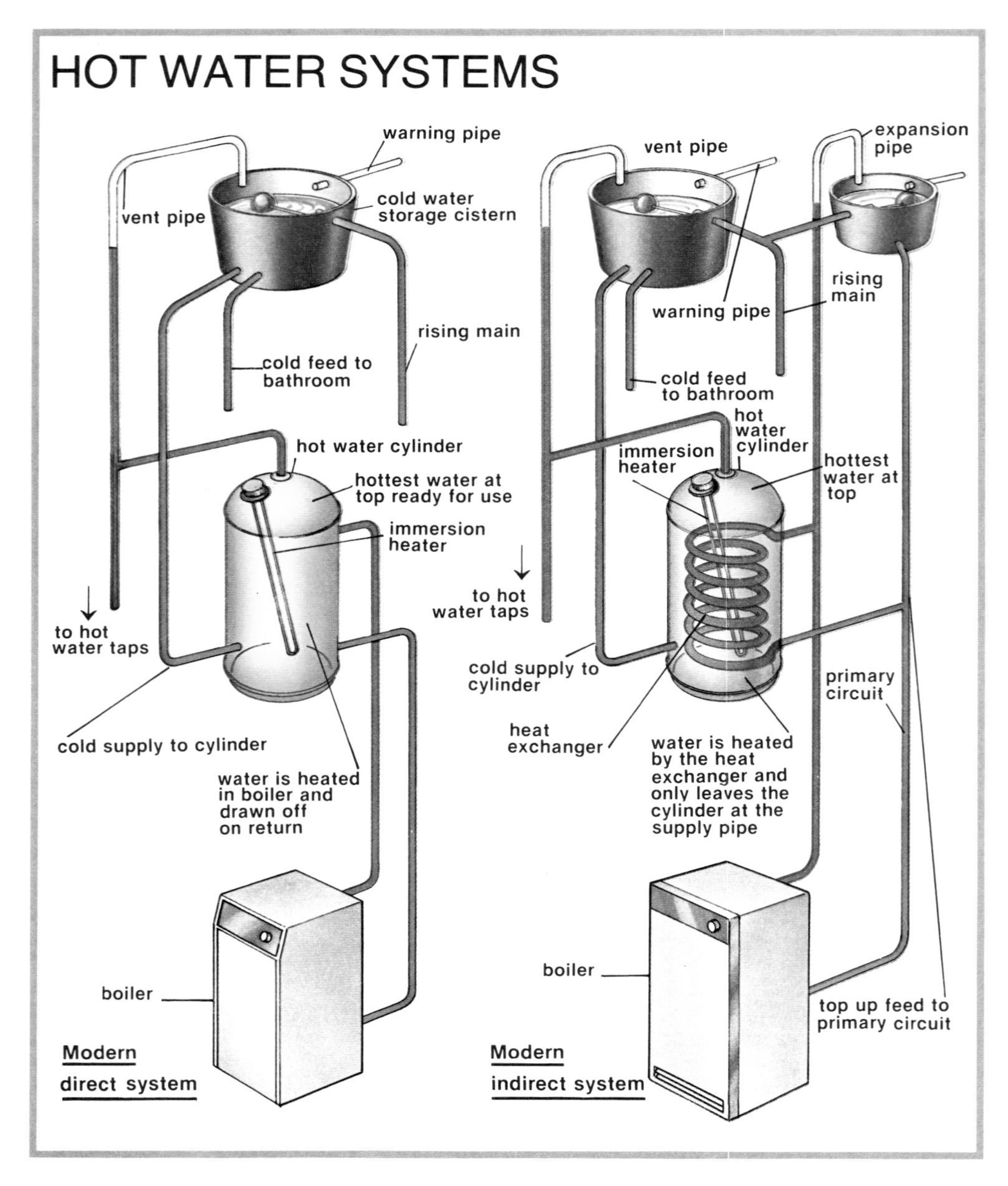


But many heating engineers are suspicious of these cylinders which they do not consider to give the same positive separation of the primary from the domestic hot water as would a conventional indirect system.

### Choice of system

Before replacing a hot water cylinder it is essential to identify whether the existing cylinder is direct or indirect. You may think you can do this quite easily by checking whether or not there is, in addition to the main cold water storage cistern, a small feed and expansion tank in the roof space. The presence of a feed and expansion tank does indicate an indirect system, but of course self-priming indirect cylinders don't need them.

Another difficulty in identification is the 'two-in-one' or packaged plumbing system that has been developed in recent years to provide instant hot water systems in homes that had previously lacked this amenity. They are very often provided where a large house has been converted into a number of self-contained flats.

A packaged plumbing system is simply a hot water cylinder with a cold water storage cistern directly above it in the same unit. Some packaged plumbing units have a small cold water storage cistern – which is only adequate for the supply of the hot water cylinder. Others have a full sized 275 litre (50 gal) cistern that is capable of providing bathroom cold water supplies as well as supplying the hot water cylinder immediately beneath it.

Packaged plumbing systems may be direct, indirect, or self-priming indirect. The feed and expansion tank of a conventional indirect packaged plumbing system is usually contained within the walls of the main cold water storage cistern.

How then can you tell whether your hot water cylinder is direct or indirect? Well, if the water in it is heated by an electrical immersion heater only, you can be quite sure that it is direct. Indirect cylinders are never used in this situation.

If you have a boiler which, as well as supplying domestic hot water, serves a central heating system that has been giving trouble-free service, you can be pretty certain that you have an indirect cylinder of one kind or another. Look in the roof space, or within the main cold water storage cistern, if it is a packaged unit, for a small feed and expansion tank. If one exists then you definitely have a conventional indirect cylinder.

Self-priming indirect cylinders are normally marked as such but there is only one way to be absolutely certain whether your existing cylinder is indirect (though possibly self-priming) or direct.

The flow and return pipe connections for direct cylinders are always female screwed tappings, into which a male cylinder connector is screwed. The flow and return pipe connections for indirect cylinders (whether conventional or self-priming) are always male screwed connectors projecting from the heat exchanger within the cylinder, through the cylinder wall.

Armed with these clues you should find it possible to identify your cylinder; it's a good idea to do this for your own information before a leak or other emergency makes its replacement a matter of urgency.

### Draining the system

The cylinder must, of course, be drained before it can be replaced. You can't do this simply by turning off the main stop-valve and opening up the hot taps. Since the distribution pipes to these taps are taken from the vent pipe above the cylinder, the cylinder will still be full of water when the taps cease to flow.

Boiler-heated systems, whether direct or indirect, will normally have a drain-cock fitted into the return pipe from cylinder to boiler, immediately beside the boiler. After letting out, or turning off, the boiler and switching off any immersion heater, drain off from this drain-cock by means of a length of hose, to an outside gully. You'll have to create a siphon by filling the pipe first. This will drain the primary circuit of an indirect system but it will not drain the domestic hot water in the outer part of the cylinder. To drain this use another drain-cock, usually fitted at the base of the cold water supply pipe just before it enters the cylinder. A drain-cock should also be provided in this position where a cylinder is heated by an immersion heater only as it could well prove to be useful.

## REMOVING THE OLD CYLINDER

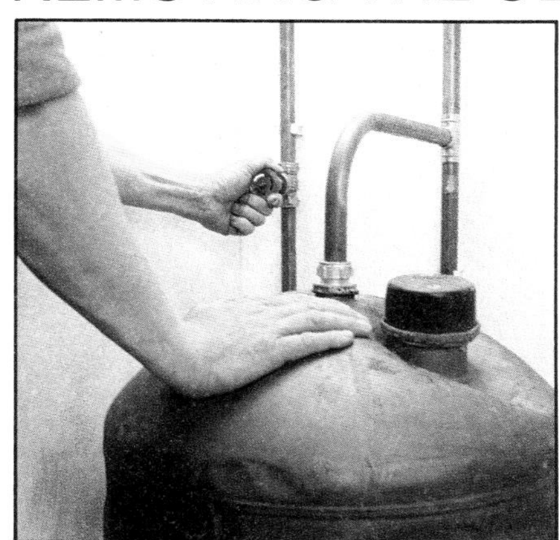

*1 Identify the cold water feed, and turn off the supply using the gate-valve. If there isn't one, turn off the mains and drain the cistern.*

*2 Drain the contents of the cylinder by attaching one end of a hose to the drain-cock and undoing the nut with a drain-cock spanner.*

*3 When the water stops flowing, pull the hose away from the drain-cock. A little more water may flow out, so have some mopping up cloths handy.*

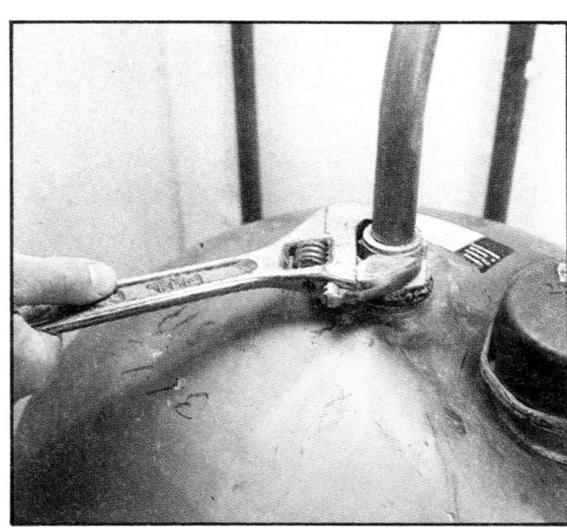

*4 Start to disconnect the pipework attached to the cylinder. It should be easy to unscrew the connections using an adjustable spanner.*

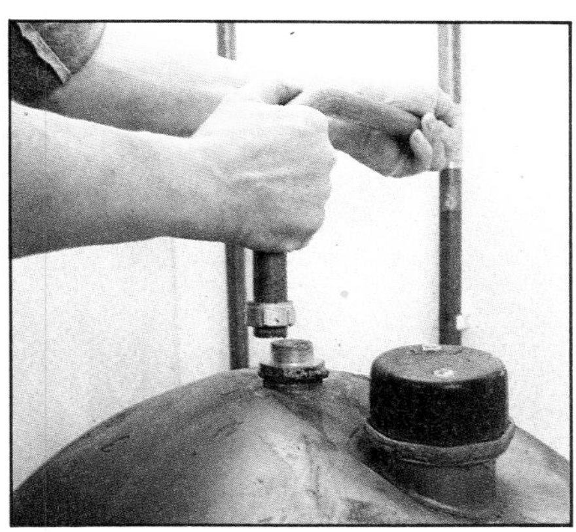

*5 As you disconnect the pipes make sure they will pull free from the cylinder; if not, gently bend them by hand, supporting them evenly.*

*6 The primary circuit connections are the trickiest to disconnect as the male iron cylinder connector may start to turn.*

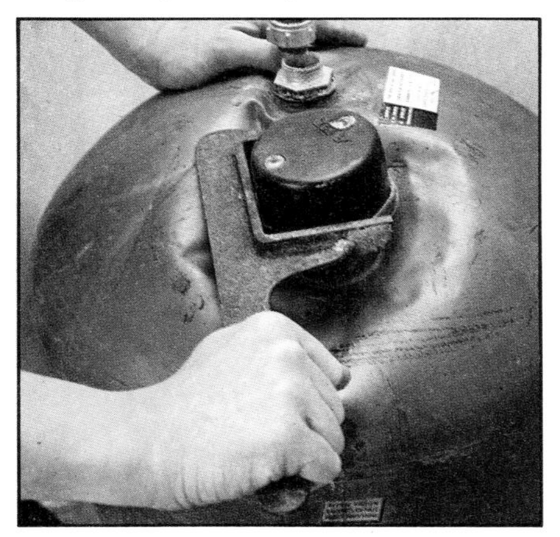

*7 Disconnect the electrical supply to the immersion heater. If you want to reuse the immersion heater, hire a special spanner and unscrew it.*

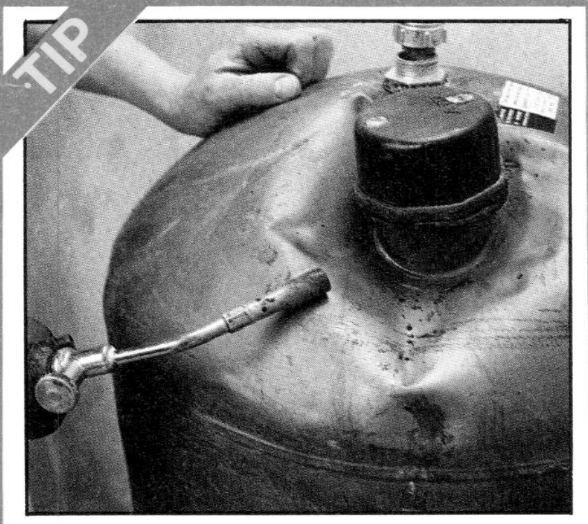


*8 If the immersion heater will not unscrew, heat the cylinder boss with a blow-torch. Then allow it to cool and try the spanner again.*

*9 When you have disconnected the cylinder, pull it free from the pipework and dispose of it. It may be worth selling it for scrap.*

### Renewing a hot water cylinder

After checking the type of your cylinder, you must also check its size before you can buy a new one.

Common cylinder capacities are 115 litres (25 gal), 140 litres (30 gal) and 160 litres (35 gal). Most cylinders are 900mm (36in) or 1050mm (42in) high, while common diameters are 400mm (16in) and 450mm (18in). When you are ready to begin, drain the cylinder. If the cylinder is not provided with adequate drain-cocks it can be emptied by siphonage. Unscrew the nut at the top of the cylinder, but be prepared for the water that will flow as you do so; it may be as much as a litre or so. Fill a hose with water and secure both ends. Thrust one end deeply into the cylinder through the tapping at its apex and allow the other to discharge over an outside gully. Siphonage will empty the cylinder.

To remove the immersion heater from the old cylinder, you'll have to hire a special extra-large immersion heater spanner. If you are installing a new one in the new cylinder, there's no need to take the old one out. The other tappings should be straightforward.

With the new cylinder in position you may find that the connections don't quite coincide with those of the old one. If not, lengthen or shorten the connecting pipes as appropriate using soldered capillary or compression fittings (see pages 20 to 24). You can alter the height of the new cylinder if necessary by raising it on stout strips of wood. The connections to the cylinder are made watertight by binding the male threads of the screwed joints in every case with PTFE thread sealing tape.

When you refill the system with water, check for leaks. When refilling a direct system, or the primary circuit of an indirect system, it is a good idea to use a length of hose to connect the cold tap over the kitchen sink with a drain-cock beside the boiler. Open up the tap and the drain-cock and the system will fill upwards; this will drive air in front of it and thus reduce the risk of air-locks forming. If the system is connected to a central heating circuit, the air vents on the radiators, and any other air vents, elsewhere, should be left open until water starts to flow through them.

When you are satisfied that the system is water-tight and leak-free you can switch on the immersion heater or boiler again. When the system heats up, check again for leaks. The cylinder and pipework will have expanded which may loosen some of your joints if you haven't tightened them properly, or used enough PTFE tape. Last of all, add an insulating jacket to the new cylinder. This is an extremely worthwhile investment as, without an efficient one, you'll lose a lot of the heat from your water which will add considerably to your bills.

## PUTTING IN A NEW CYLINDER

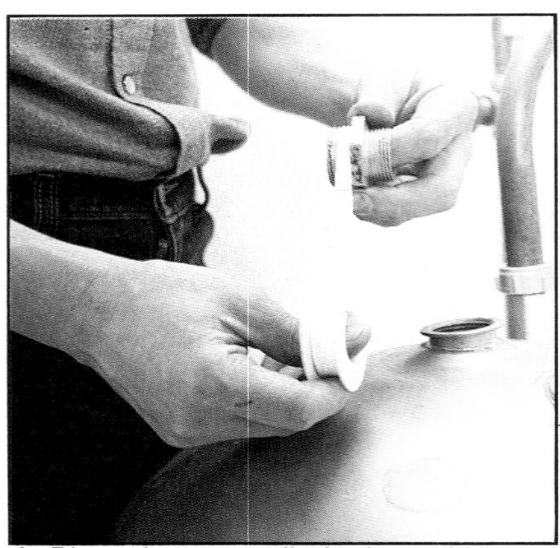

**1** *Place the new cylinder in position and check that all the old connections are reusable. Wind new PTFE tape round the outlet male iron connector.*

**2** *Put some jointing compound round the thread; then screw the connector back into the outlet, making sure you don't cross the thread.*

**5** *Connectors on the primary circuit are connected in exactly the same way, but you may have to adjust the pipe runs to match your new cylinder.*

**6** *Check that the male to female iron connectors are tightly screwed into the cylinder; they may have come loose in transport.*

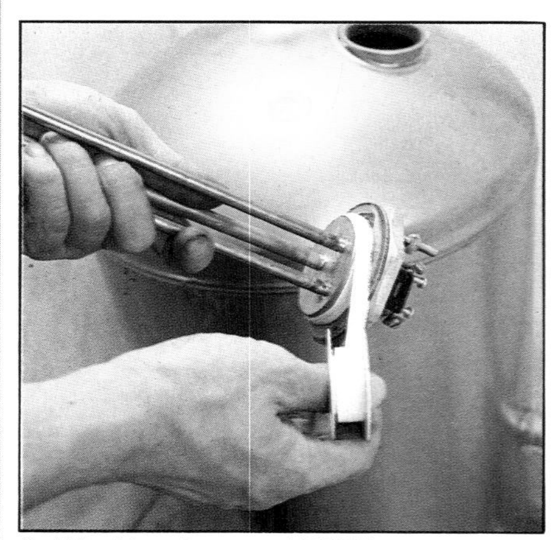

**9** *Wind two layers of PTFE tape round the thread before inserting the immersion heater into the cylinder boss, and screwing it finger tight.*

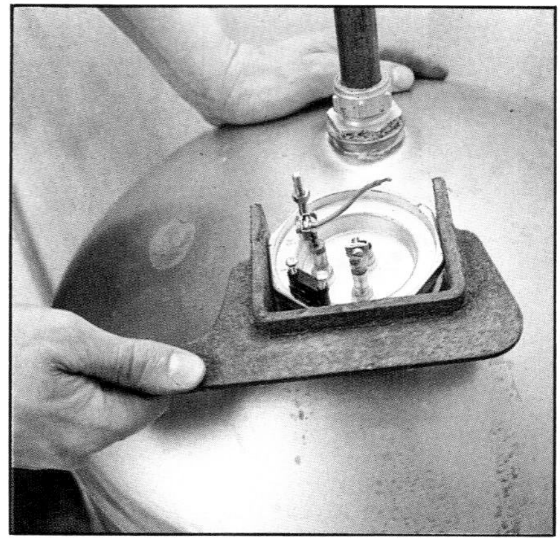

**10** *Tighten the immersion heater carefully until it is completely home using the immersion heater spanner. Then check all the connections.*

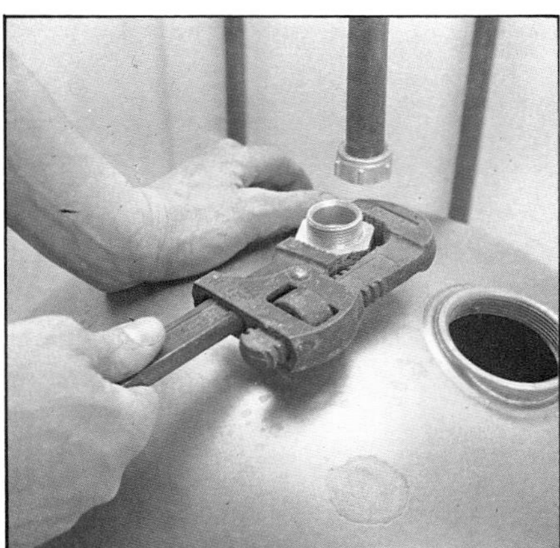

**3** *Tighten the connector into place and screw up the cap-nut making sure that the olive is in position. If it's worn you should replace it.*

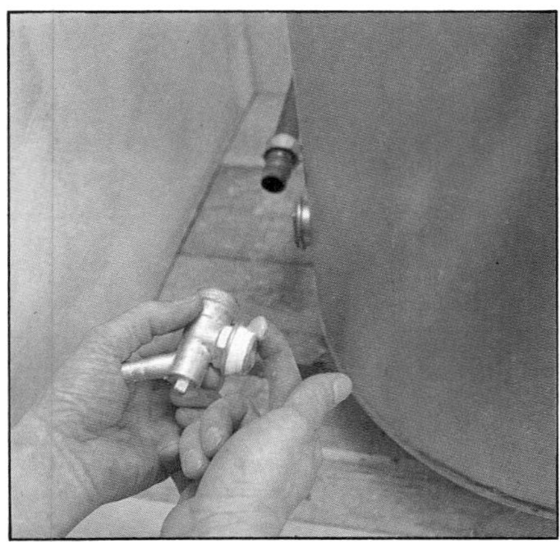

**4** *Carry on making the pipe connections, using PTFE tape and pipe jointing compound each time to ensure that they are watertight.*

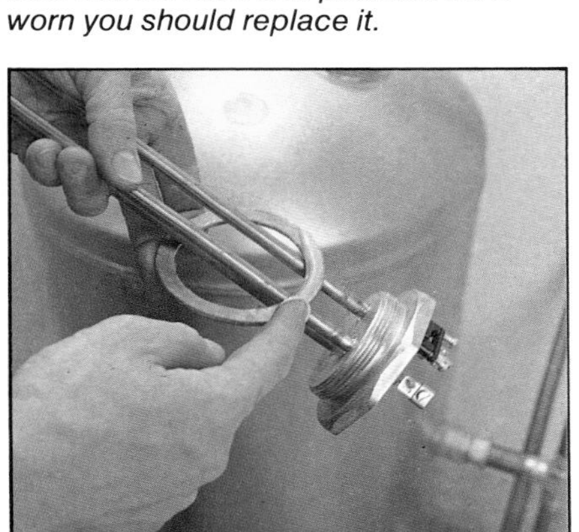

**7** *With a new immersion heater, remove the protective cap, then take the larger washer supplied and coat the underside with jointing compound.*

**8** *Press the washer firmly into place against the underside of the head-nut. Try not to damage it when pushing it over the thread.*

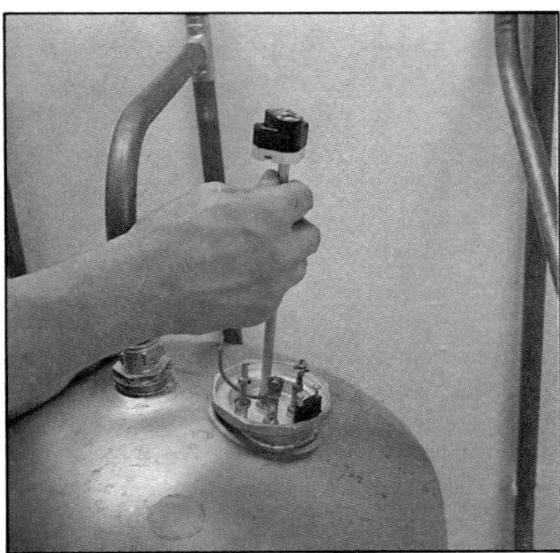

**11** *Place the immersion heater thermostat in its channel. Make sure it runs smoothly, and set it to the correct temperature.*

**12** *Turn the water back on and check for leaks, then wire up the immersion heater and replace its cover. Finally fit a cylinder insulation jacket.*

# Ready Reference

## KNOW YOUR SYSTEM

**Direct cylinders** may be heated by an immersion heater; or by water which is heated by the boiler, and returned to the cylinder for use.

**Indirect cylinders** keep the water heated by the boiler separate from the water that you use, passing on the heat by means of a heat exchanger.
Indirect cylinders must have a small feed and expansion cistern, which is situated in the loft or inside the main cistern in a packaged system, or they may be self-priming with the unit inside the cylinder.

Female flow and return tappings for connection to the boiler mean a **direct system.**

Male flow and return tappings mean an **indirect system.**

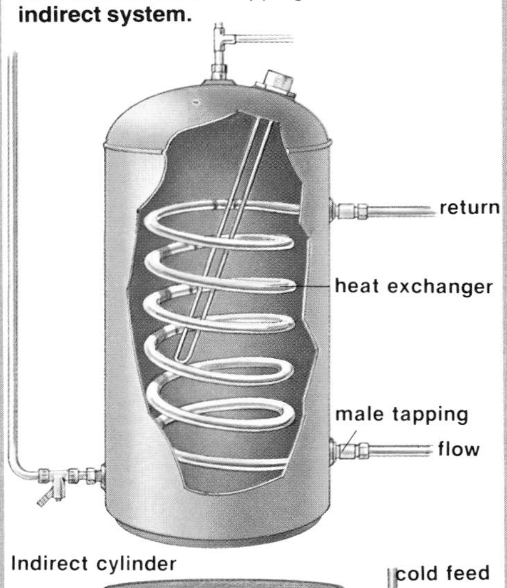


Indirect cylinder

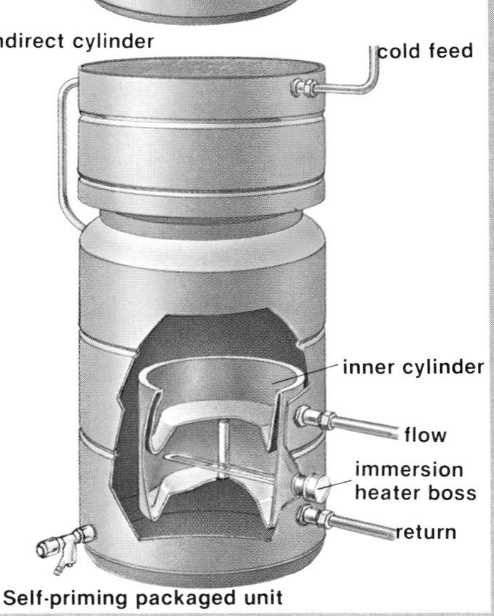


Self-priming packaged unit

# REPLACING AN IMMERSION HEATER

**Immersion heaters are a versatile way of heating water, but can be expensive if used carelessly. They are also a useful back-up for conventional heating systems.**

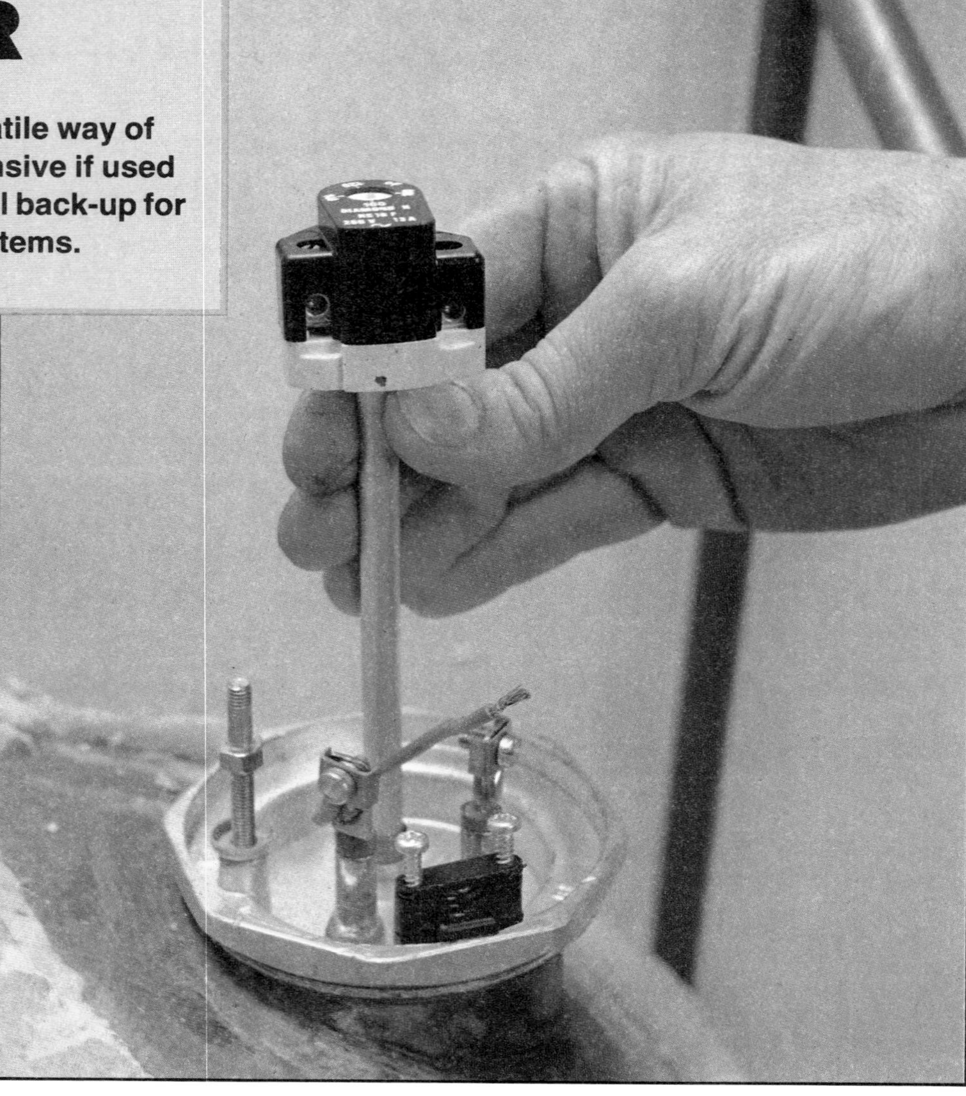

An electric immersion heater may be used either as the sole means of providing domestic hot water, or as a supplement – perhaps during the summer months – to a solid fuel, gas- or oil-fired boiler. It provides the simplest means of heating water and is the cheapest to install. However, with constantly rising electricity prices an immersion heater can prove to be prohibitively expensive to use, unless it is operated intelligently in a carefully designed and insulated hot water system.

Immersion heaters raise the temperature of the water in the storage cylinder or tank in which they are installed by conduction and convection. Water in direct contact with the element is heated by conduction. Since warm water is lighter than cold, it rises to 'float' on top of the cold and other, cooler, water takes its place in contact with the element and is heated in its turn. This has the effect of setting up convection currents within the cylinder, and circulation continues until all the water above the level of the immersion heater has been raised to the required temperature. The thermostat then switches the immersion heater off.

Consequently, only water above the immersion heater element is heated. This is an important fact that must be borne in mind when deciding whether an immersion heater is to be fitted horizontally or vertically, and, in the latter case, the length of the heater required. You can buy the heating elements in lengths ranging from 275 to 900mm (11 to 36in) and these are provided with a thermostat. In soft water areas this should be set at 70°C (160°F), but in hard water areas a setting of 60° (140°F) is quite adequate for normal domestic use and will not cause water scale or 'fur' to precipitate.

## Purpose-made immersion heaters

These heaters are known as 'whole house' electric water heaters because they can supply hot water for all domestic needs, and they are used when the sole means of heating water is by electricity. They are sometimes called under-draining board or UDB heaters because of the position in which they are usually situated. They are heavily insulated and look like rather squat hot water storage cylinders with a capacity of some 113 litres (25 gal). Inside there are usually two immersion heaters fitted horizontally, one above the other. The upper one is positioned about one quarter of the distance from the top of the cylinder and is intended to be kept switched on throughout the period during which hot water may be required. This ensures that there are always about 15 litres (3½gal) of hot water available for personal washing, washing-up, household cleaning and so on. The lower element is fitted a little way up from the base of the cylinder and you have to use this when you need larger quantities of hot water say for a bath or washing laundry. Normally you have to turn it on about half an hour to an hour before you need the water; but it's worth keeping a close eye on the time needed to heat your water, as this could save money.

## Immersion heaters in hot water cylinders

Modern hot water storage cylinders, both direct and indirect, intended for use with a boiler as the primary source of heat, are usually fitted with an immersion heater boss in the dome of the cylinder. This means you can fit an immersion heater so it protrudes downwards into the water. And, if it is to heat all the water in the cylinder, when the boiler is off, it must extend almost to the base of the cylinder. Some immersion heaters, intended for vertical fitting, have two elements. A short one performs the same function as the upper element in a UDB; it ensures that there is always a basic amount of hot water stored in the upper part of the cylinder. Similarly, like the lower element of a purpose-made electric water heater, the longer element is switched on prior to a demand for a larger volume of hot water.

## TAKING OUT THE OLD HEATER

**1** *Try to unscrew the immersion heater boss. If it's stiff then remove any insulating material in the immediate vicinity.*

**2** *Use a blow-torch to heat the boss and screw fitting; the differing expansion between the materials should loosen the thread.*

**3** *Use the special immersion heater spanner to unscrew the boss gently. Don't wrench too hard or the cylinder may get dented.*

**4** *Remove the old heater and clean up the screw thread. Make sure it isn't damaged or else you may have to replace the cylinder.*

### Using immersion heaters efficiently

As an immersion heater is the most expensive means of heating water, it is worth bearing a few things in mind. Perhaps the most important factor in making it economical to use is the amount of insulation packed round the cylinder in which it is fitted. A 130 litre (30gal) copper cylinder will, if it is unlagged and the water temperature maintained at 60°C (140°F), waste no less than 86 units (kWh) of electricity a week. If it is provided with a 50mm (2in) thick lagging jacket, the loss will be cut to only 8.8 units per week. Increase the thickness of the insulation to 75mm (3in) and the weekly heat loss will be reduced to 6 units. In fact, 75mm (3in) is the optimum thickness of a lagging jacket. Further increases in thickness do not produce commensurate savings.

Some people remove, or partly remove, the lagging jacket for clothes airing, but it's not cost effective to do this, and in any case enough warmth will still escape from the cylinder and its pipework to warm the average airing cupboard. If more heat is needed, you will find it far more economical to provide a low powered electric airing cupboard heater.

Water heated by an electric immersion heater must never be allowed to circulate through the central heating system. Electrically-heated water at 60°C circulating through 15mm (½in) copper tube will waste 1.36 units of electricity for each 300mm (1ft) of pipe run per week. It sometimes happens that pipework to a towel rail is run from a direct hot water system. If the system is sometimes heated by an electric immersion heater, the towel rail pipework should be kept wholly below the level of the heater, or alternatively, a gate-valve must be provided and must be turned off to prevent circulation whenever the heater is switched on.

## Ready Reference

### CHOOSE THE RIGHT HEATER

There are several types of immersion heater available, and it's important to select the type that matches your needs.

For straightforward water heating, or as back-up for a conventional central heating system, install a single-element heater.

For the most economical use, link the heater to a timeswitch. This will turn it on a short while before you want to use the hot water, usually first thing in the morning and in the early evening.

To cope with variable demand, you can either:

- fit a dual-element heater (A) in the usual position, or
- install two short heaters (B) through holes cut in the side of the cylinder.

When only small quantities of hot water are needed, you switch on the short element or the upper heater only; for heavy demand, both elements or heaters are on.

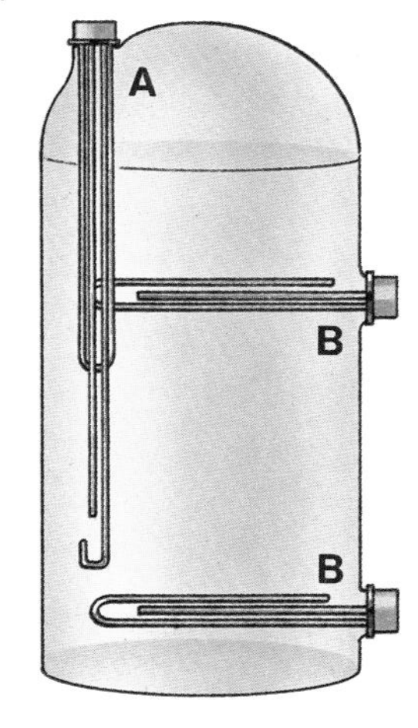


### TIP: RESCUE THE CUT-OUT

If you have to cut a hole in your cylinder to install your heater, drill a series of holes in a circle and complete the cutting with a hacksaw blade. To stop the cut-out falling into the cylinder:

- drill a hole in its centre before cutting round it.
- insert a toggle (nail or dowel, for example) tied to a piece of string, so you can retrieve the cut-out when it's severed.

Alternatively use a hook made from something like coat-hanger wire.

The cylinder, with its immersion heater should be positioned as closely as possible to the hot water tap in most constant use, not the one from which the greatest volumes of hot water are drawn. This will normally be the hot tap over the kitchen sink. Where the position of a hot water draw-off point, over a cloakroom washbasin for example, involves a run of more than 7m (20ft), you ought to consider installing a small instantaneous water heater to serve that particular fitting.

Finally, if an immersion heater is to be used economically, it must also be used intelligently. No matter how thoroughly a cylinder is lagged, the water stored within it will slowly lose heat. It's rare that hot water is required in any amount between, say 11.00pm and 7.00am. It's sensible therefore to switch off the immersion heater at about 10.00pm and to switch it on again at about 6.30am. When a house is empty for most of the day, it's also wise to switch off the immersion heater during the period that the house is usually unoccupied.

This doesn't have to be done manually. Nowadays there are clock-controlled time switches available that will switch the immersion heater off and on again at pre-determined times. These controls normally have a manual over-ride for use at weekends or other occasions when the house is occupied throughout the day.

## PUTTING IN THE NEW HEATER

**1** *Take the new heater and remove the cap. Put some plumber's sealant on the metal washer and run some PTFE tape round the thread.*

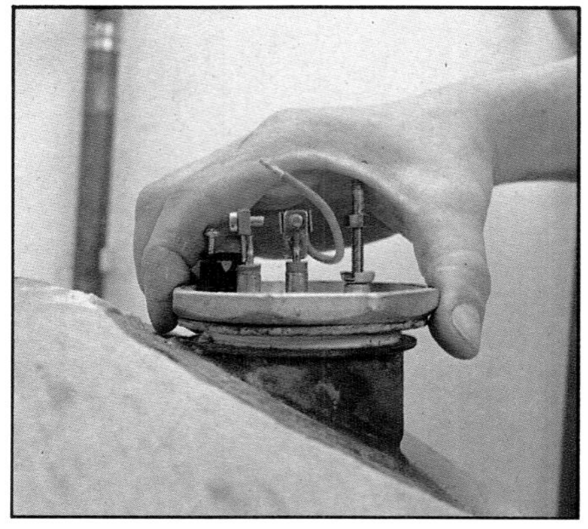

**2** *Put the heater element inside the cylinder and gently screw up the boss nut, ensuring the thread doesn't cross, then tighten with the spanner.*

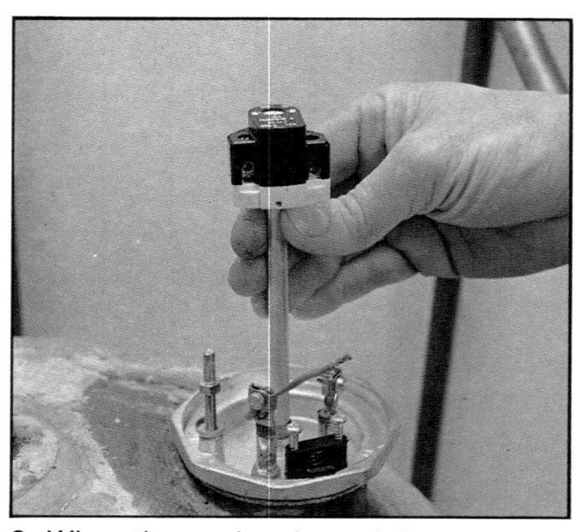

**3** *When the nut has been fully tightened, fill the cylinder with water and check for leaks, then insert the thermostat in its housing.*

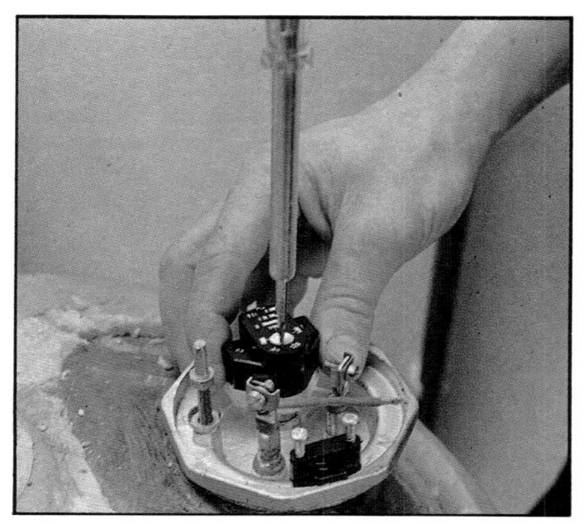

**4** *Adjust the thermostat to the temperature you require, and then complete the electrical connection and replace the cap.*

### Replacing or installing an immersion heater

When you're dealing with an immersion heater, one tool you will have to get hold of, (and it's worth hiring it for the day rather than buying), is an immersion heater spanner. No other use has been found for this dinosaur amongst spanners, as you'll understand when you see its gigantic proportions. (If there were another purpose, it would probably be in connection with constructing marine diesel engines for oil tankers!)

Before starting work you must turn off the heater, if you already have one, and drain the cylinder. You don't actually need the whole cylinder drained but because of the way they are constructed it's all or nothing, unless you want to go to the trouble of siphoning a small quantity out through the vent pipe hole in the top. See the previous section for how to go about draining the cylinder. Don't forget that the cylinder cannot be drained from the hot taps alone.

If you're installing an immersion heater in a cylinder that doesn't have one, there should be a boss plug in the top to take it. If not, then you may have to think about buying a new cylinder. However, you can carefully cut out a hole using a hole cutter. If all you've got is a drill then you'll have to draw a circle on the cylinder the same diameter as the screw boss and then drill a series of holes on the inside of this circle. Once you've done this you can cut out the circle of the metal with a hacksaw blade and smooth off the inside edges of the hole with a half-round file. You then have to insert a solderless flange into which the immersion heater can be screwed.

If there is a boss plug or an old heater, then you will need the special immersion heater spanner to remove it before you can put the new heater in. With an old heater it's quite likely that you'll have to play a blow-torch over the fitting to make it easier to loosen the screw, but make sure there is no combustible material around. If it doesn't turn after you've heated it you'll have to leave it for a few moments to cool and then try again. Applying heat once or twice should do the trick.

You must get the right length of heater to extend almost to the base of the cylinder. When you fit it you'll need to bind PTFE tape round the thread of the new heater boss and put some plumbers' sealant between the metal washer and the boss head. Then insert the heater into the body of the cylinder and gently screw it up tight.

Once you've done this you can fill the cylinder with water and check for any leaks round the boss. When you're satisfied that everything is in order you can deal with the electrics (see opposite). This entails running a heat-resisting flex from the heater to a double-pole isolating switch, which in turn is connected to a separate radial circuit. Most switches are sited in the cupboard which houses the heater or just outside the door, but for greater convenience you could install a second switch, say, in the kitchen. Finally, you'll need to insert the thermostat and adjust it so that it heats the water to the temperature which you require.

## CHECKING THE ELECTRICS

When replacing an immersion heater it's a good idea to check that the existing cable runs and switch are not worn or poorly installed. It is quite likely that if the heater has been in for some time the cable may need replacing, and a more modern switch may be desirable. If you are installing an immersion heater from scratch, you will have to install new wiring, and it is vital that this meets Wiring Regulations requirements.

An immersion heater must be controlled by an isolating double-pole switch fitted close to it. This is usually a double-pole 20A switch, which may have a neon indicator. The normal way to provide the supply is by a 15A radial circuit connected to a spare fuseway in the consumer unit, or to a separate switchfuse unit if no spare fuseway is available. For heaters rated at 3kW or less, the connection can also be via a socket-outlet connected to a radial or ring circuit, or via a fused connection unit looped off a suitable ring circuit or radial feed from the consumer unit.(see below).

A special switch is needed for a dual immersion heater and this may be sited elsewhere in the house for convenience – usually in the kitchen. Alternatively, there may be a change-over switch on the heater head itself.

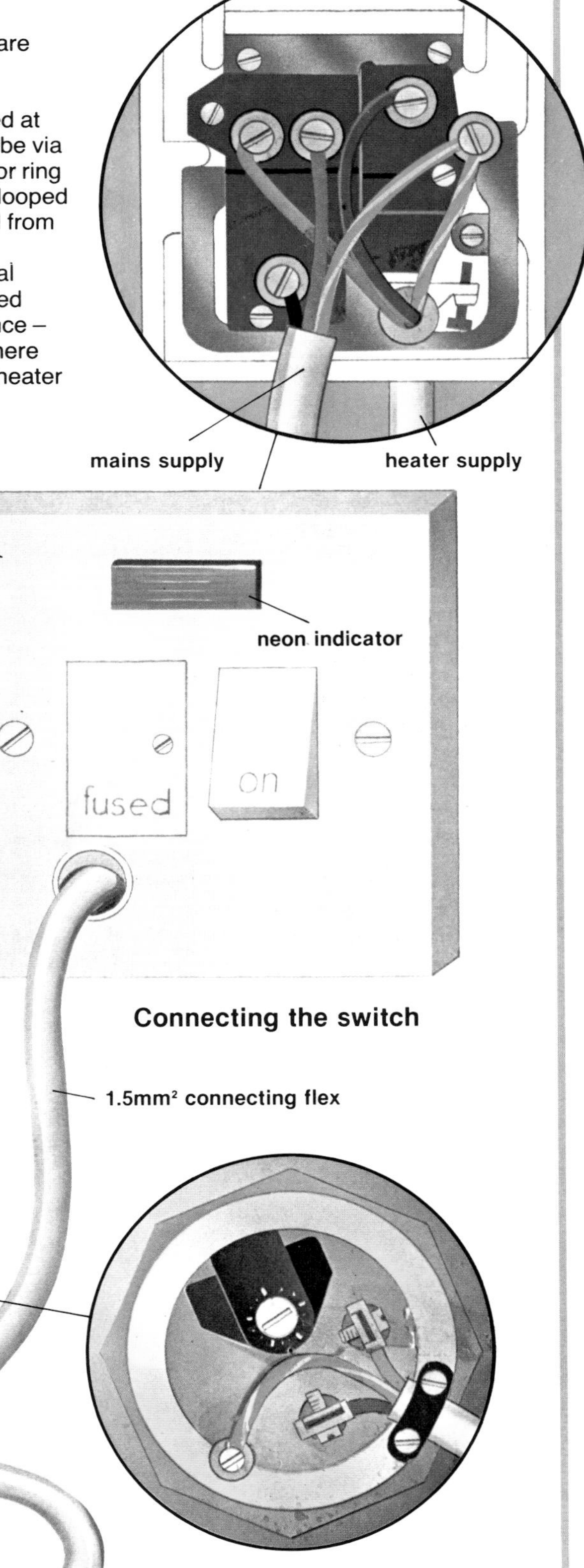


Connecting the switch

Connections at the heater

# REPLACING A CISTERN

**Because a cold water storage cistern is out of sight does not mean it should be out of mind. It should be inspected at least twice a year: at the beginning and the end of winter. Otherwise a leak or overflow may have disastrous consequences.**

You may well wonder why it's necessary to have a cold water cistern. After all it's possible to supply all cold water fittings direct from the rising main, using what is known as a direct supply system (as described on pages 9 to 13). However, in new or converted properties, most water authorities require homes to have an indirect cold water system, in which only the cold tap over the kitchen sink, and possibly a garden water tap, come direct from the main. The reason for this is that at times of peak demand the water mains may be incapable of supplying water as quickly as it is drawn off, so the storage cistern acts as a 'shock absorber' and evens out fluctuations in the flow. The cistern also provides a reserve of water which can be used for several hours, while the supply is cut off during repairs to the main, or when supply is reduced at times of water shortage. A leak from a pipe under pressure from a storage cistern is also likely to be less devasting than one from a pipe under mains pressure. However, one of the most important uses of a cold water cistern is to provide a source of water under constant, relatively low pressure for a cylinder storage hot water system.

If your home was built more than thirty years ago the chances are that it'll have a galvanised mild steel cold water storage cistern, unless it's already been replaced. Nowadays cisterns are usually built to a standard capacity of 227 litres (50 gal). In pre-metrication days it was common practice to install a cistern of 20 or 25 gal capacity if it supplied a hot water system only, and one of 40 gal capacity if it also supplied the WC cistern and the bathroom cold taps.

### Why replace the cistern?

Galvanised steel cisterns are tough and hardwearing which is why there are still so many of them in use. But they are subject to corrosion and this failing has become much more common since the almost universal adoption of copper pipe for water supply and distribution. The mains water supply is never completely pure and contains minerals and salts which may make it slightly acid or alkaline. Where the mains water supply is very slightly acid, a galvanised steel cistern can be turned into a giant electric cell or battery. This won't give you any electric power, but it can be disastrous for the cistern. Current will flow between the zinc coating of the galvanised steel and the copper pipes connected to the cistern, and the thin zinc protective layer will dissolve away, leaving the steel beneath exposed to corrosive attack and rusting. This phenomenon is known as electrolytic corrosion. Never, therefore, connect copper pipes to a galvanised steel cistern without taking appropriate steps to protect the zinc coating (see below).

When you inspect your cistern you should look for rust. Once you've removed the cistern's cover, play a torch beam into the interior. Rust may appear as a light dusting on the cistern walls, in larger patches concentrated round pipe connections, or even as a cauliflower-like growth protruding inwards from the cistern walls.

A cistern that doesn't show evidence of corrosion can be protected by means of a 'sacrificial anode'. This consists of a lump of magnesium (the anode), placed in the cistern and connected to the outside metal wall. One well-known make is made up of a clamp which is attached to the magnesium anode by a length of copper wire. The clamp is fixed firmly to the cistern wall, which has to be rubbed down to the bare metal to ensure a good electrical contact. The magnesium is then hung over a batten placed across the cistern and suspended in the water below. The magnesium very slowly dissolves away – is 'sacrificed' – and the zinc coating of the galvanised steel is protected.

The presence of rust doesn't necessarily mean that the cistern must instantly be replaced. If the extent of corrosion is limited, the cistern can be reconditioned. After it has been drained and dried, every trace of rust has to be removed and the pit-holes filled with an epoxy resin filler. All the inside surfaces then have to be treated with two coats of a tasteless and odourless bituminous paint. It's best to disconnect the water supply and distribution pipes before doing this work.

# THE OLD CISTERN

**1** *Turn off the mains supply, drain the entire system and bail out the water that remains in the cistern below the outlet pipes.*

**2** *Disconnect all pipes attached to the cistern, the supply at the ball-valve, the overflow, and any distribution pipes.*

**3** *It's quicker to saw off the pipe connections if connections to the new cistern are going to be in a different position.*

### Modern cisterns

Modern non-corroding cisterns may be made either of asbestos cement or a variety of plastics, perhaps reinforced with glass fibre. Although asbestos cement cisterns cannot corrode, they are rather heavy and tend to become heavier as they absorb water. They are also prone to accidental breakage. It's best to use a plastic cistern of one kind or another as they have a number of advantages. They are light in weight and easy to raise into the roof space, which means they can be installed by one person. And you won't need many tools as the walls are easy to drill and the pipe connections are simple to make. These cisterns are also quite flexible, which is handy if the opening to the loft is not very large, (see below). The smooth internal angles also make cleaning out easy.

### Installing the cistern

It's likely that if you have an old galvanised steel cistern, it'll be resting directly across the joists in the roof space. But a plastic cistern must have a flat level base. Two or three pieces of floorboard or a square of chipboard will serve this purpose. However, you may decide to take the opportunity of raising the level of the cistern, particularly if you want to improve the pressure in the supply to a shower. This can be done by constructing a platform on a substantial wooden frame 600 or 900mm (2 or 3ft) above the joists. A shower works best if there is a vertical distance of 1500mm (5ft) or more between the shower rose and the base of the storage cistern: 900mm (3ft) is the minimum (see pages 111 to 113).

If you are raising the new cistern onto a platform of this kind you needn't worry too much about unscrewing the back-nuts securing the water pipes to the existing cistern. Just cut the pipes near the cistern. You'll have to extend them anyway.

Before purchasing your new cistern, make sure that it will go through the trap-door into your roof space. Round black polythene cisterns can often be flexed through a relatively small opening. If it is quite impossible to pass it through the existing trap door you can install two smaller cisterns, linked together by a short length of 28mm pipe connected 50mm (2in) above their bases. To avoid the risk of stagnating water, it's a good idea to take the distribution pipes from one cistern and to connect the ball-valve inlet to the other. This will ensure a through-flow from one cistern to the other one.

Installation instructions are usually supplied with a new cistern; read them carefully and follow them exactly. Usually, all pipes must be connected squarely to the plastic walls so as not to strain them. The

## Ready Reference

### CISTERN INSPECTION

Always check the cistern twice a year in spring and autumn:

- if there is any sign of rust then drain it out and look more closely
- if the rust is not extensive and thin consider cleaning if off and coating with special bitumen.
- if the rust is extensive or deep, replace the cistern as soon as possible.

### CISTERN REPLACEMENT

First turn off the water supply at the rising main. Then:

- empty the cistern
- disconnect the cistern
- connect the new cistern to the existing pipework
- turn on the water and check for leaks.

### CONNECTIONS TO THE CISTERN

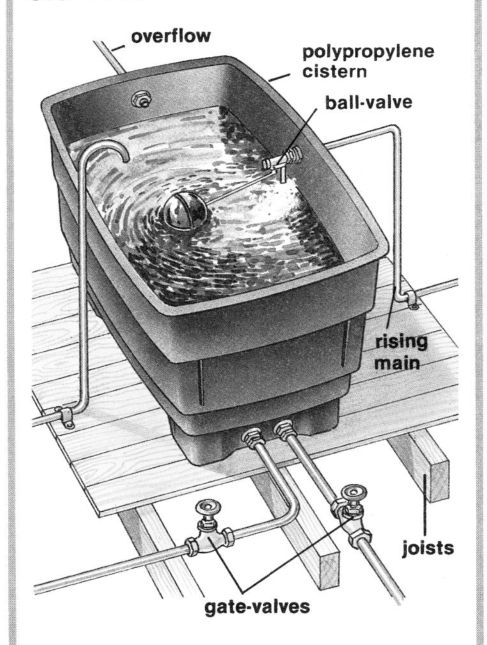


### WHAT YOU'LL NEED

Here is the equipment you may need:

- new plastic cistern
- new ball-valve if old one is not in good condition
- 15 and 22mm pipe for new connections to old pipework
- tank connectors
- drill with bit and hole saw of the same diameter as the connections
- wrenches for pipe connections
- PTFE tape
- hacksaw if you want to cut the old connections.

## INSTALLING THE NEW CISTERN

*1 Place the new cistern in position, check that any expansion pipe fits over the edge, and cut the overflow pipe to the right length.*

*2 Mark the position of the outlet holes you need to cut out, then use a drill bit and hole saw to make the aperture to fit the tank connectors.*

*3 Clean up the hole with a fine file or glasspaper so that there is no swarf left round it. Check that the connector fits fairly tightly.*

*5 Push the connector into the hole from the inside of the cistern, place another plastic washer on the thread and screw up the connector nut.*

*6 Measure up the necessary linkage from the new cistern to the outlet pipework and make up suitable pipe lengths for the connections.*

*7 Fit stop-valves close to the outlet exits: these are useful if you have to make any repairs to some other part of the system.*

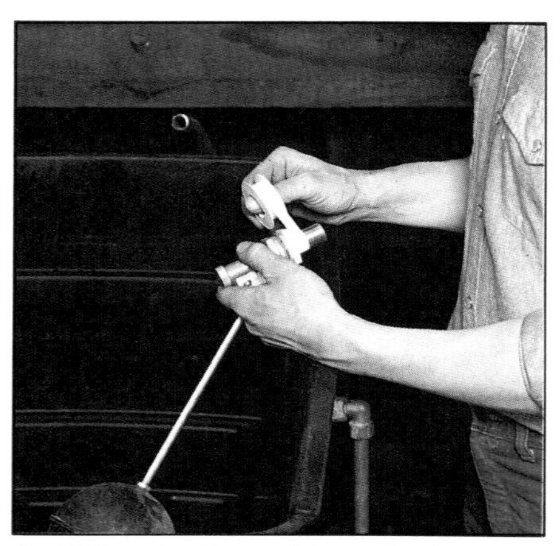

*9 Fit the plastic washer and nut on the ball-valve tail, then wind PTFE tape round the thread and push it through the hole.*

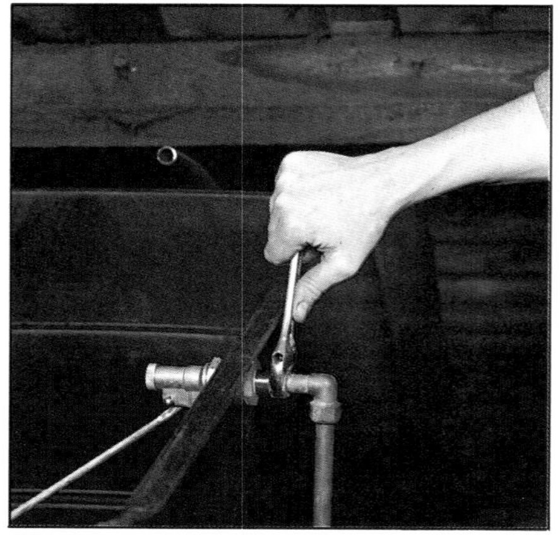

*10 Connect the inlet and support the pipe against the roof timbers to prevent any vibration. Finally, check that the ball arm lifts easily.*

*11 When you're sure the connections are firm and tight, turn the water back on, after you have turned off the outlet stop-valves.*

4 *Place a plastic washer on the thread of the connector and run some PTFE tape around the thread right up to the end.*

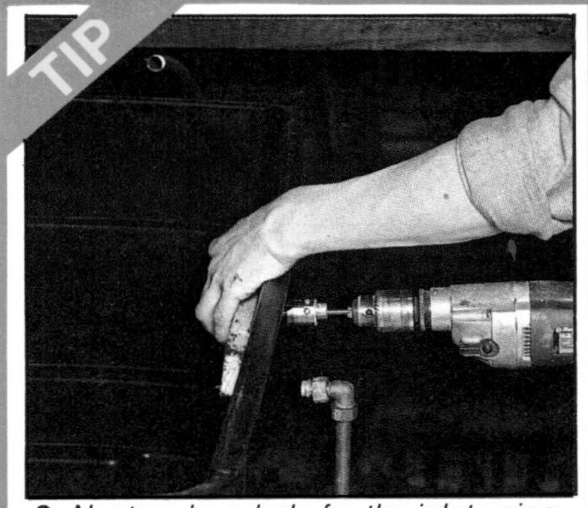


8 *Next make a hole for the inlet using a hole saw. It's a good idea to support the wall of the cistern with a piece of scrap wood.*

12 *Check that the ball-valve works. Then place the cover on the cistern, having made a hole for an expansion pipe, and install the lagging.*

connections should be made with one large plastic washer and one large metal washer on each side of the cistern wall, with the plastic washer in direct contact with the wall. No sealant or other jointing agent should be used in contact with the plastic.

### Carrying out the work

Before you start the job, turn off the main stop-valve to prevent water flowing into the cistern and drain it by opening the bathroom cold taps. As long as you don't use the hot taps while carrying out the work there's no need to shut down the boiler if you have one. As the distribution pipes are taken from a point about 50mm (2in) above the base of the cistern, a certain amount of water will have to be bailed out.

When you've emptied the cistern you'll have to disconnect the ball-valve inlet, overflow (warning) pipe, and distribution pipes. Then you'll have to move it out of the way.

An old galvanised cistern will be quite heavy, so make sure you have strong helpers before attempting to lower it through the trap-door. If possible use a stout rope to support it. There's a good chance that it won't go through, as in many houses the cistern was installed before the roof was put on. You could cut it up with a hacksaw, but this is extremely arduous and if there is plenty of room in the roof space there's no great harm in simply leaving it there.

Before you make the connections to the new cistern you will have to mark and cut holes in the right places. You can use the fittings that will occupy these holes as templates to determine the correct size and position. In the case of the ball-valve this will be the ball-valve tail. The overflow and distribution pipes will be connected by a compression joint to the male screw tank connector, so use the threaded male end to determine the diameter.

A round polythene cistern will be supplied complete with a supporting plate for the ball-valve, which will determine the level at which the ball-valve is fitted. For other cisterns the ball-valve should be fitted about 25mm (1in) below the cistern rim. The hole for the overflow (warning) pipe should be cut about 50mm (2in) below the ball-valve inlet. The holes for the distribution pipes should be cut 50mm (2in) above the base of the cistern.

### Water knocking

It sometimes happens that, after installing a new plastic cold water cistern, a plumbing system that has previously been quiet and unobtrusive, suddenly becomes intolerably noisy. This is because the old galvanised steel cistern, whatever its faults, did give very good support to the rising main. A plastic cistern does not. As water flows in through the ball-valve, a copper rising main supported only by the cistern wall may vibrate uncontrollably. The remedy is to secure it firmly to the roof timbers. This is particularly important where the new cistern has been raised onto a platform in the roof space and the rising main lengthened. In these circumstances it should be secured to the platform.

## Ready Reference

### TRAP DOOR PROBLEMS

If your loft entry is too small to get the old cistern out:

- just move it to one side and leave it in the roof space, or
- cut it into pieces – but this is hard work.

A modern plastic cistern will bend to a certain extent, but if it won't fit the loft entry. Buy two smaller ones that will give you the same capacity as a larger one. These should be connected together in series so there is no risk of the water stagnating:

- position the cisterns side-by-side
- connect them together 50mm (2in) from the bottom with 28mm pipe
- connect the mains supply to the side of one cistern
- connect the outlet and the overflow to the side of the other.

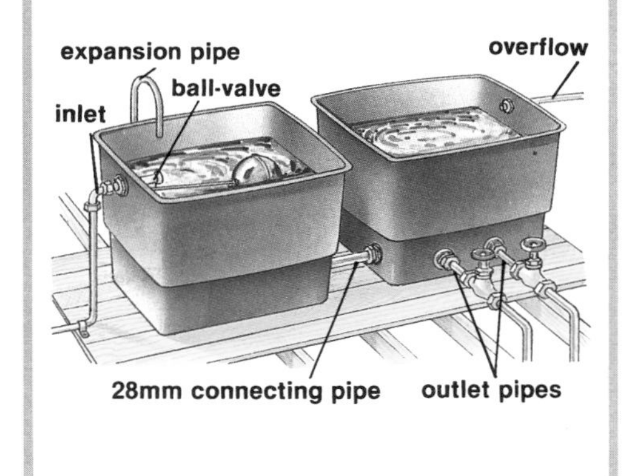


### Freezing

Plastic cisterns have a built-in frost resistance and, if the water in them should freeze, they are unlikely to be damaged. Insulation isn't therefore quite as important with a plastic cistern as with one of galvanised steel or asbestos. It is, however, well worth protecting it with glass fibre tank-wrap or similar lagging material. A dust-proof, but not air-tight, cover should always be fitted. Many manufacturers supply one as an optional extra, but it is quite easy to make one from a sheet of exterior grade plywood.

CHAPTER 7

# DRAINAGE AND OUTDOOR PLUMBING

**Plumbing jobs need not necessarily be confined to indoors; there are many jobs that require plumbing skills outdoors as well. Foremost among these is the maintenance and repair of the rainwater system – the gutters and downpipes. Another problem area outdoors is the gullies into which rainwater downpipes and the waste pipes from downstairs sinks and appliances discharge.**

# REPAIRING AND REPLACING GUTTERING

**The chances are you won't realise there is anything wrong with your home's guttering until it leaks. Note where the water is coming from, and, once the rain has stopped, get up a ladder and see what's wrong.**

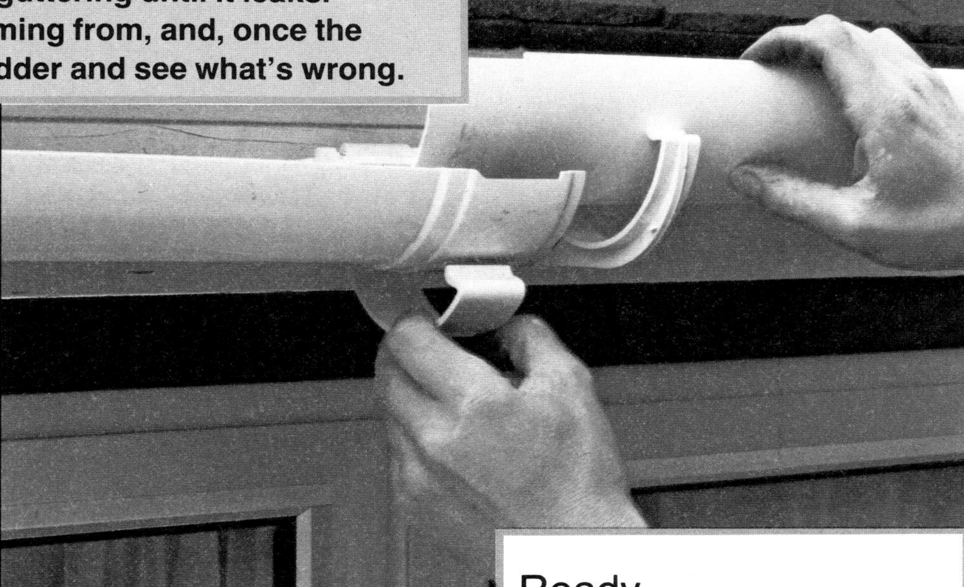

The gutters on your home are supposed to capture all the rain falling on the roof and channel it to one or more downpipes. In turn these downpipes take the water into the main drain, a storm drain, or to a soakaway in your garden. This efficient removal of rainwater is important to keep your outside walls sound. Any missing, damaged, or blocked guttering will result in water cascading down the face of your wall, leading to dampness, and eventually mortar and brick decay. You may be able to repair it; or you may be faced with having to replace whole sections or the complete system.

Until the mid-1940s most guttering was made of cast iron, although asbestos enjoyed a brief popularity. Cast iron had the disadvantage of being very heavy to work with – as you'll find if you take some of it down. It is also prone to rusting if not properly maintained. Asbestos was heavy, looked rather bulky in appearance and was easily damaged. When plastic piping and guttering was introduced, it became an obvious choice. It is light to work with, doesn't need painting and its smooth surface allows water to flow through it more effectively. In any case, cast iron is very expensive these days, and not particularly easy to obtain.

### Blockages

You should check why a blockage has occurred in the first place. This may be due to sagging, or poor installation preventing a free run for the water. Or the blockage may be combined with a faulty joint which may be possible to repair. But if cast iron guttering is at all cracked it needs replacing.

If your gutter overflows during heavy rain, the chances are that it's blocked with leaves.

## PREPARING FOR WORK

**1** *Access is always a problem when working on guttering – a convenient garage roof made this job a lot easier. Scaffold towers are useful on high roofs.*

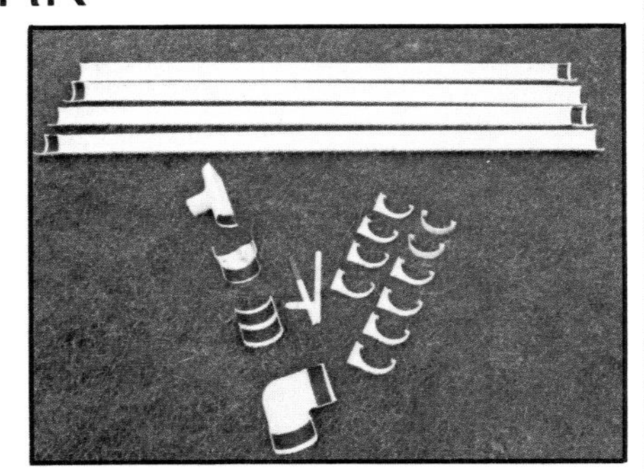

**2** *Before you start work assemble all the components you will need. You can check them off against the existing guttering.*

## Ready Reference

### GUTTER SIZES

Plastic gutters come in three common sizes (measured as the width from lip to lip):

- 75mm (3in) – for extensions and outbuildings
- 100mm (4in) – for most house roofs
- 150mm (6in) – for house roofs of very large surface area

The 150mm size carries roughly seven times the volume of water that the 75mm size can take, and three times as much as the 100mm size.

### A CAST IRON ALTERNATIVE

It is still possible to buy a new cast iron guttering in several 'classic' profiles as a match for existing gutters, but it's expensive and very awkward to install.

If you want the look of cast iron you could consider hiring a specialist firm to produce seamless extruded aluminium guttering for your house.

### GUTTER PROFILES

nominal half-round　　true half-round　　square

## REMOVING OLD GUTTERING

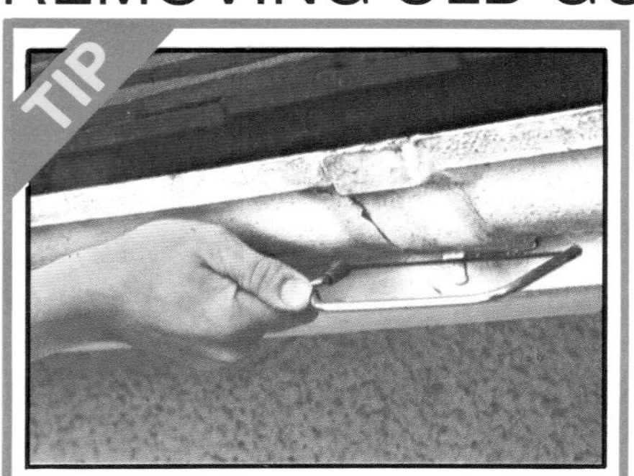


**1** *Gutter sections are usually bolted together and these bolts won't come out easily. Saw through the nut.*

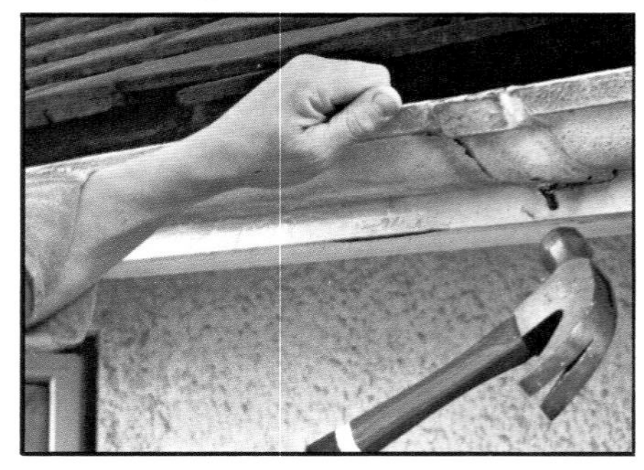

**2** *When the nut has been detached try to hammer the bolt out but don't use too much force as the gutter itself may crack and collapse dangerously.*

**3** *You may need to use a hammer and chisel to get the joints moving. Loosen the joints before unscrewing the gutter sections.*

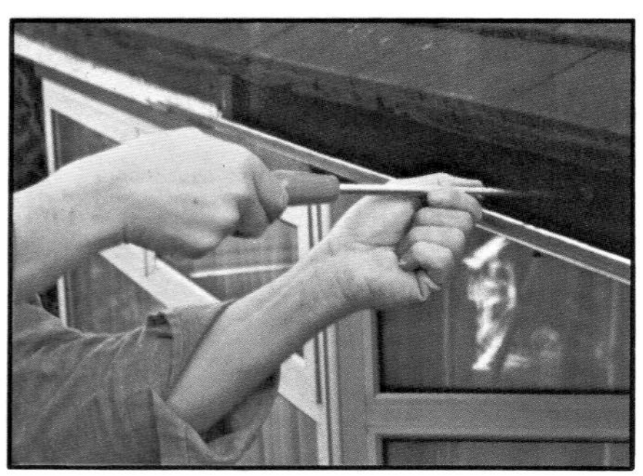

**4** *Cast iron guttering is supported by brackets or screws depending on its profile. You can lift it off brackets, or in this case unscrew it.*

**5** *Start to take down the guttering at the point closest to the down pipe – it should come free quite easily even if it's attached directly to the pipe.*

**6** *Detach and lift off each succeeding section in turn – remember that cast iron is heavier than it looks. Be careful not to overbalance.*

**7** *Always carry pieces of guttering down to the ground, never throw them down – you may cause the cast iron to splinter dangerously.*

**8** *Thoroughly brush down the fascia board to remove dirt and cobwebs, then fill any holes using a filler suitable for outside work.*

**9** *If the fascia board has not been painted, use this opportunity to do the work. Sand down first and then apply primer and topcoats.*

You can use an old dustpan brush to clean it out, scraping the debris into piles and scooping them out with gloved hands. But prevent any bits from getting into the down-pipe or this may get blocked as well.

### Coping with sags

If a section of guttering has sagged, making it lower than the top of the downpipe, the water will not drain away properly. And you will be able to see this from puddles of water collecting in the guttering itself. You must decide whether to raise the sagging section, or lower the mouth of the downpipe to bring everything back into line. If you flex cast iron guttering more than about 25mm (1in) you'll break the seal on the joints, causing a leak. So choose the option that involves moving the guttering least.

In order to reset the guttering to the correct gradient you'll need to fix a piece of string taut between two nails hammered into the fascia board. You can then use this as a guide as you reposition each gutter support in turn.

### Leaking joints

Joints in cast iron gutters are made by over-lapping the two lengths of gutter, and bolting them together with a layer of sealant in between to form a watertight seal. As this sealant begins to deteriorate with age, the joint starts to leak.

To make the repair, first remove the bolt holding the joint together. Often this is too rusty to undo, so hacksaw off the bolt between the nut and the guttering, or drill out the rest of the bolt. Lever the joint apart with an old chisel, and scrape away all the old sealant. Clean up the joint with a wire brush, then apply a finger-thick sausage of new sealant and bolt the sections back together using a new nut and bolt and a couple of washers. Scrape off any sealant that has oozed out before giving the repair a coat of bitumen-based paint on the inside of the gutter.

### Dealing with rust

If one bit of guttering has rusted right through, it won't be long before the rest follows suit, so you may as well save yourself a lot of trouble and replace it all. If meanwhile you want a temporary repair, there are several suitable repair kits on the market. They consist of a sort of wide metal sticky tape which you apply inside the guttering and over the holes with bitumen adhesive.

### Choosing a replacement

Assuming you won't be using cast iron again – you'll have a job getting hold of it and even more of a job putting it up, apart from the fact that it's expensive – your choice is between aluminium and plastic. Plastic guttering is made of UPVC (unplasticised polyvinyl chloride). It's probably the better choice for a do-it-yourself installation: it is far more widely available than aluminium, and has the edge in terms of cost and durability.

Two different cross-sections are commonly available – half-round and 'square'. The latter is often given a decoratively moulded face similar to the more ornate ogee cast iron guttering. In addition, a semi-elliptical guttering is available – it looks a bit like half-round but is deeper and more efficient. This, together with some brands of conventional profile, can be camouflaged by being boxed in with a clip-on fascia panel. Which type you choose is largely a matter of personal taste, but try to choose something that blends into the style of your home.

More important than looks is the size of the gutter. Too small, and it will be forever overflowing; too large, and you will have paid more for the installation than is necessary. It's all to do with relating the amount of water the guttering can carry to the amount of water likely to come off the roof during a heavy rainstorm. These calculations are complicated, but you can assume that they were done when the guttering was originally installed. Just measure the existing guttering at its widest point to find its size, and buy the same again. The most commonly available sizes are 75mm (3in), 100mm (4in), 112mm (4½in), 125mm (5in), and 150mm (6in). If in doubt, consult the manufacturer's literature.

The actual cross-section of the gutter may vary from brand to brand; this can make it difficult to join with existing guttering: for example, the guttering belonging to a neighbour on a semi-detached or terraced house. Most firms offer adaptors to link their product with cast iron guttering, or with a different size from within their range. However, they tend not to offer adaptors to tie in with the equivalent size from another brand, so if possible stick to one brand throughout the installation. If you have to link up with a neighbour's gutter, find out which brand was used, and try to use the same.

There are many different fittings as well as lengths of guttering available on the market. Before you start buying your new guttering get hold of a manufacturer's brochure from the stockist you use and carefully check to ensure you have all the fittings you will need. Make sure you understand how the particular system works before you buy anything.

### Taking down old guttering

Cast iron guttering is heavy, and may also be rusted into place, so removing it can be tricky. But there is no need to be gentle with it: it doesn't matter if it breaks. The important thing is to work in safe conditions. If you are wrenching things apart, do it in a controlled way so you don't fall off the ladder, and so that great chunks of gutter don't fall down. Try not to drop cast iron guttering to the ground: it shatters easily, and, if it lands on a hard surface, dangerous fragments can fly off. If you toss the guttering clear of the house you might overbalance and fall off the ladder, so aim to lower larger sections gently to the ground with a rope.

Begin with the section linking gutter and downpipe. Cut through the old bolts holding the sections together. Then, if you lift the gutter slightly, you should be able to pull it free from the downpipe. Once it's out of the way, unmake the joints between the sections of gutter (as if you were repairing them), and lift the guttering off its supporting brackets. It may, of course, be screwed directly to the fascia board.

You can now turn your attention to the brackets themselves. These are usually screwed to the fascia board just beneath the eaves of the roof, and can either be unscrewed or levered off with a claw hammer. In older houses the brackets may be screwed to the tops or sides of the roof rafters, to support the weight of the iron guttering. If there is a fascia board to which

## Ready Reference

### HALF-ROUND GUTTER FITTINGS

This is the most common style of fitting available for gutter work. The means of joining varies according to manufacturer.

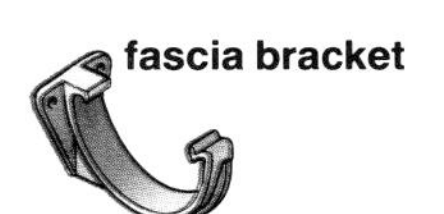


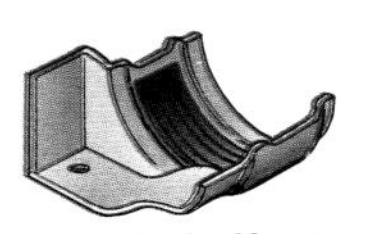


An ogee/half-round adaptor will help you join up to your neighbour's gutter if it has an ogee profile. Other adaptors will connect new PVC guttering to half-round and square cast iron profiles.

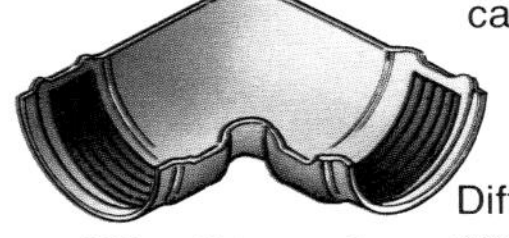


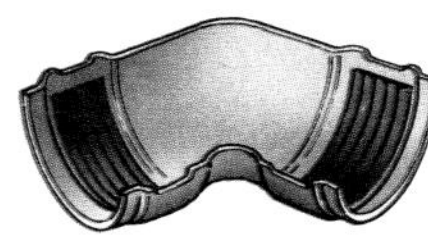


Different gutter angles are available to get round corners which aren't square. Various fascia brackets make fixing possible under low eaves; measure up carefully so that you buy the right ones.

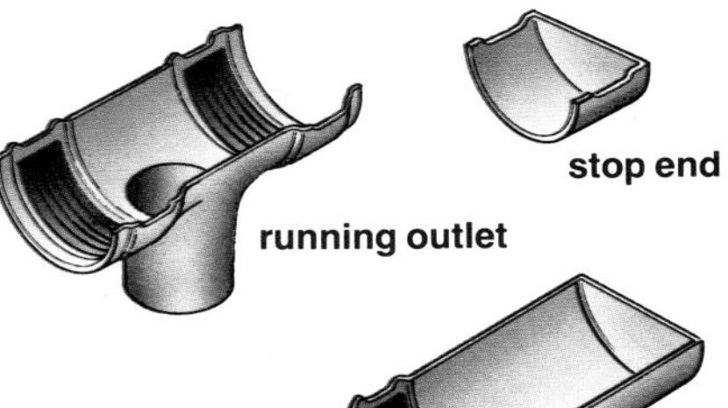


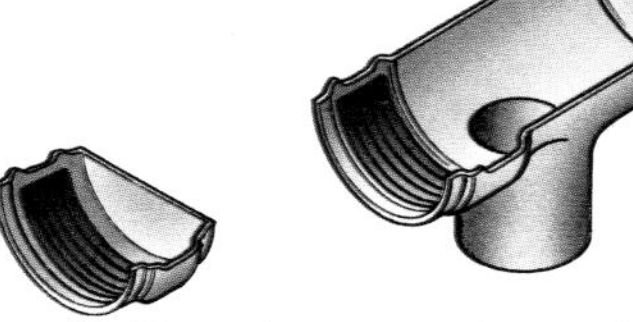


The gutter outlet should fit *inside* the top of the downpipe. Measure the downpipe diameter before you buy a new outlet.

## PUTTING UP PLASTIC GUTTERING

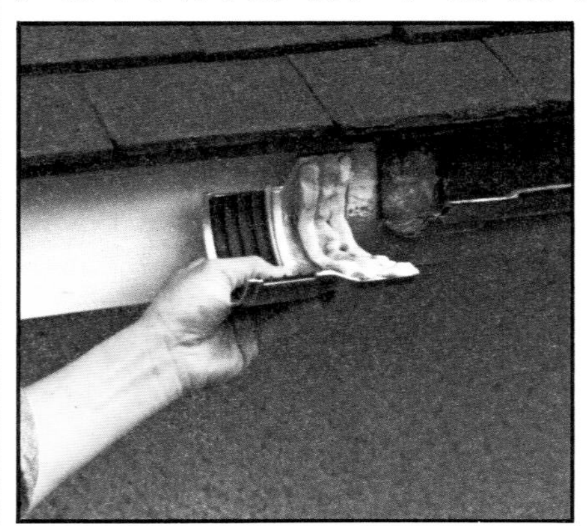

**1** *If you are joining onto your neighbour's gutter you'll need a special adaptor. Line it with a lump of mastic and bolt it into place.*

**2** *Fix a string at the level of the top of the adaptor or end furthest from the downpipe. Hammer a nail into position to hold it in place.*

**3** *Pull the string taut and fix it with a nail at the other end of the gutter run. Make sure it is horizontal, then lower it enough for the correct fall.*

**4** *Fix the brackets to the fascia board at intervals of about 1m (39in), making sure their tops are aligned with the string.*

**5** *You can now put in the first section of guttering so that it is resting on the brackets, and connect it to the end piece or adaptor.*

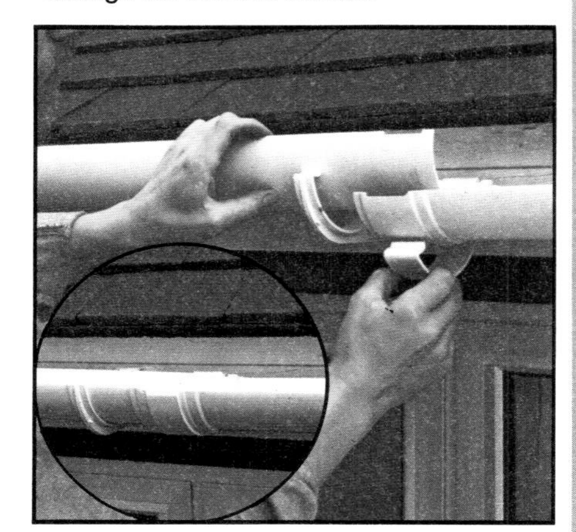

**6** *Each manufacturer has a different system for making joints. Here the next section rests in the previous one and is then firmly held with a clip.*

**7** *You will very likely have to cut a section of guttering. Measure it exactly at roof level, then cut it squarely.*

**8** *In this system, once a section is cut, new notches must be made in the end for the clip. To do this you can use a proprietary notch cutter or a wood file.*

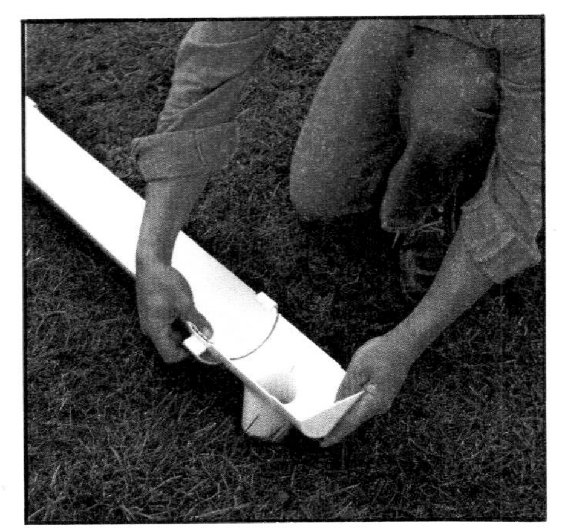

**9** *The final corner piece and down-pipe fitting is made up on the ground which is the easiest procedure when dealing with small sections.*

you can fit the new gutter, the ends of the brackets can be hacksawed off. Otherwise, you will have to lift off some of the roofing to remove them.

When all the old guttering has been removed, inspect the fascia board to make sure it is sound and securely fixed. If it is, fill the old screw holes and paint it before fixing the new guttering. If it isn't, it will have to be replaced.

### Fixing new guttering

The obvious first step is to assemble the various bits and pieces you need, and you can use the old guttering system as a model to decide what's required. It's best to measure up the length of the guttering itself, allowing a little extra to be safe.

At the end of the run furthest from the downpipe, fix a gutter support bracket as high up the fascia as possible, and about 150mm (6in) from the end. The fixings here, and elsewhere, are made with 25mm (1in) screws. Choose ones that are galvanised to stop them rusting. Insert a nail into the fascia board level with the top of the bracket.

At the other end of the run, 150mm from the downpipe, fix another nail, tie a length of string tightly between the two, and use a spirit level to check that this string is level. When it is, lower the second nail by the amount needed to ensure that the guttering runs downhill towards the outlet. This 'fall', as it's called, varies according to the type of guttering, so check the manufacturer's recommendations. Usually, it is in the region of 5mm (1/4in) for every metre (3ft) of gutter run. Once you've found the right line for the gutter, fix another bracket level with the lowest nail.

The next job is to fix the next bracket 1m (39in) from the one at the downpipe end of the run, using the string as a guide to set it at the correct level. Use these two brackets to support a length of gutter with the downpipe outlet attached.

Exactly how you join the gutter to the outlet – or indeed make any other joins in the guttering – will vary from brand to brand. With some, you slip the ends of the components into a special jointing piece called a union, and clip the whole lot together. With others, one of the components will have a union built into its end.

Now work your way along, building up the gutter run as you go and adding additional support brackets as required, again using the string as a guide. In most cases, you will need a bracket every metre, plus one on each side of every join – though some ranges contain combined unions and support brackets. Check the manufacturer's recommendations.

The only problem you may run into is when you have to cut the guttering to length, either to go round a corner, or to finish the run with a stop end. Do the cutting on the ground using a hacksaw, making sure that you cut the end square. Any roughness left by the saw should be cleaned up with a file. If you want to turn a corner, fix the corner piece before cutting the straight piece of gutter to length. You can then use it to work out exactly how long the straight gutter length needs to be. When cutting to finish at a stop end, it is usual to leave about 50mm (2in) of gutter projecting beyond the ends of the fascia.

When you've finished the job and checked to see that all the joints are properly connected, take a bucket of water to the highest point of the gutter and pour it down. If the gutter doesn't drain all the water then go back and check your work.

**10** *The made-up section is fixed in place taking care to locate the down-pipe end into the hopper head. Any pipe connection needs a sealant joint.*

**11** *When the whole system is up, you should check that it will work by pouring water in at the point furthest from the downpipe.*

## Ready Reference

### SQUARE GUTTER FITTINGS

These fittings may be preferred to the half-round profile although they are slightly less efficient in discharging water.

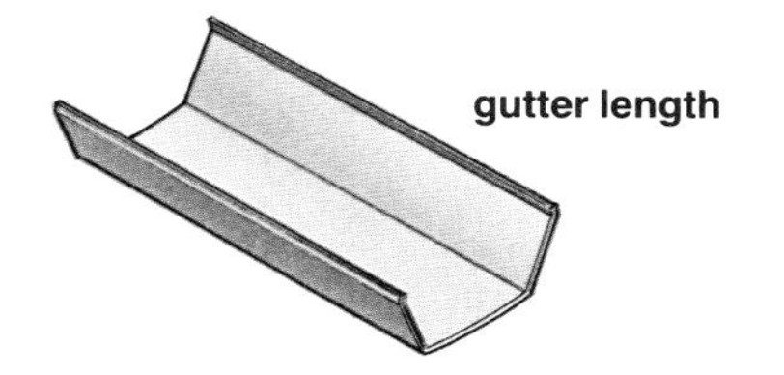


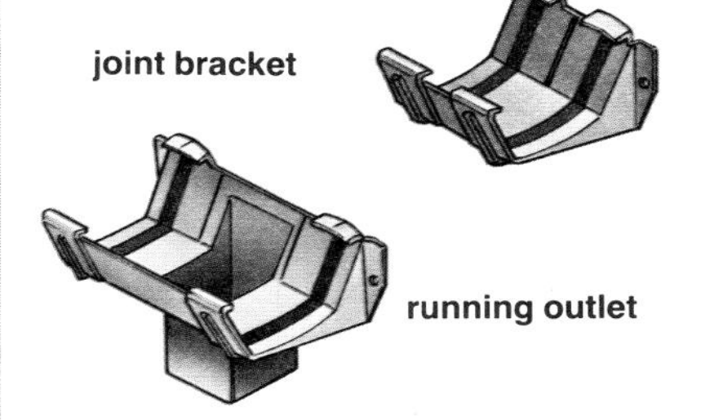


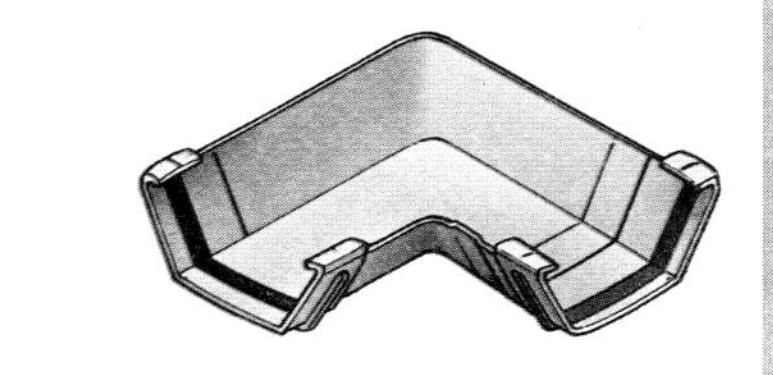


stop end outlet

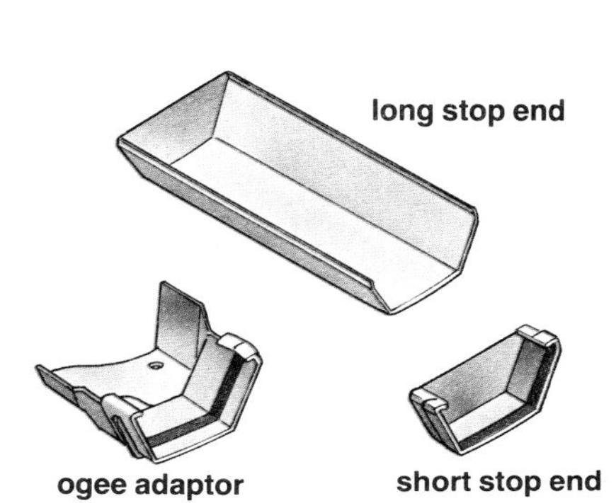


Remember that if you have old square or ogee profile cast iron guttering matched with round downpipes, you will have to replace the downpipes as well when you fit new square-profile guttering.

# REPLACING DOWNPIPES

**If your downpipes are blocked, damaged or badly fixed, the overflowing rainwater can damage your house (and soak passers-by). Routine maintenance is half the battle, but complete replacement may ultimately be the only solution.**

The rainwater that falls on your house cannot be allowed to run off freely over the sides of the roof. If it were, it would soak the walls below, flood the ground all about, and drench anybody unlucky enough to be walking underneath. So it is taken away harmlessly by what is known as a rainwater disposal system. This consists of gutters that collect the water flowing off the roof, and convey it to downpipes which carry it to the drains. At one time most gutters and downpipes were made of cast iron. But although this is a tough material, gutters and downpipes made from it suffer from two big disadvantages: in use they are prone to attack by rust, a big drawback in something that comes into such close contact with water; they need to be kept well painted to ensure that corrosion is held at bay; and during installation (or removal) they are heavy and cumbersome to handle.

Because of this, alternative materials were sought for gutters and downpipes, and for a time they were made in asbestos. This was, however, a rather bulky material and is now recognised as a potential health hazard. So, when the full potential of plastics became apparent during the late 1940s, the opportunity was seized to manufacture rainwater systems in a plastic material – UPVC (unplasticised polyvinyl chloride). As a result, cast iron systems have just about disappeared from the scene and it's difficult to buy them at all. When a rainwater disposal system nowadays is being renewed in whole or in part, it is invariably plastic goods that are used.

UPVC gutters and downpipes have many bonuses. They seem to be everlasting (unless actually broken); they don't need painting, although they take paint if you don't like the colours in which they are available; they are also light to handle, and easy to cut with a sharp hacksaw. In fact, their only drawback is that they are not as rigid as cast iron, and so cannot support such things as ladders.

## Simple maintenance

The faults that occur with downpipes are very much the sort of thing you get with gutters. For instance, you may occasionally get a blockage, caused by dirt, leaves or other debris being washed off the roof. You should clear this out as soon as possible, otherwise the surrounding wall of your house will get soaked with escaping water, and damp could find its way inside the house. You will see at a glance in which section of a downpipe the trouble has occurred because the joins between various lengths are not sealed. Thus when during a downpour water bubbles out of a join, you will know that the trouble lies in the section below.

The fact that the sections are just loosely joined also means that a blocked one can be taken down for clearance. You merely lift it up and pull it away, rather like a sliding door that operates in a groove.

On a straight run, you can usually push out the blockage with a long stick, although in stubborn cases you might have to tie a wad of rags to the end of the stick to make a sort of plunger. Bends will have to be poked clear with a length of wire or cane. Then clean them thoroughly by pulling through a piece of rope with a rag tied to the end of it.

Should the system have a hopper head, scoop debris out with a trowel. You should wear protective gloves as you do this. Take care not to push anything down the pipe; in fact, it's a wise precaution to push a rag bung into the top of the pipe as you work. When everything has been cleared up, fit netting to the top of the pipe so that the trouble will not occur again.

Another fault that sometimes develops is that one or more of the clips holding the pipe to the wall may become damaged or displaced in some way, and the pipe then becomes loose at the joint. The remedy is obvious: refix the clip securely (or replace it if it is badly damaged) and push the pipe back into place. Sections of pipe, too, may be badly damaged, or missing altogether. Again, you should replace them although minor damage on cast iron can be repaired with a glass fibre repair kit.

If you have cast iron downpipes, then a lot of these faults may arise because of rust, for unless you keep them well painted, they will eventually corrode. Even householders who are meticulous about regularly re-painting the exterior of the house tend to neglect the back of the downpipes because they cannot be seen, and it is difficult to treat them without getting paint all over the wall. There is one simple solution to this last problem: protect the wall with a scrap piece of card or hardboard as you work. Obviously, corrosion can take place just as readily at the back as at the front, so it is as well to be meticulous when you paint.

When one length of old downpipe becomes defective, you can replace it with a new one, and there is no problem about inserting a

## PARTS OF A DOWNPIPE

*Select downpipe components carefully to ensure a well-designed and well-fitting installation.*

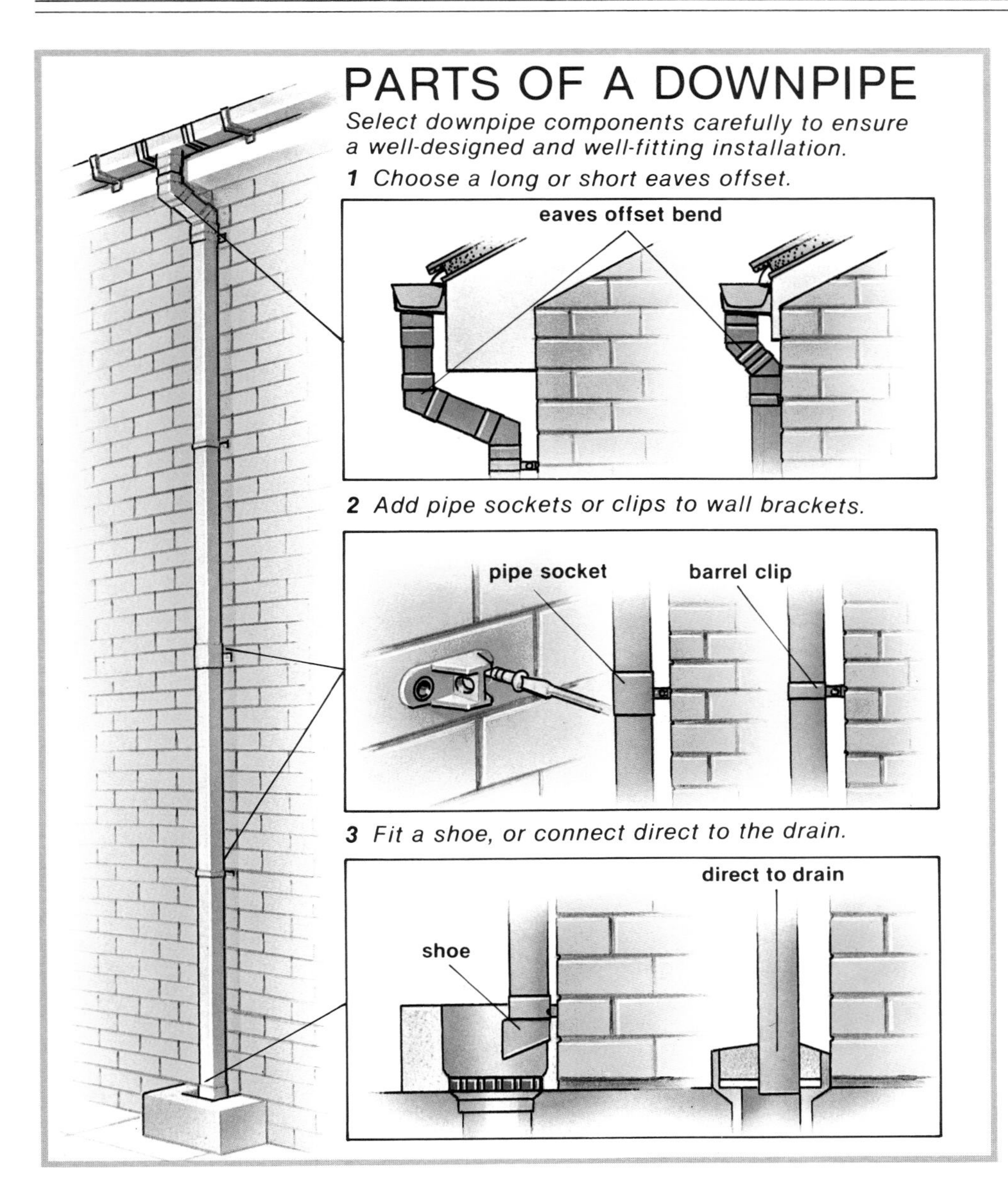


length of plastic pipe in a cast iron system. It merely sits loosely in place, so you do not have to worry about sealing joints, as you do with gutters.

However, if one section of pipe corrodes, it is a good bet that all are coming to the end of their useful life. And, of course, if the whole system becomes ramshackle, it is time to replace the lot. This is especially true if you are fitting new gutters.

### Putting in new pipes

There are a number of brands to select from, but little to choose between them, so settle for one which is available from a convenient store. If you are fitting new gutters, the pipes should be of the same brand to ensure that you can link the two at the eaves. With only a short length of guttering, consider replacing the whole gutter and downpipe system.

Begin by getting a manufacturer's catalogue. With this in one hand, inspect your existing downpipe system, and note down the exact replacements you will need. The pipes come in three common diameters – 75mm (3in) for extensions and the like, 100mm (4in) for most normal houses, and 150mm (6in) for very large roofs. Your pipes must, of course, match the gutters in size.

You have to begin the work by what is really the only troublesome part of the job, and that's taking down and getting rid of the old metal or asbestos pipes. Once you've freed each section you can lower it gently to the ground. Don't drop it as it may shatter. The clips holding the pipe to the wall can now be removed. If held by screws, there's a fair chance they will have rusted into place and will be virtually impossible to turn. However, there is a trick you can use to start the screw

## Ready Reference

### PIPE FITTINGS

Here are all the different sorts of downpipe fittings which you are likely to require. They are available in the square profile shown here or in the traditional round profile. Colours tend to be grey, white and black.

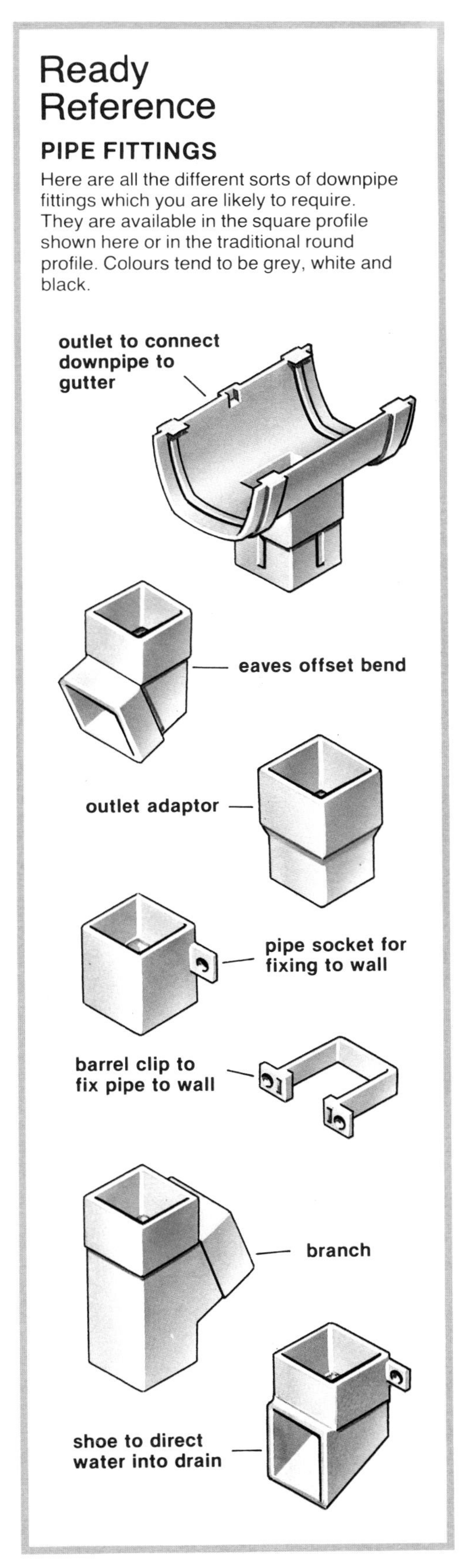

## REMOVING AN ASBESTOS SYSTEM

**1** *Try to unscrew the old downpipe brackets; if they won't move then lever them out of the wall with a hammer and cold chisel.*

**2** *Ease the lowest pipe section away and remove it. Wear a mask and protective gloves when you're handling asbestos materials.*

**3** *Work upwards, removing each section in turn. Once the brackets are off, the downpipe should come apart easily, so don't let any sections fall.*

**4** *Once you've removed the downpipes, take down the guttering as well. Asbestos gutters are not usually screwed down, and should lift out.*

**5** *When you've got the guttering down, remove the brackets. If they are old and rusted in, you may need a hacksaw to cut them off.*

**6** *NEVER break up old asbestos pipe or guttering. Soak it thoroughly to avoid creating dust, and cut it up with a hacksaw.*

moving. Insert the screw-driver blade in the slot of the screw, then give the handle a short sharp blow with a mallet (if it's wooden). This should free the screw so you can turn it. Alternatively, the brackets may be held in place by large galvanised nails cemented into the mortar. These will have to be prised out. If all else fails, cut everything loose with a hacksaw.

The pipe itself comes in a series of standard lengths and you'll probably have to join two or more sections together with a special socket, or cut one down to size, to make up the required run. You should leave an expansion gap of 10mm (3/8in) at the end.

Plastic pipes are held to the wall by a series of small clips. These may come, according to the make, as one unit, or in two parts – a separate back-plate and clip. A clip should be placed at each joint socket, and at the manufacturer's recommended spacings in between – possibly every 2m (6ft 6in). Incidentally, there is no need to go to the trouble of drilling holes in brickwork to take the plugs for the screws that hold the clips in place. The pipes are so light that you will get a fixing by drilling the holes into the mortar.

On a simple structure, such as a garden shed, the gutter outlet may well be fitted directly into the top of the pipe without being sealed, and this makes it easier to locate and to deal with blockages. However, houses have eaves, which means the gutters won't be flush with the wall on which the downpipe is situated. So some form of fitting is needed to make the connection: this is known as an offset or 'swan neck'. You can make one of these yourself from an offset socket, an offset spigot, and a short length of pipe – perhaps an offcut from one of the main lengths – as shown in the diagram overleaf. The joins between the gutter outlet and the offset socket and spigot should be solvent-welded, for these do need to be watertight. The same is true of any section of the system that is not vertical.

Once you've made up the offset you can position it to work out where you can fix the downpipe. And this will also allow you to site the clip that holds the socket which connects the offset to the downpipe itself.

With this clip in place, you can plumb the drop of the pipe and mark the positions of the clips on the wall with chalk, so that they will all be directly underneath each other. Then fix these clips in place, and fit the pipe sections.

If your downpipes discharge into an open gully at the bottom, a curved or angled end, known as a shoe, is fitted. A clip will, of course, be needed here, as at every other joint. The shoe should be pointing away from the house wall, and should be only 50mm (2in) or so higher than the grating, so that splashes will not get onto the wall. Should the connection be direct to the drain, a special adaptor is required.

# INSTALLING THE NEW SYSTEM

**1** *Brush down the fascia and make good any damage to the wood. Fill the holes in the wall where the old pipe brackets were positioned.*

**2** *Paint the fascia. If it's at all rotten you should replace it, as the new guttering is likely to last longer than an untreated wooden fascia.*

**3** *Put up the new guttering brackets and use a taut line and a spirit level to make sure there is a slight fall along the run.*

TIP

**4** *Assemble the guttering and clip it into the support brackets. Pour some water into it to make sure it flows away properly.*

**5** *Attach the outlet to the gutter, using clips to make a watertight seal. Check that the outlet is vertically above the drain or gully below.*

**6** *Measure the length of downpipe you need and cut it using a hacksaw. Remember to allow for an adaptor or a shoe at the bottom.*

**7** *Attach the shoe to the last section of downpipe using solvent-weld cement. Check that the shoe will discharge directly over the gully.*

**8** *Connect the downpipe to the outlet; this may mean inserting a 'swan neck' offset (see page 167) on buildings with overhanging eaves.*

**9** *Attach the brackets to the wall using screws and wallplugs. When the system is complete, test it with water to make sure it doesn't leak.*

# REPLACING A HOPPER

**Most drainage systems operate without trouble year in, year out. But if your system incorporates hopper heads to collect rainwater or upstairs waste water, then these may need your attention from time to time.**

A hopper head is simply a funnel-shaped container with a vertical outlet in its base that is used for collecting water from different sources. Indeed, its original purpose was to receive water draining from two roofs, perhaps at different levels, so that this could be conducted away in one main downpipe. In short, hoppers made for a neater simpler drainage system.

The introduction of two-pipe drainage (see WASTE WATER SYSTEMS) gave hopper heads another, yet very similar, use. With this system, the waste from sinks, baths, basins and showers – anything, in fact, except the waste from a WC, urinal and slop-sink – had to enter the underground drainage system via a trapped yard gully. This didn't present any problems for fittings situated on the ground floor, but dealing with the upstairs waste water was not as straightforward. To get round the need for individual downpipes casting an unsightly web over the wall of the house, plumbers seized on the idea of using a hopper head to collect all the waste water at one point on the outside wall and then to take it via a downpipe to a yard gully.

This arrangement remained in vogue for many years before being superseded by single-stack drainage in the 1940s, although there are hundreds of thousands of homes where the two-pipe drainage system is still functioning perfectly adequately. However, because of the age of these systems and their inherent design drawbacks, particularly concerning the hopper head itself, it's likely that they have begun to cause trouble.

## WHERE HOPPERS ARE USED

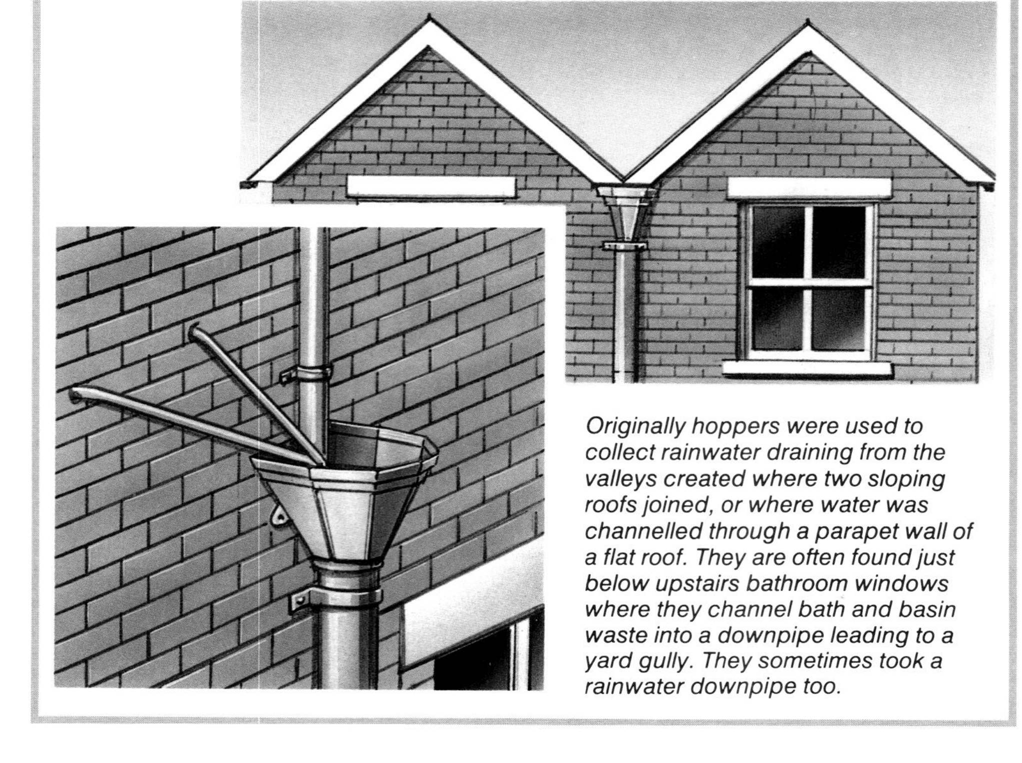

*Originally hoppers were used to collect rainwater draining from the valleys created where two sloping roofs joined, or where water was channelled through a parapet wall of a flat roof. They are often found just below upstairs bathroom windows where they channel bath and basin waste into a downpipe leading to a yard gully. They sometimes took a rainwater downpipe too.*

### Problems with hoppers

The original iron hopper was, and is, a common source of nuisance. It has a rough interior surface that tends to hold back any debris or scum the waste water discharges into it. Inevitably, this dries and decomposes to produce unpleasant smells in the vicinity of the bathroom window. Furthermore, during cold weather, if you leave a bathroom tap dripping overnight it can quickly fill the hopper with ice, so blocking the outlet and possibly causing a flood in the morning when more waste water is discharged. In a similar manner, the open top of a hopper provides a

## FITTING A NEW HOPPER

*1 The hopper head will be fixed to the wall with bolts or screws – often rusted securely in place. Unscrew them if possible or lever them out.*

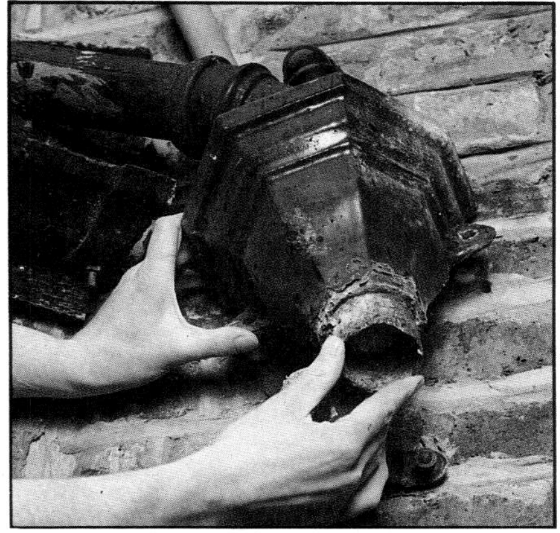

*2 Lift the hopper head clear of the downpipe. Cast iron ones are heavy and there may be sharp rusted edges, so take care and lower it carefully to the ground.*

*3 Use a filling knife or trowel to fill the holes left by the old fixing bolts with a small amount of mortar or some exterior-quality filler.*

*4 Hold the new hopper in place and mark the position of the new fixing holes which go through the back wall. Check that they're level then drill and plug them.*

*5 Choose No. 10 round-headed screws about 38mm (1 1/2in) long. They will need to be rust-proof so use zinc-plated or sherardised ones.*

*6 There will probably be a poor fit between the hopper and downpipe so seal this with some bitumen mastic. The sort applied by a gun is most convenient.*

convenient receptacle for falling leaves, which in turn can cause blockages even in the downpipe itself. Corrosion can also be a problem and metal hoppers should be protected by regular painting. But so often the interior surfaces are ignored, and if this is the case, rust is the inevitable outcome.

All this makes the hopper head seem like an unsavoury fitting, yet many of the drawbacks can be alleviated by regular maintenance. Cleaning the inside with caustic soda and coating the surfaces with paint aren't daunting or time-consuming jobs. And some chicken wire fixed over the top will prevent leaves blocking the outlet.

If, however, the hopper has deteriorated beyond repair, then more drastic action is needed. You may think that this is as good an opportunity as any to convert your existing drainage into a single-stack system (as described on pages 172 to 176) rather than replacing the hopper. Admittedly, this gets round the problems of the hopper, but it's not as simple as it seems. The existing soil pipe, for example, may not be suitable for single stack use and the length of the gradient of the bath and basin wastes may make it impossible to take them to a single stack without realignment. You may even need to reposition the bath or basin. So before you take the plunge remember that a well-designed and satisfactorily functioning two-pipe system is far better than a bad conversion to a single-stack one.

For this reason, often the simplest answer is just to replace the hopper itself. Metal ones are still available to match old metal downpipes, but it's advisable to fit a modern streamlined hopper made of UPVC or similar plastic. This won't need any decoration or protection from corrosion. Its internal surfaces are smooth and far less likely to hold back debris from bath or basin water. And there is less likelihood of frost damage. However, if you choose this option you'll probably have to replace the downpipe as well (see the previous section) even if it's in good repair as it may look unsightly to have a plastic hopper set on an old metal pipe.

A new plastic hopper head will probably be about 280mm (11in) wide, 150mm (6in) deep from front to back, and 280mm (11in) from rim to outlet. Normally, there are two pre-drilled fixing holes just below the rim on the back of the hopper. Ideally, these holes should coincide with a mortar joint when the hopper is being fitted, but often this won't be possible especially if the downpipe isn't being replaced at the same time. In any event, make sure you plug the drill holes and use zinc-plated or sherardised steel screws. Also remember that cast iron hoppers are heavy so be extra careful when taking one down. Make sure you secure your ladders in position and have all the necessary tools to hand.

# REPLACING AN OUTSIDE SOIL STACK

**You can't make new connections into an old cast iron soil pipe. So changing your indoor plumbing system will mean fitting a new soil stack too.**

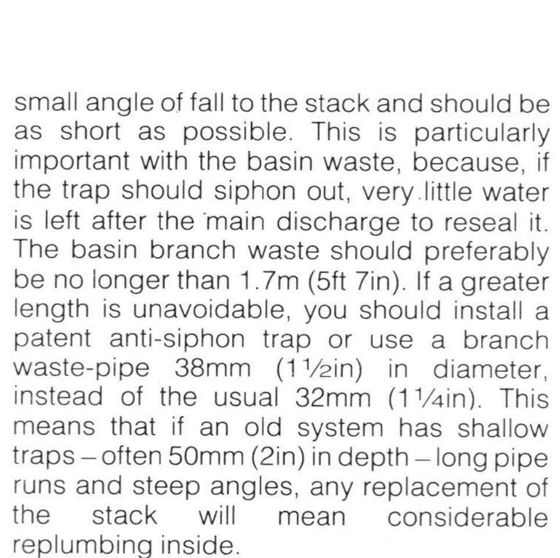

If your house was built before the mid-1950s it will almost certainly have a 'two-pipe' above-ground drainage system made of cast iron. This system was originally devised by Victorian sanitary engineers in a determined effort to keep 'drain air', which was believed by the public health experts of the time to be the cause of virtually all human disease, out of the home. The system made a distinction between 'soil appliances' – WCs – and 'waste appliances' – basins, sinks, baths, etc. Soil was sent down one pipe to the underground drain, and waste was sent down another (although it eventually reached the same drain). Drain smells were, and still are, prevented from spreading inside the house by the use of water traps at the outlet of each appliance.

Modern homes are provided with 'single stack' above-ground drainage systems using PVC or similar plastic waste pipes. In a single stack system no distinction is made between soil and waste appliances. All discharges go into one main stack which, as with the old soil pipe, terminates open-ended above eaves level. To make these systems safe they must be in strict accordance with the regulations. For more explanation of two-pipe and single stack systems see WASTE WATER SYSTEMS.

In most cases it is possible to replace an obsolete two-pipe system with a modern single stack one, but the local council's Building Inspector must be consulted about your plans in advance, and very careful attention should be paid to the design of the new system if it is to be both efficient and safe. In new houses the single stack is often located inside the house, in a boxed service duct, but this isn't a legal requirement and replacement of an existing external soil stack by a single stack in the same position is perfectly acceptable.

## Single stack requirements

In order to prevent water from siphoning out of the traps of baths and basins which have pipe connections to a single stack, deep-seal 75mm (3in) traps must be used. For the same reason, branch waste pipes from baths and basins have to be laid with a very small angle of fall to the stack and should be as short as possible. This is particularly important with the basin waste, because, if the trap should siphon out, very little water is left after the main discharge to reseal it. The basin branch waste should preferably be no longer than 1.7m (5ft 7in). If a greater length is unavoidable, you should install a patent anti-siphon trap or use a branch waste-pipe 38mm (1½in) in diameter, instead of the usual 32mm (1¼in). This means that if an old system has shallow traps – often 50mm (2in) in depth – long pipe runs and steep angles, any replacement of the stack will mean considerable replumbing inside.

The branch soil pipe from the WC suite must be connected to the main soil and waste stack by a swept joint in the direction of the soil flow. To prevent waste outlets from baths, basins or bidets from being fouled or obstructed by discharges of soil from the WC, no connection may be made to the opposite side of the main stack within 200mm (8in) of the centre point of the connection of the soil branch. Special boss sockets are available which allow connections to be made at apparently the same level as the lavatory outlet. In fact, inside the boss the waste is deflected downwards to flow into the stack itself below the level of the soil pipe entry.

The main soil and waste stack, which must have an internal diameter of at least 100mm (4in), must connect to the underground drain with a bend of at least 200mm (8in) radius. In some cases this will mean that, as well as replacing the old soil pipe, it will be necessary to replace the – usually short – length of underground drain between the foot of the soil-pipe and the drain inspection chamber. This job is not too difficult but must be done with great precision to ensure efficient drainage.

Although the single stack is now the most popular system for the drainage of appliances on first floors and above, there is little, if anything, to be gained by converting ground floor drainage to a single stack system. Ground floor WCs may quite conveniently be connected direct to the nearest inspection chamber by means of a branch from the underground drain, and there is no objection to ground floor sinks, baths and basins discharging over a yard gully. These discharges should however enter the gully above the water level but below the level of the gully grid. Slotted grids are available to allow existing gullies to be adapted in this way.

## Assembling the new system

Get an illustrated catalogue of plastic above-ground drainage components from your local builder's merchant, or send away for one. Using this, have a look at the existing

# SOIL AND WASTE PIPE FITTINGS

*The choice of modern plastic soil and waste pipes and fittings is quite bewildering. You will have to make a careful survey of the job to work out the individual components you will need. Try and get hold of a manufacturer's brochure which will show you the range available. Most soil fittings are made of unplasticised polyvinyl chloride (UPVC), but waste pipes may be of polypropylene (PP) and waste fittings of acrylonitrile butadiene styrene (ABS) or polyethylene. There are two systems for joining plastic pipes and fittings, push-fit and solvent welding (as described on pages 38 to 42). Push-fit fittings should be used where particularly hot water passes through the waste system, as they allow for expansion.*

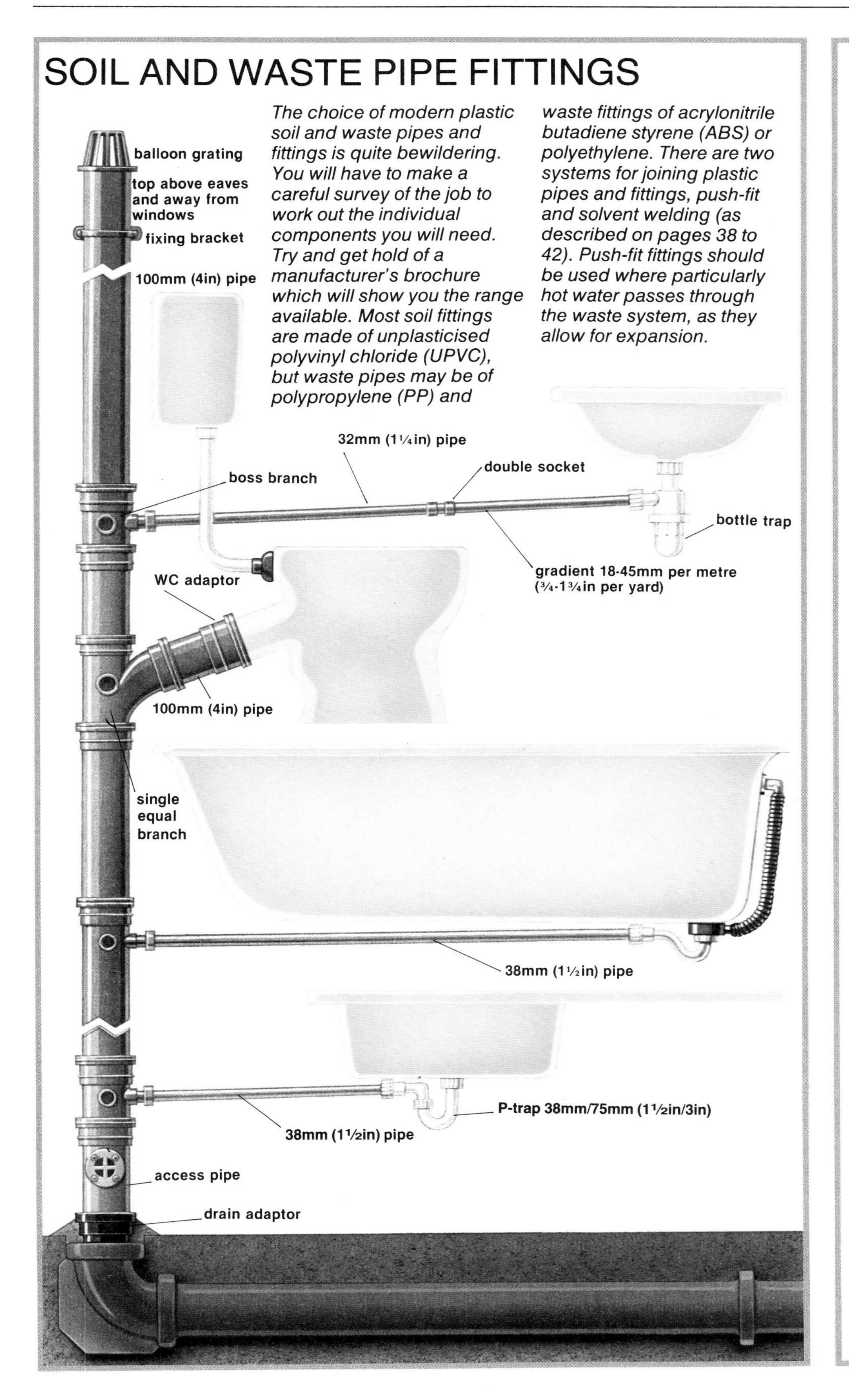


## Ready Reference

### CHECKING REGULATIONS

Before you install a single drainage stack you should consult your local Building Inspector to ensure that your plans are in compliance with the Building Regulations. He may also want to inspect the work after you have finished it. Remember:

- basins, baths, showers, washing machines and dishwashing machine outlets need P-traps. The depth of trap seal, except on baths and showers should always be 75mm (3in). The exception is WC pans which can have integral S-traps (see WASTE WATER SYSTEMS)
- wash basins and bidets need a 32mm (1¼in) diameter trap and branch pipe, if the branch is up to 1.7m (5ft 7in) long. If it is more – up to a maximum of 2.3m (7ft 6in) – use a 38mm (1½in) trap and pipe
- baths, sinks and showers need a 38mm (1½in) diameter trap and branch pipe
- washing machines should have a vertical standpipe (usually about 600mm/24in high) with a 32mm (1¼in) diameter trap, at the bottom of which should be a P- or running P-trap. You need an air gap where the hose enters the stack pipe
- WC branch pipes should be 100mm (4in) in diameter with a maximum length of 6m (20ft) from stack to pan, though a shorter run is preferable
- branch pipe gradients should have an angle of between 1° and 2½° (18-45mm per metre/¾-1¾in per yard)
- ground floor WCs can connect directly into the underground drain as long as the top of the trap is less than 1.5m (5ft) above the point of entry into the main drain
- there should be no connection nearer than 200mm (8in) below the WC branch connection from the opposite side of the stack
- the lowest connection to the stack must be at least 450mm (18in) above the bottom of the bend at the base of the stack
- the bend at the base of the stack where the pipe turns to flow into the underground drain must have a radius of at least 200mm (8in)
- stack pipes must be at least the same diameter as the WC outlet
- the top of the stack pipe, capped with a grille, must be above the eaves and at least 0.9m (35in) above any window which is within 3m (10ft) of the pipe.

## REMOVING THE OLD PIPEWORK

**1** *Start on the old waste pipe; use a club hammer and chisel to loosen the brackets supporting the pipe and lever them out.*

**2** *The pipe should now come free from the hopper head connection. If you can't move it easily, then tap gently downwards with a club hammer.*

**3** *When you've got the waste pipe out of the way, remove any other inflows, including the old bath overflow pipe which is illustrated here.*

TIP

**4** *The top part of the soil stack, with an eaves level vent, needs a lot of care. If you can't lift it free, try and break up the pipe.*

**5** *When you have cracked the old pipe, lift the section clear. It will be quite heavy, so be careful how you lower it to the ground.*

**6** *Move further down the stack and break each joint in turn. Lift each section clear and carry it carefully down to the ground.*

**7** *When you get to the old outlet from the WC pan, lever it gently out through the wall. Try not to dislodge any bricks in the wall.*

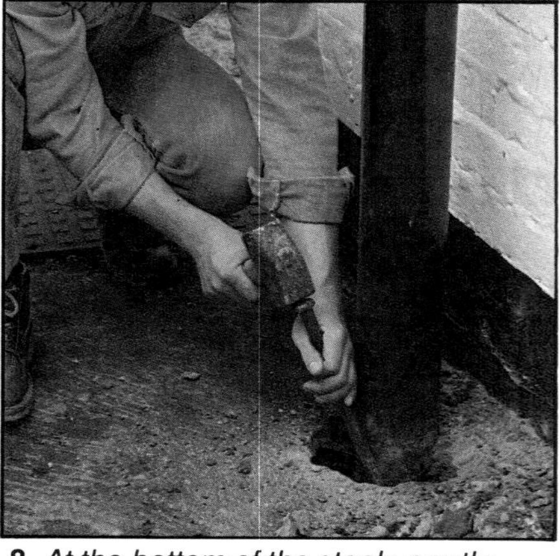

**8** *At the bottom of the stack, gently chip away the concrete round the base of the pipe, until it starts to loosen and come free.*

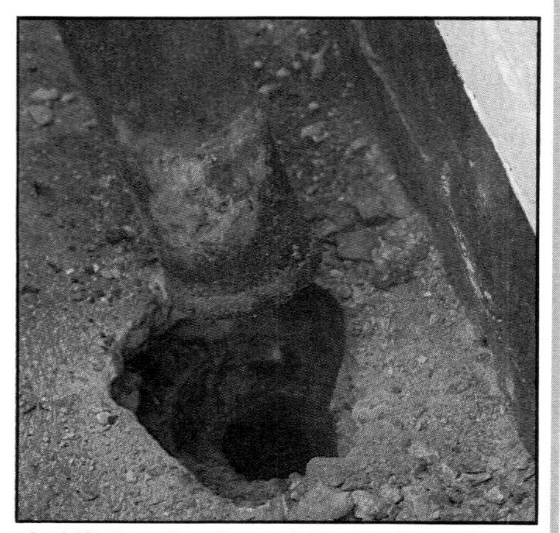

**9** *Lift the pipe free of the drain socket connection. Ensure that no pieces of broken concrete and debris fall into the opening.*

## ASSEMBLING THE STACK

**1** *Carefully clean out the old underground drain connection. It may need replacing if the bend is too tight; check the Regulations.*

**2** *Install new outlet connections so that they emerge flush with the outside wall surface. Don't fix them rigidly in place yet.*

**3** *Using a drain connector and access branch, start to make up the base of the stack. Use push-fit or solvent-weld fittings.*

**4** *Mortar in the drain connector to the underground drain joint, using a quick-dry mortar. Check that the pipe is truly vertical.*

**5** *When the mortar joint is firm, start to extend the stack upwards, using sockets according to the connections you want to make.*

**6** *Support the stack with brackets about every 2m (6ft 6in). These are easily fixed by drilling into the wall and using wall plugs.*

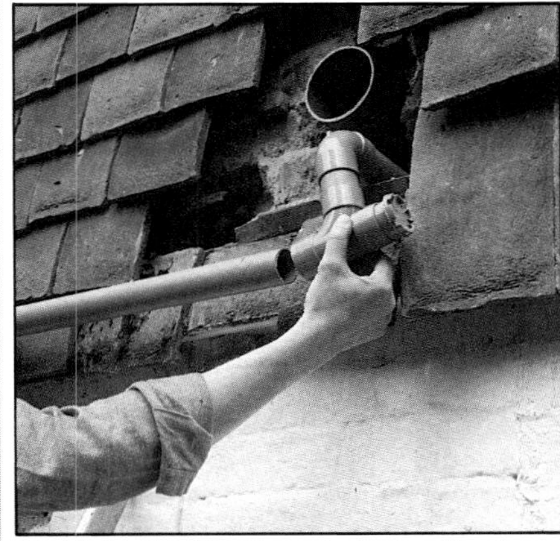

**7** *Make the lowermost connection to the stack using the appropriate plastic-pipe fitting technique. Here an inspection junction is being fitted.*

**8** *Make sure the connections to the stack are firm, and don't finally fix the through-wall connections (see 2) until these are made.*

**9** *In the case of solvent-weld jointing (as used here), further connections should only be made when the previous ones are completely firm.*

## COMPLETING THE STACK

**1** *Attach the swept branch for the WC/soil pipe connection; check that you have fulfilled all the Regulations regarding these connections.*

**2** *Make the soil pipe bend connection to the pipe emerging through the wall. Check that the angle of the soil pipe is correct.*

**3** *Connect the soil pipe to the stack and then continue the stack upwards, installing any other branch connections that are necessary.*

**4** *Fix the remaining connections, still making sure that no movement takes place in those lower down, and that the stack remains vertical.*

**5** *Make up the top section of the stack. Don't forget to fix the balloon grating in place; this is required by the Regulations.*

**6** *Fix the top section of the stack, and attach any necessary support brackets to the wall. Again, check that the stack remains vertical.*

drainage system and work out what components you will need. You must stick to the products of one manufacturer throughout. When you have a clear idea of the new system you want to install, draw out some plans and go to see the local Building Inspector and get his approval for your proposals (and his advice, if you need it).

Dismantling the old pipe stacks needs a lot of care. If you have to work at any great height you should seriously consider hiring a scaffold tower. Try and take the old stacks apart by levering out the fixing brackets and pulling out each section of pipe, starting from the top. If this is difficult you'll have to break up the pipe with a club hammer, but be careful of splinters. Then either lower each piece to the ground with a length of rope or carry it down.

When you've taken out all the old pipework clean and tidy up carefully the underground drain connection. Start the new installation by connecting the new stack to the underground drain (unless the bend needs replacing). The drain connector should be fixed in place with quick-setting mortar, and should be supported to make sure that it remains firmly vertical during setting. When this connection is in place you can continue upwards using brackets at roughly 1m (39in) intervals to support the stack against the wall. Depending on the pipe system you are using, the joints will be either push-fit or solvent-welded (as described on pages 38 to 42). You may have to fit new deep-seal traps to basins and sinks, and run plastic pipe from the trap outlets to the bosses provided in the boss-branch of the main stack.

The job is easier if you can use the existing cast-iron branch soil pipe from the WC. You can do this if the stack is made of UPVC by slipping a neoprene sealing ring over the spigot of the iron pipe. Insert the spigot, with the ring round it, into the UPVC socket, then gently heat the socket with a blow torch until it shrinks round the spigot with its neoprene ring seal. If you have to replace the soil pipe it may even mean a new WC pan if the connection is mortared in.

When you get to the top of the stack you must finish it off with a balloon grating to stop debris, in particular birds' nests, from falling in. This is in fact a requirement of the Regulations. Put the balloon onto the last section of the stack before you fix it in place.

When you have finished erecting the whole system check carefully for leaks. You may then receive a visit from the Building Inspector to make sure that all is in order. If there are any problems with the new system he will be able to suggest the causes and what you should do about them.

# GULLIES AND SOAKAWAYS

**Gullies and soakaways are an integral part of the household drainage system, getting rid of waste water and rainwater quickly and efficiently. But things can go wrong, and prompt action is needed when they do.**

The yard gully, over which the waste pipes from household sinks, baths and wash basins discharge, is a legacy of the Victorian conviction that 'drain air' was a primary cause of virtually all the ills to which the flesh is heir. It was provided to permit household waste to flow into the underground drainage system without the least risk of the supposedly noxious gases from the drain entering the house. This was achieved by discharging household wastes (other than those from 'soil fittings' such as WCs) in the open air over the gully grid. The gully had a trapped outlet, usually with a 50mm (2in) water seal, that was then connected to the underground drain. Drain gases couldn't pass that water seal and, even if they did, they would disperse inoffensively in the open air, not within the home. However, even this safeguard failed to satisfy all Victorian hygienists. The now-obsolete byelaws of some local authorities required that sink and other wastes must discharge, not directly over the gully, but into a glazed half-channel at a point at least 450mm (18in) away from it. The wastes then flowed down this half-channel into the gully itself. It is still possible to see this arrangement in some older properties, particularly in rural areas.

## Stoneware gullies

Gullies provided up to World War II and for a decade or so afterwards (that is to say, the overwhelming majority of gullies still in use in this country) were usually made in one piece in glazed stoneware. The inlet was square in plan and was covered with a metal grid to prevent leaves and other debris washing into the drain to produce a blockage. The gully was set onto a 150mm (6in) thick concrete base and its spigot outlet was connected to the socket of a 100mm (4in) stoneware branch drain with a neat cement joint or, more likely perhaps, a joint made with a mix of two parts cement to one of sand. Very frequently, gullies were installed below the level of the adjacent yard surface in a purpose-made pit with cement-rendered sides, to drain surface water away from the yard. The yard surface might well be sloped to improve drainage into the gully.

This kind of gully, installed as described, often produced more problems than it solved. In this it resembled the rainwater hopper-head – another device intended to keep 'drain air' out of the home. For a start, it failed to meet what nowadays would be regarded as the very first requirement of any sanitary appliance: it was not self-cleansing. The self-cleansing flow of the waste water from a sink or bath was broken by discharging it over the gully grid, from which it descended into the water in the trap below in a gentle rain. Debris, if it was not retained by the grid, fell into the trap and stayed there, decomposing as water gently overflowed from the gully outlet above it into the drain. Much debris was, of course, retained by the grid and the scrubbing and cleansing of these grids was a revoltingly unpleasant regular household chore. Householders with a solid fuel open fire or boiler often solved the problem by extracting the grid with a poker and consigning it to the cleansing effect of the flames for half an hour or so. This, of course, could only be done with the old-fashioned metal grids, not the more modern plastic ones.

Then again, it needed only half a dozen fallen autumn leaves or a wind-blown paper bag to block the gully grid and so to produce a flooded yard. This was bad enough in bungalows or two-storey domestic premises, but if the gully took waste pipes from multi-storey buildings it was quite possible for people to continue to use sinks and basins on upper floors, totally oblivious of the havoc that they were creating at ground or basement level.

A flooded yard gully is one of the ways in which a blocked drain may manifest itself. But before getting out the drain rods and raising the drain manhole covers, it is always wise to raise the grid and probe into the flooding gully itself. The chances are that the water will instantly flow away. Sometimes, of course, the water will not flow away and raising the manhole covers may reveal no other evidence of drain blockage. In these circumstances the obstruction must be between the yard gully and the drain inspection chamber into which the branch drain from the gully discharges, and is most probably in the gully trap itself. It can usually be cleared quite quickly and easily by plunging, preferably with a purpose-made drain plunger (a 100mm/4in diameter rubber disc screwed onto the end of a drain clearing rod) but an old-fashioned long-handled domestic mop, or even a bundle or rags tied *securely* to the end of a broom handle, can be used in an emergency. Lower the disc or mop head into the gully and plunge it up and down sharply three or four times. If this doesn't do the trick, try passing a piece of flexible wire (expanding spring curtain wire, for instance) round the trap of the gully, or else rod back towards the gully from the drain inspection

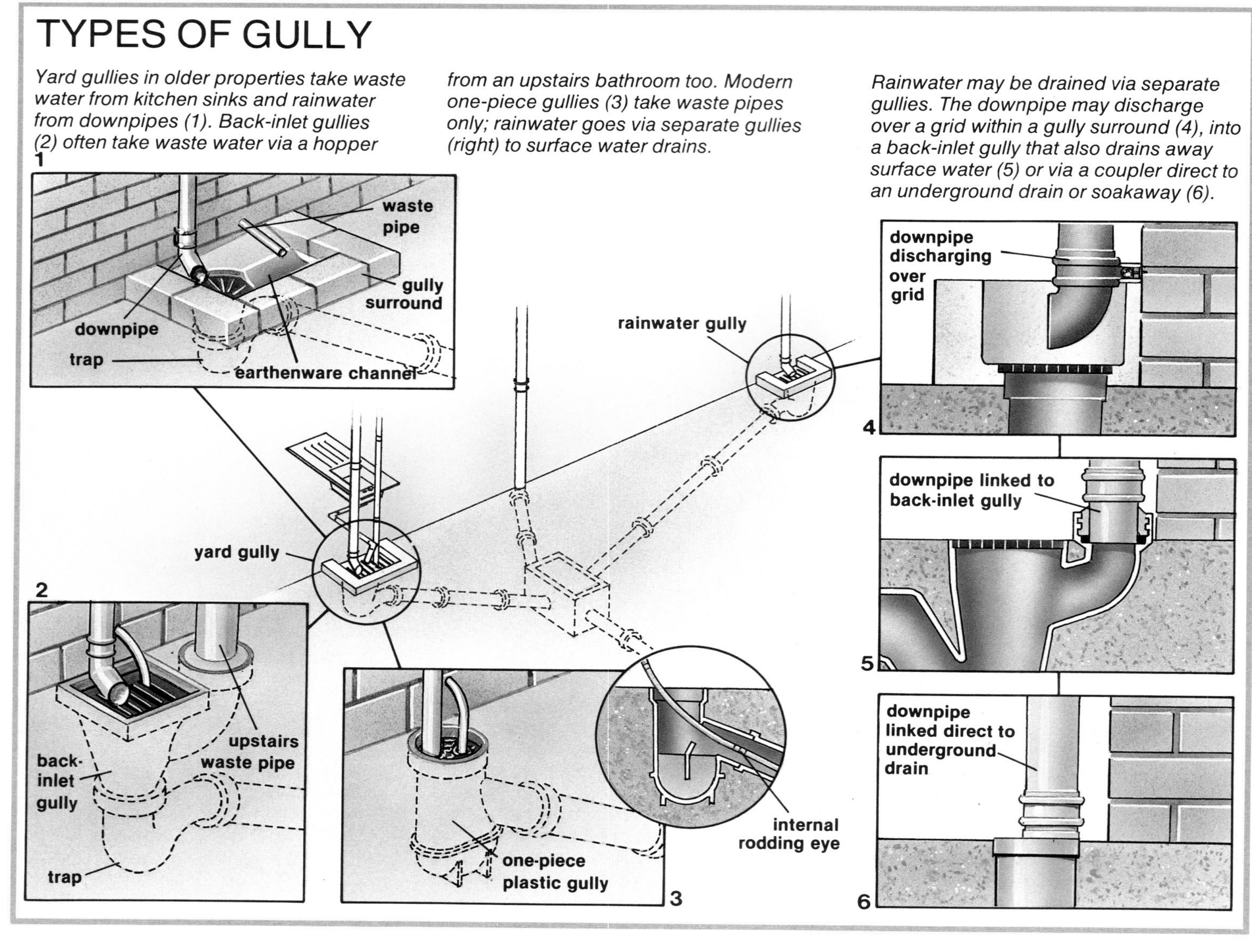


## TYPES OF GULLY

*Yard gullies in older properties take waste water from kitchen sinks and rainwater from downpipes (1). Back-inlet gullies (2) often take waste water via a hopper from an upstairs bathroom too. Modern one-piece gullies (3) take waste pipes only; rainwater goes via separate gullies (right) to surface water drains.*

*Rainwater may be drained via separate gullies. The downpipe may discharge over a grid within a gully surround (4), into a back-inlet gully that also drains away surface water (5) or via a coupler direct to an underground drain or soakaway (6).*

chamber into which its branch drain discharges, using a set of drain-cleaning rods – see pages 72 to 75.

### Grid problems

Most of the troubles to which old-fashioned gullies are prone are caused by the grid which dissipates the force of waste discharges from sinks, baths and wash basins and thus prevents the gully from being self-cleansing. Debris trapped by the grid is a source of drain smells, and an obstructed grid is a common cause of yard flooding, as already described.

The remedy was an obvious one – to discharge the kitchen and bathroom wastes into the gully *above* water level but *below* the grid. To this end, back-inlet and side-inlet gullies were manufactured – often in two pieces – to be connected directly to the outlets of the branch waste pipes. They yielded an immediate benefit. The gully was thoroughly scoured out, and any silt and other debris that it contained was washed into the drain, every time a bath or sink was emptied into it. The gully grid no longer collected its evil smelling fragments; and anything obstructing the gully grid could no longer be the cause of a flood.

Back-inlet and side-inlet gullies were naturally more expensive than the older type. Furthermore, rather longer waste pipes were needed to connect to them and connection was a longer – and therefore slightly more expensive – job than simply discharging the waste over the grid in the traditional manner. Consequently, despite the fact that the advantages of the improved gullies were well-known to hygienists and sanitary engineers, they remained for many years the exception rather than the rule in the provision of domestic drainage systems.

### Plastic gullies

The revolution, which produced the present generation of yard gullies and resulted in thousands of older gullies being converted to under-grid discharge, came with the widespread development of plastics in underground drainage, and (at about the same time) with the Building Regulations of the early 1960s which insisted upon under-grid discharge in all new drainage work.

A typical modern plastic gully assembly comprises three components – the gully inlet with two or more socket inlets for waste and rainwater pipes, the trap itself, and the outlet pipe. One-piece gullies are also available. Some manufacturers provide an access cap on the outlet pipe which eliminates the need for an inspection chamber at the point where the branch drain from the gully joins the main drain. Any blockage that occurs in this branch can be cleared by removing the cap and

## REMOVING THE OLD GULLY

*1 Use a club hammer and cold chisel to break away the old gully surround. Don't worry at this stage about debris falling into the old gully trap.*

*2 Chop away surrounding concrete to expose the hopper, and then start to excavate carefully until you have exposed the nearby drain run.*

*3 Once you have exposed the joint between trap and drain, cut through it cleanly behind the socket with an angle grinder and cutting disc.*

*4 Use a club hammer to break up the trap outlet, taking care not to damage the cut drain pipe. Then lift out the old gully in one piece.*

inserting drain rods through the opening.

The three components are usually solvent-welded into one unit on the site, care being taken to ensure that the gully inlet is positioned so as best to accept the waste pipes to be connected to it and that the gully trap is positioned with its outlet pointing towards the main drain. To make solvent-weld joints, the surface of the spigot and the inside of the socket are roughened with medium-grade abrasive paper. Then an even coat of solvent cement is applied to the spigot and the interior of the socket, using a wooden spatula to stroke the cement along (rather than round) the surfaces to be joined together.

To assemble the joint the spigot is pushed into the socket with a slight twist, and is held in position for a few seconds. The joint can be handled within minutes, but the gully should not be used for at least 24 hours.

Ring-seal 'push-fit' joints may be used instead of solvent-welded ones to link the gully components. To make a joint of this kind, first clean the recess inside the socket and insert the sealing ring. You should then smear a small amount of petroleum jelly round the ring to lubricate it, and push the spigot firmly past the joint ring into the socket (or thrust the socket over the spigot if this is more convenient). Finally, you have to withdraw the spigot by 10mm (3⁄8in) to allow for expansion.

### Gully repairs

An existing one-piece stoneware yard gully can be converted to under-grid discharge by discarding the existing metal grid and replacing it with a modern plastic one, provided with a slot through which the waste pipes can pass. All that is then necessary to convert the gully into a modern self-cleansing one is to lengthen the waste pipes so that they pass through this slot to terminate

## Ready Reference

### CLEARING BLOCKAGES

If a gully overflows, the likeliest site for a blockage is in the gully trap itself. To clean it:

- lift off the grating or cover
- scoop out solid debris with a gloved hand or an old tin
- mop out all the water
- scrub the gully and trap with hot water and soda
- flush it through with clean water from a garden hose.

If the blockage is between the gully and the next inspection chamber, rod the branch drain from the chamber to clear it – see CLEARING BLOCKAGES.

### REPLACING A GULLY CHANNEL

The earthenware half-channel in an old gully may cause damp if it is cracked or the rendering in which it is set has become porous. To replace it:

- cover the gully grating with cardboard to catch debris
- break out the old channel, rendering and gully surround – usually bricks laid on edge
- buy a straight half-section of glazed earthenware pipe, lay it on a bed of sand and cut it carefully to the length required with a cold chisel and club hammer

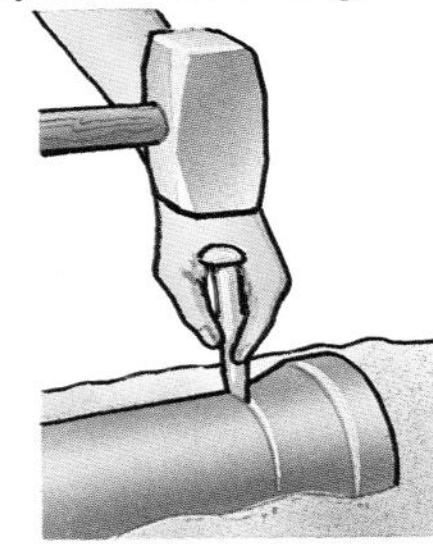

- bed the channel in mortar at a slight slope towards the gully
- build up the gully surround with new bricks, mortared into place
- slope mortar upwards from the half-channel to the gully surround and smooth it off.

### TIP: COVER GULLIES

Provided that all the pipes entering a gully discharge below the gully grating, you can help to keep debris out of the trap by making a simple cover to fit over the grating and within the gully surround itself (so wind cannot lift it and blow it away). The simplest cover is a piece of exterior-grade plywood cut to the size required, with cut-outs to match the pipes passing through it.

## INSTALLING THE NEW GULLY

**1** *Use rapid-hardening cement to bed a PVC-to-clay adaptor on the cut end of the drain run. Hold the joint for a few minutes to ensure a sound bond.*

**2** *Shovel a layer of almost-dry concrete mix into the hole, bed the gully trap in it and test the fit of the trap outlet to the adaptor.*

**3** *Push the trap outlet firmly into the adaptor and check that the concrete bed supports the trap. Then hold the hopper in place to check its level.*

**4** *If the hopper level is too low, you will have to insert a short length of pipe and another coupler. Lubricate the sealing rings with petroleum jelly.*

**5** *Cut the extra pipe to length with a hacksaw, push it into place in the top of the trap and then add the coupler immediately above it.*

**6** *Now you can position the gully hopper and press its outlet down firmly into the coupler. Make sure you align the hopper head with the wall.*

**7** *With the hopper in place, use a spirit level to check that it is sitting flush with (or even fractionally below) the surrounding surface.*

**8** *Back-fill round the gully with a fairly dry coarse concrete mix, treading it down well to ensure that all voids are filled. Fill to just below the surface level.*

**9** *Finish off the surface round the gully with fine concrete, and check that the gully trap is clear of debris. Finally, add the gully grid.*

## CREATING A SOAKAWAY

*A soakaway is used to drain rainwater where no main surface water drain is provided. It's just a pit dug at least 1.2m (4ft) deep, filled with loosely-packed bricks and rubble and covered with heavy-duty polythene to prevent soil washing in and silting it up. The underground pipe should reach to its centre.*

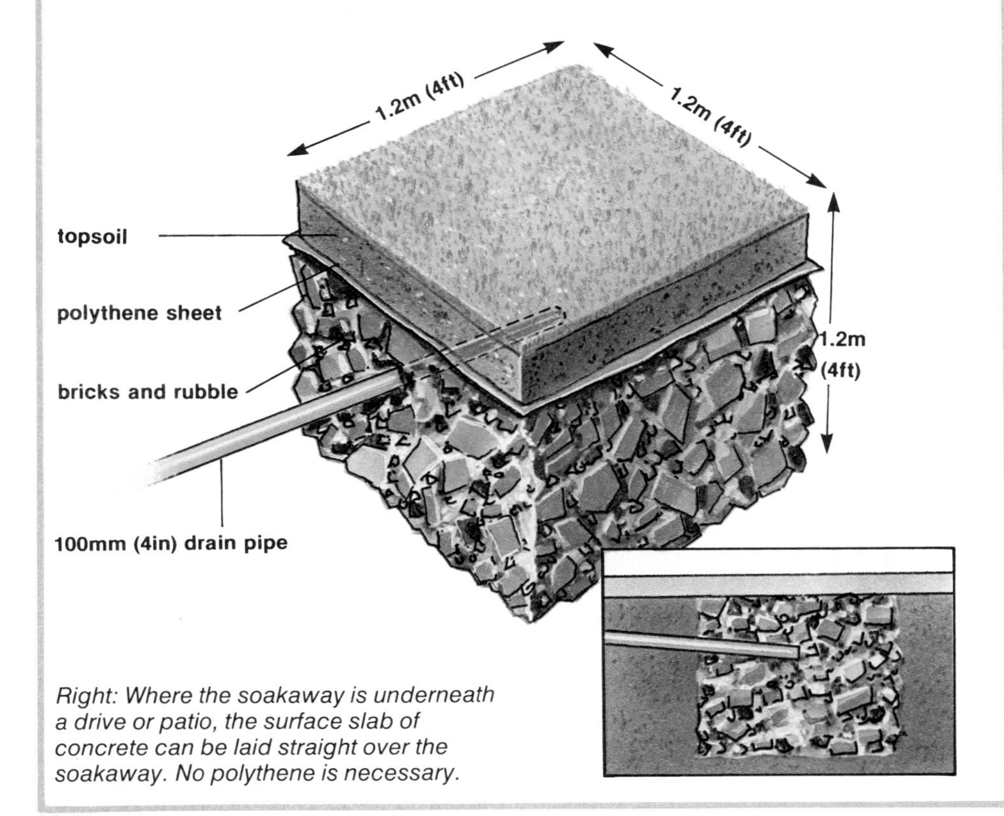


*Right: Where the soakaway is underneath a drive or patio, the surface slab of concrete can be laid straight over the soakaway. No polythene is necessary.*

below the grid but above water level.

Stoneware gullies, once installed, are virtually impervious to damage but the same cannot be said about the cement-rendered gully surround. The cement rendering is very liable to crack, chip or flake off, leaving cracks into which potentially smelly waste water can seep. Defects of this kind can be repaired using a pre-packed sand and cement rendering mix. It is wise to add a PVA bonding agent to the mix to ensure good adhesion of the new mortar to existing surfaces.

### Replacing a gully

Occasionally it may be necessary (or at least desirable) to replace an existing glazed stoneware gully with a modern plastic one. As with so many other plumbing and drainage operations the most difficult part is likely to be the removal of the old fitting.

You will, of course, first have to excavate the surrounding surface to expose the old gully and its connection to the stoneware branch drain. Using a cold chisel and a club hammer, deliberately break the old gully so as to leave only the jagged end of its spigot outlet protruding from the drain socket. Remove the main part of the gully. Now attempt to remove the spigot and its jointing material from the drain socket *without* damaging the socket. Proceed carefully and with patience, using the cold chisel and a hammer. Keep the blade of the chisel pointing inwards towards the centre of the socket and try to break the spigot right down to the shoulder of the socket at one point. Having done this, the rest of the socket will probably come away fairly easily. Alternatively, cut through the drain pipe just beyond the socket using a cutting disc and an angle grinder.

Manufacturers of UPVC drainage systems provide various means of connecting plastic gully outlets (or other UPVC drainage components) to existing stoneware drains. Typically, a 'caulking bush' component is provided which is either solvent-welded or push-fit-jointed to the gully outlet. The other end of the caulking bush is then connected to the socket of the stoneware drain with a gasket (to centre the bush and to prevent mortar entering the drain) and the joint is completed with mortar.

### Rainwater drainage

Yard gullies, as well as taking ground floor and (in older properties) upper floor wastes, may also take at least some rainwater from the roof and from the yard surface. Nowadays though, local authorities and water authorities usually require that rain water must be excluded from the main sewerage system and taken either to a separate surface water drain (where one is provided) or else to a soakaway. Surface water drains usually discharge their contents untreated into a ditch or stream. It is therefore vitally important, where a dual system of sewers is provided, to ensure that domestic waste cannot flow into the surface water drain.

Where there is such a system, trapped yard gullies should be used to collect the rainwater from roofs and yard surfaces. The trap serves a useful purpose in preventing the surface water drainage system from becoming an underground highway for rats and other vermin.

### Building a soakaway

The alternative of a soakaway works best where the subsoil is light and the subsoil water level low. Typically it consists of a pit, dug up to 10m (11yds) from the walls of the house, some 1.2m (4ft) deep and perhaps 1.2m (4ft) square in plan. This is filled to within about 300mm (12in) of the surface with brick and other builders' rubble. In order to reduce the risk of the soakaway silting up, a sheet of heavy-duty polythene should then be laid over this rubble, before the soil is filled in and the surface made good. The pit can be capped with a 100mm (4in) concrete slab if desired. Rainwater pipes may be taken *untrapped* to a soakaway of this kind, though there is some advantage in providing a 'rainwater shoe with access plate' at the bottom of the rainwater downpipe to permit rodding if a blockage occurs. Pipes should enter the soakaway near the top of the rubble layer, and should reach approximately to the centre of the pit.

There are nowadays precast concrete ring soakaways on the market; these consist of concrete rings that are laid to the required depth and are perforated to permit soakage of water into the surrounding subsoil. These are provided with a concrete cover or with a manhole cover set into a frame, for access purposes.

It must be stressed that a soakaway should be used *only* for the disposal of rain and surface water; it should never be used for the waste from a sink, a bath, a washing machine or a dishwasher, and such use is contrary to the requirements of the Building Regulations.

# DRAINING PATIOS & GARDENS

**Poor drainage can ruin your enjoyment of your garden. Remedying this state of affairs is relatively straightforward, and the results will be well worth the effort involved.**

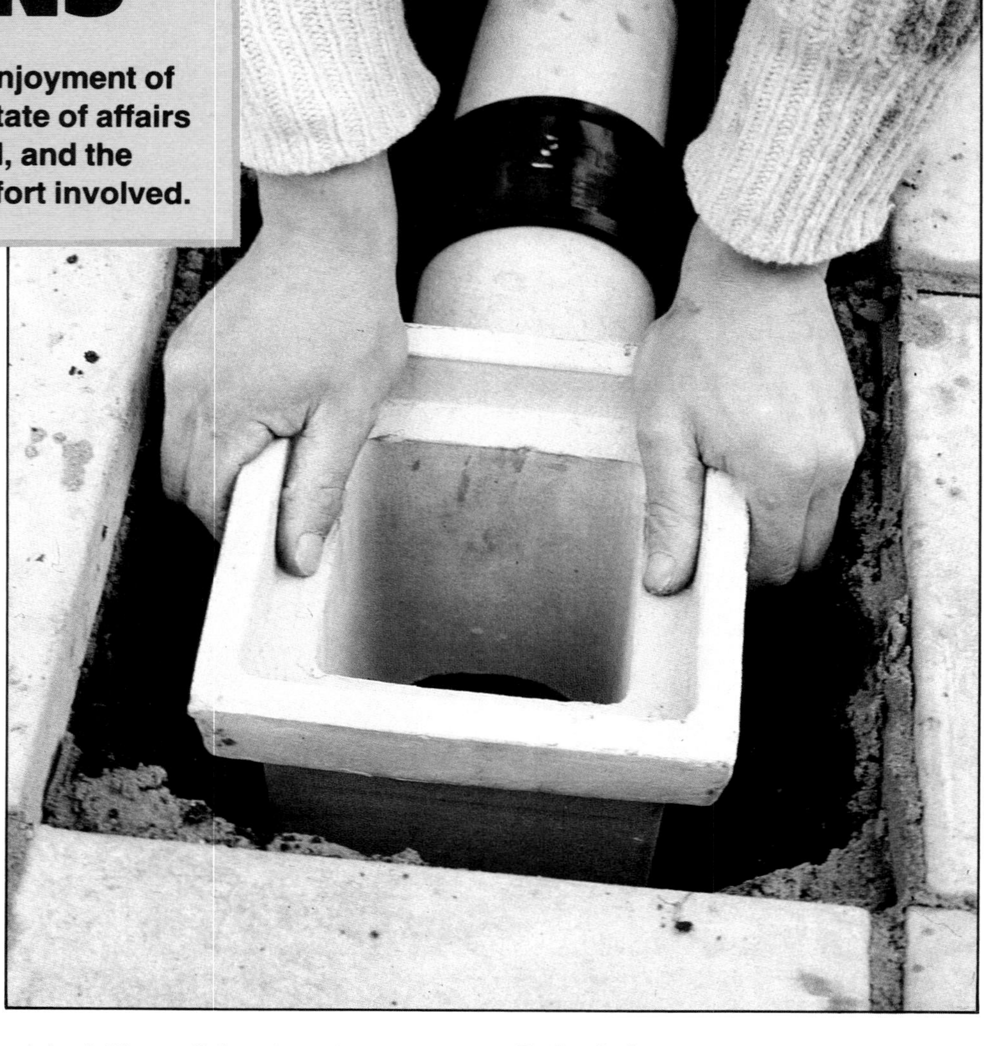

You may be a keen gardener, growing a stunning array of plants and flowers each year, or you might simply enjoy sitting out of doors for meals and to relax. Whatever your pleasure, it is likely to be ruined if the drainage in your garden or on your patio is insufficient – a continually soggy lawn or patio covered in puddles will make life a misery. The answer is to provide adequate drainage for all parts of your garden.

## How do the problems arise?

Unless your home is poorly sited or your garden has an exceptionally heavy clay soil, the chances are that the garden's soil will be able to cope perfectly adequately with the amount of water that falls as rain or snow throughout the year. Of course, you may occasionally get heavy storms that will cause standing pools on lawns, flower beds and vegetable plots, but this is nothing to worry about provided they all clear within a few hours. If the water can drain immediately into the subsoil the chances are that it'll disappear quite quickly.

However, where drainage is denied – by a patio, say, that incorporates no channelling or slope for the water to drain away – then there's likely to be a problem. The water will have nowhere to go and will disappear only gradually as it evaporates.

Flooding in the garden is unlikely to be caused merely by intense rainfall. More likely the cause will be the overflow of streams or rivers carrying away surface water from higher land, or the inability of the local storm drains to cope with a bout of particularly intense rainfall running off roofs, streets and pavements.

## Dealing with small paved areas

A paved footpath in your garden is unlikely to create serious problems. The paved area involved is quite small compared to the length of the sides of the path along which rain can flow freely. The worst that can happen in a period of intense rainfall is the temporary flooding of the flower beds or grass on either side.

Most driveways slope from the garage or house towards the road, and the problems that are likely to arise from heavy rain are minimal. Water will flow down the drive and via the road gutter into a roadside gully and the local storm drain.

You may find you have problems if your drive slopes upwards from the garage to the road and in this case you may have to take action to ensure that surface water from the road can't use it as a route into your home. One solution is to install a low ramp just before the point at which the drive connects to the pavement crossing. Whether or not any other measures will be necessary will depend on the length and slope of the drive and whether or not a yard gully already exists into which run-off from the drive can flow. If there's a gully at the lowest point, then setting a channel across the entrance to the garage or carport so that surface water will run into the gully will prevent any flooding. For further information on installing a new gully see the previous section.

## Patio drainage

If you're intending to lay a patio in your garden then you'll certainly have to have some kind of drainage for it. Patios are often surrounded by walls to provide privacy and a wind break, and after heavy rain a patio without a drainage system will become a paddling pool for a few days. Even where the patio is bordered directly by flower beds or shrubberies, the substantial paved area from which the rain water must flow will mean that these are regularly flooded or waterlogged.

When you're creating a patio, the simplest way of providing some sort of drainage is to ensure that its surface slopes imperceptibly to a shallow channel along one side. You'll have to make sure that the channel has a slight fall to a gully provided at one end so that the water can be disposed of.

A conventional glazed stoneware gully can be used, but you may find it easiest to fit

## LAYING LAND DRAINS

**1** *Dig a trench about 750mm (2ft 6in) deep away from the area you want to drain. Make sure there is a slight fall on the run. Then line the base with shingle.*

**2** *Next set the drain in the trench. If you're using perforated pipes the holes should face downwards so silt can't enter and block the run.*

**3** *At the start of the drain run, block up the exposed pipe end, for example, with a piece of slate, in order to prevent soil getting in.*

**4** *Butt join the lengths of pipe together and prevent soil entering by covering the join with slate. You can then backfill the trench with soil.*

a one-piece bottle gully made of UPVC. This has a 'Q' outlet (halfway between the almost horizontal P outlet and the vertical S outlet) and so is particularly convenient for connection to a downward-sloping pipe run leading to a soakaway. The gully is also fitted with a polypropylene grating and baffle which can be conveniently removed to give access to the drain for rodding and the removal of washed-through leaves and other debris that could otherwise cause a blockage.

You'll have to set the gully on a 100mm (4in) thick concrete base for stability, and it's best to fix it with its inlet about 25mm (1in) below the level of the outlet of the drainage channel to ensure a smooth flow for the water.

It's important to realise that your local authority won't permit a gully draining a patio or any other paved area to be connected to an ordinary household drain. And even if a separate surface water drain is provided, the advantages of connecting the gully to this will probably be outweighed by the prohibitive cost and extra work. The problem of what to do with the water can be solved by discharging it by means of a short length of UPVC drain pipe into a garden soakaway.

### Building a soakaway

Your soakaway should consist of a pit 1.2m (4ft) square and about 1.5m (5ft) deep. Fill it to within 300mm (1ft) of the surface with hardcore; before reinstating the topsoil lay a sheet of heavy-duty polythene over the rubble. This will lengthen the life of the soakaway by reducing the amount of silt that can be washed into it and so preventing it from clogging up.

Soakaways are most effective where the subsoil is light and crumbly. However, there is a chance that when digging one you could

## Ready Reference

### TEST NATURAL DRAINAGE

It's wise to test your garden's drainage before undertaking any work. You should:

- dig a hole about 600mm (2ft) deep
- fill it with water or wait for heavy rain.

If you have good drainage the hole will empty completely within 24 hours, but with poor drainage the water will still be there after 48 hours or more.

### NATURAL DRAINAGE IMPROVEMENTS

Although your garden may have poor drainage there are a number of simple remedies you can make which do away with the necessity of laying special land drainage. You can:

- dig an impervious clay soil deeply to aerate it
- mix in organic matter such as peat or compost to make its texture more porous
- improve its texture by adding inorganic material such as sand
- introduce lime into a clay soil in order to break it up
- use a tining fork to make deep holes which should be then filled with fine gravel.

### TIP: PERFORATED PIPES

When laying perforated pipes in a trench make sure the perforated side is laid on the bottom of the trench. That way water will seep up into the pipes, so preventing silt from getting into them and reducing their water-carrying capacity.

### A LINED SOAKAWAY

An alternative to a hardcore-filled soakaway is a lined one. You should:

- dig the soakaway
- line it with dry brickwork, dry stone walling or perforated concrete liners
- top it with a 150mm (6in) thick concrete cover fitted 250mm (10in) below the top soil surface, so that grass and plants will have enough soil in which to grow.

A lined soakaway will have a greater capacity for water and will seldom need cleaning out.

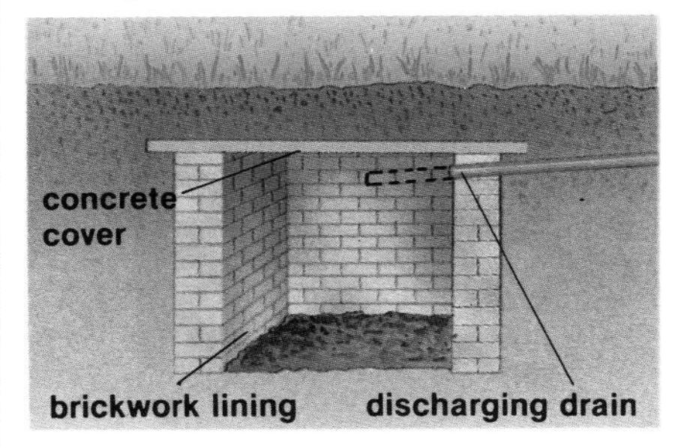

hit a layer of impervious clay at a depth of 600 to 900mm (2 to 3ft); in this case there's little point in digging any further. You should change your tactics and dig an extended soakaway – making up in length what it lacks in depth. Dig out a trench say 5 to 7m (15 to 20ft) long, 750mm (2ft 6in) deep and about 450mm (18in) wide across your lawn from the outlet of the gully. Lay a 150mm (6in) thick layer of pebbles or hardcore in the bottom of the trench and, after checking that it's level, lay land drain pipes along the trench.

Traditional unglazed agricultural drain pipes butt-jointed together will be perfectly adequate, but you'll probably find that UPVC drain pipes specially perforated for land drainage will be easier to lay.

Lay more pebbles and clinker in the trench so that you cover the pipes by at least 150mm (6in). Again, before filling in the last 150mm (6in) of the trench and reinstating the turf it's a good idea to lay a sheet of polythene over the clinker or pebbles in the trench to prevent silting.

### Draining the garden

Land drainage, consisting of a series of pipes in trenches, can be used to prevent the continual waterlogging of a garden. This is often the result of subsoil water flowing from higher levels of land through the garden to a natural outlet. The remedy in this case is to intercept the water and divert it along a particular path. Dig a trench along the wettest part of the garden and a similar one connecting to it at right angles and leading down to an outlet at the front of the property. Lay the drains as before and make sure that those running across the property fall very slightly towards those laid down at the side. It's also a good idea to provide an inspection chamber at the point where the pipe run changes direction. This need not be watertight and can be just a simple square brick chamber covered by a concrete slab.

If your garden is consistently waterlogged and it's not just a question of subsoil water flowing through it, then you'll probably have to lay a different system of drainage. There are several to choose from. A natural system has the pipes following the contours of your garden and, like a grid system, takes the water to a main drain at one side of the property in much the same way as described above. A fan system will also direct the water to an outlet, while a herring-bone system consists of a main drain with a number of branch drains laid parallel with each other. With a herring-bone system the drains should be laid in at a gradient of no more than 1:250; otherwise there would be too little time for the water to soak in to the pipes. Once you've laid the pipes it's wise to protect their butt joints with a couple of pieces of slate to prevent soil entering them.

## BUILDING A SOAKAWAY

**1** *Dig a pit 1.2m (4ft) square and about 1.5m (5ft) deep. If you hit an impervious layer of clay extend the length of the soakaway to make up for the lack of depth.*

**2** *Fill the bottom of the soakaway with a layer of hardcore. This will help to disperse the water quickly and so make the soakaway that much more efficient.*

**3** *Extend the drainage pipe run to the middle of the soakaway, resting it on the hardcore. The water will then reach the optimum area of drainage of the soakaway.*

**4** *Next, cover the drainage pipe and fill the rest of the soakaway to within 300mm (1ft) of the top with hardcore. Gently tamp it down to prevent later settling.*

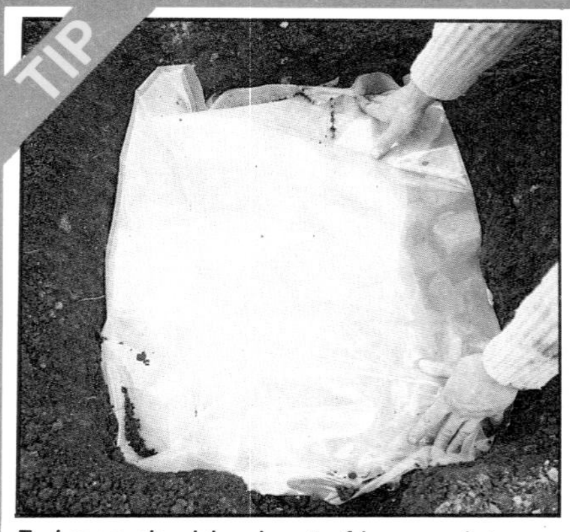


**5** *Lay a double sheet of heavy duty polythene over the hardcore. This will lengthen the life of the soakaway by stopping soil being washed into it.*

**6** *Finally, reinstate the topsoil. Be careful if you dig over the ground in the future that you don't pierce the polythene sheet with a spade or fork.*

# INSTALLING PATIO DRAINAGE

*1 To stop your patio from getting waterlogged install a gully and drainage system running into a soakaway. First lift the slabs where the water collects.*

*2 Dig a hole deep enough to accommodate a gully. Then excavate a trench directly to the site of your soakaway (see opposite).*

*3 Make the hole for the gully deep enough to allow you to lay a 100mm (4in) concrete base on which it is set. This will give the gully a stable foundation.*

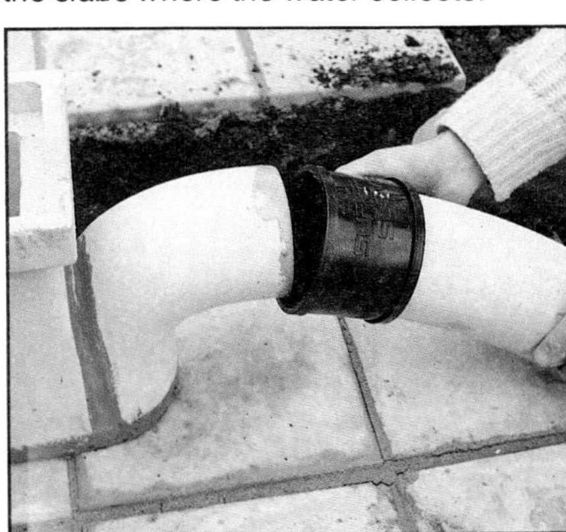

*4 Use a one-piece UPVC gully fitted with a Q outlet. Alternatively, you can install a conventional stoneware gully fitted with a suitable adaptor.*

*5 Set the gully and outlet on the concrete base. Make sure the gully inlet is fixed about 25mm (1in) below the surface of the patio.*

*6 Secure the gully in position by packing round it with hardcore. Check several times as you do this that it remains completely level.*

*7 Fix a short length of pipe to the outlet and then fit an elbow to this pipe to reduce the 45° slope of the system, otherwise you'll have to dig much deeper.*

*8 After running the drainage pipes to the soakaway you can start backfilling. Make sure you tamp this down firmly to prevent settlement of the slabs.*

*9 Finally, replace the slabs and set a mortar fillet round the gully. Allow for the thickness of the grid, which should lay just below the patio surface.*

# OUTSIDE TAPS AND PIPES

**It's vital to know where your main water supply pipes are buried, so you don't damage them by accident and can trace a leak if one occurs. And it's useful to be able to install an outside tap.**

Apart from any outside pipes you have, say, supplying a garden tap, the pipe you have to worry about is the service pipe which runs as a branch from the authority's main to supply your house's plumbing system. Usually it will run in a straight line from the authority's stop-valve to the point at which it enters the house and rises through the floor (usually in the kitchen) to become the rising main (see pages 9 to 13).

Because the service pipe is probably the most important water pipe in the home, it's vital that you know where the authority's stop-valve – which controls the flow of water in the pipe – is located. Often you'll find it under a small square or round hinged metal cover set in the pavement just outside the front gate, or in the concrete of your front garden path. It's quite likely that the valve will be protected in a guard pipe beyond the reach of a groping hand. It may have an ordinary crutch handle (the type found on old-fashioned taps) or a specially-shaped square head that can be turned only with one of the water authority's turnkeys.

Provided that you have another 'householder's stop-valve' where the service pipe enters your home, you will rarely have occasion to turn off the authority's stop-valve, but it's nice to be able to feel that you can do so should the need arise. Long-handled keys are available for turning crutch handles, or you may be able to improvise one by cutting a notch in the end of a piece of 75mm x 25mm (3in x 1in) timber and nailing another piece of wood across the other end to serve as a handle. You may have difficulty getting hold of a turnkey for the square-headed type of valve, as the water authority likes to feel that it can turn it off in the event of non-payment of the water rate, without the prospect of it being promptly turned on again, but they are usually entrusted to plumbers in whom the authority has confidence. It's really worth checking out what sort of tap you have, and if you find you haven't got a stop-valve on the rising main inside, you should definitely consider installing one. At the same time you can also make sure the guard pipe is clear of debris; having raised its cover, make sure you replace it securely. You could be liable to heavy damages if a pedestrian were injured as a result of tripping over a cover that you had left open.

### The service pipe stop-valve

The service pipe will run underground directly to your home. It should rise slightly as it does so to prevent any air bubbles being trapped, but it should be at least 800mm (2ft 8in) below the surface of the ground throughout its length. This is an important frost precaution. Even in the most severe winters experienced in this country, frost is very unlikely to penetrate as deeply as this into the soil. Make sure that you don't reduce this protection by, for instance, digging a drainage channel or creating a sunken garden above the service pipe.

Where the service pipe passes under the foundations or 'footings' of the house wall, it should be threaded through a length of drainpipe to protect it against any settlement which could fracture it. Generally it will rise into the home through the solid floor of a kitchen. Where, however, it rises through the gap between the oversite concrete and a hollow boarded floor, it must be protected against the icy draughts that may whistle through the sub-floor space. This is best done by threading the pipe, when it is first installed, through the centre of a 150mm (6in) stoneware drainpipe placed vertically on the oversite concrete and filling the space between the service pipe and the inner walls of the drainpipe with vermiculite chips or other similar insulating material.

It isn't, of course, practical to do this with an existing installation. In such a case the length of pipe in the sub-floor area should be bound with a 100mm (4in) thickness of glass fibre tank wrap or glass fibre roof insulating blanket, which should then be covered with a polythene sheet to prevent it from becoming damp and so useless as insulation.

### A leaking service pipe

An underground leak may go undetected for a long period, but there are some tell-tale signs which should raise your suspicions. The main ones include the sound of trickling water when no tap has been in use in the house for a long period, a persistent noise from the main pipework, a loss of pressure in the flow of water from the cold tap over the kitchen sink, or a persistently damp patch on the garden path or on the wall of a basement. If you suspect a leak, contact the water authority. They have listening apparatus with which they are supposed to be able to fix the position of a leak. At least they can advise you on how best to track down the leak.

It is generally best to get professional help to deal with a leak in the underground service pipe. In an older house – where a leak is most likely to occur – this pipe will be of lead or iron which is difficult to repair. If the pipe is a modern copper one it will probably be leaking at a joint. To reduce the risk of this happening, water authorities normally insist upon the use of special manipulative (Type B) compression joints in underground locations. With these the pipe ends have to be widened

## PLANNING THE PIPE RUNS

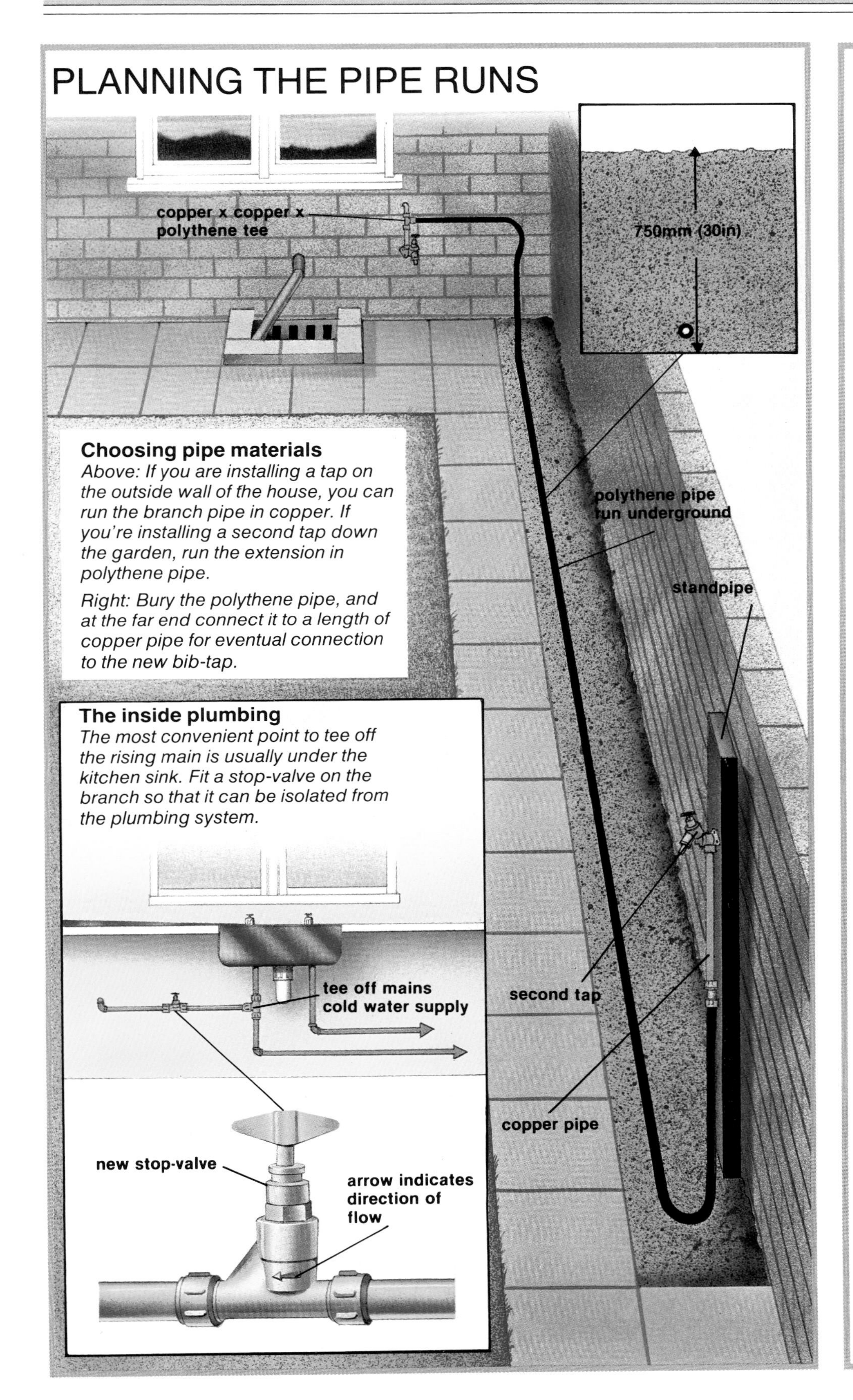


**Choosing pipe materials**
*Above: If you are installing a tap on the outside wall of the house, you can run the branch pipe in copper. If you're installing a second tap down the garden, run the extension in polythene pipe.*

*Right: Bury the polythene pipe, and at the far end connect it to a length of copper pipe for eventual connection to the new bib-tap.*

**The inside plumbing**
*The most convenient point to tee off the rising main is usually under the kitchen sink. Fit a stop-valve on the branch so that it can be isolated from the plumbing system.*

## Ready Reference

### TURNING OFF THE SUPPLY

You can control the flow of water in the service pipe supplying your home by turning off the stop-valve located

- under the kitchen sink
- under the stairs
- in the cellar
- in a guard pipe by the front fence
- just outside your front fence under the pavement.

### TIP: CHECK THE STOP-VALVE

Occasionally turn all stop-valves off and on to check that they aren't jammed. You don't want to find in an emergency that they're not working.

### A NEW OUTSIDE TAP

The most common outside taps are bib-taps. These have a plain brass finish and often there is no easy-clean cover to protect the headgear.

### NEW PIPE RUNS

If a new outside tap is to be fitted to the house wall, use copper pipe. If the tap is to be situated away from the house use polythene pipe run underground.

### TIP: FIT A STOP-VALVE

Fit a stop-valve on the new pipe run in the inside of the house. Turn the valve off in winter and leave the outside tap open to reduce the risk of freezing water causing damage to the pipe run.

## INSTALLING AN OUTSIDE TAP

**1** *After turning off the main stop-valve, cut out a small section of pipe and insert a compression tee in the rising main.*

**2** *Insert a stop-valve in the branch supply as close to the tee as possible. Make sure that the arrow on the tap points in the direction of the flow.*

**3** *Work out where you want the branch pipe to emerge from the inside. Then working from the outside (or the inside) drill a hole through the wall.*

**4** *Feed the branch pipe through the wall, then screw a backplate elbow in place just below it; this will act as the fixing for a new bib-tap.*

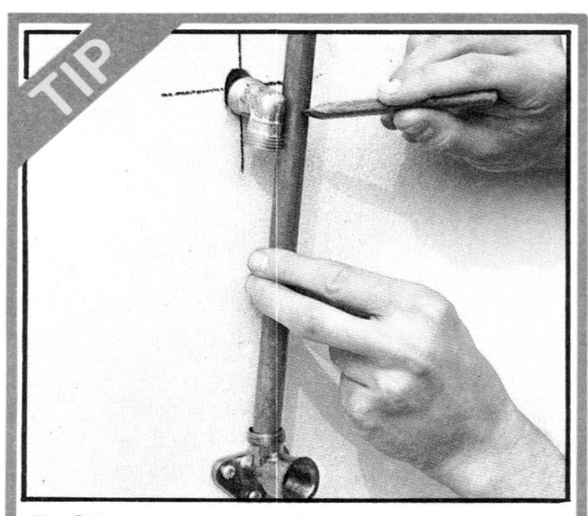


**5** *Slip a compression elbow over the branch pipe and measure the length of pipe needed to reach the backplate. Cut and fit it in place.*

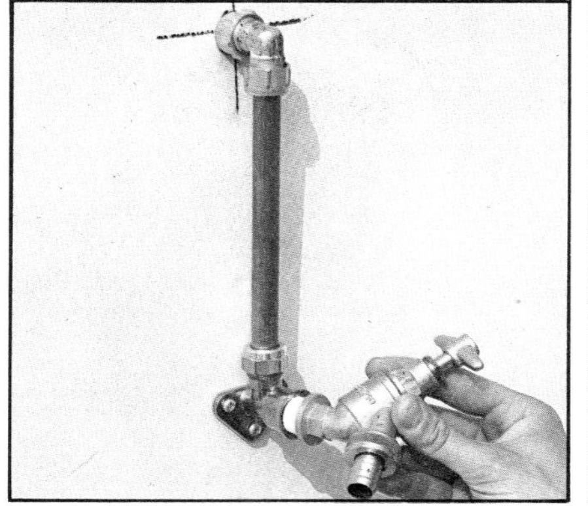

**6** *Wind PTFE tape several times round the thread of the bib-tap. Screw the tap into place, making sure it is upright when you finish.*

– 'manipulated' – with a special tool as the joint is assembled. You may consider it better to replace the existing pipe with a single length of soft-temper copper tubing. This is obtainable on reels in long lengths that eliminate the need for underground joints.

Many water authorities nowadays also permit the use of black polythene piping. This too is obtainable in long lengths and has the added advantage that its thick walls help to insulate the pipe against frost. And in the unlikely event of the water within the pipe freezing, polythene pipe is sufficiently resilient to accommodate the expansion of the freezing water without bursting.

### Putting in an outside tap

The only occasion when you are likely to need a permanent supply of water out of doors is when you put in an outside garden or garage tap. Before doing this you should always seek the permission of the water authority. This is likely to be granted readily enough, but it will involve an additional charge on the water rate, particularly if you are going to use the tap for a hose pipe or sprinkler system. If you already have an outside tap you'll agree that the convenience of not having the garden hose snaking through the kitchen window, and putting the domestic water supply out of action while it is in use, makes this extra payment well worthwhile. Provided that your home has modern copper plumbing, fitting an outside tap is a straightforward job.

If the outside tap is to be fixed to the wall outside the kitchen, you will need a bib-tap with a horizontal inlet for outside water supply, with a threaded nozzle for a hose connector and an angled handle that you can turn without grazing your knuckles on the wall. You'll also need a 15mm wall-plate elbow with a compression elbow bend, one 15mm equal-ended compression tee joint, a screw-down stop-valve with 15mm compression inlet and outlet and a length of 15mm copper tubing – how much will depend on the distance between the rising main and the new outside tap.

As far as tools are concerned, you'll require a couple of wrenches, a hacksaw, a tin of jointing compound, a roll of PTFE thread-sealing tape and some means of cutting through the wall to take the pipe-run outside. It's best to hire a heavy duty electric drill with hole-cutting attachments; the job can be done with a hammer and cold chisel, but this takes longer and is not as neat.

Turn off the main stop-valve and drain the rising main from the cold tap above the kitchen sink and, if there is one, from the drain-cock above the stop-valve. Cut the rising main at a convenient point to take off a

## ADDING A SECOND TAP

**1** *Fit a 15x15x22mm compression tee into the existing branch. Use a piece of copper pipe to hold the fitting secure while it's tightened.*

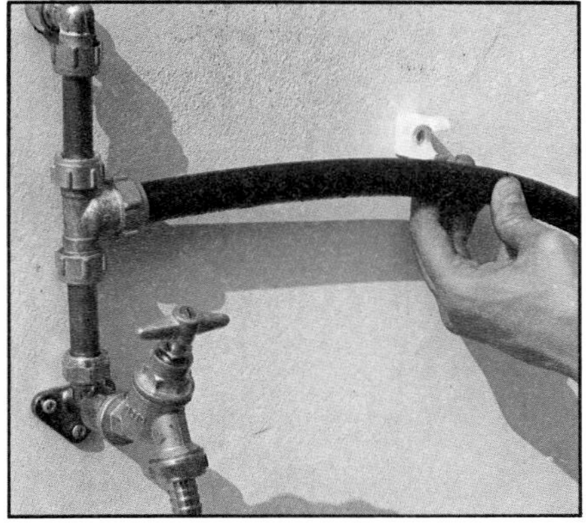

**2** *Fit the polythene pipe to the tee. Then clip it to the wall and take it down to a prepared trench at least 750mm (30in) deep.*

**3** *At the other end of the trench, attach the second tap and a short length of pipe. Then run the polythene pipe up the foot of the post.*

**4** *Link the polythene pipe to the copper using a 22x15mm compression coupling. Finally turn on the supply, check for leaks and back-fill the trench.*

feed branch pipe. If there isn't a drain-cock above the main stop-valve a little water will flow out as you do this, so be prepared for it. Make another cut 18mm (3/4in) away from the first one and remove the 18mm segment of pipe.

Insert the 15mm compression tee into the cut pipe (described on pages 20 to 24) so that the branch outlet of the tee points along the kitchen wall in the direction of the position of the new tap. Cut a short length of copper pipe, say 150mm (6in), and fit it into the outlet of the tee. To the other end of this fit the screw-down stop-valve by means of its compression joint inlet.

There are two points to watch as you do this. Make sure that the arrow engraved on the body of the stop-valve points away from the rising main and towards the position of the new tap. Make sure, too, that the stop-valve handle is angled away from the wall so you have enough room to turn it with ease.

The first phase of the job is now complete. You can turn off the new stop-valve and turn on the main stop-valve to check for leaks. Because this will restore water to the rest of the house you can carry out the rest of the job in your own time.

Drill a hole – sufficiently large to take a 15mm copper pipe – through the wall above the position of the new tap. When deciding exactly where on the outside wall you want your tap to be positioned, remember that you'll want enough room to be able to put buckets and watering cans beneath it. Then cut two more lengths of copper pipe, one long enough to pass through the house wall and to protrude by 25mm (1in) at each end, and the other long enough to reach from the new stop-valve to the hole that you have made in the wall. Join these two lengths with a compression elbow and push the correct length through the hole in the wall. Connect the other end of the other length to the outlet of the new stop-valve.

Next you can go outside and cut the projecting pipe so that 25mm (1in) projects through the wall. Connect the other elbow to this so that its outlet points downward to the position of the new tap. Cut another short piece of pipe to reach the position of the new tap. Fit the wall-plate elbow to one end of this and connect the other end to the projecting elbow bend. Drill and plug the wall, and screw the wall-plate elbow into place. You'll then have to bind PTFE tape round the threaded tail of the tap and screw it into the outlet of the wall-plate elbow. If the tap doesn't point downwards when screwed fully home, you'll have to remove it and add washers to its tail until it does.

The job is now complete, apart from making good the hole through the wall with some mastic filler. With the onset of winter, turn off the new stop-valve and open the outside tap to drain the short branch to protect it from the risk of frost damage. There is no need to insulate the section of pipe on the outside wall.

### Installing a garden standpipe

If you have a large garden, or a garage at some distance from the house, one tap fitted against the outside wall of the house may be insufficient, and you may need another standpipe to provide an adequate outside supply. This is an excellent opportunity to use polythene pipe for the water supply because of the long lengths in which it can be obtained. In fact, when new houses are built today this piping is usually chosen for all underground runs.

In order to install a second outside tap you have to carry out the preliminary work described above, but instead of fitting the tap into a backplate elbow, you can use a backplate tee. It is from the lower outlet of this tee that the additional garden supply is taken. You may not be able to get a tee of this kind to which polythene pipe can be directly connected. In this case fit a short length of 15mm copper pipe into the tee outlet and connect the end of the polythene pipe to it by means of a 15mm copper to 1/2in polythene compression coupling. However, probably the easiest method is to tee off the short section of supply pipe feeding the outside tap already installed.

Although polythene pipe will not be damaged by frost, it should still be laid in a trench about 750mm (30in) deep to avoid the risk of accidental damage from gardening operations. The pipe can be taken underground to any point required, and then connected to a tap fixed to a post or to the wall of an outbuilding by means of the usual backplate elbow.

# INDEX